Emily Goldberg

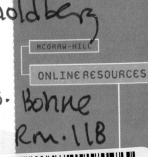

Ms. Bohne
Rm. 118

IMPORTANT:

HERE IS YOUR REGISTRATION CODE TO ACCESS YOUR PREMIUM McGRAW-HILL ONLINE RESOURCES.

For key premium online resources you need THIS CODE to gain access. Once the code is entered, you will be able to use the Web resources for the length of your course.

If your course is using **WebCT** or **Blackboard**, you'll be able to use this code to access the McGraw-Hill content within your instructor's online course.

Access is provided if you have purchased a new book. If the registration code is missing from this book, the registration screen on our Website, and within your WebCT or Blackboard course, will tell you how to obtain your new code.

Registering for McGraw-Hill Online Resources

To gain access to your McGraw-Hill web resources simply follow the steps below:

1. USE YOUR WEB BROWSER TO GO TO: **www.mhhe.com/maderap5**
2. CLICK ON **FIRST TIME USER**.
3. ENTER THE REGISTRATION CODE* PRINTED ON THE TEAR-OFF BOOKMARK ON THE RIGHT.
4. AFTER YOU HAVE ENTERED YOUR REGISTRATION CODE, CLICK **REGISTER**.
5. FOLLOW THE INSTRUCTIONS TO SET-UP YOUR PERSONAL UserID AND PASSWORD.
6. WRITE YOUR UserID AND PASSWORD DOWN FOR FUTURE REFERENCE. KEEP IT IN A SAFE PLACE.

TO GAIN ACCESS to the McGraw-Hill content in your instructor's **WebCT** or **Blackboard** course simply log in to the course with the UserID and Password provided by your instructor. Enter the registration code exactly as it appears in the box to the right when prompted by the system. You will only need to use the code the first time you click on McGraw-Hill content.

Thank you, and welcome to your McGraw-Hill online Resources!

REGISTRATION CODE

77KW–CGBH–TGY7–9NPP–HHDU

FIFTH EDITION

Understanding Human Anatomy & Physiology

Sylvia S. Mader

Special Contributions by:

Susannah N. Longenbaker, M.S.,
Columbus State Community College, Columbus, Ohio

Michael W. Squires, Ph. D.
Columbus State Community College, Columbus, Ohio

Dianne M. Jedlicka, Ph. D.
Columbia College, Chicago, Illinois

Boston   Burr Ridge, IL   Dubuque, IA   Madison, WI   New York   San Francisco   St. Louis
Bangkok   Bogotá   Caracas   Kuala Lumpur   Lisbon   London   Madrid   Mexico City
Milan   Montreal   New Delhi   Santiago   Seoul   Singapore   Sydney   Taipei   Toronto

UNDERSTANDING HUMAN ANATOMY & PHYSIOLOGY, FIFTH EDITION

4 5 6 7 8 9 0 VNH/VNH 0 9 8 7 6

ISBN-13: 978–0-07–246437–5 (softcover)
ISBN-10: 0–07–246437–2

Publisher: *Martin J. Lange*
Sponsoring editor: *Michelle Watnick*
Senior developmental editor: *Patricia Hesse*
Director of development: *Kristine Tibbetts*
Marketing manager: *James F. Connely*
Senior project manager: *Jayne Klein*
Lead production supervisor: *Sandy Ludovissy*
Senior media project manager: *Tammy Juran*
Media technology producer: *Renee Russian*
Design manager: *K. Wayne Harms*
Cover/interior designer: *Christopher Reese*
Cover image: *Lori Adamski Peek/GettyImages*
Senior photo research coordinator: *Lori Hancock*
Supplement producer: *Brenda A. Ernzen*
Compositor: *The GTS Companies/Los Angeles, CA Campus*
Typeface: *10/12 Giovanni Book*
Printer: *Von Hoffmann Corporation*

The credits section for this book begins on page 435 and is considered an extension of the copyright page.

Library of Congress Cataloging-in-Publication Data

Mader, Sylvia S.
 Understanding human anatomy & physiology / Sylvia S. Mader—5th ed.
  p.   cm.
 Includes bibliographical references and index.
 ISBN 0–07–246437–2 (hard copy : alk. paper)
  1. Human physiology. 2. Human anatomy. I. Title.

QP34.5.M353   2005
612—dc22   2003022859
                                            CIP

I

www.mhhe.com

Brief Contents

Contents

Boxed Readings

Clinical Connections

Preface

We cannot teach people anything; we can only help them discover it within themselves. Galileo Galilei

Over the years, it has been my privilege to meet many of the adopters of my texts at various meetings around the country. At one such meeting, I met a professor who told me that he and his colleagues were using my book, *Human Biology* for an anatomy and physiology course because they wanted to use a Mader text. When I returned home, I pondered over this and decided that I would write an anatomy and physiology text so that professors teaching that course would have a more appropriate Mader textbook. Thus, began the development of this text, *Understanding Human Anatomy and Physiology*, which is now in its fifth edition.

I wanted to write a text that would appeal to a wide audience—from those in traditional allied health fields to others who are a bit removed from traditional endeavors. The book should be clear and direct, with objectives that are achievable by students who have no previous science background and even by those who are science shy. This goal was reached.

Diane Kelly, of Broome Community College, writes, *"I think the text is very readable, clear, and user friendly. The art is a wonderful complement to the author's writing; together, the information is clearly presented."*

Mader texts are well known for their pedagogical features, and those for this text are described in the Guided Tour on pages xv–xx. Also, as with other Mader texts, the illustrations are excellent.

William J. Burke, of Madison Area Technical College, states, *"This text has some very good art. It is well labeled and has a good color scheme that helps it stand out. The inclusion of the many tables and charts is also an excellent learning tool for the students."*

My vision for *Understanding Human Anatomy and Physiology* encompasses three goals. I want students to develop a working knowledge of (1) anatomy and physiology that is based on conceptual understanding rather than rote memory; (2) medical terminology that will increase the student's confidence in their chosen field; and (3) clinical applications to broaden their horizons beyond the core principles.

Dr. Philip Swartz, of Houston Community College system, writes, *"Each chapter includes salient clinical concepts that will be fascinating to the reader and enhance his or her understanding of the material being presented."*

About the Author   Sylvia S. Mader

In her 20-year career with McGraw-Hill, Dr. Mader has written an impressive collection of textbooks. Aside from *Understanding Human Anatomy and Physiology*, now in its fifth edition, Dr. Mader has written *Biology*, eighth edition; *Human Biology*, eighth edition, and *Inquiry into Life*, tenth edition, through which Dr. Mader has successfully helped innumerable students learn biology as well as human anatomy and physiology.

Dr. Mader's interest in anatomy and physiology began when she took courses at the Medical School of St. Andrews University, in Scotland, during her junior year abroad. As a fledgling faculty member, she was called upon to teach a variety of courses, among them was human anatomy and physiology. As a textbook writer she discovered that the teaching and learning techniques she so successfully used in the classroom were appropriate for her biology texts and then later for her anatomy and physiology text. Dr. Mader's direct writing style and carefully constructed pedagogy provide students with an opportunity to learn the basics of biology and anatomy and physiology.

What's New to This Edition?

New Design and Illustrations

A new, colorful design and revised illustrations enhance the features of *Understanding Human Anatomy and Physiology*, fifth edition.

Organization

This edition follows the same general sequence as the earlier editions. It is divided into five parts:

Part I, "Human Organization," provides an understanding of how the body is organized and the terminology used to refer to various body parts and their locations. Chapters 2 through 4 describe the chemistry of the cell, cell structure and function, and the tissues and membranes of the body.

Part II, "Support, Movement, and Protection," includes the integumentary system in addition to the skeletal and muscular systems.

Part III, "Integration and Coordination," explains that the nervous and endocrine systems are vitally important to the coordination of body systems, and therefore homeostasis, while the sensory system provides the nervous system with information about the internal and external environments.

Part IV, "Maintenance of the Body," describes how the cardiovascular, lymphatic, respiratory, digestive, and urinary systems contribute to the maintenance of homeostasis.

Part V, "Reproduction and Development," concerns the reproductive systems, development, and the basics of human genetics, including modern advances.

Homeostasis

The theme of homeostasis is strengthened in this edition. As before, Chapter 1 describes how various feedback mechanisms work to maintain the internal environment within a narrow range. New to this edition, each systems chapter ends with a major section on homeostasis to accompany the "Human Systems Work Together" illustration. This section describes how the system under discussion, with the help of the other systems, maintains homeostasis.

New Readings

Understanding Human Anatomy and Physiology, fifth edition, has two types of readings. Previously, the book had two types of readings called Medical Focus and MedAlert. In this edition, the readings are Medical Focus and What's New. Some of the Medical Focus readings from the fourth edition have been removed, and most of the others have been revised. The What's New readings, which are new to this edition, tell of treatments that are now experimental but promise to be particularly helpful in the future. For example, a What's New box in the first chapter tells about organs made in the laboratory that are now being transplanted into patients. The What's New reading in Chapter 8 describes a "pacemaker" for Parkinson disease.

Chapter Openers

Scanning electron micrographs, X-rays, and MRI images open the chapters for a closer look into the wonders of the human body. The integrated outline has been retained with the addition of a numbering system for each major concept found in the chapter, including the summary.

Visual Focus

Visual Focus illustrations are included in several chapters. With the addition of boxed statements, these in-depth illustrations, which contain several art pieces, cover a process from start to finish. For example, Figure 7.3 outlines contraction of a muscle from the macroscopic to the microscopic perspective.

Chapter End Matter

This edition includes updated Selected New Terms, Summaries, Study Questions, Objective Questions, Medical Terminology Reinforcement Exercises, and Website Links to the Online Learning Center.

Objective Questions

Labeling exercises have been added to chapters 8, 11, 14, and 18 to reinforce the concepts of the chapter.

Chapter Updates and Additions

Chapter 1: Organization of the Body

New illustrations, tables, and a reading titled "Organs for Transplant" introduce the student to the human body. The discussion of negative feedback now includes temperature control as an example and also includes a discussion of positive feedback, as requested by reviewers.

Chapter 2: Chemistry of Life

This chapter has been reorganized and rewritten to help students understand fundamental chemistry concepts. Carbohydrates, lipids, proteins, and nucleic acids each have their own major section.

Chapter 3: Cell Structure and Function

Cellular Organization, Crossing the Plasma Membrane, and The Cell Cycle are clearly defined as chapter sections. Tables

3.1, 3.2, and all art are new to this edition. The Medical Focus reading, "Dehydration and Water Intoxication" is also new to this edition.

Chapter 4: Body Tissues and Membranes

Each type of tissue now has its own major section. In addition to body membranes, connections between cells and different types of glands are discussed in respective sections. Art and tables have been revised for this chapter.

Chapter 5: The Integumentary System

Section 5.5. Homeostasis is new to this edition. It shows how the various functions of the skin assist the body in maintaining homeostasis. Also discussed are hyperthermia and hypothermia, which occur when homeostasis has been overcome. The section is accompanied by an updated Human Systems Work Together illustration.

Chapter 6: The Skeletal System

New illustrations, each of which is on the same or a facing page to its reference, much improve this chapter. More information is given about each bone and joint discussed. The chapter ends with a review of the many ways the skeletal system helps maintain homeostasis.

Chapter 7: The Muscular System

The first two illustrations in this chapter are new: The first shows the three types of muscles, and the second describes the connective tissue coverings within and around a skeletal muscle. Instructors and students will appreciate the new in-depth discussion of the sources of energy for muscle contraction, which is also accompanied by a new illustration.

Chapter 8: The Nervous System

This chapter was rewritten. In particular, the discussion of the cerebrum has been expanded to include not only the various lobes but also the areas within these lobes. The somatic system of the peripheral nervous system is now clearly defined, and the spinal reflex has been moved to this section. New illustrations support improved discussions of all aspects of the nervous system.

Chapter 9: The Sensory System

Types of senses, rather than types of receptors, are now used to organize this chapter. The discussions of the anatomy and physiology of the eye and ear are better organized, with an emphasis on how information regarding vision and sound is generated and transmitted to the brain. The sense of equilibrium is now divided into rotational and gravitational equilibrium.

Chapter 10: The Endocrine System

An overview of the endocrine glands now precedes an improved discussion of each gland. A new illustration shows how the adrenal medulla and the adrenal cortex are involved in short-term and long-term stress, respectively. Other new illustrations pertain to regulation of blood calcium, regulation of blood pressure, Addison disease, and Cushing syndrome. The chapter also includes a discussion of chemical signals in general and how hormones affect cellular metabolism.

Chapter 11: Blood

A detailed description of the composition and function of blood now opens the chapter. There follows a more comprehensive look at the formed elements. The section on platelets centers around hemostasis, including coagulation. The transport function of blood is illustrated by considering capillary exchange. The last section of the chapter, Blood Typing and Transfusions, is supported by new art that clearly illustrates blood types and agglutination.

Chapter 12: The Cardiovascular System

An overview of the cardiovascular system, supported by an illustration, offers a much-improved introduction to the chapter, which has been reorganized into five parts: the anatomy of the heart, the physiology of the heart, the anatomy of blood vessels, the physiology of circulation, and circulatory routes. A better discussion of cardiac output and peripheral resistance improves the presentation of the chapter.

Chapter 13: The Lymphatic System and Body Defenses

As requested by reviewers, the lymphatic organs are now divided into those that are primary and those that are secondary. The discussion of specific immunity is much improved by new illustrations depicting the action of B cells and T cells. A new reading on emerging diseases modernizes the chapter.

Chapter 14: The Respiratory System

An improved Table 14.1, which includes a description of the respiratory organs, adds to the discussion of the respiratory system. The respiratory membrane is better described and is accompanied by a new illustration. The section entitled Mechanism of Breathing is better organized so that regulation of breathing rates now has its own subsection. Following reviewers' suggestions, the chapter is more student friendly because gas exchange and transport no longer require a knowledge of partial pressures. All readings are new or extensively revised.

Chapter 15: The Digestive System

New illustrations of stomach and small intestine anatomy add to the improved and extended discussion of these topics. Chemical digestion now benefits by having its own separate section. The Medical Focus reading "Human Teeth" has been moved to a logical location early in the chapter. Liver structure, function, and disorders are more logically and thoroughly presented. The chapter ends with an added discussion of three eating disorders: obesity, bulimia nervosa, and anorexia nervosa.

Chapter 16: The Urinary System and Excretion

The functions of the urinary system are discussed more thoroughly than in the fourth edition. The discussion of a nephron has been improved by the addition of micrographs. The role of the loop of the nephron and various hormones in water reabsorption is better explained, and the topic of acid-base balance has been expanded to discuss all the ways the body can adjust the pH of the blood. The chapter ends with a discussion of treatments for kidney failure.

Chapter 17: The Reproductive System

The topic of meiosis has been moved to this chapter so that spermatogenesis and oogenesis can be better understood by students. Coverage of the reproductive organs has been improved by the inclusion of both sagittal and posterior views of the systems. Following reviewers' suggestions, the menstrual (instead of the ovarian and uterine cycles) is discussed. New Health Focuses are provided on endocrine-disrupting contaminants, shower checks for cancer, and preventing transmission of STDs.

Chapter 18: Human Development and Birth

The addition of new figures depicting fertilization, extraembryonic membranes, and the primary germ layers improves this chapter. Extensive revision is obvious due to the addition of new readings entitled "Therapeutic Cloning" and "Preventing Birth Defects." A discussion of the development of male and female organs has been added, and the chapter ends with a new and extended discussion of the effects of pregnancy on the mother.

Chapter 19: Human Genetics

Aside from having all sections revised and updated, the chapter uses cystic fibrosis to show the connection between a genetic disorder and the function of a protein and to illustrate the levels of genetic counseling, from doing a pedigree to performing a preimplantation genetic study. The chapter ends with a Medical Focus outlining the future benefits from the modern field of genomics.

Teaching and Learning Supplements

McGraw-Hill offers various tools and teaching products to support the fifth edition of *Understanding Human Anatomy & Physiology*. Students can order supplemental study materials by contacting their local bookstore. Instructors can obtain teaching aids by calling the Customer Service Department at 800-338-3987, visiting our A & P website at www.mhhe.com, or contacting their local McGraw-Hill sales representative.

The ***Digital Content Manager***, 0-07-246443-7, is a multimedia collection of visual resources that allows instructors to utilize artwork from the text in multiple formats to create customized classroom presentations, visually-based tests and quizzes, dynamic course website content, or attractive printed support materials. The digital assets on this cross-platform CD-ROM are grouped by chapter within the following easy-to-use folders.

- **Active Art Library** Key Process Figures are saved in manipulable layers that can be isolated and customized to meet the needs of the lecture environment.

- **Animations Library** Numerous full-color animations of key physiological processes are provided. Harness the visual impact of processes in motion by importing these files into classroom presentations or course websites.

- **Art Libraries** Full-color digital files of all illustrations in the book, plus the same art saved in unlabeled and gray scale versions, can be readily incorporated into lecture presentations, exams, or custom-made classroom materials. These images are also pre-inserted into blank PowerPoint slides for ease of use.

- **Photo Libraries** Digital files of instructionally significant photographs from the text—including cadaver, bone, histology, and surface anatomy images—can be reproduced for multiple classroom uses.

- **PowerPoints** Ready-made image presentations cover each of the 19 chapters of the text. Tailor the PowerPoints to reflect your preferred lecture topics and sequences.
- **Tables Library** Every table that appears in the text is provided in electronic form. You can quickly preview images and incorporate them into PowerPoint or other presentation programs to create your own multimedia presentations. You can also remove and replace labels to suit your own preferences in terminology or level of detail.

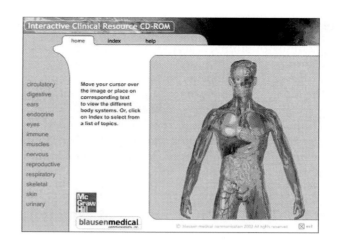

Instructor Testing and Resource CD-ROM, 0-07-246441-0, is a cross-platform CD-ROM providing a wealth of resources for the instructor. Supplements featured on this CD-ROM include a computerized test bank utilizing Brownstone Diploma® testing software to quickly create customized exams. This user-friendly program allows instructors to search for questions by topic or format, edit existing questions or add new ones, and scramble questions and answer keys for multiple versions of the same test.

Other assets on the Instructor's Testing and Resource CD-ROM are grouped within easy-to-use folders. The Instructor's Manual and Clinical Applications Manual are available in both Word and PDF formats. Word files of the test bank are included for those instructors who prefer to work outside of the test generator software.

The *Instructor's Manual,* by Dr. Patrick Galliart includes chapter summaries and outlines, suggested student activities, answers to objective questions and to medical terminology reinforcement exercises, and a list of audiovisual materials. The Instructor's Manual is available on Instructor Testing and Resource CD-ROM and the Instructor Edition of the Online Learning Center.

McGraw-Hill provides 200 *Overhead Transparencies,* 0-07-246438-0 of key text line art and photographs.

English/Spanish Glossary for Anatomy and Physiology, 0-07-283118-9, is a complete glossary that includes every key term used in a typical anatomy and physiology course. Definitions are provided in both English and Spanish. A phonetic guide to pronunciation follows each word in the glossary.

Course Delivery Systems With help from our partners, WebCT, Blackboard, TopClass, eCollege, and other course management systems, professors can take complete control over their course content. These course cartridges also provide online testing and powerful student tracking features. *Understanding Human Anatomy & Physiology* Online Learning Center is available within all of these platforms.

For the Student

Interactive Clinical Resource CD-ROM

The **Interactive Clinical Resource CD-ROM** offers one hundred fifty-one 3D animations and 3D models of human disease and disorders. It also contains 13 sections of clinical content (and nearly every body system) including Urinary, Skeletal, Reproductive, Nervous, Muscular, Immune, Digestive, Circulatory, and Endocrine. The Interactive Clinical Resource CD-ROM may be used as a classroom lecture tool or study guide for students post lecture. Students can use the Interactive Clinical Resource CD-ROM to play the 3D animations, explore the 3D models, print the associated text, and view the slides with labels and definitions of key structures related to the disease/disorder. Students will learn how the various diseases/disorders affect the human body system along with possible treatments. The Interactive Clinical Resource CD-ROM is the perfect way to reinforce and relate the physiological concepts taught in the classroom to real life.

Online Learning Center (http://www.mhhe.com/maderap5) The OLC offers an extensive array of learning and teaching tools. The site includes quizzes for each chapter, links to websites related to each chapter, clinical applications, interactive activities, art labeling exercises, and case studies. Instructor resources at the site include lecture outlines, technology resources, clinical applications, and case studies.

- **Student Center, Online Essential Study Partner** The ESP contains 120 animations and more than 800 learning activities to help your students grasp complex concepts. Interactive diagrams and quizzes will make learning stimulating and fun for your students. The Essentials Study Partner can be accessed via the Online Learning Center.

- **Live News Feeds**
  The OLC offers course specific real-time news articles to help students stay current with the latest topics in anatomy and physiology.

- **Tutorial Service**
  This free "homework hotline" offers you the opportunity to discuss text questions with our A&P consultant.

- **GetBodySmart.com** is an online examination of human anatomy and physiology. This program is available on the Student Edition of the Online Learning Center.

- **Access Science** is the online version of McGraw-Hill's Encyclopedia of Science & Technology. Link to this site free of charge from the Online Learning Center.

Physiology Interactive Lab Simulations (Ph.I.L.S)
0-07-287167-9
The Ph.I.L.S CD-ROM contains eleven laboratory simulations that allow students to perform experiments without using expensive lab equipment or live animals. This easy-to-use software offers students the flexibility to change the parameters of every lab experiment, with no limit to the amount of times a student can repeat experiments or modify variables. This power to manipulate each experiment reinforces key physiology concepts by helping students to view outcomes, make predictions, and draw conclusions.

The *Anatomy and Physiology Laboratory Textbook Essentials Version*, 0-07-232363-9, by Gunstream, contains several frog dissections and may be used with any anatomy and physiology text.

Human Anatomy and Physiology Laboratory Manual-Fetal Pig Dissection, **Second Edition** 0-07-243814-2, by Terry R. Martin, Kishwaukee College, provides excellent full-color photos of the dissected fetal pig with corresponding labeled art. It includes World Wide Web activities for many chapters.

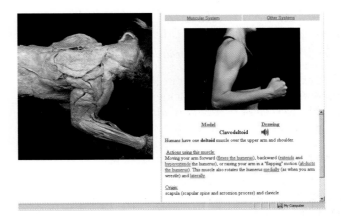

Virtual Anatomy Dissection Review, CD-ROM, 0-07-285621-1, by John Waters, Pennsylvania State University. This multimedia program contains vivid, high quality, labeled cat dissection photographs. The program helps students easily identify and review the corresponding structures and functions between the cat and the human body.

Laboratory Atlas of Anatomy and Physiology, fourth edition, 0-07-243810-X, by Eder et al., is a full-color atlas containing histology, human skeletal anatomy, human muscular anatomy, dissections, and reference tables.

Acknowledgments

I would like to acknowledge the valuable contributions of all professors and their students who have provided detailed recommendations for improving chapter content and illustrations for the fifth edition.

Bert Atsma
Union County College

William J. Burke
Madison Area Technical College

Richard Ceroni
Carnegie Institute of Integrative Medicine

Jay P. Clymer III
Marywood University

Mark Eberle
Central Oregon Community College

Diana Godish
Ball State University

Michelle A. Green
Alfred State College

Gary W. Hunt
Tulsa Community College

Dianne M. Jedlicka
The School of the Art Institute of Chicago

Geoffrey Jowett
Savannah College of Art and Design

Diane M. Kelly
Broome Community College

Kenneth M. Kosten
Community College of Denver

John J. Kulig
Central Massachusetts School of Massage and Therapy

Karen Magatagan
Cochise College

Jacqueline S. McLaughlin
Pennsylvania State University—Berks/Lehigh Valley

Kenneth Moore
Seattle Pacific University

Albert Moraska
Boulder College of Massage Therapy

Scott Murdoch
Moraine Valley Community College

Linda R. Nichols
Santa Fe Community College

Robin R. Patterson
Butler County Community College

Susan Pazynski
Glen Oaks Community College

Joel H. Scott
Blue Cliff College

Marilyn M. Shannon
Indiana University-Purdue University—Fort Wayne

F. Christopher Sowers
Wilkes Community College

Michael Squires
Columbus State Community College

James D. Tipton
Chattahoochee Valley Community College

Harry A. Tracy, Jr.
University of Texas at San Antonio

Ricky K. Wong
Los Angeles Trade-Technical College

The Focus is Understanding . . .

- Students develop a working knowledge of anatomy and physiology based upon conceptual understanding.
- Clinical Applications broaden students' horizons beyond the core principles.
- Self-confidence increases as students master medical terminology and key concepts.

Art Program

Art presents and reinforces the dynamic processes within the human body.

Dynamic Photos

give students a closer look inside the wonders of the human body through the technology of scanning electron micrographs.

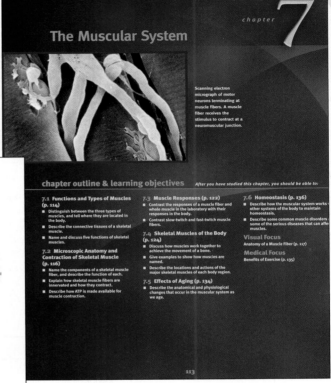

chapter **7**

The Muscular System

Scanning electron micrograph of motor neurons terminating at muscle fibers. A muscle fiber receives the stimulus to contract at a neuromuscular junction.

chapter outline & learning objectives *After you have studied this chapter, you should be able to:*

7.1 Functions and Types of Muscles (p. 114)
- Distinguish between the three types of muscles, and tell where they are located in the body.
- Describe the connective tissues of a skeletal muscle.
- Name and discuss five functions of skeletal muscles.

7.2 Microscopic Anatomy and Contraction of Skeletal Muscle (p. 116)
- Name the components of a skeletal muscle fiber, and describe the function of each.
- Explain how skeletal muscle fibers are innervated and how they contract.
- Describe how ATP is made available for muscle contraction.

7.3 Muscle Responses (p. 122)
- Contrast the responses of a muscle fiber and whole muscle in the laboratory with their responses in the body.
- Contrast slow-twitch and fast-twitch muscle fibers.

7.4 Skeletal Muscles of the Body (p. 124)
- Discuss how muscles work together to achieve the movement of a bone.
- Give examples to show how muscles are named.
- Describe the locations and actions of the major skeletal muscles of each body region.

7.5 Effects of Aging (p. 134)
- Describe the anatomical and physiological changes that occur in the muscular system as we age.

7.6 Homeostasis (p. 136)
- Describe how the muscular system works with other systems of the body to maintain homeostasis.
- Describe some common muscle disorders and some of the serious diseases that can affect muscles.

Visual Focus
Anatomy of a Muscle Fiber (p. 117)

Medical Focus
Benefits of Exercise (p. 135)

113

visual focus

bundle of muscle fibers

muscle fiber

T tubules

nucleus

sarcoplasm

sarcoplasmic reticulum

calcium storage sites

skeletal muscle fiber

Muscle fiber has many myofibrils.

one myofibril

one sarcomere

Z line

Z line

sarcolemma

Myofibril has many sarcomeres.

cross-bridge

myosin

actin

Sarcomere is relaxed.

H zone

Z line

A band

I band

Sarcomere is contracted.

Figure 7.3 Anatomy of a muscle fiber. A muscle fiber contains many myofibrils with the components shown. A myofibril has many sarcomeres that contain myosin and actin filaments whose arrangement gives rise to the striations so characteristic of skeletal muscle. Muscle contraction occurs when sarcomeres contract and actin filaments slide past myosin filaments.

Visual Focus

illustrates difficult concepts that relate structure to function, using a step-by-step process.

Figure 7.15 Muscles of the posterior shoulder. The right trapezius is removed to show deep muscles that move the scapula and the rotator cuff muscles.

trapezius

deltoid

rotator cuff muscles

latissimus dorsi

New and Revised Art

focuses on the main concepts by using concise labeling methodology that keeps students from getting bogged down with excessive detail.

Muscles of the Abdominal Wall

The abdominal wall has no bony reinforcement (Fig. 7.14). The wall is strengthened by four pairs of muscles that run at angles to one another. The external and internal obliques and the transversus abdominis occur laterally, but the fasciae of these muscle pairs meet at the midline of the body, forming a tendinous area called the linea alba. The rectus abdominis is

Muscles of the Shoulder

Muscles of the shoulder are shown in Figures 7.14 and 7.15. They are also listed in Table 7.4 on page 130. The muscles of the shoulder attach the scapula to the thorax and move the scapula; they also attach the humerus to the scapula and move the arm.

"The most beautiful thing we can experience is the mysterious. It is the source of all true art and science."

– Albert Einstein

XV

Figure 6.2 Anatomy of a long bone. **a.** A long bone is encased by the periosteum except at the epiphyses, which are covered by articular cartilage. Spongy bone of the epiphyses contains red bone marrow. The diaphysis contains yellow bone marrow and is bordered by compact bone. **b.** The detailed anatomy of spongy bone and compact bone is shown in the enlargement, along with a blowup of an osteocyte in a lacuna.

epiphyseal plates

Epiphysis

articular cartilage

spongy bone
(contains red
bone marrow)

compact
bone

endosteum

periosteum

osteon

lamella

medullary
cavity
(contains
yellow bone
marrow)

blood
vessel

Spongy Bone

Diaphysis

trabeculae

canaliculi

central canal

Compact Bone

b.

osteocyte
within
lacuna

blood vessels

Epiphysis

a.

Humerus

Macro to Micro Presentation

helps students make the connection between gross anatomy and microscopic anatomy.

4.2 Connective Tissue

Connective tissue binds structures together, provides support and protection, fills spaces, produces blood cells, and stores fat. The body uses this stored fat for energy, insulation, and organ protection. As a rule, connective tissue cells are widely separated by an extracellular **matrix** composed of an *organic ground substance* that contains *fibers* and varies in consistency from solid to semifluid to fluid. Whereas the functional and physical properties of epithelial tissues are derived from its cells, connective tissue properties are largely derived from the characteristics of the matrix (Table 4.2).

The fibers within the matrix are of three types. White fibers contain *collagen*, a substance that gives the fibers flexibility and strength. Yellow fibers contain *elastin*, which is not as strong as collagen but is more elastic. *Reticular fibers* are very thin, highly branched, collagenous fibers that form delicate supporting networks.

Figure 4.5 Loose (areolar) connective tissue. This tissue has a loose network of fibers.

ground
substance
fibroblast

elastic fiber

collagenous
fiber

Loose (Areolar) Connective Tissue

Location:
Between muscles; beneath the skin;
beneath most epithelial layers

Function:
Binds organs together

Correlation of Photomicrographs with Line Art

makes it easier for students to identify specific structures.

Reference Figures

of the human body have been added to give students an additional resource in the study of body structure.

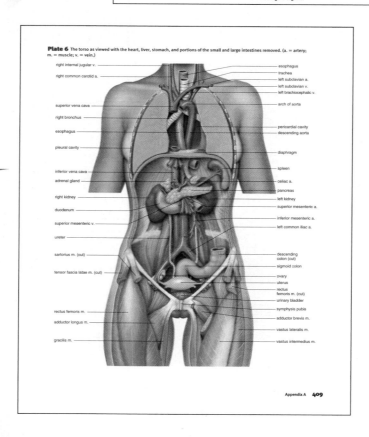

Plate 6 The torso as viewed with the heart, liver, stomach, and portions of the small and large intestines removed. (a. = artery; m. = muscle; v. = vein.)

right internal jugular v.

right common carotid a.

esophagus
trachea
left subclavian a.
left subclavian v.
left brachiocephalic v.

superior vena cava

right bronchus

esophagus

pleural cavity

arch of aorta

pericardial cavity
descending aorta

diaphragm

inferior vena cava

adrenal gland

right kidney

duodenum

superior mesenteric v.

ureter

sartorius m. (cut)

tensor fascia latae m. (cut)

rectus femoris m.

adductor longus m.

gracilis m.

spleen

celiac a.

pancreas

left kidney

superior mesenteric a.

inferior mesenteric a.

left common iliac a.

descending
colon (cut)

sigmoid colon

ovary

uterus

rectus
femoris m. (cut)

urinary bladder

symphysis pubis

adductor brevis m.

vastus lateralis m.

vastus intermedius m.

Clinical Connections

Additional readings engage the students by creating a richer understanding of the concepts presented and provide a real life connection to anatomy and physiology.

Medical Focus Readings

encourage students to explore clinical examples that they may see throughout their health care career or within their own family.

What's New Readings

offer fascinating information on treatments that are now experimental but promise to be particularly helpful in the future.

Effects of Aging

presents some of the age-related physical and functional changes that occur in the body.

"Education is not preparation for life; education is life itself."

– John Dewey

Homeostasis

Each system chapter ends with a major section on homeostasis to accompany the "Human Systems Work Together" illustration. Together, they describe how the system under discussion, with the help of other body systems, maintains a stable internal environment.

Human Systems Work Together   **SKELETAL SYSTEM**

How the Skeletal System works with other body systems

Integumentary System
Bones provide support for skin.
Skin protects bones; helps provide vitamin D for Ca²⁺ absorption.

Muscular System
Bones provide attachment sites for muscles; store Ca²⁺ for muscle function.
Muscular contraction causes bones to move at joints; muscles help protect bones.

Nervous System
Bones protect sense organs, brain, and spinal cord; store Ca²⁺ for nerve function.
Receptors send sensory input from bones to joints.

Endocrine System
Bones provide protection for glands; store Ca²⁺ used as second messenger.
Growth hormone regulates bone development; parathyroid hormone and calcitonin regulate Ca²⁺ content.

Cardiovascular System
Rib cage protects heart; red bone marrow produces blood cells; bones store Ca²⁺ for blood clotting.
Blood vessels deliver nutrients and oxygen to bones, carry away wastes.

Lymphatic System/Immunity
Red bone marrow produces white blood cells involved in immunity.
Lymphatic vessels pick up excess tissue fluid; immune system protects against infections.

Respiratory System
Rib cage protects lungs and assists breathing; bones provide attachment sites for muscles involved in breathing.
Gas exchange in lungs provides oxygen and rids body of carbon dioxide.

Digestive System
Jaws contain teeth that chew food; hyoid bone assists swallowing.
Digestive tract provides Ca²⁺ and other nutrients for bone growth and repair.

Urinary System
Bones provide support and protection.
Kidneys provide active vitamin D for Ca²⁺ absorption and help maintain blood level of Ca²⁺, needed for bone growth and repair.

Reproductive System
Bones provide support and protection of reproductive organs.
Sex hormones influence bone growth and density in males and females.

6.6 Homeostasis

The illustration in Human Systems Work Together on page 109 tells how the skeletal system assists other systems (buff color) and how other systems assist the skeletal system (aqua color). Let's review again the functions of the skeletal system, but this time as they relate to the other systems of the body.

Functions of the Skeletal System

The bones protect the internal organs. The rib cage protects the heart and lungs; the skull protects the brain; and the vertebrae protect the spinal cord. The endocrine organs, such as the pituitary gland, pineal gland, thymus, and thyroid gland, are also protected by bone. The nervous system and the endocrine system work together to control the other organs and, ultimately, homeostasis.

The bones assist all phases of respiration (Fig. 6.23). The rib cage assists the breathing process, enabling oxygen to enter the blood, where it is transported by red blood cells to the tissues. Red bone marrow produces the blood cells, including the red blood cells that transport oxygen. Without a supply of oxygen, the cells of the body could not efficiently produce ATP. ATP is needed for muscle contraction and for nerve conduction as well as for the many synthesis reactions that occur in cells.

The bones store and release calcium. The storage of calcium in the bones is under hormonal control. A dynamic equilibrium is maintained between the concentrations of calcium in the bones and in the blood. Calcium ions play a major role in muscle contraction and nerve conduction. Calcium ions also help regulate cellular metabolism. Protein hormones, which cannot enter cells, are called the first messenger, and a second messenger such as calcium ions jump-starts cellular metabolism, directing it to proceed in a particular way.

The bones assist the lymphatic system and immunity. Red bone marrow produces not only the red blood cells but also the white blood cells. The white cells, which congregate in the lymphatic organs, are involved in defending the body against

pathogens and cancerous cells. Without the ability to withstand foreign invasion, the body may quickly succumb to disease and die.

The bones assist digestion. The jaws contain sockets for the teeth, which chew food, and a place of attachment for the muscles that move the jaws. Chewing breaks food into pieces small enough to be swallowed and chemically digested. Without digestion, nutrients would not enter the body to serve as building blocks for repair and a source of energy for the production of ATP.

The skeleton is necessary to locomotion. Locomotion is efficient in human beings because they have a jointed skeleton for the attachment of muscles that move the bones. Our jointed skeleton allows us to seek out and move to a more suitable external environment in order to maintain the internal environment within reasonable limits.

Functions of Other Systems

How do the other systems of the body help the skeletal system carry out its functions?

The integumentary system and the muscles help the skeletal system protect internal organs. For example, anteriorly, the abdominal organs are only protected by muscle and skin.

The digestive system absorbs the calcium from food so that it enters the body. The plasma portion of blood transports calcium from the digestive system to the bones and any other organs that need it. The endocrine system regulates the storage of calcium in the bones.

The thyroid gland, a lymphatic organ, is instrumental in the maturity of certain white blood cells produced by the red bone marrow. The cardiovascular system transports the red blood cells as they deliver oxygen to the tissues and as they return to the lungs where they pick up oxygen.

Movement of the bones would be impossible without contraction of the muscles. In these and other ways, the systems of the body help the skeletal systems carry out its functions.

Figure 6.23 The skeletal system and cardiovascular system work together. **a.** Red bone marrow produces the blood cells, including the red and white blood cells. **b.** As the red blood cells pass through the capillaries, they deliver oxygen to the body's cells. Some white blood cells exit blood and enter the tissues at capillaries, where they phagocytize pathogens. Others stay in the blood (and lymph), where they produce antibodies against invaders.

red blood cell
white blood cells
red bone marrow
a. Production of blood cells

b. Red blood cells in capillaries

Clinical Key Terms

expand students' understanding of medical terminology and offer the chance to brush up on phonetic pronunciations of terms often used in clinical situations.

Selected New Terms

Basic Key Terms

abduction (ab-duk′shun), p. 106
adduction (uh-duk′shun), p. 106
appendicular skeleton (ap″en-dik′yū-ler skel′ē-ton), p. 97
articular cartilage (ar-tik′yū-ler kar′ti-lij), p. 84
articulation (ar-tik′yū-la′shun), p. 84
axial skeleton (ak′se-al skel′ē-ton), p. 89
bursa (bur′suh), p. 104
circumduction (ser″kum-duk′shun), p. 106
compact bone (kom′pakt bōn), p. 84
diaphysis (di-af′i-sis), p. 84
epiphyseal plate (ep″i-fiz′e-al plāt), p. 86
epiphysis (ē-pif′i-sis), p. 84
eversion (e-ver′zhun), p. 106
extension (ek-sten′shun), p. 106
flexion (flek′shun), p. 106
fontanel (fon″tuh-nel′), p. 90
hematopoiesis (hem″ah-to-poi-e′sis), p. 84
intervertebral disk (in″ter-ver′tē-bral disk), p. 94
inversion (in-ver′zhun), p. 106
ligament (lig′uh-ment), p. 104
medullary cavity (med′u-lār″e kav′i-te), p. 84
meniscus (mē-nis′kus), p. 104
ossification (os′-i-fi-ka′shun), p. 86
osteoblast (os′te-o-blast″), p. 86
osteoclast (os′te-o-klast″), p. 86

osteocyte (os′te-o-sit), p. 86
pectoral girdle (pek′tor-al ger′dl), p. 97
pelvic girdle (pel′vik ger′dl), p. 100
periosteum (per″e-os′te-um), p. 84
pronation (pro-na′shun), p. 106
red bone marrow (red bōn már′o), p. 84
rotation (ro-ta′shun), p. 106
sinus (si′nus), p. 90
spongy bone (spunj′e bōn), p. 84
supination (su″pi-na′shun), p. 106
suture (su′cher), p. 90
synovial fluid (si-no′ve-al flu′id), p. 104
synovial joint (si-no′ve-al joint), p. 104
synovial membrane (si-no′ve-al mem′brān), p. 104
vertebral column (ver′tē-bral kah′lum), p. 94

Clinical Key Terms

bursitis (ber-si′tis), p. 104
fracture (frak′cher), p. 87
herniated disk (her′ne-a-ted disk), p. 94
kyphosis (ki-fo′sis), p. 94
lordosis (lor-do′sis), p. 94
mastoiditis (mas″toi-di′tis), p. 90
osteoarthritis (os″te-o-ar-thri′tis), p. 107
osteoporosis (os″te-o-po-ro′sis), p. 107
rheumatoid arthritis (ru′muh-toid ar-thri′tis), p. 107
scoliosis (sko″le-o′sis), p. 94

Summary

6.1 Skeleton: Overview

A. The skeleton supports and protects the body; produces red blood cells; serves as a storehouse for inorganic calcium and phosphate ions and fat; and permits flexible movement.

B. A long bone has a shaft (diaphysis) and two ends (epiphyses), which are covered by articular cartilage. The diaphysis contains a medullary cavity with yellow marrow and is bounded by compact bone. The epiphyses contain spongy bone with red bone marrow that produces red blood cells.

C. Bone is a living tissue. It develops, grows, remodels, and repairs itself. In all these processes, osteoclasts

break down bone, and osteoblasts build bone.

D. Fractures are of various types, but repair requires four steps: (1) hematoma, (2) fibrocartilaginous callus, (3) bony callus, and (4) remodeling.

6.2 Axial Skeleton

The axial skeleton lies in the midline of the body and consists of the skull, the hyoid bone, the vertebral column, and the thoracic cage.

A. The skull is formed by the cranium and the facial bones. The cranium includes the frontal bone, two parietal bones, one occipital bone, two temporal bones, one sphenoid bone, and one ethmoid bone. The facial bones include two maxillae,

two palatine bones, two zygomatic bones, two lacrimal bones, two nasal bones, the vomer bone, two inferior nasal conchae, and the mandible.

B. The U-shaped hyoid bone is located in the neck. It anchors the tongue and does not articulate with any other bone.

C. The typical vertebra has a body, a vertebral arch surrounding the vertebral foramen, and a spinous process. The first two vertebrae are the atlas and axis. The vertebral column has four curvatures and contains the cervical, thoracic, lumbar, sacral, and coccygeal vertebrae, which are separated by intervertebral disks.

The Learning System

Students differ in how they learn best and how they respond to different learning situations. Effective instruction and lasting retention don't just happen; they result from materials that are carefully planned and organized in a logical sequence so that learning will occur.

Outline and Learning Objectives

An integrated outline and learning objectives that number the major topics of the chapter, give students the overall plan and sequence for the chapter.

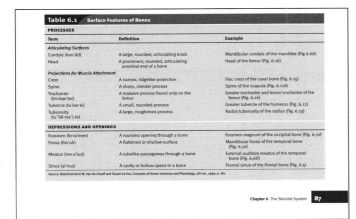

Key points are emphasized using a *variety of presentation techniques*, photos, drawings, and tables.

Key Boldface Terms

anchor students' under-standing of chapter concepts.

"I hear and I forget. I see and I remember. I do and I understand."

— Confucius

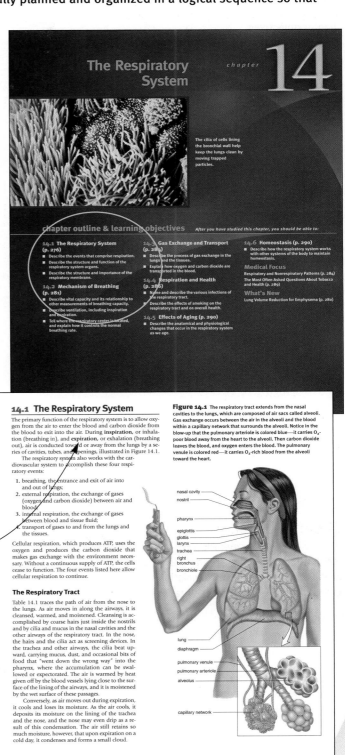

Learners are actively involved in end of chapter *questions and reinforcement activities* to confirm mastery of the chapter objectives.

D. The rib cage contains the thoracic vertebrae, ribs and associated cartilages, and the sternum.

6.3 **Appendicular Skeleton**
The appendicular skeleton consists of the bones of the pectoral girdle, upper limbs, pelvic girdle, and lower limbs.
A. The pectoral (shoulder) girdle contains two clavicles and two scapulae.
B. The upper limb contains the humerus, the radius, the ulna, and the bones of the hand (the carpals, metacarpals, and phalanges).
C. The pelvic girdle contains two coxal bones, as well as the sacrum and coccyx. The female pelvis is generally wider and more shallow than the male pelvis.
D. The lower limb contains the femur, the patella, the tibia, the fibula, and the bones of the foot (the tarsals, metatarsals, and phalanges).

6.4 **Joints (Articulations)**
A. Joints are regions of articulation between bones. They are

classified according to their degree of movement. Some joints are immovable, some are slightly movable, and some are freely movable (synovial). The different kinds of synovial joints are ball-and-socket, hinge, condyloid, pivot, gliding, and saddle.
B. Movements at joints are broadly classified as angular (flexion, extension, adduction, abduction); circular (circumduction, rotation, supination, and pronation); and special (inversion, eversion, elevation, and depression).

6.5 **Effects of Aging**
Two fairly common effects of aging on the skeletal system are arthritis and osteoporosis.

6.6 **Homeostasis**
A. The bones protect the internal organs: The rib cage protects the heart and lungs; the skull protects the brain; and the vertebrae protect the spinal cord.

B. The bones assist all phases of respiration. The rib cage assists the breathing process, and red bone marrow produces the red blood cells that transport oxygen.
C. The bones store and release calcium. Calcium ions play a major role in muscle contraction and nerve conduction. Calcium ions also help regulate cellular metabolism.
D. The bones assist the lymphatic system and immunity. Red bone marrow produces not only the red blood cells but also the white blood cells.
E. The bones assist digestion. The jaws contain sockets for the teeth, which chew food, and a place of attachment for the muscles that move the jaws.
F. The skeleton is necessary for locomotion. Locomotion is efficient in human beings because they have a jointed skeleton for the attachment of muscles that move the bones.

Study Questions

1. What are five functions of the skeleton? (p. 84)
2. What are five major categories of bones based on their shapes? (p. 84)
3. What are the parts of a long bone? What are some differences between compact bone and spongy bone? (pp. 84–85)
4. How does bone grow in children, and how is it remodeled in all age groups? (pp. 86–87)
5. What are the various types of fractures? What four steps are required for fracture repair? (p. 87)
6. List the bones of the axial and appendicular skeletons. (Fig. 6.4, p. 89)
7. What are the bones of the cranium and the face? What are the special features

of the temporal bones, sphenoid bone, and ethmoid bone? (pp. 90–93)
8. What are the parts of the vertebral column, and what are its curvatures? Distinguish between the atlas, axis, sacrum, and coccyx. (pp. 94–95)
9. What are the bones of the rib cage, and what are several of its functions? (p. 96)
10. What are the bones of the pectoral girdle? Give examples to demonstrate the flexibility of the pectoral girdle. What are the special features of a scapula? (p. 97)
11. What are the bones of the upper limb? What are the special features of these bones? (pp. 98–100)
12. What are the bones of the pelvic girdle, and what are their functions? (pp. 100–101)

13. What are the false and true pelvises, and what are several differences between the male and female pelvises? (p. 101)
14. What are the bones of the lower limb? Describe the special features of these bones. (pp. 102–3)
15. How are joints classified? Give examples of each type of joint. (p. 104)
16. How can joint movements permitted by synovial joints be categorized? Give an example of each category. (p. 106)
17. How does aging affect the skeletal system? (p. 107)
18. What functions of the skeletal system are particularly helpful in maintaining homeostasis? (pp. 108–9)

Objective Questions

I. **Match the items in the key to the bones listed in questions 1–6.**
Key:
   a. forehead
   b. chin
   c. cheekbone
   d. elbow
   e. shoulder blade
   f. hip
   g. ankle
1. temporal and zygomatic bones
2. tibia and fibula
3. frontal bone
4. ulna
5. coxal bone
6. scapula
II. **Match the items in the key to the bones listed in questions 7–13.**

Key:
   a. external auditory meatus
   b. cribriform plate
   c. xiphoid process
   d. glenoid cavity
   e. olecranon process
   f. acetabulum
   g. greater and lesser trochanters
7. scapula
8. sternum
9. femur
10. temporal bone
11. coxal bone
12. ethmoid bone
13. ulna
III. **Fill in he blanks.**
14. Long bones are _____ than they are wide.
15. The epiphysis of a long bone contains _____ bone,

where red blood cells are produced.
16. The _____ are the air-filled spaces in the cranium.
17. The sacrum is a part of the _____, and the sternum is a part of the _____.
18. The pectoral girdle is specialized for _____, while the pelvic girdle is specialized for _____.
19. The term *phalanges* is used for the bones of both the _____ and the _____.
20. The knee is a freely movable (synovial) joint of the _____ type.

Medical Terminology Reinforcement Exercise

Consult Appendix B for help in pronouncing and analyzing the meaning of the terms that follow.

1. chondromalacia (kon″dro-muh-la′she-uh)
2. osteomyelitis (os″te-o-mi″e-li′tis)
3. craniosynostosis (kra″ne-o-sin″os-to′sis)
4. myelography (mi″ĕ-log′ruh-fe)
5. acrocyanosis (ak″ro-si″uh-no′sis)
6. syndactylism (sin-dak′ti-lizm)
7. orthopedist (or″tho-pe′dist)
8. prognathism (prog′nah-thizm)
9. micropodia (mi″kro-po′de-uh)
10. arthroscopic (ar″thro-skop′ik)
11. bursectomy (ber-sek′to-me)
12. synovitis (sin-o-vi′tis)
13. acephaly (a-sef′uh-le)
14. sphenoidostomy (sfe-noy-dos′to-me)
15. acetabuloplasty (as-ĕ-tab′yŭ-lo-plas-te)

Website Link

Visit the Student Edition of the Online Learning Center at http://www.mhhe.com/maderap5 for additional quizzes, interactive learning exercises, and other study tools.

Organization of the Body

Magnetic resonance imaging (MRI) of the head and neck in sagittal section. MRI is particularly useful in viewing soft tissues such as the brain.

chapter outline & learning objectives

After you have studied this chapter, you should be able to:

1.1 The Human Body (p. 2)
- Define anatomy and physiology, and explain how they are related.
- Describe each level of organization of the body with reference to an example.

1.2 Anatomical Terms (p. 3)
- Use anatomical terms to describe the relative positions of the body parts, the regions of the body, and the planes by which the body can be sectioned.

1.3 Body Cavities and Membranes (p. 6)
- List the cavities of the body, and state their locations.

- Name the organs located in each of the body cavities.
- Name the membranes that line each body cavity and adhere to the organs.

1.4 Organ Systems (p. 8)
- List the organ systems of the body, and state the major organs associated with each.
- Describe in general the functions of each organ system.

1.5 Homeostasis (p. 10)
- Describe how a feedback system maintains homeostasis.
- Define disease, and explain the difference between a local and a systemic disease.

Medical Focus
Imaging the Body (p. 14)

What's New
Organs for Transplant (p. 9)

Part I

Figure 1.1 Levels of organization of the human body. Each level is more complex than the previous level.

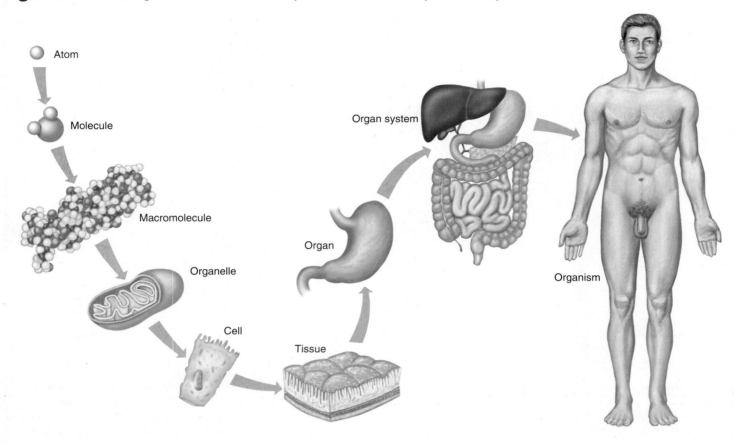

Atom

Molecule

Macromolecule

Organelle

Cell

Tissue

Organ

Organ system

Organism

1.1 The Human Body

Anatomy and physiology is the study of the human body. **Anatomy** is concerned with the structure of a part. For example, the stomach is a J-shaped, pouchlike organ (Fig. 1.1). The stomach wall has thick folds, which disappear as the stomach expands to increase its capacity. **Physiology** is concerned with the function of a part. For example, the stomach temporarily stores food, secretes digestive juices, and passes on partially digested food to the small intestine.

Anatomy and physiology are closely connected in that the structure of an organ suits its function. For example, the stomach's pouchlike shape and ability to expand are suitable to its function of storing food. In addition, the microscopic structure of the stomach wall is suitable to its secretion of digestive juices, as we shall see in Chapter 15.

Organization of Body Parts

The structure of the body can be studied at different *levels of organization* (Fig. 1.1). First, all substances, including body parts, are composed of chemicals made up of submicroscopic particles called **atoms.** Atoms join to form **molecules,** which

can in turn join to form **macromolecules.** For example, molecules called amino acids join to form a macromolecule called protein, which makes up the bulk of our muscles.

Macromolecules are found in all **cells,** the basic units of all living things. Within cells are **organelles,** tiny structures that perform cellular functions. For example, the organelle called the nucleus is especially concerned with cell reproduction; another organelle, called the mitochondrion, supplies the cell with energy.

Tissues are the next level of organization. A **tissue** is composed of similar types of cells and performs a specific function. An **organ** is composed of several types of tissues and performs a particular function within an **organ system.** For example, the stomach is an organ that is a part of the digestive system. It has a specific role in this system, whose overall function is to supply the body with the nutrients needed for growth and repair. The other systems of the body (see page 13) also have specific functions.

All of the body systems together make up the **organism**—such as, a human being. Human beings are complex animals, but this complexity can be broken down and studied at ever simpler levels. Each simpler level is organized and constructed in a particular way.

Figure 1.2 Directional terms. Directional terms tell us where body parts are located with reference to the body in anatomical position.

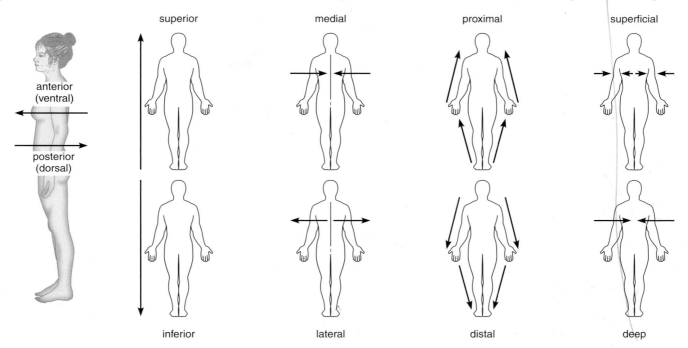

1.2 Anatomical Terms

Certain terms are used to describe the location of body parts, regions of the body, and imaginary planes by which the body can be sectioned. You should become familiar with these terms before your study of anatomy and physiology begins. Anatomical terms are useful only if everyone has in mind the same position of the body and is using the same reference points. Therefore, we will assume that the body is in the *anatomical position:* standing erect, with face forward, arms at the sides, and palms and toes directed forward, as illustrated in Figure 1.1.

Directional Terms

Directional terms are used to describe the location of one body part in relation to another (Fig. 1.2):

Anterior (ventral) means that a body part is located toward the front. The windpipe (trachea) is anterior to the esophagus.

Posterior (dorsal) means that a body part is located toward the back. The heart is posterior to the rib cage.

Superior means that a body part is located above another part, or toward the head. The face is superior to the neck.

Inferior means that a body part is below another part, or toward the feet. The navel is inferior to the chin.

Medial means that a body part is nearer than another part to an imaginary midline of the body. The bridge of the nose is medial to the eyes.

Lateral means that a body part is farther away from the midline. The eyes are lateral to the nose.

Proximal means that a body part is closer to the point of attachment or closer to the trunk. The elbow is proximal to the hand.

Distal means that a body part is farther from the point of attachment or farther from the trunk or torso. The hand is distal to the elbow.

Superficial (external) means that a body part is located near the surface. The skin is superficial to the muscles.

Deep (internal) means that the body part is located away from the surface. The intestines are deep to the spine.

Central means that a body part is situated at the center of the body or an organ. The central nervous system is located along the main axis of the body.

Peripheral means that a body part is situated away from the center of the body or an organ. The peripheral nervous system is located outside the central nervous system.

Figure 1.3 Terms for body parts and areas. **a.** Anterior. **b.** Posterior.

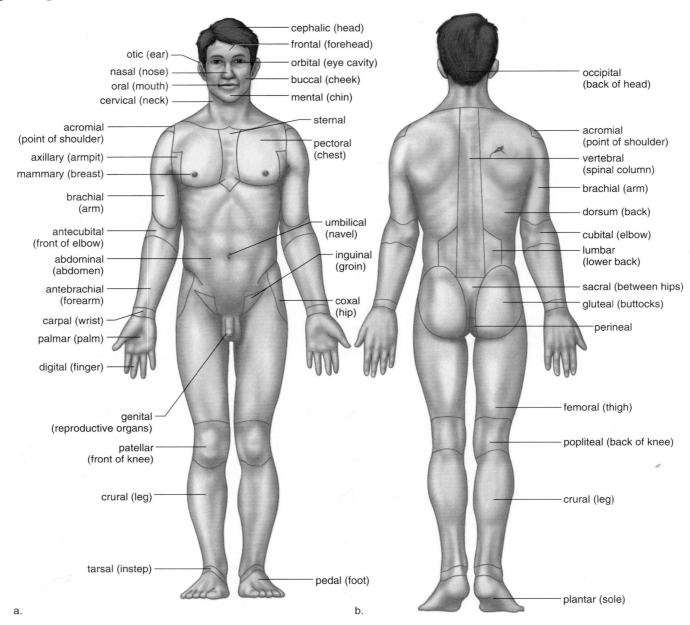

cephalic (head)
frontal (forehead)
otic (ear)
nasal (nose)
oral (mouth)
cervical (neck)
orbital (eye cavity)
buccal (cheek)
mental (chin)
acromial
(point of shoulder)
axillary (armpit)
mammary (breast)
sternal
pectoral
(chest)
brachial
(arm)
antecubital
(front of elbow)
abdominal
(abdomen)
antebrachial
(forearm)
carpal (wrist)
palmar (palm)
digital (finger)
umbilical
(navel)
inguinal
(groin)
coxal
(hip)
genital
(reproductive organs)
patellar
(front of knee)
crural (leg)
tarsal (instep)
pedal (foot)

occipital
(back of head)
acromial
(point of shoulder)
vertebral
(spinal column)
brachial (arm)
dorsum (back)
cubital (elbow)
lumbar
(lower back)
sacral (between hips)
gluteal (buttocks)
perineal
femoral (thigh)
popliteal (back of knee)
crural (leg)
plantar (sole)

a.

b.

Regions of the Body

The human body can be divided into axial and appendicular portions. The **axial portion** includes the head, neck, and trunk. The trunk can be divided into the thorax, abdomen, and pelvis. The pelvis is that part of the trunk associated with the hips. The **appendicular portion** of the human body includes the limbs—that is, the upper limbs and the lower limbs.

The human body is further divided as shown in Figure 1.3. The labels in Figure 1.3 do not include the word "region." It is understood that you will supply the word region in each case. The scientific name for each region is followed by the common name for that region. For example, the cephalic region is commonly called the head.

Notice that the upper arm includes among other parts the brachial region (arm) and the antebrachial region (forearm), and the lower limb includes among other parts the femoral region (thigh) and the crural region (leg). In other words, contrary to common usage, the terms arm and leg refer to only a part of the upper limb and lower limb, respectively.

Most likely, it will take practice to learn the terms in Figure 1.3. One way to practice might be to point to various regions of your own body and see if you can give the scientific name for that region. Check your answer against the figure.

Figure 1.4 Body planes and sections. The planes shown in **(a)**, **(b)**, and **(c)** are typically used as sites for sectioning the body as shown in **(d)**, **(e)**, and **(f)**.

a. Sagittal (median) plane

b. Frontal (coronal) plane

c. Transverse (horizontal) plane

d. Sagittal section of
pelvic cavity

e. Frontal section of
thoracic cavity

f. Transverse section of
head at eye level

Planes and Sections of the Body

To observe the structure of an internal body part, it is customary to section (cut) the body along a plane. A plane is an imaginary flat surface passing through the body. The body is customarily sectioned along the following planes (Fig. 1.4):

A **sagittal** (median) **plane** extends lengthwise and divides the body into right and left portions. A midsagittal plane passes exactly through the midline of the body. The pelvic organs are often shown in midsagittal section (Fig. 1.4*d*). Sagittal cuts that are not along the midline are called parasagittal sections.

A **frontal** (coronal) **plane** also extends lengthwise, but it is perpendicular to a sagittal plane and divides the body or an organ into anterior and posterior portions. The thoracic organs are often illustrated in frontal section (Fig. 1.4*e*).

A **transverse** (horizontal) **plane** is perpendicular to the body's long axis and therefore divides the body horizontally to produce a cross section. A transverse cut divides the body or an organ into superior and inferior portions. Figure 1.4*f* is a transverse section of the head at the level of the eyes.

The terms *longitudinal section* and *cross section* are often applied to body parts that have been removed and cut either lengthwise or straight across, respectively.

Figure 1.5 The two major body cavities and their subdivisions. **a.** Left lateral view **b.** Frontal view.

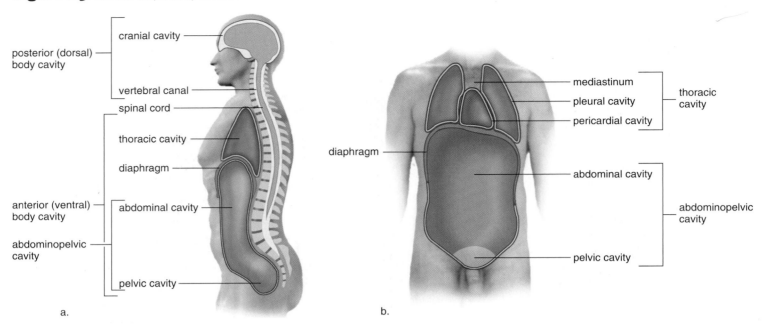

a.

b.

1.3 Body Cavities and Membranes

During embryonic development, the body is first divided into two internal cavities: the posterior (dorsal) body cavity and the anterior (ventral) body cavity. Each of these major cavities is then subdivided into smaller cavities. The cavities, as well as the organs in the cavities (called the **viscera**), are lined by membranes.

Posterior (Dorsal) Body Cavity

The posterior body cavity is subdivided into two parts: (1) The **cranial cavity**, enclosed by the bony cranium, contains the brain. (2) The **vertebral canal**, enclosed by vertebrae, contains the spinal cord (Fig. 1.5a)

The posterior body cavity is lined by three membranous layers called the **meninges**. The most inner of the meninges is tightly bound to the surface of the brain and the spinal cord. The space between this layer and the next layer is filled with cerebrospinal fluid. **Spinal meningitis**, a serious condition, is an inflammation of the meninges usually caused by an infection.

Anterior (Ventral) Body Cavity

The large anterior body cavity is subdivided into the superior **thoracic cavity** and the inferior **abdominopelvic cavity** (Fig. 1.5a). A muscular partition called the **diaphragm** separates the two cavities. Membranes that line these cavities are called **serous membranes** because they secrete a fluid that has just about the same composition as serum, a component of

blood. Serous fluid between the smooth serous membranes reduces friction as the viscera rub against each other or against the body wall.

To understand the relationship between serous membranes and an organ, imagine a ball that is pushed in on one side by your fist. Your fist would be covered by one membrane (called a **visceral membrane**), and there would be a small space between this inner membrane and the outer membrane (called a **parietal membrane**):

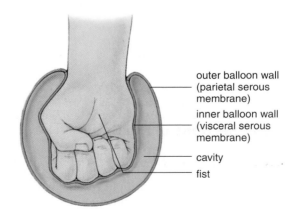

Thoracic Cavity

The thoracic cavity is enclosed by the rib cage, and has three portions: the left, right, and medial portions. The medial portion, called the **mediastinum,** contains the heart, thymus gland, trachea, esophagus, and other structures (Fig. 1.5b).

Figure 1.6 Clinical subdivisions of the abdomen into quadrants. These subdivisions help physicians identify the location of various symptoms.

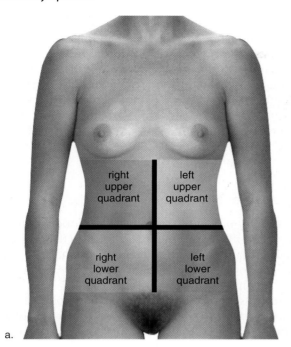

right upper quadrant | left upper quadrant

right lower quadrant | left lower quadrant

a.

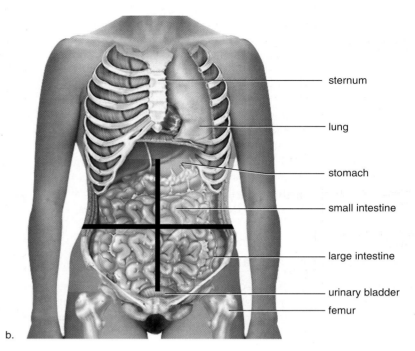

- sternum
- lung
- stomach
- small intestine
- large intestine
- urinary bladder
- femur

b.

The right and left portions of the thoracic cavity contain the lungs. The lungs are surrounded by a serous membrane called the **pleura**. The **parietal pleura** lies next to the thoracic wall, and the **visceral pleura** adheres to a lung. In between the two pleura, the *pleural cavity* is filled with *pleural fluid*. Similarly, in the mediastinum, the heart is covered by the two-layered membrane called the pericardium. The **visceral pericardium** which adheres to the heart is separated from the **parietal pericardium** by a small space called the *pericardial cavity* (Fig. 1.5*b*). This small space contains *pericardial fluid*.

Abdominopelvic Cavity

The abdominopelvic cavity has two portions: the superior **abdominal cavity** and the inferior **pelvic cavity**. The stomach, liver, spleen, gallbladder, and most of the small and large intestines are in the abdominal cavity. The pelvic cavity contains the rectum, the urinary bladder, the internal reproductive organs, and the rest of the large intestine. Males have an external extension of the abdominal wall, called the **scrotum**, where the testes are found.

Many of the organs of the abdominopelvic cavity are covered by the **visceral peritoneum**, while the wall of the abdominal cavity is lined with the **parietal peritoneum**. *Peritoneal fluid* fills the cavity between the visceral and parietal peritoneum. **Peritonitis,** another serious condition, is an inflammation of the peritoneum, again usually caused by an infection. Table 1.1 summarizes our discussion of body cavities and membranes.

Clinically speaking, the abdominopelvic cavity is divided into four quadrants by running a transverse plane across the midsagittal plane at the point of the navel (Fig. 1.6*a*). Physicians commonly use these quadrants to identify the locations of patients' symptoms. The four quadrants are: (1) right upper quadrant, (2) left upper quadrant, (3) right lower quadrant, and (4) left lower quadrant.

Figure 1.6*b* shows the organs that lie within these four quadrants.

Table 1.1	Body Cavities and Membranes	
Name of Cavity	**Contents**	**Membranes**
POSTERIOR BODY CAVITY		
Cranial cavity	Brain	Meninges
Vertebral canal	Spinal cord	Meninges
ANTERIOR BODY CAVITY		
Thoracic Cavity		
	Lungs	Pleura
	Heart	Pericardium
Abdominopelvic Cavity		
Abdominal cavity	Digestive organs, liver, kidneys	Peritoneum
Pelvic cavity	Reproductive organs, urinary bladder, rectum	Peritoneum

1.4 Organ Systems

The organs of the body work together in systems. Today, certain diseased organs can be replaced by **organ transplantation,** during which a healthy organ is received from a donor. In the future, tissue engineering may provide organs for transplant, as discussed in the Medical Focus on page 9.

The reference figures in Appendix A can serve as an aid to learning the 11 organ systems and their placement. The type of illustration that will be used at the end of each of the organ system chapters is introduced on page 13. In this chapter, the illustration demonstrates the general functions of the body's organ systems. The corresponding illustrations in the organ system chapters will show how a particular organ system interacts with all the other systems. In this text, the organ systems of the body have been divided into four categories, as discussed next.

Support, Movement, and Protection

The **integumentary system,** discussed in Chapter 5, includes the skin and accessory organs, such as the hair, nails, sweat glands, and sebaceous glands. The skin protects underlying tissues, helps regulate body temperature, contains sense organs, and even synthesizes certain chemicals that affect the rest of the body.

The **skeletal system** and the **muscular system** give the body support and are involved in the ability of the body and its parts to move.

The skeletal system, discussed in Chapter 6, consists of the bones of the skeleton and associated cartilage, as well as the ligaments that bind these structures together. The skeleton protects body parts. For example, the skull forms a protective encasement for the brain, as does the rib cage for the heart and lungs. Some bones produce blood cells, and all bones are a storage area for calcium and phosphorus salts. The skeleton as a whole serves as a place of attachment for the muscles.

Contraction of *skeletal muscles,* discussed in Chapter 7, accounts for our ability to move voluntarily and to respond to outside stimuli. These muscles also maintain posture and are responsible for the production of body heat. *Cardiac muscle* and *smooth muscle* are called involuntary muscles because they contract automatically. Cardiac muscle makes up the heart, and smooth muscle is found within the walls of internal organs.

Integration and Coordination

The **nervous system,** discussed in Chapter 8, consists of the brain, spinal cord, and associated nerves. The nerves conduct nerve impulses from the sense organs to the brain and spinal cord. They also conduct nerve impulses from the brain and spinal cord to the muscles and glands.

The *sense organs,* discussed in Chapter 9, provide us with information about the outside environment. This information is then processed by the brain and spinal cord, and the individual responds to environmental stimuli through the muscular system.

The **endocrine system,** discussed in Chapter 10, consists of the hormonal glands that secrete chemicals that serve as messengers between body parts. Both the nervous and endocrine systems help maintain a relatively constant internal environment by coordinating and regulating the functions of the body's other systems. The nervous system acts quickly but has a short-lived effect; the endocrine system acts more slowly but has a more sustained effect on body parts. The endocrine system also helps maintain the proper functioning of the male and female reproductive organs.

Maintenance of the Body

The internal environment of the body is the blood within the blood vessels and the tissue fluid that surrounds the cells. Five systems add substances to and/or remove substances from the blood: the cardiovascular, lymphatic, respiratory, digestive, and urinary systems.

The **cardiovascular system,** discussed in Chapter 12, consists of the heart and the blood vessels that carry blood through the body. Blood transports nutrients and oxygen to the cells, and removes waste molecules to be excreted from the body. Blood also contains cells produced by the **lymphatic system,** discussed in Chapter 13. The lymphatic system protects the body from disease.

The **respiratory system,** discussed in Chapter 14, consists of the lungs and the tubes that take air to and from the lungs. The respiratory system brings oxygen into the lungs and takes carbon dioxide out of the lungs.

The **digestive system** (see Fig. 1.1), discussed in Chapter 15, consists of the mouth, esophagus, stomach, small intestine, and large intestine (colon), along with the accessory organs: teeth, tongue, salivary glands, liver, gallbladder, and pancreas. This system receives food and digests it into nutrient molecules, which can enter the cells of the body.

The **urinary system,** discussed in Chapter 16, contains the kidneys and the urinary bladder. This system rids the body of nitrogenous wastes and helps regulate the fluid level and chemical content of the blood.

Reproduction and Development

The male and female **reproductive systems,** discussed in Chapter 17, contain different organs. The *male reproductive system* consists of the testes, other glands, and various ducts that conduct semen to and through the penis. The *female reproductive system* consists of the ovaries, uterine tubes, uterus, vagina, and external genitalia. Both systems produce sex cells, but in addition, the female system receives the sex cells of the male and also nourishes and protects the fetus until the time of birth. Development before birth and the process of birth are discussed in Chapter 18.

Organs for Transplant

Transplantation of a human kidney, heart, liver, pancreas, lung, and other organs is now possible due to two major breakthroughs. First, solutions have been developed that preserve donor organs for several hours. This made it possible for one young boy to undergo surgery for 16 hours, during which time he received five different organs. Second, rejection of transplanted organs is now prevented by immunosuppressive drugs; therefore, organs can be donated by unrelated individuals, living or dead. Even so, rejection is less likely to happen if the donor's tissues "match" those of the recipient—that is, their cell surface molecules should be similar to one another. Living individuals can donate one kidney, a portion of their liver, and certainly bone marrow, which quickly regenerates.

After death, it is still possible to give the "gift of life" to someone else—over 25 organs and tissues from the same person can be used for transplants at that time. A liver transplant, for example, can save the life of a child born with biliary atresia, a congenital defect in which the bile ducts do not form. Dr. Thomas Starzl, a pioneer in this field, reports a 90% chance of complete rehabilitation among children who survive a liver transplant. (He has also tried animal-to-human liver transplants, but so far, these have not been successful.) So many heart recipients are now alive and healthy that they have formed basketball and softball teams, demonstrating the normalcy of their lives after surgery.

One problem persists: The number of Americans waiting for organs now stands at over 80,000 and is getting larger by the day. Although it is possible for people to signify their willingness to donate organs at the time of their death, only a small percentage do so. Organ and tissue donors need only sign a donor card and carry it at all times. In many states, the back of the driver's license acts as a donor card. Age is no drawback, but the donor should have been in good health prior to death. Organ and tissue donation does not interfere with funeral arrangements, and most religions do not object to the donation. Family members should know ahead of time about the desire to become a donor because they will be asked to sign permission papers at the time of death.

Especially because so many Americans are waiting for organs and a chance for a normal life, researchers are trying to develop organs in the laboratory. Just a few years ago, scientists believed that transplant organs had to come from humans or other animals. Now, however, tissue engineering is demonstrating that it is possible to make some bioartificial organs—hybrids created from a combination of living cells and biodegradable polymers. Presently, lab-grown hybrid tissues are on the market. For example, a product composed of skin cells growing on a polymer is used to temporarily cover the wounds of burn patients. Similarly, damaged cartilage can be replaced with a hybrid tissue produced after chondrocytes are harvested from a patient. Another connective tissue product made from fibroblasts and collagen is available to help heal deep wounds without scarring. Soon to come are a host of other products, including replacement corneas, heart valves, bladder valves, and breast tissue.

The ultimate goal of tissue engineering is to produce fully functioning transplant organs in the laboratory. After nine years, a Harvard Medical School team headed by Anthony Atala has produced a working urinary bladder. After testing the bladder in laboratory animals, the Harvard group is ready to test it in humans whose own bladders have been damaged by accident or disease, or will not function properly due to a congenital birth defect. Another group of scientists has been able to grow arterial blood vessels in the laboratory. Tissue engineers are hopeful that they will one day produce more complex organs such as a liver or kidney.

Figure 1A Laboratory-produced bladder. This urinary bladder was made in the laboratory by tissue engineering.

1.5 Homeostasis

Homeostasis is the relative constancy of the body's internal environment. Because of homeostasis, even though external conditions may change dramatically, internal conditions stay within a narrow range. For example, regardless of how cold or hot it gets, the temperature of the body stays around 37°C (97° to 99°F). No matter how acidic your meal, the pH of your blood is usually about 7.4, and even if you eat a candy bar, the amount of sugar in your blood is just about 0.1%.

It is important to realize that internal conditions are not absolutely constant; they tend to fluctuate above and below a particular value. Therefore, the internal state of the body is often described as one of *dynamic* equilibrium. If internal conditions change to any great degree, illness results. This makes the study of homeostatic mechanisms medically important.

Negative Feedback

Negative feedback is the primary homeostatic mechanism that keeps a variable close to a particular value, or set point. A homeostatic mechanism has three components: a sensor, a regulatory center, and an effector (Fig. 1.7a). The sensor detects a change in the internal environment; the regulatory center activates the effector; the effector reverses the change and brings conditions back to normal again. Now, the sensor is no longer activated.

Mechanical Example

A home heating system illustrates how a negative feedback mechanism works (Fig. 1.7b). You set the thermostat at, say, 68°F. This is the set point. The thermostat contains a thermometer, a sensor that detects when the room temperature falls below the set point. The thermostat is also the regulatory center; it turns the furnace on. The furnace plays the role of the effector. The heat given off by the furnace raises the temperature of the room to 70°F. Now, the furnace turns off.

Notice that a negative feedback mechanism prevents change in the same direction; the room does not get warmer and warmer because warmth inactivates the system.

Human Example: Regulation of Blood Pressure

Negative feedback mechanisms in the body function similarly to the mechanical model. For example, when blood pressure falls, sensory receptors signal a regulatory center in the brain (Fig. 1.7c). This center sends out nerve impulses to the arterial walls so that they constrict. Once the blood pressure rises, the system is inactivated.

Figure 1.7 Negative feedback. In each example, a sensor detects an internal environmental change and signals a regulatory center. The center activates an effector, which reverses this change. **a.** The general pattern. **b.** A mechanical example. **c.** A human example.

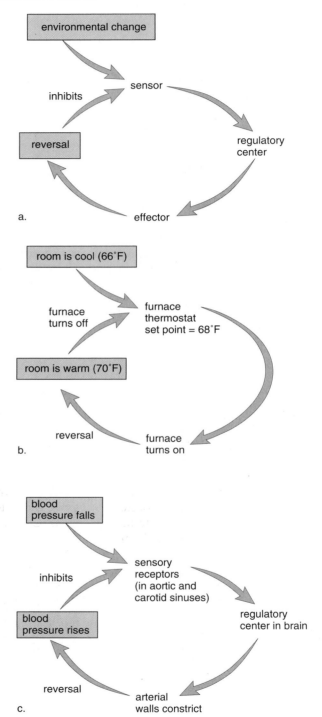

Figure 1.8 Homeostasis and body temperature regulation. Negative feedback mechanisms control body temperature so that it remains relatively stable at 37°C. These mechanisms return the temperature to normal when it fluctuates above and below this set point.

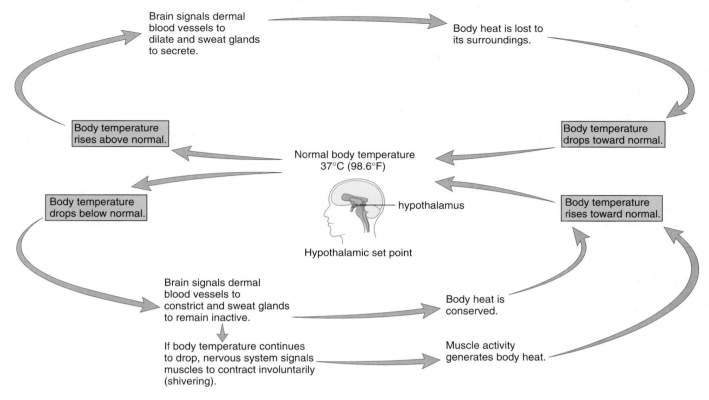

Human Example: Regulation of Body Temperature

The thermostat for body temperature is located in a part of the brain called the hypothalamus. When the body temperature falls below normal, the regulatory center directs (via nerve impulses) the blood vessels of the skin to constrict (Fig.1.8). This conserves heat. If body temperature falls even lower, the regulatory center sends nerve impulses to the skeletal muscles, and shivering occurs. Shivering generates heat, and gradually body temperature rises to 37°C. When the temperature rises to normal, the regulatory center is inactivated.

When the body temperature is higher than normal, the regulatory center directs the blood vessels of the skin to dilate. This allows more blood to flow near the surface of the body, where heat can be lost to the environment. In addition, the nervous system activates the sweat glands, and the evaporation of sweat helps lower body temperature. Gradually, body temperature decreases to 37°C.

Positive Feedback

Positive feedback is a mechanism that brings about an ever greater change in the same direction. A positive feedback mechanism can be harmful, as when a fever causes metabolic changes that push the fever still higher. Death occurs at a body temperature of 45°C because cellular proteins denature at this temperature and metabolism stops.

Still, positive feedback loops such as those involved in blood clotting, the stomach's digestion of protein, and childbirth assist the body in completing a process that has a definite cutoff point.

Consider that when a woman is giving birth, the head of the baby begins to press against the cervix, stimulating sensory receptors there. When nerve impulses reach the brain, the brain causes the pituitary gland to secrete the hormone oxytocin. Oxytocin travels in the blood and causes the uterus to contract. As labor continues, the cervix is ever more stimulated, and uterine contractions become ever stronger until birth occurs.

Homeostasis and Body Systems

The internal environment of the body consists of blood and tissue fluid. Tissue fluid, which bathes all the cells of the body, is refreshed when molecules such as oxygen and nutrients move into tissue fluid from the blood, and when wastes move from tissue fluid into the blood (Fig. 1.9). Tissue fluid remains constant only as long as blood composition remains constant.

As described in the Human Systems Work Together illustration on page 13, all systems of the body contribute toward maintaining homeostasis and therefore a relatively constant internal environment. The cardiovascular system conducts blood to and away from capillaries, where exchange occurs. The heart pumps the blood and thereby keeps it moving toward the capillaries. The formed elements also contribute to homeostasis. Red blood cells transport oxygen and participate in the transport of carbon dioxide. Platelets participate in the clotting process. The lymphatic system is accessory to the cardiovascular system. Lymphatic capillaries collect excess tissue fluid, and this is returned via lymphatic veins to the cardiovascular veins. Lymph nodes help purify lymph and keep it free of pathogens. This action is assisted by the white blood cells that are housed within lymph nodes.

The respiratory system adds oxygen to and removes carbon dioxide from the blood. It also plays a role in regulating blood pH because removal of CO_2 causes the pH to rise and helps prevent acidosis. The digestive system takes in and digests food, providing nutrient molecules that enter the blood and replace the nutrients that are constantly being used by the body cells. The liver, an organ that assists the digestive process by producing bile, also plays a significant role in regulating blood composition. Immediately after glucose enters the blood, any excess is removed by the liver and stored as glycogen. Later, the glycogen can be broken down to replace the glucose used by the body cells; in this way, the glucose composition of blood remains constant. The liver also removes toxic chemicals, such as ingested alcohol and other drugs. The liver makes urea, a nitrogenous end product of protein metabolism. Urea and other metabolic waste molecules are excreted by the kidneys, which are a part of the urinary system. Urine formation by the kidneys is extremely critical to the body, not only because it rids the body of unwanted substances, but also because urine formation offers an opportunity to carefully regulate blood volume, salt balance, and pH.

The integumentary, skeletal, and muscular systems protect the internal organs we have been discussing. In addition, the integumentary system produces vitamin D, while the skeletal system stores minerals and produces the blood cells. The muscular system produces the heat that maintains the internal temperature.

The nervous system and the endocrine system regulate the other systems of the body. They work together to control body

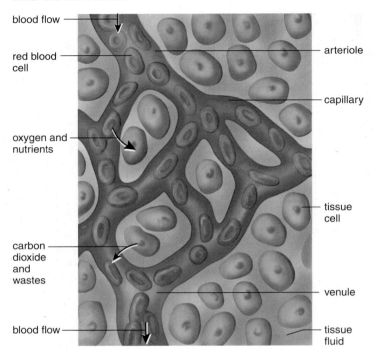

Figure 1.9 Regulation of tissue fluid composition. Cells are surrounded by tissue fluid (blue), which is continually refreshed because oxygen and nutrient molecules constantly exit the bloodstream, and carbon dioxide and waste molecules continually enter the bloodstream.

systems so that homeostasis is maintained. We have already seen that in negative feedback mechanisms, sensory receptors send nerve impulses to regulatory centers in the brain, which then direct effectors to become active. Effectors can be muscles or glands. Muscles bring about an immediate change. Endocrine glands secrete hormones that bring about a slower, more lasting change that keeps the internal environment relatively stable.

Disease

Disease is present when homeostasis fails and the body (or part of the body) no longer functions properly. The effects may be limited or widespread. A *local disease* is more or less restricted to a specific part of the body. On the other hand, a **systemic disease** affects the entire body or involves several organ systems. Diseases may also be classified on the basis of their severity and duration. **Acute diseases** occur suddenly and generally last a short time. **Chronic diseases** tend to be less severe, develop slowly, and are long term.

The medical profession has many ways of diagnosing disease including, as discussed in the Medical Focus on page 14, imaging internal body parts.

Human Systems Work Together

Integumentary System
External support and protection of body; helps maintain body temperature.

Respiratory System
Rids the blood of carbon dioxide and supplies the blood with oxygen; helps maintain the pH of the blood.

Cardiovascular System
Transport of nutrients to body cells and transport of wastes away from cells.

Skeletal System
Internal support and protection; body movement; production of blood cells.

Lymphatic System/Immunity
Drainage of tissue fluid; purifies tissue fluid and keeps it free of pathogens.

Muscular System
Body movement; production of heat that maintains body temperature.

Digestive System
Breakdown of food and absorption of nutrients into blood.

Nervous System
Regulatory centers for control of all body systems; learning and memory.

Urinary System
Maintenance of volume and chemical composition of blood.

Endocrine System
Secretion of hormones for chemical regulation of all body systems.

Reproductive System
Production of sperm and egg; transfer of sperm to female system where development occurs.

Medical Focus

Imaging the Body

Imaging the body for diagnosis of disease is based on chemical properties of subatomic particles. For example, X rays, which are produced when high-speed electrons strike a heavy metal, have long been used to image body parts. Dense structures such as bone absorb X rays well and show up as light areas; soft tissues absorb X rays to a lesser extent and show up as dark areas on photographic film. During CAT (computerized axial tomography) scans, X rays are sent through the body at various angles, and a computer uses the X-ray information to form a series of cross sections (Fig. 1B). CAT scanning has reduced the need for exploratory surgery and can guide the surgeon in visualizing complex body structures during surgical procedures.

PET (positron emission tomography) is a variation on CT scanning. Radioactively labeled substances are injected into the body; metabolically active tissues tend to take up these substances and then emit gamma rays. A computer uses the gamma-ray information to again generate cross-sectional images of the body, but this time, the image indicates metabolic activity, not structure (see Fig. 2.3). PET scanning is used to diagnose brain disorders, such as a brain tumor, Alzheimer disease, epilepsy, or stroke.

During MRI (magnetic resonance imaging), the patient lies in a massive, hollow, cylindrical magnet and is exposed to short bursts of a powerful magnetic field. This causes the protons in the nuclei of hydrogen atoms to align. Then, when exposed to strong radio waves, the protons move out of alignment and produce signals. A computer changes these signals into an image (see page 1). Tissues

Figure 1B CAT (computerized axial tomography).

with many hydrogen atoms (such as fat) show up as bright areas, while tissues with few hydrogen atoms (such as bone) appear black. This is the opposite of an X ray, which is why MRI is more useful than an X ray for imaging soft tissues. However, many people cannot undergo MRI, because the magnetic field can actually pull a metal object out of the body, such as a tooth filling, a prosthesis, or a pacemaker!

Selected New Terms

Basic Key Terms

abdominal cavity (ab-dom'ĭ-nal kav'ĭ-te), p. 7
abdominopelvic cavity (ab-dom"ĭ-no-pel'vik kav'ĭ-te), p. 6
anatomy (uh-nat'o-me), p. 2
cranial cavity (kra'ne-al kav'ĭ-te), p. 6
distal (dis'tal), p. 3
homeostasis (ho"me-o-sta'sis), p. 10
lateral (lat'er-al), p. 3
medial (me'de-al), p. 3
mediastinum (me"de-uh-sti'num), p. 6
negative feedback (neg'uh-tiv fēd'bak), p. 10
pelvic cavity (pel'vik kav'ĭ-te), p. 7
pericardium (per"ĭ-kar'de-um), p. 7
peritoneum (per"ĭ-to-ne'um), p. 7
physiology (fiz"e-ol'o-je), p. 2

pleurae (plūr'e), p. 7
positive feedback (poz'ĭ-tiv fēd'bak), p. 11
proximal (prok'sĭ-mal), p. 3
sagittal plane (saj'ĭ-tal plān), p. 5
serous membrane (sēr'us mem'brān), p. 6
thoracic cavity (tho-ras'ik kav'ĭ-te), p. 6
transverse plane (trans-vers' plān), p. 5
viscera (vis'er-uh), p. 6

Clinical Key Terms

disease (dĭ-zēz'), p. 12
organ transplantation (or'gun trans-plan-ta'shun), p. 8
peritonitis (per"ĭ-to-ni'tis), p. 7
spinal meningitis (spi'nal men"in-ji'tis), p. 6
systemic disease (sis-tem'ik dĭ-zēz'), p. 12

Summary

1.1 The Human Body

A. Anatomy is the study of the structure of body parts, and physiology is the study of the function of these parts. Structure is suited to the function of a part.

B. The body has levels of organization that progress from atoms to molecules, macromolecules, cells, tissues, organs, organ systems, and finally, the organism.

1.2 Anatomical Terms

Various terms are used to describe the location of body organs when the body is in the anatomical position (standing erect, with face forward, arms at the sides, and palms and toes directed forward).

A. The terms *anterior/posterior, superior/inferior, medial/lateral, proximal/distal, superficial/deep,* and *central/peripheral* describe the relative positions of body parts.

B. The body can be divided into axial and appendicular portions, each of which can be further subdivided into specific regions. For example, *brachial* refers to the arm, and *pedal* refers to the foot.

C. The body or its parts may be sectioned (cut) along certain planes. A sagittal (vertical) cut divides the body into right and left portions. A frontal (coronal) cut divides the body into anterior and posterior parts. A transverse (horizontal) cut is a cross section.

1.3 Body Cavities and Membranes

The human body has two major cavities: the posterior (dorsal) body cavity and the anterior (ventral) body cavity. Each is subdivided into smaller cavities, within which specific viscera are located. Specific serous membranes line body cavities and adhere to the organs within these cavities.

1.4 Organ Systems

The body has a number of organ systems. These systems have been characterized as follows:

A. Support, movement, and protection. The integumentary system, which includes the skin, not only protects the body, but also has other functions. The skeletal system contains the bones, and the muscular system contains the three types of muscles. The primary function of the skeletal and muscular systems is support and movement, but they have other functions as well.

B. Integration and coordination. The nervous system contains the brain, spinal cord, and nerves. Because the nervous system communicates with both the sense organs and the muscles, it allows us to respond to outside stimuli. The endocrine system consists of the hormonal glands. The nervous and endocrine systems coordinate and regulate the activities of the body's other systems.

C. Maintenance of the body. The cardiovascular system (heart and vessels), lymphatic system (lymphatic vessels and nodes, spleen, and thymus), respiratory system (lungs and conducting tubes), digestive system (mouth, esophagus, stomach, small and large intestines, and associated organs), and urinary system (kidneys and bladder) all perform specific processing and transporting functions to maintain the normal conditions of the body.

D. Reproduction and development. The reproductive system in males (testes, other glands, ducts, and penis) and in females (ovaries, uterine tubes, uterus, vagina, and external genitalia) carries out those functions that give humans the ability to reproduce.

1.5 Homeostasis

Homeostasis is the relative constancy of the body's internal environment, which is composed of blood and the tissue fluid that bathes the cells.

A. Negative feedback mechanisms help maintain homeostasis. Positive feedback also occurs.

B. All of the body's organ systems contribute to homeostasis. Some, including the respiratory, digestive, and urinary systems, remove and/or add substances to blood.

C. The nervous and endocrine systems regulate the activities of other systems. Negative feedback is a self-regulatory mechanism by which systems and conditions of the body are controlled.

Study Questions

1. Distinguish between the study of anatomy and the study of physiology. (p. 2)

2. Give an example that shows the relationship between the structure and function of body parts. (p. 2)

3. List the levels of organization within the human body in reference to a specific organ. (p. 2)

4. What purpose is served by directional terms as long as the body is in anatomical position? (p. 3)

5. Distinguish between the axial and appendicular portions of the body. State at least two anatomical terms that pertain to the head, thorax, abdomen, and limbs. (p. 4)

6. Distinguish between a midsagittal section, a transverse section, and a coronal section. (p. 5)

7. Distinguish between the posterior and anterior body cavities, and name two smaller cavities that occur within each. (pp. 6–7)

8. Name the four quadrants of the abdominopelvic cavity. (p. 7)

9. Name the major organ systems, and describe the general functions of each. (p. 8)

10. List the major organs found within each organ system. (p. 8)

11. Define homeostasis, and give examples of negative feedback and positive feedback mechanisms. (pp. 10–11)

12. Discuss the contribution of each body system to homeostasis. (p. 12)

Objective Questions

I. Match the terms in the key to the relationships listed in questions 1–5.

Key:
- a. anterior
- b. posterior
- c. superior
- d. inferior
- e. medial
- f. lateral
- g. proximal
- h. distal

1. the esophagus in relation to the stomach
2. the ears in relation to the nose
3. the shoulder in relation to the hand
4. the intestines in relation to the vertebrae
5. the rectum in relation to the mouth

II. Match the terms in the key to the body regions listed in questions 6–12.

Key:
- a. oral
- b. occipital
- c. gluteal
- d. carpal
- e. palmar
- f. cervical
- g. axillary

6. buttocks
7. palm
8. back of head
9. mouth
10. wrist
11. armpit
12. neck

III. Match the terms in the key to the organs listed in questions 13–18.

Key:
- a. cranial cavity
- b. vertebral canal
- c. thoracic cavity
- d. abdominal cavity
- e. pelvic cavity

13. stomach
14. heart
15. urinary bladder
16. brain
17. liver
18. spinal cord

IV. Match the organ systems in the key to the organs listed in questions 19–25.

Key:
- a. digestive system
- b. urinary system
- c. respiratory system
- d. cardiovascular system
- e. reproductive system
- f. nervous system
- g. endocrine system

19. thyroid gland
20. lungs
21. heart
22. ovaries
23. brain
24. stomach
25. kidneys

V. Fill in the blanks.

26. A(n) _____ is composed of several types of tissues and performs a particular function.
27. The imaginary plane that passes through the midline of the body is called the _____ plane.
28. All the organ systems of the body together function to maintain _____ , a relative constancy of the internal environment.

Medical Terminology Reinforcement Exercise

Consult Appendix B for help in pronouncing, analyzing, and filling in the blanks to give a brief meaning to the terms that follow.

1. Suprapubic (su″pruh-pyū′bik) means _____ the pubis.
2. Infraorbital (in″fruh-or′bĭ-tal) means _____ the eye orbit.
3. Gastrectomy (gas-trek′to-me) means excision of the _____.
4. Celiotomy (se″le-ot′o-me) means incision (cut into) of the _____.
5. Macrocephalus (mak″ro-sef′uh-lus) means large _____.
6. Transthoracic (trans″tho-ras′ik) means across the _____.
7. Bilateral (bi-lat′er-al) means two or both _____.
8. Ophthalmoscope (of-thal′mo-skōp) is an instrument to view inside the _____.
9. Dorsalgia (dor-sal′je-uh) means pain in the _____.
10. Endocrinology (en″do-krĭ-nol′o-je) is the _____ of the endocrine system.
11. The pectoralis (pek-to-ral′is) muscle can be found on the _____.
   a. chest   b. head   c. buttocks   d. thigh
12. The sacral (sa′krul) nerves are located in the _____.
   a. lower back   b. neck   c. upper back   d. head
13. Hematuria (he-muh-tu′re-uh) means _____ in the urine.
14. Nephritis (nef-ri′tis) is _____ of the _____.
   a. lungs   b. heart   c. liver   d. kidneys
15. Tachypnea (tak-ip-ne′uh) is a breathing rate that is _____.
   a. faster than normal   b. slower than normal

Website Link

Visit the Student Edition of the Online Learning Center at http://www.mhhe.com/maderap5 for additional quizzes, interactive learning exercises, and other study tools.

Chemistry of Life

Cholesterol crystals photographed in polarized light. Cholesterol is just one of many types of organic molecules.

chapter outline & learning objectives

After you have studied this chapter, you should be able to:

2.1 Basic Chemistry (p. 18)

- Describe how an atom is organized, and tell why atoms interact.
- Define radioactive isotope, and describe how they can be used in the diagnosis and treatment of disease.
- Distinguish between an ionic bond and a covalent bond.

2.2 Water, Acids, and Bases (p. 22)

- Describe the characteristics of water and three functions of water in the human body.
- Explain the difference between an acid and a base with examples.
- Use and understand the pH scale.

2.3 Molecules of Life (p. 24)

- List the four classes of macromolecules in cells, and distinguish between a dehydration reaction and a hydrolysis reaction.
- Name the individual subunits that comprise carbohydrates, lipids, proteins, and nucleic acids.

2.4 Carbohydrates (p. 24)

- Give some examples of different types of carbohydrates and their specific functions in cells.

2.5 Lipids (p. 26)

- Describe the composition of a neutral fat, and give examples of how lipids function in the body.

2.6 Proteins (p. 28)

- State the major functions of proteins, and tell how globular proteins are organized.

2.7 Nucleic Acids (p. 31)

- Describe the structure and function of DNA and RNA in cells.
- Explain the importance of ATP in the body.

Medical Focus

Nutrition Labels (p. 30)

2.1 Basic Chemistry

Matter is anything that takes up space and has weight; it can be a solid, a liquid, or a gas. Therefore, not only are we humans matter, but so are the water we drink and the air we breathe.

Elements and Atoms

All matter is composed of basic substances called **elements**. It's quite remarkable that there are only 92 naturally occurring elements. It is even more surprising that over 90% of the human body is composed of just four elements: carbon, nitrogen, oxygen, and hydrogen.

Every element has a name and a symbol; for example, carbon has been assigned the atomic symbol C (Fig. 2.1*a*). Some of the symbols we use for elements are derived from Latin. For example, the symbol for sodium is Na because *natrium* in Latin means sodium.

Elements are composed of tiny particles called atoms. The same name is given to both an element and its atoms.

Atoms

An **atom** is the smallest unit of an element that still retains the chemical and physical properties of the element. Although it is possible to split an atom by physical means, an atom is the smallest unit to enter into chemical reactions. For our purposes, it is satisfactory to think of each atom as having a central nucleus and pathways about the nucleus called *shells*. The subatomic particles called **protons** and **neutrons** are located in the nucleus, and **electrons** orbit about the nucleus in the shells (Fig. 2.1*b*). Most of an atom is empty space. If we could draw an atom the size of a football stadium, the nucleus would be like a gumball in the center of the field, and the electrons would be tiny specks whirling about in the upper stands.

Protons carry a positive (+) charge, and electrons have a negative (−) charge. The atomic number of an atom tells you how many protons, and therefore how many electrons, an atom has when it is electrically neutral. For example, the atomic number of carbon is six; therefore, when carbon is neutral, it has six protons and six electrons. How many electrons are in each shell of an atom? The inner shell is the lowest energy level and can hold only two electrons; after that, each shell, for the atoms noted in Figure 2.1*a*, can hold up to eight electrons. Using this information, we can calculate that carbon has two shells and that the outer shell has four electrons.

The number of electrons in the outer shell determines the chemical properties of an atom, including how readily it enters into chemical reactions. As we shall see, an atom is most stable when the outer shell has eight electrons. (Hydrogen, with only one shell, is an exception to this statement. Atoms

Figure 2.1 Elements and atoms. **a.** The atomic symbol, number, and weight are given for common elements in the body. **b.** The structure of carbon shows that an atom contains the subatomic particles called protons (p) and neutrons (n) in the nucleus (colored pink) and electrons (colored blue) in shells about the nucleus.

Common Elements in Living Things				
Element	Atomic Symbol	Atomic Number	Atomic Weight	Comment
hydrogen	H	1	1	These
carbon	C	6	12	elements
nitrogen	N	7	14	make up
oxygen	O	8	16	most
phosphorus	P	15	31	biological
sulfur	S	16	32	molecules.
sodium	Na	11	23	These
magnesium	Mg	12	24	elements
chlorine	Cl	17	35	occur mainly
potassium	K	19	39	as dissolved
calcium	Ca	20	40	salts.

a.

p = protons
n = neutrons
◯ = electrons

6p
6n

Carbon

b.

atomic weight⟶ $^{12}_{6}C$ ⟵atomic number

with only one shell are stable when this shell contains two electrons.)

The subatomic particles are so light that their weight is indicated by special designations called *atomic mass units*. Protons and neutrons each have a weight of one atomic mass unit, and electrons have almost no mass. Therefore, the atomic weight of an atom generally tells you the number of protons plus the number of neutrons. How could you calculate that carbon (C) has six neutrons? Carbon's atomic weight is 12, and you know from its atomic number that it has six protons. Therefore, carbon has six neutrons (Fig. 2.1*b*).

Also, as shown in Figure 2.1*b*, the atomic number of an atom is often written as a subscript to the lower left of the atomic symbol. The atomic weight is often written as a superscript to the upper left of the atomic symbol.

Isotopes

Isotopes of the same type of atom differ in the number of neutrons and therefore in weight. For example, the element carbon has three common isotopes:

$$^{12}_{6}C \qquad\qquad ^{13}_{6}C \qquad\qquad ^{14}_{6}C*$$

*radioactive

Carbon 12 has six neutrons, carbon 13 has seven neutrons, and carbon 14 has eight neutrons. Unlike the other two isotopes of carbon, carbon 14 is unstable and breaks down over time. As carbon 14 decays, it releases various types of energy in the form of rays and subatomic particles, and therefore it is a **radioactive isotope.** The radiation given off by radioactive isotopes can be detected in various ways. You may be familiar with the use of a Geiger counter to detect radiation.

Low Levels of Radiation

The importance of chemistry to biology and medicine is nowhere more evident than in the many uses of radioactive isotopes. A radioactive isotope behaves the same as do the stable isotopes of an element. This means that you can put a small amount of radioactive isotope in a sample, and it becomes a **tracer** by which to detect molecular changes.

Specific tracers are used in imaging the body's organs and tissues. For example, after a patient drinks a solution containing a minute amount of radioactive iodine (^{131}I), the tracer becomes concentrated in the thyroid, which takes it up to make the hormone thyroxine. (No other organ takes up ^{131}I.) A subsequent image of the thyroid indicates whether it is healthy in structure and function (Fig. 2.2). Positron-emission tomography (PET) is a way to determine the comparative activity of tissues. Radioactively labeled glucose emits a subatomic particle known as a positron. When labeled glucose is injected into the body. The radiation given off is detected by sensors and analyzed by a computer. The result is a color image that shows which tissues took up glucose and are metabolically active (Fig. 2.3). A PET scan of the brain can help diagnose a brain tumor, Alzheimer disease, epilepsy, or stroke.

High Levels of Radiation

Radioactive substances in the environment can harm cells, damage DNA, and cause cancer. The release of radioactive particles following a nuclear power plant accident can have far-reaching and long-lasting effects on human health. The harmful effects of radiation can also be put to good use, however. Radiation from radioactive isotopes has been used for many years to sterilize medical and dental products. Now the possibility exists that it can be used to sterilize the U.S. mail to free it of possible pathogens, such as anthrax spores.

The ability of radiation to kill cells is often applied to cancer cells. Radioisotopes can be introduced into the body in a way that allows radiation to destroy only the cancerous cells, with little risk to the rest of the body.

Figure 2.2 Use of radiation to aid a diagnosis. After the administration of radioactive iodine, a scan of the thyroid reveals pathology. The missing portion of the gland is cancerous and therefore failed to take up the iodine.

thyroid gland

trachea (windpipe)

a. Drawing of thyroid

b. Scan of thyroid

Figure 2.3 Use of radiation to study the brain. After the administration of radioactively labeled glucose, a PET scan reveals which portions of the brain are most active.

a. Patient entering PET scanner

b. PET scan

Molecules and Compounds

Atoms often bond with each other to form a chemical unit called a **molecule.** A molecule can contain atoms of the same kind, as when an oxygen atom joins with another oxygen atom to form oxygen gas. Or the atoms can be different, as when an oxygen atom joins with two hydrogen atoms to form water. When the atoms are different, a **compound** results.

Two types of bonds join atoms: the ionic bond and the covalent bond. The first type of bond can be associated with **inorganic molecules,** which constitute nonliving matter, and the second type can be associated with **organic molecules,** which are unique to living things.

Ionic Bonds

Recall that atoms with more than one shell are most stable when the outer shell contains eight electrons. Sometimes during a reaction, atoms give up or take on an electron(s) in order to achieve a stable outer shell.

Figure 2.4 depicts a reaction between a sodium (Na) atom and a chlorine (Cl) atom. Sodium, with one electron in the outer shell, reacts with a single chlorine atom. Why? Because once the reaction is finished and sodium loses one electron to chlorine, its outer shell will have eight electrons. Similarly, a chlorine atom, which has seven electrons already, needs only to acquire one more electron to have a stable outer shell.

Ions are particles that carry either a positive (+) or negative (−) charge. When the reaction between sodium and chlorine is finished, the sodium ion carries a positive charge because it now has one more proton than electrons, and the chloride ion carries a negative charge because it now has one fewer proton than electrons. The attraction between oppositely charged sodium ions and chloride ions forms an **ionic bond.** The resulting compound, sodium chloride, is table salt, which we use to enliven the taste of foods. **Salts** characteristically form an ionic lattice that dissociates in water (Fig. 2.4b).

In contrast to sodium, why would calcium, with two electrons in the outer shell, react with two chlorine atoms? Because whereas calcium needs to lose two electrons, each chlorine, with seven electrons already, requires only one more electron to have a stable outer shell. The resulting salt ($CaCl_2$) is called calcium chloride.

The balance of various ions in the body is important to our health. Too much sodium in the blood can contribute to **hypertension** (high blood pressure); not enough calcium leads to

Figure 2.4 Ionic reaction. **a.** During the formation of sodium chloride, an electron is transferred from the sodium atom to the chlorine atom. At the completion of the reaction, each atom has eight electrons in the outer shell, but each also carries a charge as shown. **b.** In a sodium chloride crystal, bonding between ions creates a three-dimensional lattice in which each Na^+ ion is surrounded by six Cl^- ions, and each Cl^- is surrounded by six Na^+.

a. sodium atom (Na)   chlorine atom (Cl)   sodium ion (Na^+)   chloride ion (Cl^-)

sodium chloride (NaCl)

Na^+

Cl^-

b. 1 mm

rickets (a bowing of the legs) in children; too much or too little potassium results in **arrhythmia** (heartbeat irregularities). Bicarbonate, hydrogen, and hydroxide ions are all involved in maintaining the acid-base balance of the body (see page 22).

Covalent Bonds

As a result of other reactions, atoms share electrons in **covalent bonds** instead of losing or gaining them. The overlapping outermost shells in Figure 2.5 indicate that the atoms are sharing electrons. Just as two hands participate in a handshake, each atom contributes one electron to the pair that is shared. These electrons spend part of their time in the outer shell of each atom; therefore, they are counted as belonging to both bonded atoms.

Covalent bonds can be represented in a number of ways. In contrast to the diagrams in Figure 2.5, structural formulas use straight lines to show the covalent bonds between the atoms. Each line represents a pair of shared electrons. Molecular formulas indicate only the number of each type of atom making up a molecule. A comparison follows:

Structural formula: Cl—Cl
Molecular formula: Cl_2

Double and Triple Bonds   Besides a single bond, in which atoms share only a pair of electrons, a double or a triple bond can form. In a double bond, atoms share two pairs of electrons, and in a triple bond, atoms share three pairs of electrons between them. For example, in Figure 2.5, each nitrogen atom (N) requires three electrons to achieve a total of eight electrons in the outer shell. Notice that six electrons are placed in the outer overlapping shells in the diagram and that three straight lines are in the structural formula for nitrogen gas (N_2).

What would be the structural and molecular formulas for carbon dioxide? Carbon, with four electrons in the outer shell, requires four more electrons to complete its outer shell. Each oxygen, with six electrons in the outer shell, needs only two electrons to complete its outer shell. Therefore, carbon shares two pairs of electrons with each oxygen atom, and the formulas are as follows:

Structural formula: O=C=O
Molecular formula: CO_2

Figure 2.5 Covalent reactions. After a covalent reaction, each atom will have filled its outer shell by sharing electrons. To determine this, it is necessary to count the shared electrons as belonging to both bonded atoms. Oxygen and nitrogen are most stable with eight electrons in the outer shell. Hydrogen is most stable with two electrons in the outer shell.

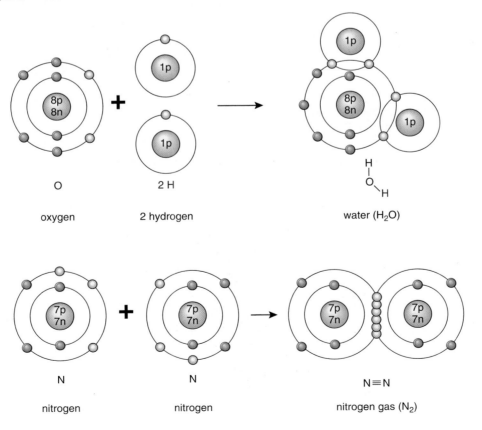

2.2 Water, Acids, and Bases

Water is the most abundant molecule in living organisms, usually making up about 60–70% of the total body weight. Even so, water is an inorganic molecule because it does not contain carbon atoms. Carbon atoms are common to organic molecules.

In water, the electrons spend more time circling the larger oxygen (O) atom than the smaller hydrogen (H) atoms. This imparts a slight negative charge (symbolized as δ^-) to the oxygen and a slight positive charge (symbolized as δ^+) to the hydrogen atoms. Therefore, water is a **polar molecule** with negative and positive ends:

The diagram on the left shows the structural formula of water, and the one on the right is called a space-filling model.

Hydrogen Bonds

A **hydrogen bond** occurs whenever a covalently bonded hydrogen is positive and attracted to a negatively charged atom nearby. A hydrogen bond is represented by a dotted line because it is relatively weak and can be broken rather easily. In Figure 2.6, you can see that each hydrogen atom, being slightly positive, bonds to the slightly negative oxygen atom of another water molecule nearby.

Figure 2.6 Hydrogen bonding between water molecules. The polarity of the water molecules causes hydrogen bonds (dotted lines) to form between the molecules.

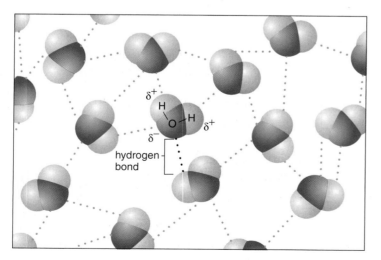

Properties of Water

Polarity and hydrogen bonding cause water to have many properties beneficial to life, including the three to be mentioned here.

1. Water is a solvent for polar (charged) molecules and thereby facilitates chemical reactions both outside and within our bodies.

   When ions and molecules disperse in water, they move about and collide, allowing reactions to occur. Therefore, water is a solvent that facilitates chemical reactions. For example, when a salt such as sodium chloride (NaCl) is put into water, the negative ends of the water molecules are attracted to the sodium ions, and the positive ends of the water molecules are attracted to the chloride ions. This causes the sodium ions and the chloride ions to separate and to dissolve in water:

The salt NaCl dissolves in water.

   Ions and molecules that interact with water are said to be **hydrophilic.** Nonionized and nonpolar molecules that do not interact with water are said to be **hydrophobic.**

2. Water molecules are cohesive, and therefore liquids fill vessels, such as blood vessels.

   Water molecules cling together because of hydrogen bonding, and yet water flows freely. This property allows dissolved and suspended molecules to be evenly distributed throughout a system. Therefore, water is an excellent transport medium. Within our bodies, the blood that fills our arteries and veins is 92% water. Blood transports oxygen and nutrients to the cells and removes wastes such as carbon dioxide from the cells.

3. Water has a high heat of vaporization. Therefore, it absorbs much heat as it slowly rises, and gives off this heat as it slowly cools.

It takes a large amount of heat to change water to steam. (Converting one gram of the hottest water to steam requires an input of 540 calories of heat energy.) Water has a high heat of vaporization because hydrogen bonds must be broken before boiling occurs and water molecules vaporize—that is, evaporate into the environment. This property of water helps keep body temperature within normal limits. Also, in a hot environment, we sweat; then the body cools as body heat is used to evaporate the sweat, which is mostly liquid water.

Acids and Bases

When water molecules dissociate (break up), they release an equal number of hydrogen ions (H^+) and hydroxide ions (OH^-):

H—O—H ⇄ H^+ + OH^-
water   hydrogen ion   hydroxide ion

Only a few water molecules at a time dissociate, and the actual number of H^+ and OH^- is very small (1×10^{-7} moles/liter).[1]

Acids are substances that dissociate in water, releasing hydrogen ions (H^+). For example, an important inorganic acid is hydrochloric acid (HCl), which dissociates in this manner:

$$HCl \longrightarrow H^+ + Cl^-$$

Dissociation is almost complete; therefore, HCl is called a strong acid. If hydrochloric acid is added to a beaker of water, the number of hydrogen ions (H^+) increases greatly. Lemon juice, vinegar, tomatoes, and coffee are all acidic solutions.

Bases are substances that either take up hydrogen ions (H^+) or release hydroxide ions (OH^-). For example, an important inorganic base is sodium hydroxide (NaOH), which dissociates in this manner:

$$NaOH \longrightarrow Na^+ + OH^-$$

Dissociation is almost complete; therefore, sodium hydroxide is called a strong base. If sodium hydroxide is added to a beaker of water, the number of hydroxide ions increases. Milk of magnesia and ammonia are common basic solutions.

pH Scale

The **pH scale**[2], which ranges from 0 to 14, is used to indicate the acidity and basicity (alkalinity) of a solution. pH 7, which is the pH of water, is neutral pH because water releases an equal number of hydrogen ions (H^+) and hydroxide ions (OH^-). Notice in Figure 2.7 that any pH above 7 is a base, with more hydroxide ions than hydrogen ions. Any pH below 7 is an acid, with more hydrogen ions than hydroxide ions. As we move toward a higher pH, each unit has 10 times the basicity of the previous unit, and as we move toward a lower pH, each unit has 10 times the acidity of the previous unit. This means that even a small change in pH represents a large change in the proportional number of hydrogen and hydroxide ions in the body.

The pH of body fluids needs to be maintained within a narrow range, or else health suffers. The pH of our blood when we are healthy is always about 7.4—that is, just slightly basic (alkaline). If the pH value drops below 7.35, the person is said to have **acidosis**; if it rises above 7.45, the condition is called **alkalosis**. The pH stability is normally possible because the body has built-in mechanisms to prevent pH changes. **Buffers** are the most important of these mechanisms. Buffers help keep the pH within normal limits because they are chemicals or combinations of chemicals that take up excess hydrogen ions (H^+) or hydroxide ions (OH^-). For example, the combination of carbonic acid (H_2CO_3) and the bicarbonate ion [HCO_3] helps keep the pH of the blood relatively constant because carbonic acid can dissociate to release hydrogen ions, while the bicarbonate ion can take them up!

Electrolytes

As we have seen, salts, acids, and bases are molecules that dissociate; that is, they ionize in water. For example, when a salt such as sodium chloride is put in water, the Na^+ ion separates from the Cl^- ion.

Substances that release ions when put into water are called **electrolytes**, because the ions can conduct an electrical current. The electrolyte balance in the blood and body tissues is important for good health because it affects the functioning of vital organs such as the heart and the brain.

Figure 2.7 The pH scale. The proportionate amount of hydrogen ions to hydroxide ions is indicated by the diagonal line. Any solution with a pH above 7 is basic, while any solution with a pH below 7 is acidic.

---

[1] In chemistry, a mole is defined as the amount of matter that contains as many objects (atoms, molecules, ions) as the number of atoms in exactly 12 grams of ^{12}C.

[2] pH is defined as the negative log of the hydrogen ion concentration [H^+]. A log is the power to which 10 must be raised to produce a given number.

2.3 Molecules of Life

Four categories of molecules, called carbohydrates, lipids, proteins, and nucleic acids, are unique to cells. They are called *macromolecules* because each is composed of many subunits:

Category	Example	Subunit(s)
Carbohydrates	Polysaccharide	Monosaccharide
Lipids	Fat	Glycerol and fatty acids
Proteins	Polypeptide	Amino acid
Nucleic acids	DNA, RNA	Nucleotide

During synthesis of macromolecules, the cell uses a **dehydration reaction,** so called because an —OH (hydroxyl group) and an —H (hydrogen atom)—the equivalent of a water molecule—are removed as the molecule forms (Fig. 2.8a). The result is reminiscent of a train whose length is determined by how many boxcars are hitched together. To break up macromolecules, the cell uses a **hydrolysis reaction,** in which the components of water are added (Fig. 2.8b).

Figure 2.8 Synthesis and degradation of macromolecules. **a.** In cells, synthesis often occurs when subunits bond following a dehydration reaction (removal of H_2O). **b.** Degradation occurs when the subunits in a macromolecule separate after a hydrolysis reaction (addition of H_2O).

a.

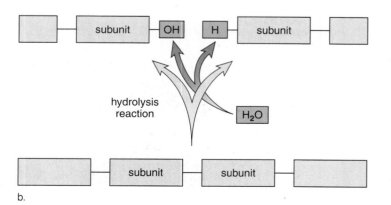

b.

2.4 Carbohydrates

Carbohydrates, like all organic molecules, always contain carbon (C) and hydrogen (H) atoms. Carbohydrate molecules are characterized by the presence of the atomic grouping H—C—OH, in which the ratio of hydrogen atoms (H) to oxygen atoms (O) is approximately 2:1. Because this ratio is the same as the ratio in water, the name "hydrates of carbon" seems appropriate. **Carbohydrates** first and foremost function for quick, short-term energy storage in all organisms, including humans. Figure 2.9 shows some foods that are rich in carbohydrates.

Simple Carbohydrates

If the number of carbon atoms in a carbohydrate is low (between three and seven), it is called a simple sugar, or **monosaccharide.** The designation **pentose** means a 5-carbon sugar, and the designation **hexose** means a 6-carbon sugar. **Glucose,** the hexose our bodies use as an immediate source of energy, can be written in any one of these ways:

Figure 2.9 Common foods. Carbohydrates such as bread and pasta are digested to sugars; lipids such as oils are digested to glycerol and fatty acids; and proteins such as meat are digested to amino acids. Cells use these subunit molecules to build their own macromolecules.

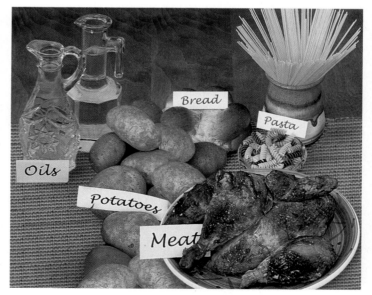

Other common hexoses are fructose, found in fruits, and galactose, a constituent of milk. A **disaccharide** (*di,* two; *saccharide,* sugar) is made by joining only two monosaccharides together by a dehydration reaction (see Fig. 2.8*a*). Maltose is a disaccharide that contains two glucose molecules:

maltose

When glucose and fructose join, the disaccharide sucrose forms. Sucrose, which is ordinarily derived from sugarcane and sugar beets, is commonly known as table sugar.

Complex Carbohydrates (Polysaccharides)

Macromolecules such as starch, glycogen, and cellulose are **polysaccharides** that contain many glucose units. Although polysaccharides can contain other sugars, we will study the ones that use glucose.

Starch and Glycogen

Starch and **glycogen** are ready storage forms of glucose in plants and animals, respectively. Some of the macromolecules

Figure 2.10 Starch structure and function. Starch has straight chains of glucose molecules. Some chains are also branched, as indicated. The electron micrograph shows starch granules in potato cells. Starch is the storage form of glucose in plants.

starch granule

cell wall

potato cells

in starch are long chains of up to 4,000 glucose units. Starch has fewer side branches, or chains of glucose that branch off from the main chain, than does glycogen, as shown in Figures 2.10 and 2.11. Flour, usually acquired by grinding wheat and used for baking, is high in starch, and so are potatoes.

After we eat starchy foods such as potatoes, bread, and cake, glucose enters the bloodstream, and the liver stores glucose as glycogen. In between eating, the liver releases glucose so that the blood glucose concentration is always about 0.1%. If blood contains more glucose, it spills over into the urine, signaling that the condition **diabetes mellitus** exists.

Cellulose

The polysaccharide **cellulose** is found in plant cell walls. In cellulose, the glucose units are joined by a slightly different type of linkage from that in starch or glycogen. Although this might seem to be a technicality, actually it is important because humans are unable to digest foods containing this type of linkage; therefore, cellulose largely passes through our digestive tract as fiber, or roughage. It is believed that fiber in the diet is necessary to good health, and some researchers have suggested it may even help prevent colon cancer.

Figure 2.11 Glycogen structure and function. Glycogen is more branched than starch. The electron micrograph shows glycogen granules in liver cells. Glycogen is the storage form of glucose in humans.

glycogen granules

liver cells

2.5 Lipids

Lipids contain more energy per gram than other biological molecules, and some function as long-term energy storage molecules in organisms. Others form a membrane that separates a cell from its environment and has inner compartments as well. Steroids are a large class of lipids that includes, among other molecules, the sex hormones.

Lipids are diverse in structure and function, but they have a common characteristic: They do not dissolve in water. Their low solubility in water is due to an absence of polar groups. They contain little oxygen and consist mostly of carbon and hydrogen atoms.

Fats and Oils

The most familiar lipids are those found in fats and oils. **Fats,** which are usually of animal origin (e.g., lard and butter), are solid at room temperature. **Oils,** which are usually of plant origin (e.g., corn oil and soybean oil), are liquid at room temperature. Fat has several functions in the body: It is used for long-term energy storage, it insulates against heat loss, and it forms a protective cushion around major organs.

Fats and oils form when one **glycerol** molecule reacts with three fatty acid molecules (Fig. 2.12). A fat is sometimes called a **triglyceride,** because of its three-part structure, or a **neutral fat,** because the molecule is nonpolar and carries no charge.

Emulsification

Emulsifiers can cause fats to mix with water. They contain molecules with a nonpolar end and a polar end. The molecules position themselves about an oil droplet so that their nonpolar ends project. Now the droplet disperses in water, which means that **emulsification** has occurred.

Emulsification takes place when dirty clothes are washed with soaps or detergents. Also, prior to the digestion of fatty foods, fats are emulsified by bile. The gallbladder stores bile for emulsifying fats prior to the digestive process.

Saturated and Unsaturated Fatty Acids

A **fatty acid** is a carbon–hydrogen chain that ends with the acidic group —COOH (Fig. 2.12). Most of the fatty acids in cells contain 16 or 18 carbon atoms per molecule, although smaller ones with fewer carbons are also known.

Fatty acids are either saturated or unsaturated. **Saturated fatty acids** have only single covalent bonds because the carbon chain is saturated, so to speak, with all the hydrogens it can hold. Saturated fatty acids account for the solid nature at room temperature of fats such as lard and butter. **Unsaturated fatty acids** have double bonds between carbon atoms wherever fewer than two hydrogens are bonded to a carbon atom. Unsaturated fatty acids account for the liquid nature of vegetable oils at room temperature. Hydrogenation of vegetable oils can convert them to margarine and products such as Crisco.

Figure 2.12 Synthesis and degradation of a fat molecule. Fatty acids can be saturated (no double bonds between carbon atoms) or unsaturated (have double bonds, colored yellow, between carbon atoms). When a fat molecule forms, three fatty acids combine with glycerol, and three water molecules are produced.

Phospholipids

Phospholipids, as their name implies, contain a phosphate group (Fig. 2.13). Essentially, they are constructed like fats, except that in place of the third fatty acid, there is a phosphate group or a grouping that contains both phosphate and nitrogen. Phospholipid molecules are not electrically neutral, as are fats, because the phosphate and nitrogen-containing groups are ionized. They form the so-called hydrophilic head of the molecule, while the rest of the molecule becomes the hydrophobic tails. Phospholipids are the backbone of cellular membranes; they spontaneously form a bilayer in which the hydrophilic heads face outward toward watery solutions and the tails form the hydrophobic interior.

Figure 2.13 Phospholipid structure and function.
a. Phospholipids are structured like fats, but one fatty acid is replaced by a polar phosphate group. **b.** Therefore, the head is polar while the tails are nonpolar. **c.** This causes the molecule to arrange itself as shown when exposed to water.

a. Phospholipid structure

b. Phospholipid symbol

c. Membrane structure

Figure 2.14 Steroids. All steroids have four rings, but they differ by attached groups. The effects of **(a)** testosterone and **(b)** estrogen on the body largely depend on the difference in the attached groups shown in red.

a. Testosterone

b. Estrogen

Steroids

Steroids are lipids that have an entirely different structure from those of fats. Steroid molecules have a backbone of four fused carbon rings. Each one differs primarily by the functional groups attached to the rings.

Cholesterol is a component of an animal cell's outer membrane and is the precursor of several other steroids, such as the sex hormones estrogen and testosterone. The male sex hormone, testosterone, is formed primarily in the testes, and the female sex hormone, estrogen, is formed primarily in the ovaries. Testosterone and estrogen differ only by the functional groups attached to the same carbon backbone, yet they have a profound effect on the body and on our sexuality (Fig. 2.14a,b). Testosterone is a steroid that causes males to have greater muscle strength than females. Taking synthetic testosterone for this purpose, however, is dangerous to your health, as will be discussed in Chapter 10.

We know that a diet high in saturated fats and cholesterol can cause fatty material to accumulate inside the lining of blood vessels, thereby reducing blood flow. As discussed in the Medical Focus on page 30, nutrition labels are now required to list the calories from fat per serving and the percent daily value from saturated fat and cholesterol.

2.6 Proteins

Proteins perform a myriad of functions, including the following:

- Proteins such as collagen and keratin (which makes up hair and nails) are fibrous structural proteins that lend support to ligaments, tendons, and skin.
- Many hormones, which are messengers that influence cellular metabolism, are proteins.
- The proteins actin and myosin account for the movement of cells and the ability of our muscles to contract.
- Some proteins transport molecules in the blood; for example, hemoglobin is a complex protein in our blood that transports oxygen.
- Antibodies in blood and other body fluids are proteins that combine with pathogens or their toxins.
- Enzymes are globular proteins that speed chemical reactions.

Structure of Proteins

Proteins are macromolecules composed of amino acid subunits. An **amino acid** has a central carbon atom bonded to a hydrogen atom and three groups. The name of the molecule is appropriate because one of these groups is an amino group and another is an acidic group. The third group is called an *R* group because it is the *Remainder* of the molecule (Fig. 2.15a). Amino acids differ from one another by their *R* group; the *R* group varies from having a single carbon to being a complicated ring structure. When two amino acids join, a dipeptide results; a **polypeptide** is a chain of amino acids (Fig. 2.15b).

Twenty different amino acids are common to polypeptides, which differ by the sequence of their amino acids.

The bond between amino acids is called a **peptide bond.** The atoms of a peptide bond share electrons unevenly; this makes hydrogen bonding possible between members of a polypeptide. Due to hydrogen bonding, the polypeptide often twists to form a coil (Fig. 2.15c). Finally, the coil bends and twists into a particular shape because of bonding between *R* groups. Hydrogen, ionic, and covalent bonding all occur in polypeptides. Also, any hydrophobic portions of a polypeptide tend to be inside, while the hydrophilic portions are outside where they can make contact with water.

Some proteins have only one polypeptide, and others have more than one polypeptide, each with its own so-called primary, secondary, and tertiary structures. If a protein has more than one polypeptide, their arrangement gives a protein a fourth level of structure.

The final three-dimensional shape of a protein is very important to its function.When proteins are exposed to extremes in heat and pH, they undergo an irreversible change in shape called **denaturation.** For example, we are all aware that the addition of acid to milk causes curdling and that heating causes egg white, which contains a protein called albumin, to coagulate. Denaturation occurs because the normal bonding between the *R* groups has been disturbed. Once a protein loses its normal shape, it is no longer able to perform its usual function. Researchers hypothesize that an alteration in protein organization may be the cause of Alzheimer disease and Creutzfeldt-Jakob disease (the human form of mad cow disease).

Figure 2.15 Levels of polypeptide structure. **a.** Amino acids are the subunits of polypeptides. Note that an amino acid contains nitrogen. **b.** Polypeptides differ by the sequence of their amino acids, which are joined by peptide bonds. **c.** A polypeptide often twists to become a coil due to hydrogen bonding between members of the peptide bonds. **d.** The third level of polypeptide structure is due to various types of bonding between the *R* groups of the amino acids.

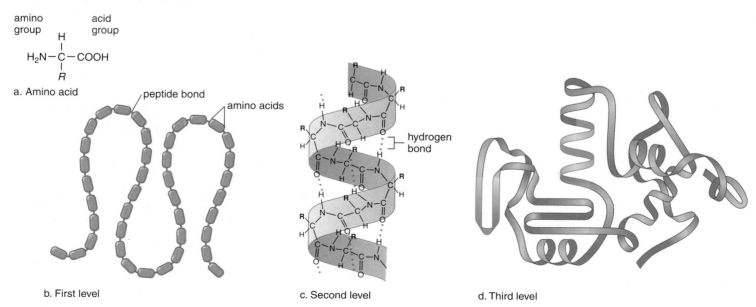

amino
group

acid
group

$$H_2N - C - COOH$$

a. Amino acid

b. First level

c. Second level

hydrogen
bond

d. Third level

Enzymatic Reactions

Metabolism is the sum of all the chemical reactions that occur in a cell. Most cellular reactions will not take place unless an enzyme is present. An **enzyme** is a protein molecule that functions as an organic catalyst to speed a particular metabolic reaction. Molecules frequently do not react with one another unless they are activated in some way. In the lab, heat is often used to increase the number of effective collisions between molecules. The energy that must be supplied is called the *energy of activation*. In the body, enzymes lower the energy of activation by forming a complex with particular molecules. In a crowded ballroom, a mutual friend can cause particular people to interact. In a cell, an enzyme brings together certain molecules and causes them to react with one another.

Enzyme-Substrate Complex

In any reaction, the molecules that interact are called *reactants*, while the substances that form as a result of the reaction are the *products*. The reactants in an enzymatic reaction are its substrate(s). Enzymes are often named for their substrate(s); for example, maltase is the enzyme that digests maltose. Enzymes have a specific region, called an *active site*, where the reaction occurs. An enzyme's specificity is caused by the shape of the active site, where the enzyme and its substrate(s) fit together, much like pieces of a jigsaw puzzle (Fig. 2.16). After a reaction is complete and the products are released, the enzyme is ready to catalyze its reaction again:

$$E + S \rightarrow ES \rightarrow E + P$$

(where E = enzyme, S = substrate, ES = enzyme-substrate complex, and P = product).

Many enzymes require cofactors. Some cofactors are inorganic, such as copper, zinc, or iron. Other cofactors are organic, nonprotein molecules called coenzymes. Cofactors assist an enzyme and may even accept or contribute atoms to the reaction. It is interesting that vitamins are often components of coenzymes.

Types of Reactions

Certain types of chemical reactions are common to metabolism.

Synthesis Reactions During **synthesis reactions,** two or more reactants combine to form a larger and more complex product (Fig. 2.16a). The dehydration synthesis reaction we have already studied (i.e., the joining of subunits to form a macromolecule) is an example of a synthesis reaction. When glucose molecules join in the liver, forming glycogen, a synthesis reaction has occurred. Notice that synthesis reactions always involve bond formation and therefore an input of energy.

Degradation Reactions During **degradation reactions,** a larger and more complex molecule breaks down into smaller, simpler products (Fig. 2.16b). The hydrolysis reactions that break down macromolecules into their subunits are examples of degradation reactions, also called decomposition reactions. When protein is digested to amino acids in the stomach, a degradation reaction has occurred.

Replacement Reactions **Replacement reactions** involve both degradation and synthesis. For example, when ADP joins with inorganic phosphate, (P), and ATP forms, the last hydrogen in ADP is replaced by a (P) (see Fig. 2.18). The (P) loses a hydroxyl group. The hydrogen and hydroxyl group join to become water.

Figure 2.16 Enzymatic action. An enzyme has an active site, where the substrates come together and react. The products are released, and the enzyme is free to act again. **a.** In synthesis, the substrates join to produce a larger product. **b.** In degradation, the substrate breaks down to smaller products.

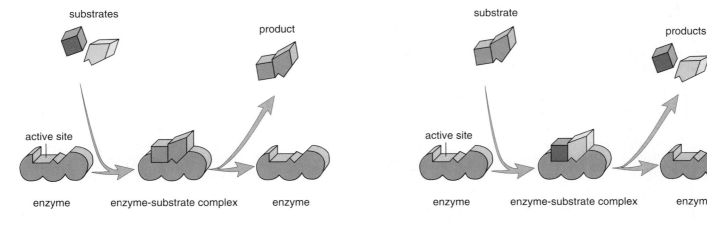

substrates   product

active site

enzyme   enzyme-substrate complex   enzyme

a. Synthesis

substrate   products

active site

enzyme   enzyme-substrate complex   enzyme

b. Degradation

Nutrition Labels

Packaged foods must have a nutrition label like the one depicted in Figure 2A. The information given is based on a serving size (that is, 1¼ cup, or 57 grams [g]) of the cereal and on a diet of 2,000 Calories for women and 2,500 Calories for men. A Calorie is a measurement of energy. One serving of the cereal provides 220 Calories, of which 20 are from fat.

Fats

The body stores excess energy from nutrients under the skin and around the organs as fat. An overconsumption of total dietary fat, saturated fat, and cholesterol can lead to obesity and have adverse effects on health. High levels of saturated fat have been implicated in cancer of the colon, pancreas, ovary, prostate, and breast. Cholesterol and saturated fat contribute to the formation of deposits of plaque, which clog arteries (called atherosclerosis) and lead to high blood pressure, strokes, and heart attacks.

A 2,000-Calorie diet should contain no more than 65 g (585 Calories) of fat because of health concerns. Knowing how a serving of the cereal will contribute to the maximum recommended daily amount of fat, saturated fat, and cholesterol is important. This information is found in the listing under % Daily Value.

Carbohydrates

Carbohydrates (simple sugars and polysaccharides) are the most readily available source of energy for the body. Breads and cereals contain complex carbohydrates, and foods such as candy and ice cream contain simple carbohydrates. Breads and cereals are preferable because they contain protein, minerals, and vitamins. Complex carbohydrates also contain fiber. Soluble fiber combines with the cholesterol in food and prevents the cholesterol from being absorbed from the digestive tract into the body. Insoluble fiber has a laxative effect. The nutrition label in Figure 2A indicates that one serving of the cereal provides 15% of the recommended daily carbohydrates.

Proteins

A woman should consume about 44 g of protein per day, and a man should have about 56 g of protein per day. Red meat is rich in protein, but it is usually also high in saturated fat. Therefore, it is considered good health sense to rely on protein from plant origins (e.g., whole-grain cereals, dark breads, rice, and legumes such as beans) to a greater extent than is customary in the United States. The nutrition label in Figure 2A shows that 5 g of protein are obtained from each serving of the cereal.

Other Molecules

The amount of dietary sodium (as in table salt) in a food product is of concern because excessive sodium intake seems to further elevate blood pressure in people already suffering from hypertension.

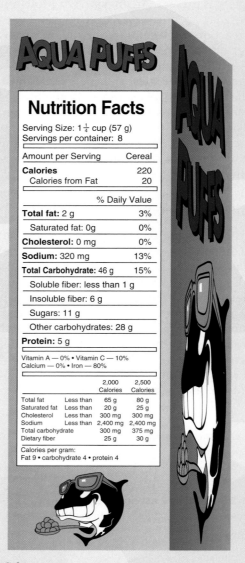

Figure 2A Nutrition label on the side panel of a cereal box.

Sodium intake should be no more than 2,400 milligrams (mg) per day for people with hypertension. What percentage of this maximum amount does a serving of the cereal in Figure 2A provide?

Vitamins are organic molecules required in small amounts in the diet for good health. Each vitamin has a recommended daily intake, and the nutrition label on food products tells what percentage of the recommended amount is provided by one serving. The nutrition label for the cereal in Figure 2A indicates that, while the cereal provides no vitamin A or calcium, one serving does contain 10% of the suggested daily intake of vitamin C and 80% of the recommended daily intake of iron.

2.7 Nucleic Acids

Nucleic acids are huge macromolecules composed of nucleotides. Every **nucleotide** is a molecular complex of three types of subunit molecules—a phosphate (phosphoric acid), a pentose sugar, and a nitrogen-containing base:

Nucleic acids store hereditary information that determines which proteins a cell will have. Two classes of nucleic acids are in cells: **DNA (deoxyribonucleic acid)** and **RNA (ribonucleic acid)**. DNA makes up the hereditary units called **genes**. Genes pass on from generation to generation the instructions for replicating DNA, making RNA, and joining amino acids to form the proteins of a cell. RNA is an intermediary in the process of protein synthesis, conveying information from DNA regarding the amino acid sequence in proteins.

The nucleotides in DNA contain the 5-carbon sugar deoxyribose; the nucleotides in RNA contain the sugar ribose. This difference accounts for their respective names. As indicated in Figure 2.17, there are four different types of bases in DNA: A = adenine, T = thymine, G = guanine, and C = cytosine. The base can have two rings (adenine or guanine) or one ring (thymine or cytosine). In RNA, the base uracil replaces the base thymine.

These structures are nitrogen-containing bases—that is, a nitrogen atom is a part of the ring. Like other bases, the presence of the nitrogen-containing base in DNA and RNA raises the pH of a solution.

Figure 2.17 Overview of DNA structure. **a.** Double helix. **b.** Complementary base pairing between strands. **c.** Ladder configuration. Notice that the uprights are composed of phosphate and sugar molecules and that the rungs are complementary paired bases.

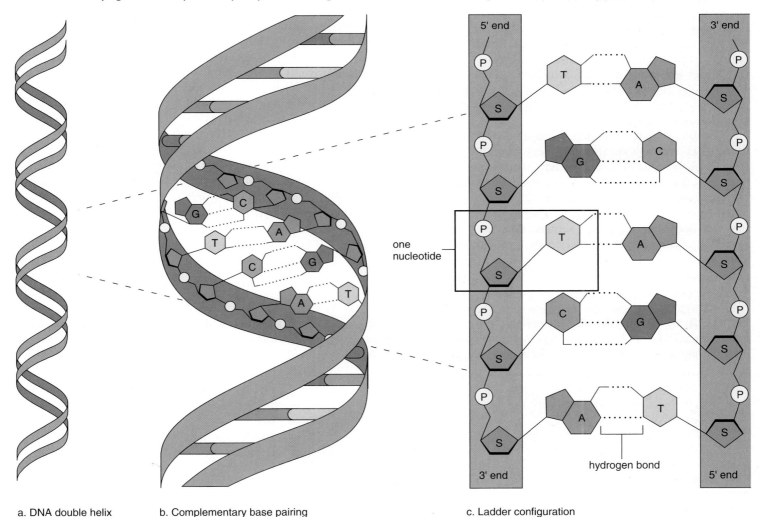

a. DNA double helix   b. Complementary base pairing   c. Ladder configuration

Table 2.1	DNA Structure Compared to RNA Structure	
	DNA	**RNA**
Sugar	Deoxyribose	Ribose
Bases	Adenine, guanine, thymine, cytosine	Adenine, guanine, uracil, cytosine
Strands	Double-stranded	Single-stranded
Helix	Yes	No

The nucleotides in DNA and RNA form a linear molecule called a *strand*. A strand has a backbone made up of phosphate-sugar-phosphate-sugar, with the bases projecting to one side of the backbone. Because the nucleotides occur in a definite order, so do the bases. Any particular DNA or RNA has a definite sequence of bases, although the sequence can vary between molecules. RNA is usually single-stranded, while DNA is usually double-stranded, with the two strands twisted about each other in the form of a double helix. The molecular differences between DNA and RNA are listed in Table 2.1.

In DNA, the two strands are held together by hydrogen bonds between the bases (see Fig. 2.17). When unwound, DNA resembles a stepladder. The sides of the ladder are made entirely of phosphate and sugar molecules, and the rungs of the ladder are made only of complementary paired bases. Thymine (T) always pairs with adenine (A), and guanine (G) always pairs with cytosine (C) (see Fig. 2.17). This is called **complementary base pairing**.

Complementary bases pair because they have shapes that fit together. We shall see that complementary base pairing allows DNA to replicate in a way that ensures the sequence of bases will remain the same. When RNA is produced, complementary base pairing occurs between DNA and RNA in which uracil takes the place of thymine. Then, the sequence of the bases in RNA determines the sequence of amino acids in a protein because every three bases code for a particular amino acid (see Chapter 3, pp. 47–48). The code is nearly universal and is the same in other organisms as it is in humans.

ATP (Adenosine Triphosphate)

Individual nucleotides can have metabolic functions in cells. Some nucleotides are important in energy transfer. When adenosine (adenine plus ribose) is modified by the addition of three phosphate groups, it becomes **ATP (adenosine triphosphate)**, the primary energy carrier in cells.

Cells require a constant supply of ATP. To obtain it, they break down glucose and convert the energy that is released into ATP molecules. The amount of energy in ATP is just right for more chemical reactions in cells. As an analogy, the energy in glucose is like a $100 bill, and the energy in ATP is like a $20 bill. Just as you might go to the bank to change a $100 bill (glucose) into $20 bills (ATP molecules), in order to spend money, cells "spend" ATP when cellular reactions require energy. Therefore, ATP is called the energy currency of cells. Cells use ATP when macromolecules such as carbohydrates and proteins are synthesized. In muscle cells, ATP is used for muscle contraction, and in nerve cells, it is used for the conduction of nerve impulses.

ATP is sometimes called a high-energy molecule because the last two phosphate bonds are unstable and easily broken. Usually in cells, the terminal phosphate bond is hydrolyzed, leaving the molecule **ADP (adenosine diphosphate)** and a molecule of inorganic phosphate, Ⓟ (Fig. 2.18). The terminal bond is sometimes called a high-energy bond, symbolized by a wavy line. But this terminology is misleading—the breakdown of ATP releases energy because the products of hydrolysis (ADP and Ⓟ) are more stable than ATP.

After ATP breaks down and the energy is used for a cellular purpose, ATP is rebuilt by the addition of Ⓟ to ADP again; this can be seen by reading Figure 2.18 from right to left. There is enough energy in one glucose molecule to build 36 ATP molecules in this way. Homeostasis is only possible because cells continually produce and use ATP molecules. The use of ATP as the energy currency of cells also occurs in other organisms, ranging from bacteria to humans.

Figure 2.18 ATP reaction. ATP, the universal energy currency of cells, is composed of adenosine and three phosphate groups (called a triphosphate). When cells require energy, ATP undergoes hydrolysis, producing ADP + Ⓟ, with the release of energy. (The Ⓟ stands for inorganic phosphate.) Later, ATP is rebuilt when energy is supplied and ADP joins with Ⓟ.

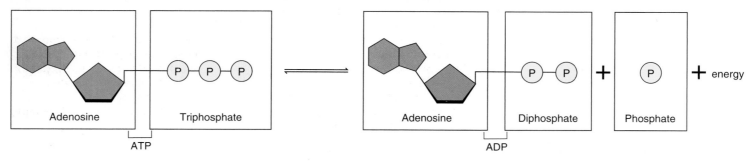

Basic Key Terms

acid (as'id), p. 23

amino acid (uh-me'no as'id), p. 28

ATP (adenosine triphosphate) (uh-den'o-sēn tri-fos'fāt), p. 32

base (bās), p. 23

buffer (buf'er), p. 23

carbohydrate (kar"bo-hi'drāt), p. 24

covalent bond (ko-va'lent bond), p. 21

disaccharide (di-sak'uh-rīd), p. 25

DNA (deoxyribonucleic acid) (de-oks'e-ri"-bo-nu-kla"ik as'id), p. 31

electrolyte (e-lek'tro-līt), p. 23

enzyme (en'zīm), p. 29

fatty acid (fat'e as'id), p. 26

gene (jēn), p. 31

glycerol (glis'er-ol), p. 26

glycogen (gli'ko-jen), p. 25

hydrogen bond (hi'dro-jen bond), p. 22

hydrolysis reaction (hi-drol'ĭ-sis re-ak'shun), p. 24

inorganic molecule (in-or-gan'ik mol'e-kyūl), p. 20

ion (i'on), p. 20

ionic bond (i-on'ik bond), p. 20

isotope (i'so-tōp), p. 19

lipid (lip'id), p. 26

monosaccharide (mon"o-sak'ah-rīd), p. 24

nucleic acid (nu-kla'ik as'id), p. 31

organic molecule (or-gan'ik mol'ĕ-kyūl), p. 20

peptide bond (pep'tīd bond), p. 28

pH scale, p. 23

polysaccharide (pol"e-sak'uh-rīd), p. 25

protein (pro'tēn), p. 28

radioactive isotope (ra"de-o-ak'tiv i'so-tōp), p. 19

RNA (ribonucleic acid) (ri"bo-nu-kla'ik as'id), p. 31

salt (sawlt), p. 20

Clinical Key Terms

acidosis (as"ĭ-do'sis), p. 23

alkalosis (al"kuh-lo'sis), p. 23

arrhythmia (uh-rith'me-uh), p. 20

diabetes (di"ah-be'tēz), p. 25

hypertension (hi"per-ten'shun), p. 20

rickets (rik'ets), p. 20

Summary

2.1 Basic Chemistry

A. All matter is composed of elements, each made up of just one type of atom. An atom has an atomic symbol, atomic number (number of protons and, therefore, electrons when neutral), and atomic weight (number of protons and neutrons). The isotopes of some atoms are radioactive and have biological and medical applications.

B. Atoms react with one another to form molecules. Following an ionic reaction, charged ions are attracted to one another. Following a covalent reaction, atoms share electrons.

2.2 Water, Acids, and Bases

A. In water, the electrons are shared unequally, and the result is a polar molecule. Hydrogen bonding can occur between polar molecules.

B. Water is a polar molecule and acts as a solvent; it dissolves various chemical substances and facilitates chemical reactions. Because of hydrogen bonding, water molecules are cohesive, and also, water heats up and cools down slowly. This

helps keep body temperature within normal limits.

C. Substances such as salts, acids, and bases that dissociate in water are called electrolytes. The electrolyte balance in the blood and body tissues is important for good health.

D. Acids have a pH less than 7, and bases have a pH greater than 7. The presence of buffers helps keep the pH of body fluids around pH 7.

2.3 Molecules of Life

A. Carbohydrates, lipids, proteins, and nucleic acids are the molecules of life.

B. A monosaccharide, such as glucose, is a subunit for larger carbohydrates. Glycerol and fatty acids are subunits for fat. Amino acids are subunits for proteins, and nucleotides are subunits for nucleic acids.

2.4 Carbohydrates

Glucose is an immediate source of energy in cells. Glycogen stores energy in the body, starch is a dietary source of energy, and cellulose is fiber in the diet.

2.5 Lipids

Lipids include neutral fat (a long-term, energy-storage molecule that

forms from glycerol and three fatty acids) and the related phospholipids, which have a charged group. Fatty acids can be saturated or unsaturated. Steroids have an entirely different structure from that of fats.

2.6 Proteins

A. Proteins, which are composed of one or more polypeptides, have both structural and physiological functions. Polypeptides have several levels of structure; the third level is their three-dimensional shape, which is necessary to their function.

B. Enzymes are proteins necessary to metabolism. The reaction occurs at the active site of an enzyme.

2.7 Nucleic Acids

A. Both DNA and RNA are polymers of nucleotides; only DNA is double-stranded. DNA makes up the genes, and along with RNA, specifies protein synthesis.

B. ATP is the energy "currency" of cells because its breakdown supplies energy for many cellular processes.

Study Questions

1. Name the subatomic particles of an atom; describe their charge, atomic mass unit, and location in the carbon atom. (p. 18)
2. What is an isotope? A radioactive isotope? Discuss the clinical uses of radioactive isotopes. (p. 19)
3. Give an example of an ionic reaction, and explain it. (p. 20)
4. Give an example of a covalent reaction, and explain it. (p. 21)
5. Relate three characteristics of water to its polarity and hydrogen bonding between water molecules (p. 22)
6. What is an acid? A base? (p. 23)
7. On the pH scale, which numbers indicate a basic solution? An acidic solution? Why? (p. 23)

8. What are buffers, and how do they function? (p. 23)
9. Name the four categories of macro–molecules in cells; give an example for each category, and name the subunits of each. (p. 24)
10. Tell how macromolecules are built up and broken down. (p. 24)
11. Name some monosaccharides, disaccharides, and polysaccharides, and give the functions for each. (pp. 24–25)
12. What is a lipid? A saturated fatty acid? An unsaturated fatty acid? What is the function of fats? (p. 26)
13. Relate the structure of a phospholipid to that of a neutral fat. What is the function of a phospholipid? (p. 27)

14. Name two steroids that function as sex hormones in humans. (p. 27)
15. What are some functions of proteins? Why do proteins stop functioning if exposed to the wrong pH or high temperature? (p. 28)
16. Discuss the levels of protein structure. (p. 28)
17. How do enzymes function? Name three types of metabolic reactions. (p. 29)
18. Discuss the structure and function of the nucleic acids DNA and RNA. (pp. 31–32)

Objective Questions

Fill in the blanks.

1. _____ are the smallest units of matter nondivisible by chemical means.
2. Isotopes differ by the number of _____ in the nucleus.
3. The two primary types of reactions and bonds are _____ and _____ .
4. A type of weak bond, called a _____ bond, exists between water molecules.

5. Acidic solutions contain more _____ ions than basic solutions, but they have a _____ pH.
6. Glycogen is a polymer of _____ , molecules that serve to give the body immediate _____ .
7. A fat hydrolyzes to give one _____ molecule and three _____ molecules.

8. A polypeptide has levels of structure. The first level is the sequence of _____ ; the second level is very often a _____ ; the third level is its final _____ .
9. _____ speed chemical reactions in cells.
10. Genes are composed of _____ , a nucleic acid made up of _____ joined together.

Medical Terminology Reinforcement Exercise

Consult Appendix B for help in pronouncing and analyzing the meaning of the terms that follow.

1. anisotonic (an-i″so-ton′ik)
2. dehydration (de″hi-dra′shun)
3. hypokalemia (hi″po-kă-le′me-uh)
4. hypovolemia (hi″po-vo-le′me-uh)
5. nonelectrolyte (non″e-lek′tro-līt)

6. lipometabolism (lip″o-mĕ-tab′o-lizm)
7. hyperlipoproteinemia (hi″per-lip″o-pro″te-in-e′me-uh)
8. hyperglycemia (hi″per-gli-se′me-uh)
9. hypoxemia (hi″pok-se′me-uh)
10. hydrostatic pressure (hi″dro-stat′-ik-presh′ur)

11. galactosemia (guh-lak-to-se′me-uh)
12. hypercalcemia (hi″per-kal-se′me-uh)
13. hyponatremia (hi″po-nuh-tre′me-uh)
14. gluconeogenesis (glu″ko-ne-o-jen′uh-sis)
15. edema (uh-de′muh)

Website Link

Visit the Student Edition of the Online Learning Center at http://www.mhhe.com/maderap5 for additional quizzes, interactive learning exercises, and other study tools.

Cell Structure and Function

Scanning electron micrograph of cellular organelles. Mitochondria (green) and the smooth endoplasmic reticulum (blue) perform specific functions in cells.

chapter outline & learning objectives

After you have studied this chapter, you should be able to:

3.1 Cellular Organization (p. 36)

- Name the three main parts of a human cell.
- Describe the structure and function of the plasma membrane.
- Describe the structure and function of the nucleus.
- Describe the structures and roles of the endoplasmic reticulum and the Golgi apparatus in the cytoplasm.
- Describe the structures of lysosomes and the role of these organelles in the breakdown of molecules.
- Describe the structure of mitochondria and their role in producing ATP.

- Describe the structures of centrioles, cilia, and flagella and their roles in cellular movement.
- Describe the structures and function of the cytoskeleton.

3.2 Crossing the Plasma Membrane (p. 43)

- Describe how substances move across the plasma membrane, and distinguish between passive and active transport.

3.3 The Cell Cycle (p. 46)

- Describe the phases of the cell cycle.

- As a part of interphase, describe the process of DNA replication.
- As a part of interphase, also describe how cells carry out protein synthesis.
- Describe the phases of mitosis, and explain the function of mitosis.

Medical Focus

Dehydration and Water Intoxication (p. 45)

3.1 Cellular Organization

Every human cell has a plasma membrane, a nucleus, and cytoplasm. The **plasma membrane,** which surrounds the cell and keeps it intact, regulates what enters and exits a cell. The plasma membrane is a phospholipid bilayer that is said to be semipermeable because it allows certain molecules but not others to enter the cell. Proteins present in the plasma membrane play important roles in allowing substances to enter the cell.

The **nucleus** is a large, centrally located structure that can often be seen with a light microscope. The nucleus contains the chromosomes and is the control center of the cell. It controls the metabolic functioning and structural characteristics of the cell. The **nucleolus** is a region inside the nucleus.

The **cytoplasm** is the portion of the cell between the nucleus and the plasma membrane. The matrix of the cytoplasm is a semifluid medium that contains water and various types of molecules suspended or dissolved in the medium. The presence of proteins accounts for the semifluid nature of the matrix.

The cytoplasm contains various **organelles** (Table 3.1 and Fig. 3.1). Organelles are small, usually membranous structures that are best seen with an electron microscope[1]. Each type of organelle has a specific function. For example, one type of organelle transports substances, and another type produces ATP for the cell. Because organelles are composed of membrane, we can say that membrane compartmentalizes the cell, keeping the various cellular activities separated from one another. Just as the rooms in your house have particular pieces of furniture that serve a particular purpose, organelles have a structure that suits their function.

Cells also have a **cytoskeleton,** a network of interconnected filaments and microtubules in the cytoplasm. The name cytoskeleton is convenient in that it allows us to compare the cytoskeleton to our bones and muscles. Bones and muscles give us structure and produce movement. Similarly, the elements of the cytoskeleton maintain cell shape and allow the cell and its contents to move. Some cells move by using cilia and flagella, which are made up of microtubules.

---

[1]Electron microscopes are high-powered instruments that are used to generate detailed photographs of cellular contents. The photographs are called electron micrographs. Scanning electron micrographs have depth (see page 35) while transmission electron micrographs are flat. Light microscopes are used to generate photomicrographs that are often simply called micrographs.

Table 3.1	Structures in Human Cells	
Name	**Composition**	**Function**
Plasma membrane	Phospholipid bilayer with embedded proteins	Selective passage of molecules into and out of cell
Nucleus	Nuclear envelope surrounding nucleoplasm, chromatin, and nucleolus	Storage of genetic information
Nucleolus	Concentrated area of chromatin, RNA, and proteins	Ribosomal formation
Ribosome	Protein and RNA in two subunits	Protein synthesis
Endoplasmic reticulum (ER)	Membranous saccules and canals	Synthesis and/or modification of proteins and other substances, and transport by vesicle formation
Rough ER	Studded with ribosomes	Protein synthesis
Smooth ER	Having no ribosomes	Various; lipid synthesis in some cells
Golgi apparatus	Stack of membranous saccules	Processing, packaging, and distribution of molecules
Vacuole and vesicle	Membranous sacs	Storage and transport of substances
Lysosome	Membranous vesicle containing digestive enzymes	Intracellular digestion
Mitochondrion	Inner membrane (cristae) within outer membrane	Cellular respiration
Cytoskeleton	Microtubules, actin filaments	Shape of cell and movement of its parts
Cilia and flagella	9 + 2 pattern of microtubules	Movement of cell
Centriole	9 + 0 pattern of microtubules	Formation of basal bodies

Figure 3.1 A generalized cell, with a blowup of the cytoskeleton.

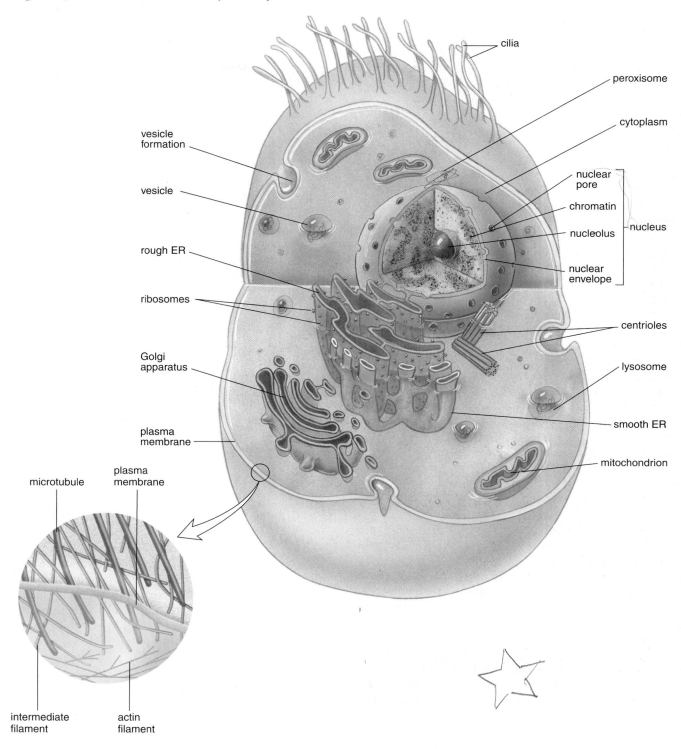

cilia

peroxisome

cytoplasm

vesicle formation

vesicle

nuclear pore

chromatin

nucleolus

nucleus

rough ER

ribosomes

nuclear envelope

centrioles

Golgi apparatus

lysosome

plasma membrane

smooth ER

mitochondrion

microtubule

plasma membrane

intermediate filament

actin filament

Figure 3.2 Fluid-mosaic model of the plasma membrane. **a.** In the phospholipid bilayer, the polar (hydrophilic) heads project outward and the nonpolar (hydrophobic) tails project inward. **b.** Proteins are embedded in the membrane. Glycoproteins have attached carbohydrate chains as do glycolipids.

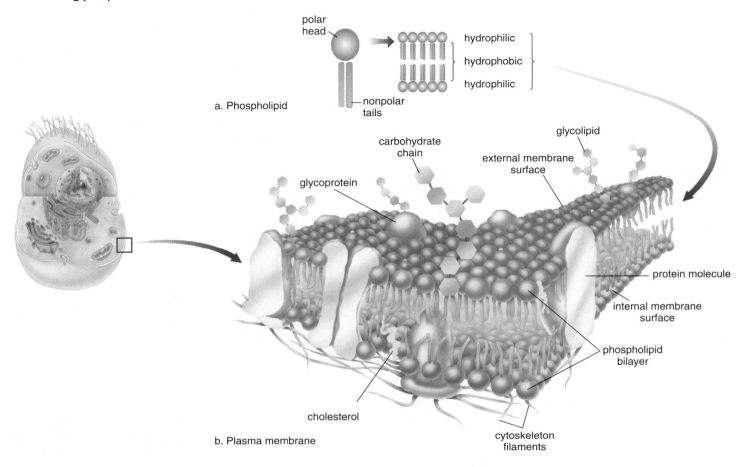

a. Phospholipid

b. Plasma membrane

The Plasma Membrane

Our cells are surrounded by an outer plasma membrane. The plasma membrane separates the inside of the cell, termed the cytoplasm, from the outside. Plasma membrane integrity is necessary to the life of the cell.

The plasma membrane is a phospholipid bilayer with attached or embedded proteins. The phospholipid molecule has a polar head and nonpolar tails (Fig. 3.2a). Because the polar heads are charged, they are *hydrophilic* (water-loving) and face outward, where they are likely to encounter a watery environment. The nonpolar tails are *hydrophobic* (water-fearing) and face inward, where there is no water. When phospholipids are placed in water, they naturally form a spherical bilayer because of the chemical properties of the heads and the tails.

At body temperature, the phospholipid bilayer is a liquid; it has the consistency of olive oil, and the proteins are able to change their positions by moving laterally. The *fluid-mosaic model*, a working description of membrane structure, suggests that the protein molecules have a changing pattern (form a mosaic) within the fluid phospholipid bilayer (Fig. 3.2b). Our plasma membranes also contain a substantial number of *cholesterol* molecules. These molecules lend stability to the phospholipid bilayer and prevent a drastic decrease in fluidity at low temperatures.

Short chains of sugars are attached to the outer surfaces of some protein and lipid molecules (called *glycoproteins* and *glycolipids*, respectively). These carbohydrate chains, specific to each cell, mark the cell as belonging to a particular individual and account for such characteristics as blood type or why a patient's system sometimes rejects an organ transplant. Some glycoproteins have a special configuration that allows them to act as a receptor for a chemical messenger such as a hormone. Some plasma membrane proteins form channels through which certain substances can enter cells, while others are carriers involved in the passage of molecules through the membrane.

The Nucleus

The nucleus is a prominent structure in human cells. The nucleus is of primary importance because it stores the genetic information that determines the characteristics of the body's cells and their metabolic functioning. Every cell contains a copy of genetic information, but each cell type has certain genes turned on, and others turned off. Activated DNA, with messenger RNA (mRNA) acting as an intermediary, controls protein synthesis (see page 48). The proteins of a cell determine its structure and the functions it can perform.

When you look at the nucleus, even in an electron micrograph, you cannot see DNA molecules, but you can see chromatin (Fig. 3.3). Chemical analysis shows that **chromatin** contains DNA and much protein, as well as some RNA. Chromatin undergoes coiling into rodlike structures called **chromosomes** just before the cell divides. Chromatin is immersed in a semifluid medium called nucleoplasm.

Most likely, too, when you look at an electron micrograph of a nucleus (Fig. 3.3), you will see one or more regions that look darker than the rest of the chromatin. These are nucleoli (sing., nucleolus) where another type of RNA, called ribosomal RNA (rRNA), is produced and where rRNA joins with proteins to form the subunits of ribosomes. (Ribosomes are small bodies in the cytoplasm that contain rRNA and proteins.)

The nucleus is separated from the cytoplasm by a double membrane known as the **nuclear envelope,** which is continuous with the endoplasmic reticulum discussed on page 40. The nuclear envelope has **nuclear pores** of sufficient size to permit the passage of proteins into the nucleus and ribosomal subunits out of the nucleus.

Figure 3.3 The nucleus. The nuclear envelope with pores (arrows) surrounds the chromatin. Chromatin has a special region called the nucleolus, where rRNA is produced and ribosomal subunits are assembled.

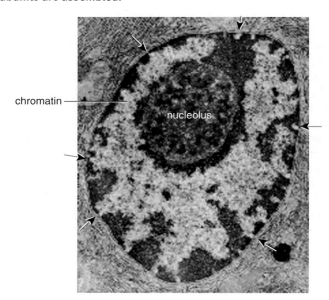

Ribosomes

Ribosomes are composed of two subunits, one large and one small. Each subunit has its own mix of proteins and rRNA. Protein synthesis occurs at the ribosomes.

Ribosomes are found free within the cytoplasm either singly or in groups called **polyribosomes.** Ribosomes are often attached to the endoplasmic reticulum, a membranous system of saccules and channels discussed next (Fig. 3.4).

Proteins synthesized by cytoplasmic ribosomes are used inside the cell for various purposes. Those produced by ribosomes attached to endoplasmic reticulum may eventually be secreted from the cell.

Figure 3.4 Rough endoplasmic reticulum is studded with ribosomes where protein synthesis occurs. Smooth endoplasmic reticulum, which has no attached ribosomes, produces lipids and often has other functions as well in particular cells.

Endomembrane System

The **endomembrane system** consists of the nuclear envelope, the endoplasmic reticulum, the Golgi apparatus, lysosomes, and **vesicles** (tiny membranous sacs) (Fig. 3.5). These components of the cell work together to produce and secrete a product.

The Endoplasmic Reticulum

The **endoplasmic reticulum (ER)**, a complicated system of membranous channels and saccules (flattened vesicles), is physically continuous with the outer membrane of the nuclear envelope. **Rough ER** is studded with ribosomes on the side of the membrane that faces the cytoplasm. Here proteins are synthesized and enter the ER interior where processing and modification begin. Some of these proteins are incorporated into membrane, and some are for export. Smooth ER, which is continuous with rough ER, does not have attached ribosomes. **Smooth ER** synthesizes the phospholipids that occur in membranes and has various other functions, depending on the particular cell. In the testes, it produces testosterone, and in the liver it helps detoxify drugs.

Regardless of any specialized function, ER also forms vesicles in which large molecules are transported to other parts of the cell. Often these vesicles are on their way to the plasma membrane or the Golgi apparatus.

The Golgi Apparatus

The **Golgi apparatus** is named for Camillo Golgi, who discovered its presence in cells in 1898. The Golgi apparatus consists of a stack of three to twenty slightly curved saccules whose appearance can be compared to a stack of pancakes (Fig. 3.5). In animal cells, one side of the stack (the inner face) is directed toward the ER, and the other side of the stack (the outer face) is directed toward the plasma membrane. Vesicles can frequently be seen at the edges of the saccules.

The Golgi apparatus receives protein and/or lipid-filled vesicles that bud from the ER. Some biologists believe that these fuse to form a saccule at the inner face and that this saccule remains a part of the Golgi apparatus until the molecules are repackaged in new vesicles at the outer face. Others believe that the vesicles from the ER proceed directly to the outer face of the Golgi apparatus, where processing and packaging occur within its saccules. The Golgi apparatus contains enzymes that modify proteins and lipids. For example, it can add a chain of sugars to proteins and lipids, thereby making them glycoproteins and glycolipids, which are molecules found in the plasma membrane.

The vesicles that leave the Golgi apparatus move to other parts of the cell. Some vesicles proceed to the plasma membrane, where they discharge their contents. Because this is secretion, note that the Golgi apparatus is involved in processing, packaging, and secretion. Other vesicles that leave the Golgi apparatus are lysosomes.

Figure 3.5 The endomembrane system. Vesicles from the ER bring proteins and lipids to the Golgi apparatus where they are modified and repackaged into vesicles. Secretion occurs when vesicles fuse with the plasma membrane. Lysosomes made at the Golgi apparatus digest macromolecules after fusing with incoming vesicles.

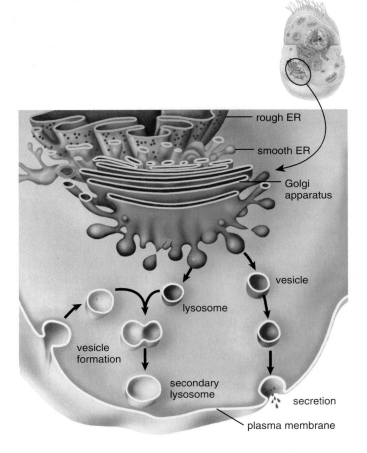

Lysosomes

Lysosomes, membranous sacs produced by the Golgi apparatus, contain hydrolytic digestive enzymes. Sometimes macromolecules are brought into a cell by vesicle formation at the plasma membrane (Fig. 3.5). When a lysosome fuses with such a vesicle, its contents are digested by lysosomal enzymes into simpler subunits that then enter the cytoplasm. Even parts of a cell are digested by its own lysosomes (called autodigestion). Normal cell rejuvenation most likely takes place in this manner, but autodigestion is also important during development. For example, when a tadpole becomes a frog, lysosomes digest away the cells of the tail. The fingers of a human embryo are at first webbed, but they are freed from one another as a result of lysosomal action.

Occasionally, a child is born with **Tay-Sachs disease,** a metabolic disorder involving a missing or inactive lysosomal enzyme. In these cases, the lysosomes fill to capacity with macromolecules that cannot be broken down. The cells become so full of these lysosomes that the child dies. Someday soon, it may be possible to provide the missing enzyme for these children.

Mitochondria

Although the size and shape of mitochondria (sing., **mitochondrion**) can vary, all are bounded by a double membrane. The inner membrane is folded to form little shelves called *cristae*, which project into the matrix, an inner space filled with a gel-like fluid (Fig. 3.6).

Mitochondria are the site of ATP (adenosine triphosphate) production involving complex metabolic pathways. As you know, ATP molecules are the common carrier of energy in cells. A shorthand way to indicate the chemical transformation that involves mitochondria is as follows:

Read as follows: As carbohydrate is broken down to carbon dioxide and water, ATP molecules are built up.

Mitochondria are often called the powerhouses of the cell: Just as a powerhouse burns fuel to produce electricity, the mitochondria convert the chemical energy of glucose products into the chemical energy of ATP molecules. In the process, mitochondria use up oxygen and give off carbon dioxide and water. The oxygen you breathe in enters cells and then mitochondria; the carbon dioxide you breathe out is released by mitochondria. Because oxygen is involved, we say that mitochondria carry on **cellular respiration.**

The matrix of a mitochondrion contains enzymes for breaking down glucose products. ATP production then occurs at the cristae. The protein complexes that aid in the conversion of energy are located in an assembly-line fashion on these membranous shelves.

Every cell uses a certain amount of ATP energy to synthesize molecules, but many cells use ATP to carry out their specialized functions. For example, muscle cells use ATP for muscle contraction, which produces movement, and nerve cells use it for the conduction of nerve impulses, which make us aware of our environment.

Figure 3.6 Mitochondrion structure. Mitochondria are involved in cellular respiration. **a.** Electron micrograph of a mitochondrion. **b.** Generalized drawing in which the outer membrane and portions of the inner membrane have been cut away to reveal the cristae.

Figure 3.7 Cilia and flagella. **a.** Cilia are common on the surfaces of certain tissues, such as the one that forms the inner lining of the respiratory tract. **b.** Flagella form the tails of human sperm cells.

a.

b.

The Cytoskeleton

Several types of filamentous protein structures form a cytoskeleton that helps maintain the cell's shape and either anchors the organelles or assists their movement as appropriate. The cytoskeleton includes microtubules, intermediate filaments, and actin filaments (see Fig. 3.1).

Microtubules are hollow cylinders whose wall is made up of 13 logitudinal rows of the globular protein tubulin. Remarkably, microtubules can assemble and disassemble. Microtubule assembly is regulated by the centrosome which lies near the nucleus. Microtubules radiate from the centrosome, helping to maintain the shape of the cell and acting as tracks along which organelles move. It is well known that during cell division, microtubules form spindle fibers, which assist the movement of chromosomes.

Intermediate filaments differ in structure and function. **Actin filaments** are long, extremely thin fibers that usually occur in bundles or other groupings. Actin filaments have been isolated from various types of cells, especially those in which movement occurs. Microvilli, which project from certain cells and can shorten and extend, contain actin filaments. Actin filaments, like microtubules, can assemble and disassemble.

Centrioles

Centrioles are short cylinders with a 9 + 0 pattern of microtubules, meaning that there are nine outer microtubule triplets and no center microtubules (see Fig. 3.1). Each cell has a pair of centrioles in the centrosome near the nucleus.

The members of each pair of centrioles are at right angles to one another. Before a cell divides, the centrioles duplicate, and the members of the new pair are also at right angles to one another. During cell division, the pairs of centrioles separate so that each daughter cell gets one centrosome.

Centrioles may be involved in the formation of the spindle that functions during cell division. Their exact role in this process is uncertain, however. Centrioles also give rise to basal bodies that direct the formation of cilia and flagella.

Cilia and Flagella

Cilia and flagella (sing., **cilium, flagellum**) are projections of cells that can move either in an undulating fashion, like a whip, or stiffly, like an oar. Cilia are shorter than flagella (Fig. 3.7). Cells that have these organelles are capable of self-movement or moving material along the surface of the cell. For example, sperm cells, carrying genetic material to the egg, move by means of flagella. The cells that line our respiratory tract are ciliated. These cilia sweep debris trapped within mucus back up the throat, and this action helps keep the lungs clean.

Each cilium and flagellum has a basal body at its base, which lies in the cytoplasm. **Basal bodies,** like centrioles, have a 9 + 0 pattern of microtubule triplets. They are believed to organize the structure of cilia and flagella even though cilia and flagella have a 9 + 2 pattern of microtubules. In cilia and flagella, nine microtubule doublets surround two central microtubules. This arrangement is believed to be necessary to their ability to move.

3.2 Crossing the Plasma Membrane

The plasma membrane keeps a cell intact. It allows only certain molecules and ions to enter and exit the cytoplasm freely; therefore, the plasma membrane is said to be **selectively permeable.** Both passive and active methods are used to cross the plasma membrane (see Table 3.2).

Diffusion

Diffusion is the random movement of molecules from the area of higher concentration to the area of lower concentration until they are equally distributed. To illustrate diffusion, imagine putting a tablet of dye into water. The water eventually takes on the color of the dye as the dye molecules diffuse.

The chemical and physical properties of the plasma membrane allow only a few types of molecules to enter and exit a cell simply by diffusion. Lipid-soluble molecules such as alcohols can diffuse through the membrane because lipids are the membrane's main structural components. Gases can also diffuse through the lipid bilayer; this is the mechanism by which oxygen enters cells and carbon dioxide exits cells. As an example, consider the movement of oxygen from the alveoli (air sacs) of the lungs to the blood in the lung capillaries. After inhalation (breathing in), the concentration of oxygen in the alveoli is higher than that in the blood; therefore, oxygen diffuses into the blood.

When molecules simply diffuse from higher to lower concentration across plasma membranes, no cellular energy is involved.

Osmosis

Osmosis is the diffusion of water across a plasma membrane. It occurs whenever an unequal concentration of water exists on either side of a selectively permeable membrane. Normally, body fluids are *isotonic* to cells (Fig. 3.8*a*)—that is, there is an equal concentration of **solutes** (substances) and solvent (water) on both sides of the plasma membrane, and

cells maintain their usual size and shape. Intravenous solutions medically administered usually have this tonicity. **Tonicity** is the degree to which a solution's concentration of solute versus water causes water to move into or out of cells.

Solutions (solute plus solvent) that cause cells to swell or even to burst due to an intake of water are said to be hypotonic solutions. If red blood cells are placed in a *hypotonic* solution, which has a higher concentration of water (lower concentration of solute) than do the cells, water enters the cells and they swell to bursting (Fig. 3.8*b*). The term *lysis* refers to disrupted cells; hemolysis, then, is disrupted red blood cells.

Solutions that cause cells to shrink or to shrivel due to a loss of water are said to be hypertonic solutions. If red blood cells are placed in a *hypertonic* solution, which has a lower concentration of water (higher concentration of solute) than do the cells, water leaves the cells and they shrink (Fig. 3.8*c*). The term *crenation* refers to red blood cells in this condition.

These changes have occurred due to osmotic pressure. *Osmotic pressure* is the force exerted on a selectively permeable membrane because water has moved from the area of higher concentration of water to the area of lower concentration (higher concentration of solute).

Filtration

Because capillary walls are only one cell thick, small molecules (e.g., water or small solutes) tend to passively diffuse across these walls, from areas of higher concentration to those of lower concentration. However, blood pressure aids matters by pushing water and dissolved solutes out of the capillary. This process is called **filtration.**

Filtration is easily observed in the laboratory when a solution is poured past filter paper into a flask. Large substances stay behind, but small molecules and water pass through.

Filtration of water and substances in the region of capillaries is largely responsible for the formation of tissue fluid, the fluid that surrounds the cells. Filtration is also at work in the kidneys when water and small molecules move from the blood to the inside of the kidney tubules.

Figure 3.8 Tonicity. The arrows indicate the movement of water.

Animal cells

plasma membrane

a. In an isotonic solution, there is no net movement of water.

b. In a hypotonic solution, water enters the cell, which may burst (lysis).

c. In a hypertonic solution, water leaves the cell, which shrivels (crenation).

Transport by Carriers

Most solutes do not simply diffuse across a plasma membrane; rather, they are transported by means of protein carriers within the membrane. During **facilitated transport,** a molecule (e.g., an amino acid or glucose) is transported across the plasma membrane from the side of higher concentration to the side of lower concentration. The cell does not need to expend energy for this type of transport because the molecules are moving down their concentration gradient.

During **active transport,** a molecule is moving contrary to the normal direction—that is, from lower to higher concentration (Fig. 3.9). For example, iodine collects in the cells of the thyroid gland; sugar is completely absorbed from the gut by cells that line the digestive tract; and sodium (Na⁺) is sometimes almost completely withdrawn from urine by cells lining kidney tubules. Active transport requires a protein carrier and the use of cellular energy obtained from the breakdown of ATP. When ATP is broken down, energy is released, and in this case the energy is used by a carrier to carry out active transport. Therefore, it is not surprising that cells involved in active transport have a large number of mitochondria near the plasma membrane at which active transport is occurring.

Proteins involved in active transport often are called pumps because just as a water pump uses energy to move water against the force of gravity, proteins use energy to move substances against their concentration gradients. One type of pump that is active in all cells but is especially associated with nerve and muscle cells moves sodium ions (Na⁺) to the outside of the cell and potassium ions (K⁺) to the inside of the cell.

The passage of salt (NaCl) across a plasma membrane is of primary importance in cells. First, sodium ions are pumped across a membrane; then, chloride ions simply diffuse through channels that allow their passage. Chloride ion channels malfunction in persons with cystic fibrosis, and this leads to the symptoms of this inherited (genetic) disorder.

Endocytosis and Exocytosis

During endocytosis, commonly called phagocytosis, a portion of the plasma membrane invaginates to envelop a substance, and then the membrane pinches off to form an intracellular vesicle (see Fig. 3.1, *top*). Digestion may be required before molecules can cross a vesicle membrane to enter the cytoplasm. During exocytosis, a vesicle fuses with the plasma membrane as secretion occurs (see Fig. 3.1, *bottom*). This is the way insulin leaves insulin-secreting cells, for instance. Table 3.2 summarizes the various ways molecules cross the plasma membrane.

Figure 3.9 Active transport through a plasma membrane. Active transport allows a molecule to cross the membrane from lower concentration to higher concentration. ① Molecule enters carrier. ② Breakdown of ATP induces a change in shape that ③ drives the molecule across the membrane.

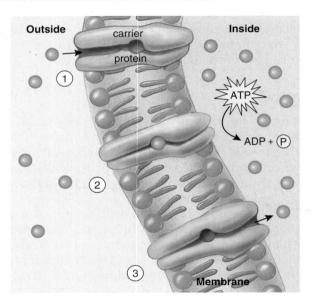

	Name	Direction	Requirement	Examples
Table 3.2	**Crossing the Plasma Membrane**			
PASSIVE METHODS	Diffusion	Toward lower concentration	Concentration gradient	Lipid-soluble molecules, water, and gases
	Facilitated transport	Toward lower concentration	Carrier and concentration gradient	Sugars and amino acids
ACTIVE METHODS	Active transport	Toward higher concentration	Carrier plus energy	Sugars, amino acids, and ions
	Endocytosis (phagocytosis)	Toward inside	Vesicle formation	Macromolecules
	Exocytosis	Toward outside	Vesicle fuses with plasma membrane	Macromolecules

Dehydration and Water Intoxication

Dehydration is due to a loss of water. The solute concentration in extracellular fluid increases—that is, tissue fluid becomes hypertonic to cells, and water leaves the cells. Common causes of dehydration are excessive sweating, perhaps during exercise, without any replacement of the water lost. Dehydration can also be a side effect of any illness that causes prolonged vomiting or diarrhea. The signs of moderate dehydration are a dry mouth, sunken eyes, and skin that will not bounce back after light pinching. If dehydration becomes severe, the pulse and breathing rate are rapid, the hands and feet are cold, and the lips are blue. Although dehydration leads to weight loss, it is never a good idea to dehydrate on purpose for this reason.

To cure dehydration, intake of a low-sodium solution is needed because water intake alone could lead to water intoxica-

tion. **Water intoxication** is due to a gain in water. The solute concentration in extracellular fluid decreases—that is, tissue fluid becomes hypotonic to the cells, and water enters the cells. Water intoxication is not nearly as common in adults as is dehydration. One cause can be the intake of too much water during a marathon race. Marathoners who collapse and have nausea and vomiting after a race are probably not suffering from a heart attack, but they may be suffering from water intoxication, which can lead to pulmonary edema and swelling in the brain. The cure, an intravenous solution containing high amounts of sodium, is the opposite of that for dehydration. Therefore, it is important that physicians be able to diagnose water intoxication in athletes who have had an opportunity to drink fluids for the past several hours.

Figure 3A Dehydration versus water intoxication. **a.** If extracellular fluid loses much water, cells lose water by osmosis, and become dehydrated. **b.** If extracellular fluid gains water, cells gain water by osmosis, and water intoxication occurs.

3.3 The Cell Cycle

The **cell cycle** is an orderly set of stages that take place between the time a cell divides and the time the resulting daughter cells also divide. The cell cycle is controlled by internal and external signals. A signal is a molecule that stimulates or inhibits a metabolic event. For example, growth factors are external signals received at the plasma membrane that cause a resting cell to undergo the cell cycle. When blood platelets release a growth factor, skin fibroblasts in the vicinity finish the cell cycle, thereby repairing an injury. Other signals ensure that the stages follow one another in the normal sequence and that each stage of the cell cycle is properly completed before the next stage begins.

The cell cycle has a number of checkpoints, places where the cell cycle stops if all is not well. Any cell that did not successfully complete mitosis and is abnormal undergoes apoptosis at the *restriction checkpoint*. **Apoptosis** is often defined as programmed cell death because the cell progresses through a series of events that bring about its destruction. The cell rounds up and loses contact with its neighbors. The nucleus fragments, and the plasma membrane develops blisters. Finally, the cell fragments, and its bits and pieces are engulfed by white blood cells and/or neighboring cells. The enzymes that bring about apoptosis are ordinarily held in check by inhibitors, but are unleashed by either internal or external signals.

Following a certain number of cell cycle revolutions, cells are apt to become specialized and no longer go through the cell cycle. Muscle cells and nerve cells typify specialized cells that rarely, if ever, go through the cell cycle. At the other extreme, some cells in the body, called stem cells, are always immature and go through the cell cycle repeatedly. There is a great deal of interest in stem cells today because it may be possible to control their future development into particular tissues and organs.

Cell Cycle Stages

The cell cycle has two major portions: interphase and the mitotic stage (Fig. 3.10).

Interphase

The cell in Figure 3.1 is in interphase because it is not dividing. During interphase, the cell carries on its regular activities, and it also gets ready to divide if it is going to complete the cell cycle. For these cells, interphase has three stages, called G_1 phase, S phase, and G_2 phase.

G_1 Phase Early microscopists named the phase before DNA replication G_1, and they named the phase after DNA replication G_2. G stood for "gap." Now that we know how metabolically active the cell is, it is better to think of G as standing for "growth." Protein synthesis is very much a part of these growth phases.

Figure 3.10 The cell cycle consists of interphase, during which cellular components duplicate, and a mitotic stage, during which the cell divides. Interphase consists of two so-called "growth" phases (G_1 and G_2) and a DNA synthesis (S) phase. The mitotic stage consists of the phases noted plus cytokinesis.

During G_1, a cell doubles its organelles (such as mitochondria and ribosomes) and accumulates materials that will be used for DNA synthesis.

S Phase Following G_1, the cell enters the S (for "synthesis") phase. During the S phase, DNA replication occurs. At the beginning of the S phase, each chromosome is composed of one DNA double helix, which is equal to a chromatid. At the end of this phase, each chromosome has two identical DNA double helix molecules, and therefore is composed of two sister chromatids. Another way of expressing these events is to say that DNA replication has resulted in duplicated chromosomes.

G_2 Phase During this phase, the cell synthesizes proteins that will assist cell division, such as the protein found in microtubules. The role of microtubules in cell division is described later in this section. Also, chromatin condenses, and the chromosomes become visible.

Mitotic Stage

Following interphase, the cell enters the M (for mitotic) stage. This cell division stage includes **mitosis** (division of the nucleus) and **cytokinesis** (division of the cytoplasm). During mitosis, daughter chromosomes are distributed to two daughter nuclei. When cytokinesis is complete, two daughter cells are present.

Events During Interphase

Two significant events during interphase are replication of DNA and protein synthesis.

Replication of DNA

During **replication,** an exact copy of a DNA helix is produced. (DNA and RNA structure are described on pages 31–32.) The double-stranded structure of DNA aids replication because each strand serves as a template for the formation of a complementary strand. A **template** is most often a mold used to produce a shape opposite to itself. In this case, each old (parental) strand is a template for each new (daughter) strand.

Figures 3.11 and 3.12 show how replication is carried out. Figure 3.12 uses the ladder configuration of DNA for easy viewing.

1. Before replication begins, the two strands that make up parental DNA are hydrogen-bonded to one another.

2. During replication, the old (parental) DNA strands unwind and "upzip" (i.e., the weak hydrogen bonds between the two strands break).

3. New complementary nucleotides, always present in the nucleus, pair with the nucleotides in the old strands. A pairs with T and C pairs with G. The enzyme DNA polymerase joins the new nucleotides forming new (daughter) complementary strands.

4. When replication is complete, the two double helix molecules are identical.

Each strand of a double helix is equal to a **chromatid,** which means that at the completion of replication each chromosome is composed of two sister chromatids. They are called **sister chromatids** because they are identical. The chromosome is called a **duplicated chromosome.**

Cancer, which is characterized by rapidly dividing cells, is treated with chemotherapeutic drugs that stop replication and therefore cell division. Some chemotherapeutic drugs are analogs that have a similar, but not identical, structure to the four nucleotides in DNA. When these are mistakenly used by the cancer cells to synthesize DNA, replication stops, and the cells die off.

Figure 3.11 Overview of DNA replication. During replication, an old strand serves as a template for a new strand. The new double helix is composed of an old (parental) strand and a new (daughter) strand.

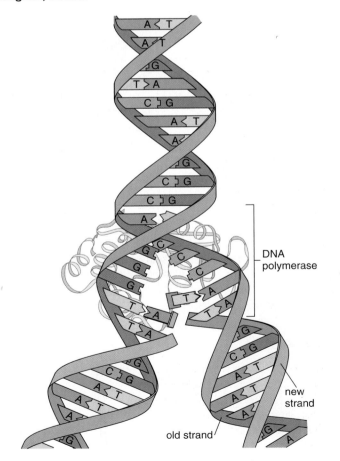

Figure 3.12 Ladder configuration and DNA replication. Use of the ladder configuration better illustrates how complementary nucleotides available in the cell pair with those of each old strand before they are joined together to form a daughter strand.

Parental DNA molecule contains so-called old strands hydrogen-bonded by complementary base pairing.

Region of replication. Parental DNA is unwound and unzipped. New nucleotides are pairing with those in old strands.

Replication is complete. Each double helix is composed of an old (parental) strand and a new (daughter) strand.

Protein Synthesis

DNA not only serves as a template for its own replication, but is also a template for RNA formation. Protein synthesis requires two steps, called transcription and translation. During **transcription,** an mRNA molecule is produced, and during **translation,** this mRNA specifies the order of amino acids in a particular polypeptide (Fig. 3.13). A gene (i.e., DNA) contains coded information for the sequence of amino acids in a particular polypeptide. The code is a **triplet code:** Every three bases in DNA (and therefore in mRNA) stands for a particular amino acid.

Transcription and Translation

During transcription, complementary RNA nucleotides from an RNA nucleotide pool in the nucleus pair with the DNA nucleotides of one strand. The RNA nucleotides are joined by an enzyme called RNA polymerase, and an mRNA molecule results. Therefore, when mRNA forms, it has a sequence of bases complementary to DNA. A sequence of three bases that are complementary to the DNA triplet code is a **codon.**

Translation requires several enzymes and two other types of RNA: transfer RNA and ribosomal RNA. **Transfer RNA (tRNA)** molecules bring amino acids to the ribosomes, which are composed of **ribosomal RNA (rRNA)** and protein. There is at least one tRNA molecule for each of the 20 amino acids found in proteins. The amino acid binds to one end of the molecule, and the entire complex is designated as tRNA–amino acid.

At the other end of each tRNA molecule is a specific **anticodon,** a group of three bases that is complementary to an mRNA codon. A tRNA molecule comes to the ribosome, where its anticodon pairs with an mRNA codon. For example, if the codon is ACC, then the anticodon is UGG and the amino acid is threonine. (The codes for each of the 20 amino acids are known.) Notice that the order of the codons of the mRNA determines the order that tRNA–amino acids come to a ribosome, and therefore the final sequence of amino acids in a polypeptide.

Figure 3.13 Protein synthesis. The two steps required for protein synthesis are transcription, which occurs in the nucleus, and translation, which occurs in the cytoplasm at the ribosomes.

1. DNA in nucleus serves as a template.

DNA

2. mRNA is processed before leaving the nucleus.

RNA

3. When mRNA is formed it has codons.

mRNA

4. mRNA moves into cytoplasm and becomes associated with ribosomes.

ribosomal subunits

amino acids

peptide chain

tRNA

5. tRNA with anticodon carries amino acid to mRNA.

anticodon

7. Peptide chain is transferred from resident tRNA to incoming tRNA.

8. tRNA departs and will soon pick up another amino acid.

6. Anticodon-codon complementary base pairing occurs.

codon

ribosome

Events During the Mitotic Stage

The mitotic stage of the cell cycle consists of mitosis and cytokinesis. By the end of interphase (Fig. 3.14, *upper left*), the centrioles have doubled and the chromosomes are becoming visible. Each chromosome is duplicated—it is composed of two chromatids held together at a centromere. As an aid in describing the events of mitosis, the process is divided into four phases: prophase, metaphase, anaphase, and telophase (Fig. 3.14). The **parental cell** is the cell that divides, and the **daughter cells** are the cells that result.

Prophase

Several events occur during **prophase** that visibly indicate the cell is about to divide. The two pairs of centrioles outside the nucleus begin moving away from each other toward opposite ends of the nucleus. Spindle fibers appear between the separating centriole pairs, the nuclear envelope begins to fragment, and the nucleolus begins to disappear.

The chromosomes are now fully visible. Although humans have 46 chromosomes, only four are shown in Figure 3.14 for ease in following the phases of mitosis. Spindle fibers attach to the centromeres as the chromosomes continue to shorten and thicken. During prophase, chromosomes are randomly placed in the nucleus.

Structure of the Spindle At the end of prophase, a cell has a fully formed spindle. A **spindle** has poles, asters, and fibers. The **asters** are arrays of short microtubules that radiate from the poles, and the fibers are bundles of microtubules that stretch between the poles. Centrioles are located in centrosomes, which are believed to organize the spindle.

Figure 3.14 The late interphase cell and the mitotic stage of the cell cycle. Although humans have 46 chromosomes, only four are shown here for convenience. The blue chromosomes were originally inherited from a father, and the red were originally inherited from a mother.

Interphase

chromatin

centrioles

spindle

nucleolus

nuclear pore

nuclear envelope

Late interphase
Chromatin is condensing into chromosomes.

Mitosis

sister chromatids

nucleolus

centromere

nuclear envelope fragments

Prophase
Duplicated chromosomes are scattered.

spindle

aster

Metaphase
Chromosomes are aligned at the equator of the spindle.

daughter cells

Daughter Cells: Early interphase
Chromosomes are decondensing.

furrow

centromere

Telophase
Daughter nuclei are forming and spindle is disappearing.

chromosome

Anaphase
Daughter chromosomes are moving to the poles.

Figure 3.15 Micrographs of mitosis occurring in a whitefish embryo.

PROPHASE

plasma membrane
aster
spindle fibers
chromosomes

METAPHASE

aster
chromosomes

ANAPHASE

TELOPHASE

Metaphase

During **metaphase,** the nuclear envelope is fragmented, and the spindle occupies the region formerly occupied by the nucleus. The chromosomes are now at the equator (center) of the spindle. Metaphase is characterized by a fully formed spindle, and the chromosomes, each with two sister chromatids, are aligned at the equator (Fig. 3.15).

Anaphase

At the start of **anaphase,** the sister chromatids separate. *Once separated, the chromatids are called chromosomes.* Separation of the sister chromatids ensures that each cell receives a copy of each type of chromosome and thereby has a full complement of genes. During anaphase, the daughter chromosomes move to the poles of the spindle. Anaphase is characterized by the movement of chromosomes toward each pole.

Function of the Spindle The spindle brings about chromosome movement. Two types of spindle fibers are involved in the movement of chromosomes during anaphase. One type extends from the poles to the equator of the spindle; there, they overlap. As mitosis proceeds, these fibers increase in length, and this helps push the chromosomes apart. The chromosomes themselves are attached to other spindle fibers that simply extend from their centromeres to the poles. These fibers get shorter and shorter as the chromosomes move toward the poles. Therefore, they pull the chromosomes apart.

Spindle fibers, as stated earlier, are composed of microtubules. Microtubules can assemble and disassemble by the addition or subtraction of tubulin (protein) subunits. This is what enables spindle fibers to lengthen and shorten, and it ultimately causes the movement of the chromosomes.

Telophase and Cytokinesis

Telophase begins when the chromosomes arrive at the poles. During telophase, the chromosomes become indistinct chromatin again. The spindle disappears as nucleoli appear, and nuclear envelope components reassemble in each cell. Telophase is characterized by the presence of two daughter nuclei.

Cytokinesis is division of the cytoplasm and organelles. In human cells, a slight indentation called a **cleavage furrow** passes around the circumference of the cell. Actin filaments form a contractile ring, and as the ring gets smaller and smaller, the cleavage furrow pinches the cell in half. As a result, each cell becomes enclosed by its own plasma membrane.

Importance of Mitosis

Because of mitosis, each cell in our body is genetically identical, meaning that it has the same number and kinds of chromosomes. Mitosis is important to the growth and repair of multicellular organisms. When a baby develops in the mother's womb, mitosis occurs as a component of growth. As a wound heals, mitosis occurs, and the damage is repaired.

Selected New Terms

Basic Key Terms

active transport (ak'tiv trans'port), p. 44

apoptosis (ap"o-to'-sis), p. 46

cell cycle (sel sī'-kl), p. 46

centriole (sen'tre-ōl), p. 42

chromatin (kro'muh-tin), p. 39

chromosome (kro'mo-sōm), p. 39

cleavage furrow (klēv'ij fur'o), p. 50

cytokinesis (si'to-kī-ne'sis), p. 46

cytoplasm (si'to-plazm), p. 36

cytoskeleton (si'to-skel"ĕ-tun), p. 36

diffusion (dĭ-fyū-zhun), p. 43

endomembrane system (en"do-mem'brān sis'tem), p. 40

endoplasmic reticulum (en-do-plaz'mic rĕ-tik'yū-lum), p. 40

facilitated transport (fuh-sil'-ĭ-tāt'id trans'port), p. 44

filtration (fil-tra'shun), p. 43

Golgi apparatus (gol'je ap"uh-rătus), p. 40

lysosome (li'so-sōm), p. 40

microtubule (mi"kro-tu'byūl), p. 42

mitochondrion (mi"to-kon'dre-on), p. 41

mitosis (mi-to'sis), p. 46

nuclear envelope (nu'kle-er en'vĕ-lōp), p. 39

nuclear pore (nu'kle-er por), p. 39

nucleolus (nu-kle'o-lus), p. 36

nucleus (nu'kle-us), p. 36

organelle (or'guh-nel), p. 36

osmosis (oz-mo'sis), p. 43

plasma membrane (plaz'muh mem'brān), p. 36

ribosomal RNA (ri'bo-sōm'al RNA), p. 48

ribosome (ri'bo-sōm), p. 39

selectively permeable (se-lĕk'tiv-le per'me-uh-bl), p. 43

solute (sol'ūt), p. 43

spindle (spin'dl), p. 49

transcription (trans-krip'shun), p. 48

transfer RNA (trans'fer RNA), p. 48

translation (trans-la'shun), p. 48

triplet code (trip'let cōd), p. 48

vesicle (ves'ĭ-kl), p. 40

Clinical Key Terms

Tay-Sachs (tā saks), p. 40

Summary

Cells differ in shape and function, but even so, a generalized cell can be described.

3.1 Cellular Organization
All human cells, despite varied shapes and sizes, have a plasma membrane and a central nucleus. The cytoplasm contains organelles and a cytoskeleton.

A. The plasma membrane, composed of phospholipid and protein molecules, regulates the entrance and exit of other molecules into and out of the cell.

B. The nucleus contains chromatin, which condenses into chromosomes just prior to cell division. Genes, composed of DNA, are on the chromosomes, and they code for the production of proteins in the cytoplasm. The nucleolus is involved in ribosome formation.

C. Ribosomes are small organelles where protein synthesis occurs. Ribosomes occur in the cytoplasm, both singly and in groups.

Numerous ribosomes are attached to the endoplasmic reticulum.

D. The endomembrane system consists of the endoplasmic reticulum (ER), the Golgi apparatus, and the lysosomes and various transport vesicles.

E. The ER is involved in protein synthesis (rough ER) and various other processes such as lipid synthesis (smooth ER). Molecules produced or modified in the ER are eventually enclosed in vesicles that take them to the Golgi apparatus.

F. The Golgi apparatus processes and packages molecules, distributes them within the cell, and transports them out of the cell. It is also involved in secretion.

G. Lysosomes are produced by the Golgi apparatus, and their hydrolytic enzymes digest macromolecules from various sources. Mitochondria are the sites of cellular respiration, a process that uses nutrients and

oxygen to provide ATP, the type of chemical energy needed by cells.

H. Mitochondria are involved in cellular respiration, a metabolic pathway that provides ATP molecules to cells.

I. Notable among the contents of the cytoskeleton are microtubules and actin filaments. The cytoskeleton maintains the shape of the cell and also directs the movement of cell parts.

J. Centrioles lie near the nucleus and may be involved in the production of the spindle during cell division and in the formation of cilia and flagella.

3.2 Crossing the Plasma Membrane
When substances enter and exit cells by diffusion, osmosis, or filtration, no carrier is required. Facilitated transport and active transport do require a carrier.

A. Some substances can simply diffuse across a plasma membrane. The diffusion of water is called osmosis.

In an isotonic solution, cells neither gain nor lose water. In a hypotonic solution, cells swell. In a hypertonic solution, cells shrink.

B. During filtration, diffusion of small molecules out of a blood vessel is aided by blood pressure.

C. During facilitated transport, a carrier is required, but energy is not because the substance is moving from higher to lower concentration. Active transport, which requires a carrier and ATP energy, moves substances from lower to higher concentration.

D. Endocytosis (phagocytosis) involves the uptake of substances by a cell through vesicle formation. Exocytosis involves the release of substances from a cell as vesicles within the cell cytoplasm fuse with the plasma membrane.

3.3 The Cell Cycle

The cell cycle consists of interphase (G_1 phase, S phase, G_2 phase) and the mitotic stage, which includes mitosis and cytokinesis.

A. During interphase, DNA replication and protein synthesis take place. DNA serves as a template for its own replication: The DNA parental molecule unwinds and unzips, and new (daughter) strands form by complementary base pairing. Protein synthesis consists of transcription and translation. During transcription, DNA serves as a template for the formation of RNA. During translation, mRNA, rRNA, and tRNA are involved in polypeptide synthesis.

B. Mitosis consists of a number of phases, during which each newly formed cell receives a copy of each kind of chromosome. Later, the cytoplasm divides by furrowing. Mitosis occurs during growth and repair.

Study Questions

1. What are the three main parts to any human cell? (p. 36)
2. Describe the fluid-mosaic model of membrane structure. (p. 38)
3. Describe the nucleus and its contents, and include the terms *DNA* and *RNA* in your description. (p. 39)
4. Describe the structure and function of ribosomes. (p. 39)
5. What is the endomembrane system? What organelles belong to this system? (p. 40)
6. Describe the structure and function of endoplasmic reticulum (ER). Include the terms smooth ER, rough ER, and ribosomes in your description. (p. 40)
7. Describe the structure and function of the Golgi apparatus. Mention vesicles and lysosomes in your description. (p. 40)
8. Describe the structure and function of mitochondria. Mention the energy molecule ATP in your description. (p. 41)
9. What is the cytoskeleton, and what role does the cytoskeleton play in cells? (p. 42)
10. Describe the structure and function of centrioles. Mention the mitotic spindle in your description. (p. 42)
11. Contrast passive transport (diffusion, osmosis, filtration) with active transport of molecules across the plasma membrane. (pp. 43–44)
12. Define osmosis, and describe the effects of placing red blood cells in isotonic, hypotonic, and hypertonic solutions. (p. 43)
13. What is the cell cycle, and what stages occur during interphase? What happens during the mitotic stage? (p. 46)
14. Describe the structure of DNA and how this structure contributes to the process of DNA replication. (p. 47)
15. Briefly describe the events of protein synthesis. (p. 48)
16. List the phases of mitosis, and tell what happens during each phase. (pp. 49–50)
17. Discuss the importance of mitosis in humans. (p. 50)

Objective Questions

I. Match the organelles in the key to the functions listed in questions 1–5.

Key:
- a. mitochondria
- b. nucleus
- c. Golgi apparatus
- d. rough ER
- e. centrioles

1. packaging and secretion
2. cell division
3. powerhouses of the cell
4. protein synthesis
5. control center for the cell

II. Fill in the blanks.

6. The fluid-mosaic model of membrane structure says that _____ molecules drift about within a double layer of _____ molecules.
7. Rough ER has _____ , but smooth ER does not.
8. Basal bodies that organize the microtubules within cilia and flagella are believed to be derived from _____ .
9. Water will enter a cell when it is placed in a _____ solution.
10. Active transport requires a protein _____ and _____ for energy.
11. Vesicle formation occurs when a cell takes in material by _____.
12. At the conclusion of mitosis, each newly formed cell in humans contains _____ chromosomes.
13. The _____ , which is the substance outside the nucleus of a cell, contains bodies called _____ , each with a specific structure and function.

III. Match the organelles in the key to the functions listed in questions 14–17.

Key:
- a. DNA
- b. mRNA
- c. tRNA
- d. rRNA

14. Joins with proteins to form subunits of a ribosome.
15. Contains codons that determine the sequence of amino acids in a polypeptide.
16. Contains a code and serves as a template for the production of RNA.
17. Brings amino acids to the ribosomes during the process of transcription.

Medical Terminology Reinforcement Exercise

Consult Appendix B for help in pronouncing and analyzing the meaning of the terms that follow.

1. hemolysis (he″mol′ĭ-sis)
2. cytology (si-tol′o-je)
3. cytometer (si-tom′ĕ-ter)
4. nucleoplasm (nu′kle-o-plazm)
5. pancytopenia (pan″si-to-pe′ne-uh)
6. cytogenic (si-to-jen′ik)
7. erythrocyte (ĕ-rith′ro-sīt)
8. apoptosis (ap″o-to′sis)
9. atrophy (at′ro-fe)
10. hypertrophy (hi-per′tro-fe)
11. oncotic pressure, colloid osmotic pressure (ong-kot′ik presh′er)(kol′oyd oz-mah′-tik presh′er)
12. hyperplasia (hi-per-pla′zhe-uh)

Website Link

Visit the Student Edition of the Online Learning Center at http://www.mhhe.com/maderap5 for additional quizzes, interactive learning exercises, and other study tools.

Body Tissues and Membranes

Spongy bone consists of bars and plates separated by irregular spaces, but it is still quite strong.

chapter outline & learning objectives

After you have studied this chapter, you should be able to:

Figure 4.1 Simple squamous epithelium. The thin and flat cells are tightly joined. The nuclei tend to be broad and thin.

free surface

plasma membrane

basement membrane

nucleus

Simple Squamous Epithelium

Location:
Lines air sacs of lungs; blood vessels; heart

Function:
Filtration; diffusion; osmosis

4.1 Epithelial Tissue

A tissue is composed of specialized cells of one type that perform a common function in the body. There are four major types of tissues: (1) Epithelial tissue, also called epithelium, covers body surfaces and organs and lines body cavities; (2) connective tissue binds and supports body parts; (3) muscular tissue contracts; and (4) nervous tissue responds to stimuli and transmits impulses from one body part to another (Table 4.1).

In **epithelial tissue,** the cells are tightly packed, with little space between them. Externally, this tissue protects the body from drying out, injury, and bacterial invasion. On internal surfaces, epithelial tissue protects, but it also may have an additional function. For example, in the respiratory tract, epithelial tissue sweeps up impurities by means of cilia. Along the digestive tract, it secretes mucus, which protects the lining from digestive enzymes. In kidney tubules, its absorptive function is enhanced by the presence of fine, cellular extensions called microvilli.

Epithelial cells readily divide to produce new cells that replace lost or damaged ones. Skin cells as well as those that line the stomach and intestines are continually being replaced. Surprisingly, then, epithelial tissue lacks blood vessels and must get its nutrients from underlying connective tissues.

Because epithelial tissue covers surfaces and lines cavities, it always has a *free surface.* The other surface is attached to underlying tissue by a layer of carbohydrates and proteins called the basement membrane.

Epithelial tissues are classified according to the shape of the cells and the number of cell layers. Simple epithelial tissue is composed of a single layer, and **stratified** epithelial tissue is composed of two or more layers. Squamous epithelium has flattened cells; cuboidal epithelium has cube-shaped cells; and columnar epithelium has elongated cells.

Squamous Epithelium

Simple squamous epithelium is composed of a single layer of flattened cells, and therefore its protective function is not as significant as that of other epithelial tissues (Fig. 4.1). It is found in areas where secretion, absorption, and filtration occur. For example, simple squamous epithelium lines the lungs where oxygen and carbon dioxide are exchanged, and it lines the walls of capillaries, where nutrients and wastes are exchanged.

Stratified squamous epithelium has many cell layers and does play a protective role. While the deeper cells may be cuboidal or columnar, the outer layer is composed of squamous-shaped cells. The outer portion of skin is stratified squamous epithelium. New cells produced in a basal layer become reinforced by keratin, a protein that provides strength, as they move toward the skin's surface. Aside from skin, stratified squamous epithelium is found lining the various orifices of the body.

Table 4.1	Epithelial Tissue
Type	**Description**
Simple squamous	One layer of flattened cells
Stratified squamous	Many layers; cell flattened at surface
Simple cuboidal	One layer of cube-shaped cells
Simple columnar	One layer of elongated cells
Pseudostratified columnar	Appears to be layered but is not layered
Transitional	When tissue stretches, layers become fewer

Figure 4.2 Simple cuboidal epithelium. The cells are cube-shaped. Spherical nuclei tend to be centrally located.

basement membrane

free surface

nucleus

Simple Cuboidal Epithelium

Location:
Lines kidney tubules; ducts of many glands; covers surface of ovaries

Function:
Secretion; absorption

Figure 4.3 Simple columnar epithelium. The cells are longer than they are wide. The nuclei are in the lower half of the cells.

free surface

mucus

goblet cell

nucleus

basement membrane

Simple Columnar Epithelium

Location:
Lines gastrointestinal tract; the ducts of many glands

Function:
Protection; secretion; absorption

Figure 4.4 Pseudostratified ciliated columnar epithelium. The cells have cilia and appear to be stratified, but each actually touches the basement membrane.

cilia
mucus
goblet cell
nucleus
basement membrane

Pseudostratified Ciliated Columnar Epithelium

Location:
Lines respiratory tract; parts of the reproductive tracts
Function:
Protection; secretion; movement of mucus and sex cells

Cuboidal Epithelium

Simple cuboidal epithelium (Fig. 4.2) consists of a single layer of cube-shaped cells attached to a basement membrane. This type of epithelium is frequently found in glands, such as salivary glands, the thyroid gland, and the pancreas, where its function is secretion. Simple cuboidal epithelium also covers the ovaries and lines most of the kidney tubules. In one part of the kidney tubule, it absorbs substances from the tubule, and in another part it secretes substances into the tubule. When the cells function in secretion, microvilli (tiny extensions from the cells) increase the surface area of cells. Also, the cuboidal epithelial cells contain many mitochondria, which supply the ATP needed for active transport.

Stratified cuboidal epithelium is mostly found lining the larger ducts of certain glands, such as the mammary glands and the salivary glands. Often this tissue has only two layers.

Columnar Epithelium

Simple columnar epithelium (Fig. 4.3) has cells that are longer than they are wide. They are modified to perform particular functions. Some of these cells are goblet cells that secrete mucus onto the free surface of the epithelium.

This tissue is well known for lining digestive organs, including the small intestine, where microvilli expand the surface area and aid in absorbing the products of digestion. Simple columnar epithelium also lines the uterine tubes. Here, many cilia project from the cells and propel the egg toward the uterus, or womb.

Stratified columnar epithelium is not very common but does exist in parts of the pharynx and the male urethra.

Pseudostratified Columnar Epithelium

Pseudostratified columnar epithelium is so named because it appears to be layered; however, true layers do not exist because each cell touches the basement membrane. In particular, the irregular placement of the nuclei in comparison to columnar epithelium makes the tissue seem stratified.

Pseudostratified ciliated columnar epithelium (Fig. 4.4) lines parts of the reproductive tract as well as the air passages of the respiratory system, including the nasal cavities and the trachea (windpipe) and its branches. Mucus-secreting goblet cells are scattered among the ciliated epithelial cells. A surface covering of mucus traps foreign particles, and upward ciliary motion carries the mucus to the back of the throat, where it may be either swallowed or expectorated.

Transitional Epithelium

The term transitional epithelium implies changeability, and this tissue changes in response to tension. It forms the lining of the urinary bladder, the ureters, and part of the urethra—organs that may need to stretch. When the walls of the bladder are relaxed, the transitional epithelium consists of several layers of cuboidal cells. When the bladder is distended with urine, the epithelium stretches, and the outer cells take on a squamous appearance. It's interesting to observe that the cells in transitional epithelium of the bladder are physically able to slide in relation to one another while at the same time forming a barrier that prevents any part of urine from diffusing into the internal environment.

4.2 Connective Tissue

Connective tissue binds structures together, provides support and protection, fills spaces, produces blood cells, and stores fat. The body uses this stored fat for energy, insulation, and organ protection. As a rule, connective tissue cells are widely separated by an extracellular **matrix** composed of an *organic ground substance* that contains *fibers* and varies in consistency from solid to semifluid to fluid. Whereas the functional and physical properties of epithelial tissues are derived from its cells, connective tissue properties are largely derived from the characteristics of the matrix (Table 4.2).

The fibers within the matrix are of three types. White fibers contain *collagen*, a substance that gives the fibers flexibility and strength. Yellow fibers contain *elastin*, which is not as strong as collagen but is more elastic. *Reticular fibers* are very thin, highly branched, collagenous fibers that form delicate supporting networks.

Figure 4.5 Loose (areolar) connective tissue. This tissue has a loose network of fibers.

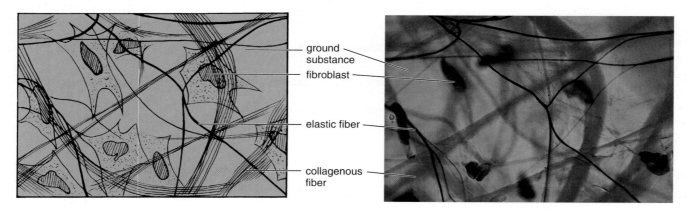

ground substance

fibroblast

elastic fiber

collagenous fiber

Loose (Areolar) Connective Tissue

Location:
Between muscles; beneath the skin; beneath most epithelial layers

Function:
Binds organs together

Figure 4.6 Adipose tissue. The cells are filled with fat droplets.

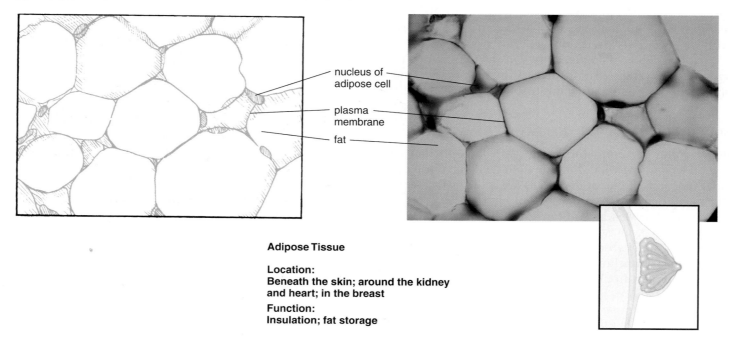

nucleus of adipose cell

plasma membrane

fat

Adipose Tissue

Location:
Beneath the skin; around the kidney and heart; in the breast

Function:
Insulation; fat storage

Table 4.2   Classification of Connective Tissue

Type	Structure	Location (Good Example)
Fibrous Connective		
Loose connective	Collagenous and elastic fibers	Between tissues and organs
Adipose	Fibroblasts enlarge and store fat	Beneath skin
Dense connective		
Regular	Bundles of parallel collagenous fibers	Tendons and ligaments
Irregular	Bundles of nonparallel collagenous fibers	Dermis of skin
Reticular connective	Reticular fibers	Lymphatic organs and liver
Cartilage		
Hyaline cartilage	Fine collagenous fibers	Ends of long bones
Elastic cartilage	Many elastic fibers	External ear
Fibrocartilage	Strong collagenous fibers	Between vertebrae
Bone		
Compact	Osteons	Skeleton
Spongy	Trabeculae, red bone marrow	Ends of long bones
Blood	Plasma plus cells	Blood vessels

Fibrous Connective Tissue

Fibrous connective tissue includes loose connective tissue and dense connective tissue. The body's membranes are composed of an epithelium and fibrous connective tissue (see page 66).

Loose (areolar) connective tissue commonly lies between other tissues or between organs, binding them together. The cells of this tissue are mainly **fibroblasts**—large, star-shaped cells that produce extracellular fibers (Fig. 4.5). The cells are located some distance from one another because they are separated by a matrix with a jellylike ground substance that contains many white (collagenous) and yellow (elastic) fibers. The white fibers occur in bundles and are strong and flexible. The yellow fibers form a highly elastic network that returns to its original length after stretching. *Adipose tissue* (Fig. 4.6) is a type of loose connective tissue in which the fibroblasts enlarge and store fat, and there is limited extracellular matrix.

The fibroblasts of *reticular connective tissue* are called reticular cells, and the matrix contains only reticular fibers. This

Figure 4.7 Dense regular connective tissue. Parallel bundles of collagenous fibers are closely packed.

fibroblasts

collagenous fibers

Dense Connective Tissue

Location: Tendons; ligaments
Function: Binds organs together

fibers. In *dense regular connective tissue*, the bundles are parallel as in **tendons** (which connect muscles to bones) and **ligaments** (which connect bones to other bones at joints). In *dense irregular connective tissue*, the bundles run in different directions. This type of tissue is found in the inner portion of the skin.

The fibroblasts of *reticular connective tissue* are called reticular cells, and the matrix contains only reticular fibers. This tissue, also called **lymphatic tissue**, is found in lymph nodes, the spleen, thymus, and red bone marrow. These organs are a part of the immune system because they store and/or produce white blood cells, particularly lymphocytes. All types of blood cells are produced in red bone marrow.

Figure 4.8 Hyaline cartilage. The matrix is solid but flexible.

matrix

lacuna

chondrocyte within lacuna

Hyaline Cartilage

Location:
Ends of long bones; anterior ends of ribs; in nose; rings of respiratory tract
Function:
Support; protection

Figure 4.9 Compact bone. Cells are arranged in a cylindrical manner about a central canal.

canaliculi

osteocyte in lacuna

central canal

Compact Bone

Location: Bones of skeleton
Function: Support; protection

Cartilage

In **cartilage**, the cells *(chondrocytes)*, which lie in small chambers called **lacunae**, are separated by a matrix that is solid yet flexible. Unfortunately, because this tissue lacks a direct blood supply, it heals very slowly. The three types of cartilage are classified according to the type of fiber in the matrix.

Hyaline cartilage (Fig. 4.8) is the most common type of cartilage. The matrix, which contains only very fine collagenous fibers, has a glassy, white, opaque appearance. This type of cartilage is found in the nose, at the ends of the long bones and ribs, and in the supporting rings of the trachea. The fetal skeleton is also made of this type of cartilage, although the cartilage is later replaced by bone.

Elastic cartilage has a matrix containing many elastic fibers, in addition to collagenous fibers. For this reason, elastic cartilage is more flexible than hyaline cartilage. Elastic cartilage is found, for example, in the framework of the outer ear.

Fibrocartilage has a matrix containing strong collagenous fibers. This type of cartilage absorbs shock and reduces friction between joints. Fibrocartilage is found in structures that withstand tension and pressure, such as the pads between the vertebrae in the backbone and the wedges in the knee joint.

Bone

Bone is the most rigid of the connective tissues. It has an extremely hard matrix of mineral salts, notably calcium salts, deposited around protein fibers. The minerals give bone rigidity, and the protein fibers provide elasticity and strength, much as steel rods do in reinforced concrete.

The outer portion of a long bone contains compact bone. **Compact bone** consists of many cylindrical-shaped units called an *osteon*, or Haversian system (Fig. 4.9). In an osteon, matrix is deposited in thin layers called lamellae that form a concentric pattern around tiny tubes called *central canals*. The canals contain nerve fibers and blood vessels. The blood vessels bring nutrients to bone cells (called *osteocytes*) that are located in lacunae between the lamellae. The nutrients can reach all of the cells because minute canals *(canaliculi)* containing thin extensions of the osteocytes connect the osteocytes with one another and with the central canals.

The ends of a long bone contain spongy bone, which has an entirely different structure. **Spongy bone** contains numerous bony bars and plates called **trabeculae** separated by irregular spaces. Although lighter than compact bone, spongy bone is still designed for strength. Like braces used for support in buildings, the solid portions of spongy bone follow lines of stress. Blood cells are formed within red marrow found in spongy bone at the ends of certain long bones.

Blood

Blood (Fig. 4.10) is a connective tissue composed of cells suspended in a liquid matrix called **plasma**. Collectively, the blood cells are called formed elements. Blood cells are of two types: **red blood cells (erythrocytes)**, which carry oxygen, and **white blood cells (leukocytes)**, which aid in fighting infection. Also present are platelets, which are important to the initiation of blood clotting. *Platelets* are not complete cells; rather, they are fragments of giant cells found in the bone marrow.

In red bone marrow, stem cells continually divide to produce new cells that mature into the different types of blood cells. The rate of cell division is high, as discussed in the Medical Focus on page 66.

Blood is unlike other types of connective tissue in that the extracellular matrix *(plasma)* is not made by the cells of the tissue. Plasma is a mixture of different types of molecules that enter blood at various organs.

Figure 4.10 Blood. When a blood sample is centrifuged, the formed elements settle out below the plasma. Plasma is the liquid portion of the blood. Red blood cells, white blood cells, and platelets are called the formed elements.

plasma

formed elements

Blood sample

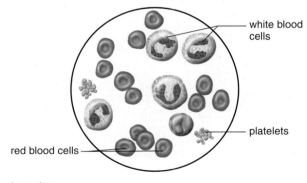

white blood cells

platelets

red blood cells

Location:
In the blood vessels

Function:
Supplies cells with nutrients and oxygen and takes away their wastes; fights infection

4.3 Muscular Tissue

Muscular (contractile) tissue is composed of cells called muscle fibers (Table 4.3). Muscle fibers contain actin and myosin, which are protein filaments whose interaction accounts for movement. The three types of vertebrate muscles are skeletal, smooth, and cardiac.

Skeletal Muscle

Skeletal muscle, also called *voluntary muscle* (Fig. 4.11), is attached by tendons to the bones of the skeleton. When skeletal muscle contracts, body parts such as arms and legs move. Contraction of skeletal muscle, which is under voluntary control, is forceful but of short duration. Skeletal muscle fibers are cylindrical and quite long—sometimes they run the length of the muscle. They arise during development when several cells fuse, resulting in one fiber with multiple nuclei. The nuclei are located at the periphery of the cell, just inside the plasma membrane. The fibers have alternating light and dark bands that give them a *striated* (striped) appearance. These bands are due to the placement of actin filaments and myosin filaments in the fiber.

Figure 4.11 Skeletal muscle. The cells are long, cylindrical, and multinucleated.

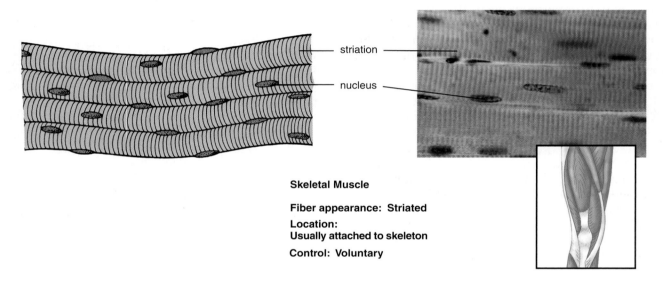

striation

nucleus

Skeletal Muscle

Fiber appearance: Striated

**Location:
Usually attached to skeleton**

Control: Voluntary

Figure 4.12 Smooth muscle. The cells are spindle-shaped.

individual smooth muscle cell

nucleus

Smooth Muscle

Fiber appearance: Spindle-shaped

Location: Walls of hollow organs (e.g., stomach, intestines, urinary bladder, uterus, blood vessels)

Control: Involuntary

Smooth Muscle

Smooth (visceral) muscle is so named because the arrangement of actin and myosin does not give the appearance of cross-striations. The *spindle-shaped cells* form layers in which the thick middle portion of one cell is opposite the thin ends of adjacent cells. Consequently, the nuclei form an irregular pattern in the tissue (Fig. 4.12).

Smooth muscle is not under voluntary control and therefore is said to be *involuntary*. Smooth muscle is found in the walls of hollow viscera, such as the intestines, stomach, uterus, urinary bladder, and blood vessels. Smooth muscle contracts more slowly than skeletal muscle but can remain contracted for a longer time. Contractility is inherent in this type of muscle, and it contracts rhythmically on its own. Even so, its contraction can be modified by the nervous system. Smooth muscle of the small intestine contracts in waves, thereby moving food along its lumen (central cavity). When the smooth muscle of blood vessels contracts, blood vessels constrict, helping to regulate blood flow.

Cardiac Muscle

Cardiac muscle (Fig. 4.13) is found only in the walls of the *heart*. Its contraction pumps blood and accounts for the heartbeat. Cardiac muscle combines features of both smooth muscle and skeletal muscle. Like skeletal muscle, it has striations, but the contraction of the heart is *involuntary* for the most part. Also like skeletal muscle, its contractions are strong, but like smooth muscle, the contraction of the heart is inherent and rhythmical. Also, its contraction can be modified by the nervous system.

Even though cardiac muscle fibers are *striated*, the cells differ from skeletal muscle fibers in that they have a single, centrally placed nucleus. The cells are branched and seemingly fused one with the other, and the heart appears to be composed of one large, interconnecting mass of muscle cells. Actually, cardiac muscle cells are separate and individual, but they are bound end-to-end at **intercalated disks,** areas where folded plasma membranes between two cells contain adhesion junctions and gap junctions (see page 65). These permit extremely rapid spread of contractile stimuli so that the fibers contract almost simultaneously.

Table 4.3	Classification of Muscular Tissue		
Type	**Fiber Appearance**	**Location**	**Control**
Skeletal	Striated	Attached to skeleton	Voluntary
Smooth	Spindle-shaped	Wall of hollow organs (e.g., intestine, urinary bladder, uterus, and blood vessels)	Involuntary
Cardiac	Striated and branched	Heart	Involuntary

Figure 4.13 Cardiac muscle. The cells are cylindrical but branched.

striation

nucleus

intercalated disk

Cardiac Muscle

Fiber appearance: Striated and branched
Location: Heart
Control: Involuntary

4.4 Nervous Tissue

Nervous tissue, found in the brain and spinal cord, contains specialized cells called neurons that conduct nerve impulses. A **neuron** (Fig. 4.14) has three parts: (1) A *dendrite* collects signals that may result in a nerve impulse; (2) the *cell body* contains the nucleus and most of the cytoplasm of the neuron; and (3) the *axon* conducts nerve impulses.

Long axons are called *fibers.* Outside the brain and spinal cord, fibers are bound together by connective tissue to form **nerves.** Nerves conduct impulses from sense organs to the spinal cord and brain, where the phenomenon called sensation occurs. They also conduct nerve impulses away from the spinal cord and brain to the muscles, causing the muscles to contract.

In addition to neurons, nervous tissue contains **neuroglia.**

Neuroglia

Neuroglia are cells that outnumber neurons nine to one and take up more than half the volume of the brain. The primary function of neuroglia is to support and nourish neurons. For example, types of neuroglia found in the brain are microglia, astrocytes, and oligodendrocytes. *Microglia,* in addition to supporting neurons, engulf bacterial and cellular debris. Astrocytes provide nutrients to neurons and produce a hormone known as glia-derived growth factor, which someday might be used as a cure for Parkinson disease and other diseases caused by neuron degeneration. *Oligodendrocytes* form myelin, a protective layer of fatty insulation.

Schwann cells are the type of neuroglia that encircles all long nerve fibers located outside the brain or spinal cord. Each Schwann cell encircles only a small section of a nerve fiber. The gaps between Schwann cells are called **nodes of Ranvier.** Collectively, the Schwann cells provide nerve fibers with a myelin sheath interrupted by the nodes. The **myelin sheath** speeds conduction because the nerve impulse jumps from node to node. Because the myelin sheath is white, all nerve fibers appear white.

Figure 4.14 Nervous tissue. Neurons are surrounded by neuroglia, such as Schwann cells, which envelope axons. Only neurons conduct nerve impulses.

cell body

nucleus

dendrite

axon

nucleus of Schwann cell

myelin sheath

impulse

nodes of Ranvier

Nervous Tissue

Location: Brain; spinal cord; nerves

Function: Conduction of nerve impulses

4.5 Extracellular Junctions, Glands, and Membranes

Extracellular Junctions

The cells of a tissue can function in a coordinated manner when the plasma membranes of adjoining cells interact. The junctions that occur between cells help cells function as a tissue.

A **tight junction** forms an impermeable barrier because adjacent plasma membrane proteins actually join, producing a zipperlike fastening (Fig. 4.15a). In the small intestine, gastric juices stay out of the body, and in the kidneys, the urine stays within kidney tubules because epithelial cells are joined by tight junctions. A **gap junction** forms when two adjacent plasma membrane channels join (Fig. 4.15b). This lends strength, but it also allows ions, sugars, and small molecules to pass between the two cells. Gap junctions in heart and smooth muscle ensure synchronized contraction. In an **adhesion junction** (desmosome), the adjacent plasma membranes do not touch but are held together by extracellular filaments firmly attached to cytoplasmic plaques, composed of dense protein material (Fig. 4.15c).

Glands

A **gland** consists of one or more cells that produce and secrete a product. Most glands are composed primarily of epithelium in which the cells secrete their product by exocytosis. During secretion, the contents of a vesicle are released when the vesicle fuses with the plasma membrane.

The mucus-secreting goblet cells within the columnar epithelium lining the digestive tract are single cells (see Fig. 4.3). Glands with ducts that secrete their product onto the outer surface (e.g., sweat glands and mammary glands) or into a cavity (e.g., pancreas) are called *exocrine glands*. Ducts can be simple or compound, as illustrated in Figure 4.16.

Glands that no longer have a duct are appropriately known as the ductless glands, or endocrine glands. *Endocrine glands* (e.g., pituitary gland and thyroid) secrete their products internally so they are transported by the bloodstream. Endocrine glands produce hormones that help promote homeostasis. Each type of hormone influences the metabolism of a particular target organ or cells.

Glands are composed of epithelial tissue, but they are supported by connective tissue, as are other epithelial tissues.

Figure 4.15 Extracellular junctions. Tissues are held together by (a) tight junctions that are impermeable; (b) gap junctions that allow materials to pass from cell to cell; and (c) adhesion junctions that allow tissues to stretch.

a. Tight junction b. Gap junction c. Adhesion junction

Figure 4.16 Multicellular exocrine glands. Exocrine glands have ducts that can be simple or compound. Compound glands vary according to the placement of secretory portions.

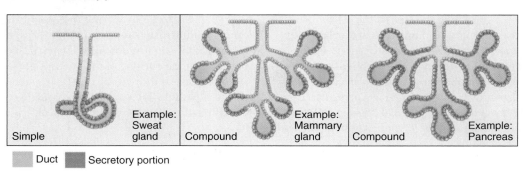

Simple — Example: Sweat gland | Compound — Example: Mammary gland | Compound — Example: Pancreas

☐ Duct ■ Secretory portion

Membranes

Membranes line the internal spaces of organs and tubes that open to the outside, and they also line the body cavities discussed on page 6.

Mucous Membranes

Mucous membranes line the interior walls of the organs and tubes that open to the outside of the body, such as those of the digestive, respiratory, urinary, and reproductive systems. These membranes consist of an epithelium overlying a layer of loose connective tissue. The epithelium contains goblet cells that secrete mucus.

The mucus secreted by mucous membranes ordinarily protects interior walls from invasion by bacteria and viruses; for example, more mucus is secreted when a person has a cold, resulting in a "runny nose." In addition, mucus usually protects the walls of the stomach and small intestine from digestive juices, but this protection breaks down when a person develops an *ulcer*.

Serous Membranes

As also discussed on page 6, **serous membranes** line cavities, including the thoracic and abdominopelvic cavities, and cover internal organs such as the intestines. The term **parietal** refers to the wall of the body cavity, while the term **visceral** pertains to the internal organs. Therefore, parietal membranes line the interior of the thoracic and abdominopelvic cavities, and visceral membranes cover the organs.

Serous membranes consist of a layer of simple squamous epithelium overlying a layer of loose connective tissue. They secrete a watery fluid that keeps the membranes lubricated. Serous membranes support the internal organs and tend to compartmentalize the large thoracic and abdominopelvic cavities. This helps hinder the spread of any infection.

In the thorax, the **pleura** are serous membranes that form a double layer around the lungs. The parietal pleura lines the inside of the thoracic wall, while the visceral pleura adheres to the surface of the lungs. Similarly a double-layered serous membrane is a part of the **pericardium**, a covering for the heart.

The **peritoneum** is the serous membranes within the abdomen. The parietal peritoneum lines the abdominopelvic wall, and the visceral peritoneum covers the organs. In between the organs, the visceral peritoneum comes together to form a double-layered **mesentery** that supports these organs.

Synovial Membranes

Synovial membranes line freely movable joint cavities and are composed of connective tissues. They secrete synovial fluid into the joint cavity; this fluid lubricates the ends of the bones so that they can move freely. In *rheumatoid arthritis*, the synovial membrane becomes inflamed and grows thicker. Fibrous tissue then invades the joint and may eventually become bony so that the bones of the joint are no longer capable of moving.

Meninges

The **meninges** are membranes found within the posterior cavity (see Fig. 1.5). They are composed only of connective tissue and serve as a protective covering for the brain and spinal cord. *Meningitis* is a life-threatening infection of the meninges.

Cutaneous Membrane

The **cutaneous membrane,** or skin, forms the outer covering of the body. It consists of an outer portion of keratinized stratified squamous epithelium attached to a thick underlying layer of dense irregular connective tissue. The skin is discussed in detail in Chapter 5.

Medical Focus

Classification of Cancers

Cancers are classified according to the type of tissue from which they arise. **Carcinomas,** the most common type, are cancers of epithelial tissues (skin and linings); **sarcomas** are cancers arising in connective tissue (muscle, bone, and cartilage); **leukemias** are cancers of the blood; and **lymphomas** are cancers of reticular connective tissue. The chance of cancer occurring in a particular tissue is related to the rate of cell division; epithelial cells reproduce at a high rate, and carcinomas account for 90% of all human cancers.

Different methods are used to obtain tissues to screen for cancer. During a **Pap smear** (named for George Papanicolaou, the Greek doctor who first described the test), epithelial tissue lining the cervix at the opening of the uterus is obtained using a cotton swab. A **biopsy** is the removal of sample tissue using a plungerlike device. A **pathologist** is skilled at recognizing the abnormal characteristics that allow for the **diagnosis** of a disease.

Selected New Terms

Basic Key Terms

cartilage (kar'tĭ-lij), p. 61

connective tissue (kŏ-nek'tiv tish'u), p. 58

cutaneous membrane (kyū-ta'ne-us mem'brān), p. 66

epithelial tissue (epi"ĭ-the'le-al tish'u), p. 55

lacuna (luh-ku'na), p. 61

matrix (ma'triks), p. 58

meninges (mĕ-nin'jēz), p. 66

mesentery (mes'en-tĕr"e), p. 66

mucous membrane (myū'kus mem'brān), p. 66

muscular tissue (mus'kyū-ler tish'u), p. 62

myelin sheath (mi'ĕ-lin shēth), p. 64

nervous tissue (ner'vus tish'u), p. 64

neuroglia (nu-rog'le-uh), p. 64

neuron (nu'ron), p. 64

parietal (puh-ri'ĕ-tal), p. 66

peritoneum (pĕr"i-to-ne'um), p. 66

pseudostratified (su"do-strat'ĭ-fīd), p. 57

serous membrane (sĕr'us mem'brān), p. 66

stratified (strat'ĭ-fīd), p. 55

synovial membrane (sĭ-no've-al mem'brān), p. 66

visceral (vis'er-al), p. 66

Clinical Key Terms

biopsy (bi'op-se), p. 66

carcinoma (kar-sĭ-no'muh), p. 66

diagnosis (di-ahg-no'sis), p. 66

leukemia (lu-ke'me-uh), p. 66

lymphoma (lim-fo'muh), p. 66

Pap smear (pap smēr), p. 66

pathologist (puh-thol'uh-jist), p. 66

sarcoma (sar-ko'muh), p. 66

Summary

4.1 Epithelial Tissue
  A. Body tissues are categorized into four types: epithelial, connective, muscular, and nervous.
  B. Epithelial tissue. This tissue is classified according to cell shape and number of layers. The cell shape may be squamous, cuboidal, or columnar. Simple tissues have one layer of cells, and stratified tissues have several layers.

4.2 Connective Tissue
  A. In connective tissue, cells are separated by a matrix (organic ground substance plus fibers).
  B. Fibrous connective tissue can be loose connective tissue, in which fibroblasts are separated by a jellylike ground substance, or dense connective tissue, which contains bundles of collagenous fibers. Adipose tissue is a type of loose connective tissue in which the fibroblasts enlarge and store fat.

  C. Cartilage and bone are support tissues. Cartilage is more flexible than bone because the matrix is rich in protein, rather than the mineral salts found in bone.
  D. Blood is a connective tissue in which the matrix is plasma.

4.3 Muscular Tissue
  Muscular tissue contains actin and myosin protein filaments. These form a striated pattern in skeletal and cardiac muscle, but not in smooth muscle. Cardiac and smooth muscle are under involuntary control. Skeletal muscle is under voluntary control.

4.4 Nervous Tissue
  Nervous tissue contains conducting cells called neurons. Neurons have processes called axons and dendrites. Outside the brain and spinal cord, long axons (fibers) are found in nerves.

4.5 Extracellular Junctions, Glands, and Membranes

  A. In a tissue, cells can be joined by tight junctions, gap junctions, or adhesion junctions.
  B. Glands are composed of epithelial tissue that produces and secretes a product, usually by exocytosis. Glands can be unicellular or multicellular. Multicellular exocrine glands have ducts and secrete onto surfaces; endocrine glands are ductless and secrete into the bloodstream.
  C. Mucous membranes line the interior of organs and tubes that open to the outside. Serous membranes line the thoracic and abdominopelvic cavities, and cover the organs within these cavities. Synovial membranes line certain joint cavities. Meninges are membranes that cover the brain and spinal cord. The skin forms a cutaneous membrane.

1. What is a tissue? (p. 55)
2. Name the four major types of tissues. (p. 55)
3. What are the functions of epithelial tissue? Name the different kinds of epithelial tissue, and give a location for each. (pp. 55–57)
4. What are the functions of connective tissue? Name the different kinds of connective tissue, and give a location for each type. (pp. 58–61)
5. Contrast the structure of cartilage with that of bone, using the words *lacunae* and *central canal* in your description. (p. 61)
6. Describe the composition of blood, and give a function for each type of blood cell. (p. 61)
7. What are the functions of muscular tissue? Name the different kinds of muscular tissue, and give a location for each. (pp. 62–63)
8. What types of cells does nervous tissue contain? Which organs in the body are made up of nervous tissue? (p. 64)
9. Name three types of junctions, and state the function of each with examples. (p. 65)
10. Describe the structure of a gland. What is the difference between an exocrine gland and an endocrine gland? (p. 65)
11. Name the different types of body membranes, and associate each type with a particular location in the body. (p. 66)

I. Fill in the blanks.
1. Most organs contain several different types of _____ .
2. Pseudostratified ciliated columnar epithelium contains cells that appear to be _____ , have projections called _____ , and are _____ in shape.
3. Connective tissue cells are widely separated by a _____ that usually contains _____ .

4. Both cartilage and blood are classified as _____ tissue.
5. A mucous membrane contains _____ tissue overlying _____ tissue.

II. Match the organs in the key to the epithelial tissues listed in questions 6–9.
Key:
  a. kidney tubules
  b. small intestine
  c. air sacs of lungs
  d. trachea (windpipe)

6. simple squamous
7. simple cuboidal
8. simple columnar
9. pseudostratified ciliated columnar

III. Match the muscle tissues in the key to the descriptions listed in questions 10–12.
Key:
  a. skeletal muscle
  b. smooth muscle
  c. cardiac muscle
10. striated and branched, involuntary
11. striated and voluntary
12. visceral and involuntary

Consult Appendix B for help in pronouncing and analyzing the meaning of the terms that follow.

1. epithelioma (ep″ĭ the″le-o′muh)
2. fibrodysplasia (fi″bro-dis-pla′se-uh)
3. meningoencephalopathy (mĕ-ning″go-en-sef″ul-lop′uh-the)
4. pericardiocentesis (per″i-kar″de-o-sen-te′sis)
5. peritonitis (per″ĭ-to-ni′tis)
6. intrapleural (in″tra-plūr′al)
7. neurofibromatosis (nu″ro-fi″bro″muh-to′sis)
8. submucosa (sub″myū-ko′suh)
9. polyarthritis (pol″e-ar-thri′tis)
10. cardiomyopathy (kar′de-o-mi-ah′puh-the)
11. encephalitis (en-sef′-uh-li-tis)
12. glioma (gle-o′-muh)
13. pleurisy (plūr′ĭ-se)
14. chondroblast (kon′-dro-blast)
15. osteology (os′te-ol′-o-je)

Visit the Student Edition of the Online Learning Center at http://www.mhhe.com/maderap5 for additional quizzes, interactive learning exercises, and other study tools.

The Integumentary System

chapter

Longitudinal section of
skin showing a hair
follicle and oil
(sebaceous) glands that
empty into the follicle

chapter outline & learning objectives

After you have studied this chapter, you should be able to:

5.1 Structure of the Skin (p. 70)
■ Describe the regions of the skin and the hypodermis.
■ Name two main epidermal layers, and describe their structure and function.

5.2 Accessory Structures of the Skin (p. 72)
■ Describe the structure and growth of hair and nails.
■ Name three glands of the skin, and describe their structure and function.

5.3 Disorders of the Skin (p. 74)
■ Name the three types of skin cancer, and state their risk factor.

■ Name and describe four types of burns with regard to depth.
■ Describe how the "rule of nines" may be used to estimate the extent of a burn.
■ Describe the steps by which a skin wound heals.

5.4 Effects of Aging (p. 77)
■ Describe the anatomical and physiological changes that occur in the integumentary system as we age.

5.5 Homeostasis (p. 78)
■ List and discuss four functions of the skin that contribute to homeostasis.

Medical Focus
The Link Between UV Radiation and Skin Cancer (p. 77)
Development of Cancer (p. 80)

Part II

Figure 5.1 Skin anatomy. Skin is composed of two regions: the epidermis and the dermis. The hypodermis, or subcutaneous layer, is located beneath the skin.

5.1 Structure of the Skin

The skin covers the entire surface of the human body. In an adult, the skin has a surface area of about 1.8 square meters (20.83 square feet).

The skin is sometimes called the **cutaneous membrane** or the **integument.** Because the skin has several accessory organs, it is also possible to speak of the **integumentary system.** The skin (Fig. 5.1) has two regions: the epidermis and the dermis. The **hypodermis,** a subcutaneous tissue, is found between the skin and any underlying structures, such as muscle. Usually, the hypodermis is only loosely attached to underlying muscle tissue, but where no muscles are present, the hypodermis attaches directly to bone. For example, there are *flexion creases* where the skin attaches directly to the joints of the fingers.

Epidermis

The **epidermis** is the outer and thinner region of the skin. It is made up of *stratified squamous epithelium* divided into several layers; the deepest layer is the stratum basale, and the most superficial layer is the stratum corneum.

Stratum Basale

The basal cells of the **stratum basale** lie just superior to the dermis and are constantly dividing and producing new cells that are pushed to the surface of the epidermis in two to four weeks. As the cells move away from the dermis, they get progressively farther away from the blood vessels in the dermis. Because these cells are not being supplied with nutrients and oxygen (the epidermis itself lacks blood vessels), they eventually die and are sloughed off.

Langerhans cells are macrophages found deep in the epidermis. Macrophages are related to monocytes, white blood cells produced in red bone marrow. These cells phagocytize microbes and then travel to lymphatic organs, where they stimulate the immune system to react.

Melanocytes are another type of specialized cell located in the deeper epidermis. Melanocytes produce **melanin,** the pigment primarily responsible for skin color. Since the number of melanocytes is about the same in all individuals, variation in skin color is due to the amount of melanin produced and its distribution. When skin is exposed to the sun, melanocytes produce more melanin to protect the skin from the damaging effects of the ultraviolet (UV) radiation in sunlight. The melanin is passed to other epidermal cells, and the result is tanning, or in some people, the formation of patches of melanin called freckles. A hereditary trait characterized by the lack of ability to produce melanin is known as **albinism.** Individuals with this disorder lack pigment not only in the skin, but also in the hair and eyes. Another pigment, called carotene, is present in epidermal cells and in the dermis and gives the skin of certain Asians its yellowish hue. The pinkish color of fair-skinned people is due to the pigment hemoglobin in the red blood cells in the capillaries of the dermis.

Stratum Corneum

As cells are pushed toward the surface of the skin, they become flat and hard, forming the tough, uppermost layer of the epidermis, the **stratum corneum.** Hardening is caused by keratinization, the cellular production of a fibrous, waterproof protein called **keratin.** Over much of the body, keratinization is minimal, but the palms of the hands and the soles of the feet normally have a particularly thick outer layer of dead, keratinized cells.

The waterproof nature of keratin protects the body from water loss and water gain. The stratum corneum allows us to live in a desert or a tropical rain forest without damaging our inner cells.

The stratum corneum also serves as a mechanical barrier against microbe invasion. This protective function of skin is assisted by the secretions of *sebaceous glands* (discussed in section 5.2), which weaken or kill bacteria on the skin.

Dermis

The **dermis,** a deeper and thicker region than the epidermis, is composed of dense irregular connective tissue. The upper layer of the dermis has fingerlike projections called dermal papillae. Dermal papillae project into and anchor the epidermis. In the overlying epidermis, dermal papillae cause ridges, resulting in spiral and concentric patterns commonly known as "fingerprints." The function of the epidermal ridges is to increase friction and thus provide a better gripping surface. Because they are unique to each person, fingerprints and footprints can be used for identification purposes.

Figure 5.2 A decubitus ulcer (bedsore). The most frequent sites for bedsores are in the skin overlying a bony projection, such as on the hip, ankle, heel, shoulder, or elbow.

The dermis contains collagenous and elastic fibers. The *collagenous fibers* are flexible but offer great resistance to overstretching; they prevent the skin from being torn. The *elastic fibers* stretch to allow movement of underlying muscles and joints, but they maintain normal skin tension. The dermis also contains blood vessels that nourish the skin. Blood rushes into these vessels when a person blushes; blood is reduced in them when a person turns cyanotic, or "blue." Sometimes, blood flow to a particular area is restricted in bedridden patients, and consequently they develop **decubitus ulcers** (bedsores) (Fig. 5.2). These can be prevented by changing the patient's position frequently and by massaging the skin to stimulate blood flow.

There are also numerous sensory nerve fibers in the dermis that take nerve impulses to and from the accessory structures of the skin, which are discussed in section 5.2.

Hypodermis

Hypodermis, or **subcutaneous tissue,** lies below the dermis. From the names for this layer, we get the terms **subcutaneous injection,** performed with a **hypodermic needle.**

The hypodermis is composed of loose connective tissue, including adipose (fat) tissue. **Fat** is an energy storage form that can be called upon when necessary to supply the body with molecules for cellular respiration. Adipose tissue also helps insulate the body. A well-developed hypodermis gives the body a rounded appearance and provides protective padding against external assaults. Excessive development of adipose tissue in the hypodermis layer results in obesity.

Figure 5.3 Hair follicle and hair shaft. **a.** A hair grows from the base of a hair follicle where epidermal cells produce new cells as older cells move outward and become keratinized. **b.** A hair shaft penetrating the outer squamous epithelial cells of the epidermis.

a. Hair follicle

b. Hair shaft

5.2 Accessory Structures of the Skin

Hair, nails, and glands are structures of epidermal origin, even though some parts of hair and glands are largely in the dermis.

Hair and Nails

Hair is found on all body parts except the palms, soles, lips, nipples, and portions of the external reproductive organs. Most of this hair is fine and downy, but the hair on the head includes stronger types as well. After puberty, when sex hormones are made in quantity, there is noticeable hair in the axillary and pelvic regions of both sexes. In the male, a beard develops, and other parts of the body may also become quite hairy. When women produce more male sex hormone than usual, they can develop **hirsutism,** a condition characterized by excessive body and facial hair. Hormonal injections and electrolysis to kill roots are possible treatments.

Hairs project from complex structures called **hair follicles.** These hair follicles are formed from epidermal cells but are located in the dermis of the skin (Fig. 5.3). Certain hair follicle cells continually divide, producing new cells that form a hair. At first, the cells are nourished by dermal blood vessels, but as the hair grows up and out of the follicle, they are pushed farther away from this source of nutrients, become keratinized, and die. The portion of a hair within the follicle is called the *root,* and the portion that extends beyond the skin is called the *shaft.*

The life span of any particular hair is usually three to four months for an eyelash and three to four years for a scalp hair; then it is shed and regrows. In males, baldness occurs when the hair on the head fails to regrow. **Alopecia,** meaning hair loss, can have many causes. Male pattern baldness, or *androgenic alopecia,* is an inherited condition. *Alopecia areata* is characterized by the sudden onset of patchy hair loss. It is most common among children and young adults, and can affect either sex.

Each hair has one or more oil, or sebaceous, glands, whose ducts empty into the follicle. A smooth muscle, the **arrector pili,** attaches to the follicle in such a way that contraction of the muscle causes the hair to stand on end. If a person has had a scare or is cold, "goose bumps" develop due to contraction of these muscles.

Figure 5.4 Sagittal section of a nail. Cells produced by the nail root become keratinized, forming the nail body.

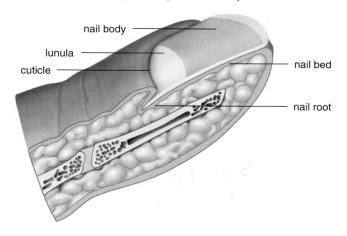

nail body
lunula
cuticle
nail bed
nail root

Figure 5.5 Types of skin glands. Apocrine glands and eccrine glands are types of sweat glands.

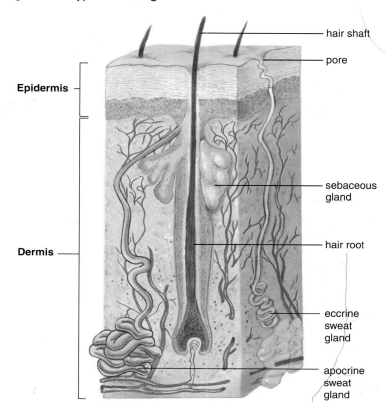

Epidermis
Dermis
hair shaft
pore
sebaceous gland
hair root
eccrine sweat gland
apocrine sweat gland

Nails grow from special epithelial cells at the base of the nail in the region called the *nail root* (Fig. 5.4). These cells become keratinized as they grow out over the nail bed. The visible portion of the nail is called the *nail body*. The cuticle is a fold of skin that hides the nail root. Ordinarily, nails grow only about 1 millimeter per week.

The pink color of nails is due to the vascularized dermal tissue beneath the nail. The whitish color of the half-moon-shaped base, or **lunula**, results from the thicker germinal layer in this area.

Glands

The *glands* in the skin are groups of cells specialized to produce and secrete a substance into ducts.

Sweat Glands

Sweat glands, or sudoriferous glands, are present in all regions of the skin. There can be as many as 90 glands per square centimeter on the leg, 400 glands per square centimeter on the palms and soles, and an even greater number on the fingertips. A sweat gland is tubular. The tubule is coiled, particularly at its origin within the dermis. These glands become active when a person is under stress.

Two types of sweat glands are shown in Figure 5.5. *Apocrine glands* open into hair follicles in the anal region, groin, and armpits. These glands begin to secrete at puberty, and a component of their secretion may act as a sex attractant. *Eccrine glands* open onto the surface of the skin. They become active when a person is hot, helping to lower body temperature as sweat evaporates. The sweat (perspiration) produced by these glands is mostly water, but it also contains salts and some urea, a waste substance. Therefore, sweat is a form of excretion. Ears contain modified sweat glands, called ceruminous glands, which produce cerumen, or earwax.

Sebaceous Glands

Most **sebaceous glands** are associated with a hair follicle. These glands secrete an oily substance called **sebum** that flows into the follicle and then out onto the skin surface. This secretion lubricates the hair and skin, and helps waterproof them.

Particularly on the face and back, the sebaceous glands may fail to discharge sebum, and the secretions collect, forming whiteheads or blackheads. If pus-inducing bacteria are also present, a boil or pimple may result.

Acne vulgaris, the most common form of acne, is an inflammation of the sebaceous glands that most often occurs during adolescence. Hormonal changes during puberty cause the sebaceous glands to become more active at this time.

Mammary Glands

The **mammary glands** are located within the breasts. A female breast contains 15 to 25 lobes, which are divided into lobules (see Fig. 17.14). Each lobule contains many alveoli. When milk is secreted, the milk enters a duct that leads to the nipple. Cells within the alveoli produce milk only after childbirth in response to complex hormonal changes occurring at that time.

5.3 Disorders of the Skin

The skin is subject to many disorders, some of which are more annoying than life-threatening. For example, **athlete's foot** is caused by a fungal infection that usually involves the skin of the toes and soles. **Impetigo** is a highly contagious disease occurring most often in young children. It is caused by a bacterial infection that results in pustules that crust over. **Psoriasis** is a chronic condition, possibly hereditary, in which the skin develops pink or reddish patches covered by silvery scales due to overactive cell division. **Eczema,** an inflammation of the skin, is caused by sensitivity to various chemicals (e.g., soaps or detergents), to certain fabrics, or even to heat or dryness. **Dandruff** is a skin disorder not caused by a dry scalp, as is commonly thought, but by an accelerated rate of keratinization in certain areas of the scalp, producing flaking and itching. **Urticaria,** or hives, is an allergic reaction characterized by the appearance of reddish, elevated patches and often by itching.

Skin Cancer

Skin cancer is categorized as either melanoma or non-melanoma.

Nonmelanoma cancers, which include basal cell carcinoma and squamous cell carcinoma, are much less likely to metastasize than melanoma cancer. **Basal cell carcinoma** (Fig. 5.6a), the most common type of skin cancer, begins when ultraviolet (UV) radiation causes epidermal basal cells to form a tumor, while at the same time suppressing the immune system's ability to detect the tumor. The signs of a tumor are varied. They include an open sore that will not heal; a recurring reddish patch; a smooth, circular growth with a raised edge; a shiny bump; or a pale mark. About 95% of patients are easily cured by surgical removal of the tumor, but recurrence is common.

Squamous cell carcinoma (Fig. 5.6b) begins in the epidermis proper. While five times less common than basal cell carcinoma, it is more likely to spread to nearby organs, and death occurs in about 1% of cases. The signs of squamous cell carcinoma are the same as those for basal cell carcinoma, except that it may also show itself as a wart that bleeds and scabs.

Melanoma (Fig. 5.6c), the type that is more likely to be malignant (see the Medical Focus on page 80), starts in the melanocytes and has the appearance of an unusual **mole.** Unlike a normal mole, which is dark, circular, and confined, a melanoma mole looks like a spilled ink spot, and a single melanoma mole may display a variety of shades. A melanoma mole can also itch, hurt, or feel numb. The skin around the mole turns gray, white, or red. Melanoma is most common in fair-skinned persons, particularly if they have suffered occasional severe burns as children. Melanoma risk increases with the number of moles a person has. Most moles appear before the age of 14, and their appearance is linked to sun exposure. Melanoma rates have risen since the turn of the century, but the incidence has doubled in the last decade. In 2002, about 54,000 cases of melanoma were diagnosed in the United States.

Raised growths on the skin, such as moles and **warts,** usually are not cancerous. Moles are due to an overgrowth of melanocytes, and warts are due to a viral infection.

Wound Healing

A wound that punctures a blood vessel will fill with blood. Chemicals released by damaged tissue cells will cause the blood to clot. The clot prevents pathogens and toxins from spreading to other tissues (Fig. 5.7a). The part of the clot exposed to air will dry and harden, gradually becoming a scab. White blood cells and fibroblasts move into the area. White blood cells help fight infection and fibroblasts are able to pull the margins of the wound together (Fig. 5.7b). Fibroblasts promote tissue regeneration: The basal layer of the epidermis begins to produce new cells at a faster than usual rate. The

Figure 5.6 Skin cancer. In each of the three types shown, the skin clearly has an abnormal appearance.

a. Basal cell carcinoma

b. Squamous cell carcinoma

c. Melanoma

Figure 5.7 The process of wound healing. **a.** A deep wound ruptures blood vessels, and blood flows out and fills the wound. **b.** After a blood clot forms, a protective scab develops. Fibroblasts and white blood cells migrate to the wound site. **c.** New epidermis forms, and fibroblasts promote tissue regeneration. **d.** Freshly healed skin.

a.

b.

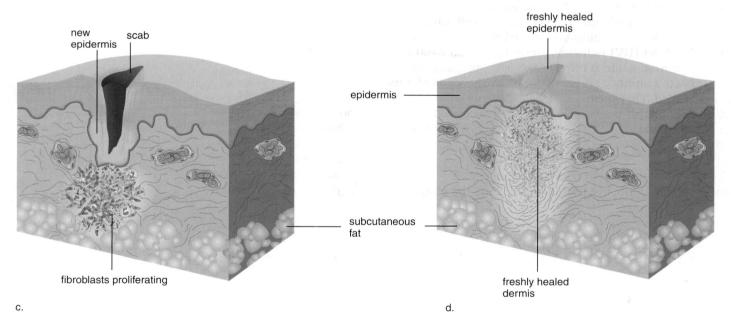

c.

d.

proliferating fibroblasts bring about scar formation; the scar may or may not be visible from the surface (Fig. 5.7c). A scar is a tissue composed of many collagen fibers arranged to pro-vide maximum strength. A scar does not contain the accessory organs of the skin and is usually devoid of feeling. In any case, epidermis and dermis have now healed (Fig. 5.7d).

Burns

The epidermal injury known as a burn is usually caused by heat but can also be caused by radioactive, chemical, or electrical agents. Two factors affect burn severity: the depth of the burn and the extent of the burned area.

A useful technique for estimating the extent of a burn, called the "rule of nines," is often employed (Fig. 5.8). In this method, the total body surface is divided into regions as follows: the head and neck, 9% of the total body surface; each upper limb, 9%; each lower limb, 18%; the front and back portions of the trunk, 18% each; and the perineum, which includes the anal and urogenital regions, 1%.

One way to classify burns is according to the depth of the burned area. In *first-degree burns,* only the epidermis is affected. The person experiences redness and pain, but no blisters or swelling. A classic example of a first-degree burn is a moderate sunburn. The pain subsides within 48–72 hours, and the injury heals without further complications or scarring. The damaged skin peels off in about a week.

A *second-degree burn* extends through the entire epidermis and part of the dermis. The person experiences not only redness and pain, but also blistering in the region of the damaged tissue. The deeper the burn, the more prevalent the blisters, which enlarge during the hours after the injury. Unless they become infected, most second-degree burns heal without complications and with little scarring in 10–14 days. If the burn extends deep into the dermis, it heals more slowly over a period of 30–105 days. The healing epidermis is extremely fragile, and scarring is common. First- and second-degree burns are sometimes referred to as partial-thickness burns.

Third-degree burns, or full-thickness burns, destroy the entire thickness of the skin. The surface of the wound is leathery and may be brown, tan, black, white, or red. The patient feels no pain because the pain receptors have been destroyed, as have blood vessels, sweat glands, sebaceous glands, and hair follicles.

Fourth-degree burns involve tissues down to the bone. Obviously, the chances of a person surviving fourth-degree burns are not good unless a very limited area of the body is affected.

The major concerns with severe burns are fluid loss, heat loss, and bacterial infection. Fluid loss is counteracted by intravenous administration of a balanced salt solution. Heat loss is minimized by placing the burn patient in a warm environment. Bacterial infection is treated by isolation and the application of an antibacterial dressing.

Figure 5.8 The "rule of nines" for estimating the extent of burns.

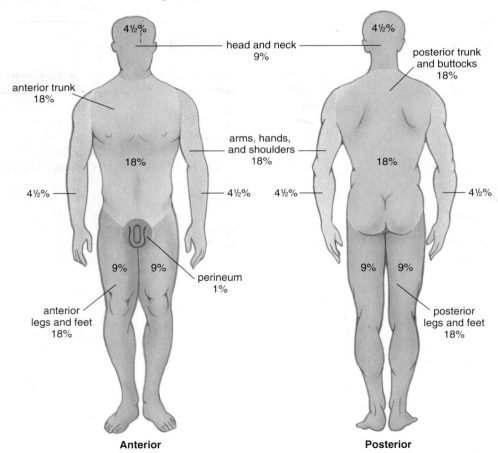

4½%

head and neck
9%

4½%

posterior trunk
and buttocks
18%

anterior trunk
18%

arms, hands,
and shoulders
18%

18%

18%

4½%

4½%

4½%

4½%

9%   9%

perineum
1%

9%   9%

anterior
legs and feet
18%

posterior
legs and feet
18%

Anterior

Posterior

As soon as possible, the damaged tissue is removed, and skin grafting is begun. The skin needed for grafting is usually taken from other parts of the patient's body. This is called *autografting*, as opposed to heterografting, in which the graft is received from another person. Autografting is preferred because rejection rates are very low. However, if the burned area is quite extensive, it may be difficult to acquire enough skin for autografting. In that case, skin can be grown in the laboratory from only a few cells taken from the patient. (See page 9.)

5.4 Effects of Aging

As aging occurs, the epidermis maintains its thickness, but the turnover of cells decreases. The dermis becomes thinner, the dermal papillae flatten, and the epidermis is held less tightly to the dermis so that the skin is looser. Adipose tissue in the hypodermis of the face and hands also decreases, which means that older people are more likely to feel cold.

The fibers within the dermis change with age. The collagenous fibers become coarser, thicker, and farther apart; therefore, there is less collagen than before. Elastic fibers in the upper layer of the dermis are lost, and those in the lower dermis become thicker, less elastic, and disorganized. The skin wrinkles because (1) the epidermis is loose, (2) the fibers are fewer and those remaining are disorganized, and (3) the hypodermis has less padding.

With aging, homeostatic adjustment to heat is limited due to less vasculature (fewer blood vessels) and fewer sweat glands. The number of hair follicles decreases, causing the hair on the scalp and extremities to thin. Because of a reduced number of sebaceous glands, the skin tends to crack.

As a person ages, the number of melanocytes decreases. This causes the hair to turn gray and the skin to become paler. In contrast, some of the remaining pigment cells are larger, and pigmented blotches appear on the skin.

Many of the changes that occur in the skin as a person ages appear to be due to sun damage. Ultraviolet radiation causes rough skin, mottled pigmentation, fine lines and wrinkles, deep furrows, numerous benign skin growths, and the various types of skin cancer discussed in section 5.3. To prevent skin cancer, follow the suggestions in the Medical Focus on this page.

Medical Focus

The Link Between UV Radiation and Skin Cancer

If an individual has experienced severe sunburns as a child, the chance of having skin cancer as a adult is greater. The sun gives off two types of UV rays: UV-A rays and UV-B rays. UV-A rays penetrate the skin deeply, affect connective tissue, and cause the skin to sag and wrinkle, and UV-A rays may help cause skin cancer. At any rate, UV-A rays are believed to increase the effects of UV-B rays, which are the primary cancer-causing rays. UV-B rays are more prevalent at midday.

No matter where you live, you need to take the following steps to protect yourself from the sun:

- Use a broad-spectrum sunscreen that protects you from both UV-A and UV-B radiation, and has a sun protection factor (SPF) of at least 15. (This means that if you usually burn, for example, after a 20-minute exposure, it will take 15 times longer, or 5 hours, before you will burn.) Children should use a higher SPF such as 30 or 45 (a sun block).
- Wear protective clothing. Choose fabrics with a tight weave, and wear a wide-brimmed hat. A baseball cap does not protect the rims of the ears, which often burn and then get

infected. Wherever the ozone layer is thinner than usual, even more protection is required. In Australia, because of a thin ozone layer due especially to the Earth's rotation, schoolchildren are allowed outside for recess only if they wear a wide-brimmed hat and long sleeves.

- Stay out of the sun altogether between the hours of 10 A.M. and 3 P.M. Some authorities believe this action will reduce annual exposure to the sun's rays by as much as 60%.
- Wear sunglasses that have been treated to absorb both UV-A and UV-B radiation. Otherwise, darkened sunglasses can expose the eyes to more damage than usual because the pupils dilate in the shade. For this reason, do not let children wear "fun" sunglasses outside in the sun. Purchase children's sunglasses only if there is a tag indicating UV-ray protection.
- Avoid tanning machines unless prescribed by a physician for Seasonal Affective Disorder (SAD). Although most tanning devices use only high levels of UV-A radiation, the deep layers of the skin become more vulnerable to UV-B radiation upon later exposure to the sun.

5.5 Homeostasis

The illustration on the next page, called Human Systems Work Together, tells how the functions of the skin assist the other systems of the body (buff color) and how the other systems help the skin carry out these functions (aqua color).

Functions of the Skin

Skin has a protective function. First and foremost, the skin forms a protective covering over the entire body, safeguarding underlying parts from physical trauma and pathogen invasion. The melanocytes in skin protect it from UV radiation, and the skin's outer dead cells also help prevent bacterial invasion. The oily secretions from sebaceous glands are acidic, which retards the growth of bacteria. The Langerhans cells in the epidermis phagocytize pathogens and then alert the immune system to their presence.

Skin helps regulate water loss. Since outer skin cells are dead and keratinized, the skin is waterproof, thereby preventing water loss. The skin's waterproofing also prevents water from entering the body when the skin is immersed. This function of the skin assists the urinary system, as do the sweat glands, which excrete some urea when sweating occurs.

Skin produces vitamin D. This function of skin is particularly useful to the digestive and skeletal systems. When skin cells are exposed to sunlight, the ultraviolet (UV) rays assist them in producing vitamin D. The cells contain a precursor molecule that is converted to vitamin D in the body after UV exposure; only a small amount of UV radiation is needed. Vitamin D leaves the skin and enters the liver and kidneys, where it is converted to a hormone called calcitriol. Calcitriol circulates throughout the body, regulating calcium uptake by the digestive system and both calcium and phosphorus metabolism in cells. Calcium and phosphorus are very important to the proper development and mineralization of the bones.

Figure 5.9 X ray of a child with rickets. Rickets develops from an improper diet and also from a lack of ultraviolet (UV) light (sunlight). Under these conditions, vitamin D does not form in the skin.

Most milk today is fortified with vitamin D, which helps prevent the occurrence of **rickets** characterized especially by soft and deformed bones (Fig. 5.9).

Skin gathers sensory information. The sensory receptors in the dermis specialized for touch, pressure, pain, hot, and cold are associated with the nervous system. These receptors supply the central nervous system with information about the external environment. The fingertips contain the greatest number of touch receptors, allowing the fingers to be used for delicate tasks. The sensory receptors also account for the use of the skin as a means of communication between people. For example, the touch receptors play a major role in sexual arousal, which assists the reproductive system.

Skin helps regulate body temperature. When muscles contract and ATP is broken down, heat is released. As described in Figure 1.8, the skin, under the direction of the brain, plays an active role in whether this heat is conserved or released to the environment in order to maintain a body temperature of 36.2°–37.7°C (97°–100°F). If body temperature starts to rise, the blood vessels in the skin, which are a part of the cardiovascular system, dilate so that more blood is brought to the surface of the skin for cooling, and the sweat glands become active. Sweat absorbs body heat, and this heat is carried away as sweat evaporates. If the weather is humid, evaporation is hindered, but cooling can be assisted by a cool breeze.

If the outer temperature is cool, the sweat glands remain inactive, and the blood vessels constrict so that less blood is brought to the skin's surface. Whenever the body's temperature falls below normal, the muscles start to contract, causing shivering, which produces heat. As mentioned previously, the arrector pili muscles attached to hair follicles are also involved in this reaction, and this is why goose bumps occur when a person is cold. If the outside temperature is extremely cold and blood flow to the skin is severely restricted for an extended period, a portion of the skin will die, resulting in *frostbite*.

Hyperthermia and Hypothermia

Hyperthermia, a body temperature above normal, and **hypothermia,** a body temperature below normal, indicate that the body's regulatory mechanisms have been overcome. In *heat exhaustion,* blood pressure may be low, and salts may have been lost due to profuse sweating. Even so, body temperature remains high. *Heat stroke* is characterized by an elevated temperature, up to 43°C (110°F), with no sweating. *Fever* is a special case of hyperthermia that can be brought on by a bacterial infection. When the fever "breaks," sweating occurs as the normal set point for body temperature returns.

At first, hypothermia is characterized by uncontrollable shivering, incoherent speech, and lack of coordination (body temperature 90°–95°F). Then the pulse rate slows, and hallucinations occur as unconsciousness develops (body temperature 80°–90°F). Breathing becomes shallow, and shivering diminishes as rigidity sets in. This degree of hypothermia is associated with a 50% mortality.

Human Systems Work Together

Skeletal System

Skin protects bones; helps provide vitamin D for Ca^{2+} absorption.

Bones provide support for skin.

Muscular System

Skin protects muscles; rids the body of or conserves heat produced by muscle contraction.

Muscle contraction provides heat to warm skin.

Nervous System

Skin protects nerves, helps regulate body temperature; skin receptors send sensory input to brain.

Brain controls nerves that regulate size of cutaneous blood vessels, activate sweat glands and arrector pili muscles.

Endocrine System

Skin helps protect endocrine glands.

Androgens activate sebaceous glands and help regulate hair growth.

Cardiovascular System

Skin prevents water loss; helps regulate body temperature; protects blood vessels.

Blood vessels deliver nutrients and oxygen to skin, carry away wastes; blood clots if skin is broken.

How the Integumentary System works with other body systems

Lymphatic System/Immunity

Skin serves as a barrier to pathogen invasion; Langerhans cells phagocytize pathogens; protects lymphatic vessels.

Lymphatic vessels pick up excess tissue fluid; immune system protects against skin infections.

Respiratory System

Skin helps protect respiratory organs.

Gas exchange in lungs provides oxygen to skin and rids body of carbon dioxide from skin.

Digestive System

Skin helps to protect digestive organs; helps provide vitamin D for Ca^{2+} absorption.

Digestive tract provides nutrients needed by skin.

Urinary System

Skin helps regulate water loss; sweat glands carry on some excretion.

Kidneys compensate for water loss due to sweating; activate vitamin D precursor made by skin.

Reproductive System

Skin receptors respond to touch; mammary glands produce milk; skin stretches to accommodate growing fetus.

Androgens activate oil glands; sex hormones stimulate fat deposition, affect hair distribution in males and females.

Development of Cancer

Cancer cells are abnormal for two reasons: First, cancer cells exhibit uncontrolled and disorganized growth. In the body, a cancer cell divides to form a growth, or **tumor,** that invades and destroys neighboring tissue. This is in contrast to **benign tumors,** which are encapsulated and stay in one place. To support their growth, cancer cells release a growth factor that causes neighboring blood vessels to branch into the cancerous tissue. This phenomenon has been termed **vascularization,** and some modes of cancer treatment are aimed at preventing vascularization.

The second abnormal characteristic of cancer cells is that they detach from the tumor and spread to other sites. Cancer cells invade the blood vessels or the lymphatic vessels and start new tumors elsewhere in the body. This process is called **metastasis.** If a tumor is found before metastasis has occurred, the chances of a cure are greatly increased. This is the rationale for using mammograms to detect early breast cancer and the Pap test to detect cancer of the cervix.

One theory says that cancer development is a two-step process involving (1) initiation and (2) promotion. *Initiators* include **carcinogens,** agents that cause gene mutations (changes). Mutagenic agents include viruses, excessive radiation, and certain chemicals. Cigarette smoke plays a significant role in the development of lung cancer because it contains chemical carcinogens. A cancer *promoter* is any influence that causes a cell to start growing in an uncontrolled manner. For example, a promoter might cause a second mutation or provide the environment for cells to form a tumor. Some evidence suggests that a diet rich in saturated fats and cholesterol is a cancer promoter. Considerable time may elapse between initiation and promotion, and this is one reason why cancer is seen more often in older rather than younger people.

Individuals should be aware of the seven danger signals for cancer (Table 5A) and inform their doctors when they notice any one of these. Cancer can be detected by physical examination, assisted by various means of viewing the internal organs. Also, specific blood tests can detect tumors that secrete a particular chemical in the blood. For example, the level of prostate-specific antigen (PSA) appears to increase in the blood according to the size of a prostate tumor.

Tumors can be surgically removed, but there is always the danger that they have already metastasized and are **malignant.** When a growth is malignant, surgery is often preceded or followed by radiation therapy and/or chemotherapy. Radiation destroys the more rapidly dividing cancer cells but causes less damage to the more slowly dividing normal cells. The use of radioactive protons is preferred over X ray because proton beams can be aimed directly at the tumor, like an automatic rifle hitting the bull's-eye of a target.

Chemotherapy is the use of drugs to kill the more actively growing cancer cells. Recently, researchers report that toxins released by diarrhea-causing bacteria can keep epithelial colon cells from dividing. Sometimes, cancer cells become resistant to chemotherapy (even when several drugs are used in combination). The plasma membrane in resistant cells contains a carrier that pumps toxic chemicals out of the cell. Researchers are testing drugs known to poison the pump in an effort to restore sensitivity to chemotherapy.

Immunotherapy and gene therapy are new, experimental ways of treating cancer. *Immunotherapy* is the use of an immune system component to treat a disease. For example, cancer patients are sometimes given cytotoxins, chemicals released by lymphocytes, a type of white blood cell. *Gene therapy* is the substitution of "good genes" for defective or missing genes in order to treat a disease. The hope is that, one day, cancer can be cured by providing a normal gene to make up for a defective or missing gene in the cells of a person with cancer.

The evidence is clear that the risk of certain types of cancer can be reduced by adopting certain behaviors. For example, avoiding excessive sunlight reduces the risk of skin cancer, and abstaining from smoking cigarettes and cigars reduces the risk of lung cancer, as well as other types of cancer. Exercise and a healthy diet are also believed to be important. Recommendations include:

1. Lowering the total fat intake
2. Eating more high-fiber foods
3. Increasing consumption of foods rich in vitamins A and C
4. Reducing consumption of salt-cured and smoked foods
5. Including vegetables of the cabbage family in the diet
6. Consuming moderate amounts of alcohol

Table 5A — Danger Signals for Cancer

C hange in bowel or bladder habits
A sore that does not heal
U nusual bleeding or discharge
T hickening or lump in breast or elsewhere
I ndigestion or difficulty in swallowing
O bvious change in wart or mole
N agging cough or hoarseness

Basic Key Terms

arrector pili (ah-rek′tor pil′i), p. 72

cutaneous membrane (kyū-ta′ne-us mem′brān), p. 70

dermis (der′mis), p. 71

epidermis (ep″ĭ-der′mis), p. 70

hair follicle (hār fol′ĭ-kl), p. 72

hypodermis (hi″po-der′mis), p. 70

integument (in-teg′yū-ment), p. 70

integumentary system (in-teg″yū-men′tar-e sis′tem), p. 70

keratin (kĕr′uh-tin), p. 71

lunula (lu′nu-luh), p. 73

melanin (mel′uh-nin), p. 71

melanocyte (mel′uh-no-sīt), p. 71

sebaceous gland (sĕ-ba′shus gland), p. 73

sebum (se′bum), p. 73

sweat gland (swet gland), p. 73

Clinical Key Terms

acne vulgaris (ak′ne vul-ga′-ris), p. 73

albinism (al′bĭ-nizm), p. 71

alopecia (al-o-pe′she-uh), p. 72

athlete's foot (ath′lēts fůt), p. 74

basal cell carcinoma (bās′al sel kar-sĭ-no′muh), p. 74

dandruff (dan′druf), p. 74

decubitus ulcer (de-kyū′bĭ-tus ul′ser), p. 71

eczema (ek′zĕ-muh), p. 74

hirsutism (her′suh-tizm), p. 72

hyperthermia (hi″per-ther′me-uh), p. 78

hypodermic needle (hi-po-der′mik ne′dl), p. 71

hypothermia (hi″po-ther′me-uh), p. 78

impetigo (im″pĕ-ti′go), p. 74

melanoma (mel-uh-no′muh), p. 74

mole (mōl), p. 74

psoriasis (so-ri′uh-sis), p. 74

rickets (rik′ets), p. 78

squamous cell carcinoma (skwa′mus sel kar-sĭ-no′muh), p. 74

subcutaneous injection (sub″kyū-ta′ne-us in-jek′shun), p. 71

urticaria (ur″tĭ-kār′e-uh), p. 74

Summary

5.1 **Structure of the Skin**
The skin has two regions: the epidermis and the dermis. The hypodermis lies below the skin.
A. The epidermis, the outer region of the skin, is made up of stratified squamous epithelium. New cells continually produced in the stratum basale of the epidermis are pushed outward and become the keratinized cells of the stratum corneum.
B. The dermis, which is composed of dense irregular connective tissue, lies beneath the epidermis. It contains collagenous and elastic fibers, blood vessels, and nerve fibers.
C. The hypodermis is made up of loose connective tissue and adipose tissue, which insulates the body from heat and cold.

5.2 **Accessory Structures of the Skin**
Accessory structures of the skin include hair, nails, and glands.
A. Both hair and nails are produced by the division of epidermal cells and consist of keratinized cells.

B. Sweat glands are numerous and present in all regions of the skin. Sweating helps lower the body temperature.
C. Sebaceous glands are associated with a hair follicle and secrete sebum, which lubricates the hair and skin.
D. Mammary glands located in the breasts produce milk after childbirth.

5.3 **Disorders of the Skin**
A. Skin cancer. Skin cancer, which is associated with ultraviolet radiation, occurs in three forms. Basal cell carcinoma and squamous cell carcinoma can usually be removed surgically. Melanoma is the most dangerous form of skin cancer.
B. Wound healing. The skin has regenerative powers and can grow back on its own if a wound is not too extensive.
C. Burns. The severity of a burn depends on its depth and extent. First-degree burns affect only the epidermis. Second-degree burns affect the entire epidermis and a

portion of the dermis. Third-degree burns affect the entire epidermis and dermis. The "rule of nines" provides a means of estimating the extent of a burn injury.

5.4 **Effects of Aging**
Skin wrinkles with age because the epidermis is held less tightly, fibers in the dermis are fewer, and the hypodermis has less padding. The skin has fewer blood vessels, sweat glands, and hair follicles. Although pigment cells are fewer and the hair turns gray, pigmented blotches appear on the skin. Exposure to the sun results in many of the skin changes we associate with aging.

5.5 **Homeostasis**
A. Skin protects the body from physical trauma and bacterial invasion.
B. Skin helps regulate water loss and gain, which helps the urinary system. Also, sweat glands excrete some urea.
C. The skin produces a precursor molecule that is converted to vitamin D following exposure to

UV radiation. A hormone derived from vitamin D helps regulate calcium and phosphorus metabolism involved in bone development.

D. The skin contains sensory receptors for touch, pressure, pain, hot, and cold, which help people to be aware of their surroundings. These receptors send information to the nervous system.

E. The skin helps regulate body temperature. When the body is too hot, surface blood vessels dilate, and the sweat glands are active. When the body is cold, surface blood vessels constrict, and the sweat glands are inactive.

F. Hyperthermia and hypothermia are two conditions that can result when the body's temperature regulatory mechanism is overcome. With hyperthermia, the body temperature rises above normal, and with hypothermia, the body temperature falls below normal.

Study Questions

1. In general, describe the two regions of the skin. (pp. 70–71)
2. Describe the process by which epidermal tissue continually renews itself. (p. 71)
3. What function does the dermis have in relation to the epidermis? (p. 71)
4. What primary role does adipose tissue play in the hypodermis? (p. 71)
5. Describe in general the structure of a hair follicle and a nail. How do hair follicles and nails grow? (pp. 72–73)
6. Describe the structure and function of sweat glands and sebaceous glands. (p. 73)
7. Describe the structure of a mammary gland. (p. 73)
8. Name the three types of skin cancer, and cite the most frequent cause of skin cancer. (p. 74)
9. Describe how a wound heals and how a scar forms. (pp. 74–75)
10. Explain how to determine the severity of a burn. Describe the proper treatment for burns. (p. 76)
11. Name five functions of the skin, and tell what system of the body is assisted by these functions and how they contribute to homeostasis. (p. 78)

Objective Questions

I. Match the terms in the key to the items listed in questions 1–5.
   Key:
      a. epidermis
      b. dermis
      c. hypodermis
   1. blood vessels and nerve fibers
   2. fat cells
   3. basal cells
   4. location of sweat glands
   5. many collagenous and elastic fibers

II. Fill in the blanks.
   6. Sebaceous glands are associated with _____ in the dermis, and they secrete an oily substance called _____ .
   7. Sweat glands are involved in body _____ regulation.
   8. Skin protects against _____ trauma, _____ invasion, and _____ gain or loss.
   9. Skin cells produce vitamin _____ , which is needed for strong bones.
   10. The severity of a burn is determined by _____ and _____ .
   11. The type of skin cancer with the highest death rate is _____ , while the most common form is _____ .

Medical Terminology Reinforcement Exercise

Consult Appendix B for help in pronouncing and analyzing the meaning of the terms that follow.

1. epidermomycosis (ep″ĭ-der″mo-mi-ko′sis)
2. melanogenesis (mel″uh-no-jen′ĕ-sis)
3. acrodermatosis (ak″ro-der″muh-to′sis)
4. pilonidal cyst (pi″lo-ni′dal sist)
5. mammoplasty (mam′o-plas″te)
6. antipyretic (an″ti-pi-ret′ik)
7. dermatome (der′muh-tōm)
8. hypodermic (hy″po-der′mik)
9. onychocryptosis (on″ĭ-ko-krip-to′sis)
10. hyperhydrosis (hi″per-hi-dro′sis)
11. scleroderma (sklēr-o-der′muh)
12. piloerection (pi′lo-e-rek′shun)
13. cellulitis (sel′yū-li′tis)
14. dermatitis (der-muh-ti′tis)
15. rhytidoplasty (rit′ĭ-do-plas-te)
16. trichopathy (tri-kop′uh-the)

Website Link

Visit the Student Edition of the Online Learning Center at http://www.mhhe.com/maderap5 for additional quizzes, interactive learning exercises, and other study tools.

The Skeletal System

Anterior view of the bones in the right hand and wrist of an adult as shown by X ray.

chapter outline & learning objectives

After you have studied this chapter, you should be able to:

6.1 Skeleton: Overview (p. 84)
- Name at least five functions of the skeleton.
- Explain a classification of bones based on their shapes.
- Describe the anatomy of a long bone.
- Describe the growth and development of bones.
- Name and describe six types of fractures, and state the four steps in fracture repair.

6.2 Axial Skeleton (p. 89)
- Distinguish between the axial and appendicular skeletons.
- Name the bones of the skull, and state the important features of each bone.
- Describe the structure and function of the hyoid bone.
- Name the bones of the vertebral column and the thoracic cage. Be able to label diagrams of them.

- Describe a typical vertebra, the atlas and axis, and the sacrum and coccyx.
- Name the three types of ribs and the three parts of the sternum.

6.3 Appendicular Skeleton (p. 97)
- Name the bones of the pectoral girdle and the pelvic girdle. Be able to label diagrams of them.
- Name the bones of the upper limb (arm and forearm) and the lower limb (thigh and leg). Be able to label diagrams that include surface features.
- Cite at least five differences between the female and male pelvises.

6.4 Joints (Articulations) (p. 104)
- Explain how joints are classified, and give examples of each type of joint.
- List the types of movements that occur at synovial joints.

6.5 Effects of Aging (p. 107)
- Describe the anatomical and physiological changes that occur in the skeletal system as we age.

6.6 Homeostasis (p. 108)
- List and discuss six ways the skeletal system contributes to homeostasis. Discuss ways the other systems assist the skeletal system.

Medical Focus
Osteoporosis (p. 88)

What's New
Coaxing the Chondrocytes for Knee Repair (p. 107)

6.1 Skeleton: Overview

The skeletal system consists of the bones (206 in adults) and joints, along with the cartilage and ligaments that occur at the joints.

Functions of the Skeleton

The skeleton has the following functions:

The skeleton supports the body. The bones of the lower limbs support the entire body when we are standing, and the pelvic girdle supports the abdominal cavity.

The skeleton protects soft body parts. The bones of the skull protect the brain; the rib cage protects the heart and lungs.

The skeleton produces blood cells. All bones in the fetus have red bone marrow that produces blood cells. In the adult, only certain bones produce blood cells.

The skeleton stores minerals and fat. All bones have a matrix that contains calcium phosphate, a source of calcium ions and phosphate ions in the blood. Fat is stored in yellow bone marrow.

The skeleton, along with the muscles, permits flexible body movement. While articulations (joints) occur between all the bones, we associate body movement in particular with the bones of the limbs.

Figure 6.1 Classification of bones. **a.** Long bones are longer than they are wide. **b.** Short bones are cube shaped; their lengths and widths are about equal. **c.** Flat bones are platelike and have broad surfaces. **d.** Irregular bones have varied shapes with many places for connections with other bones. **e.** Round bones are circular.

a.

b.

c.

d.

e.

Anatomy of a Long Bone

Bones are classified according to their shape. Long bones are longer than they are wide. Short bones are cube shaped—that is, their lengths and widths are about equal. Flat bones, such as those of the skull, are platelike with broad surfaces. Irregular bones have varied shapes that permit connections with other bones. Round bones are circular in shape (Fig. 6.1).

A long bone, such as the one in Figure 6.2, can be used to illustrate certain principles of bone anatomy. The bone is enclosed in a tough, fibrous, connective tissue covering called the **periosteum**, which is continuous with the ligaments and tendons that anchor bones. The periosteum contains blood vessels that enter the bone and service its cells. At both ends of a long bone is an expanded portion called an **epiphysis**; the portion between the epiphyses is called the **diaphysis**.

As shown in the section of an adult bone in Figure 6.2, the diaphysis is not solid but has a **medullary cavity** containing yellow marrow. Yellow marrow contains large amounts of fat. The medullary cavity is bounded at the sides by compact bone. The epiphyses contain spongy bone. Beyond the spongy bone is a thin shell of compact bone and, finally, a layer of hyaline cartilage called the **articular cartilage**. Articular cartilage is so named because it occurs where bones articulate (join). **Articulation** is the joining together of bones at a joint. The medullary cavity and the spaces of spongy bone are lined with *endosteum*, a thin, fibrous membrane.

Compact Bone

Compact bone, or dense bone, contains many cylinder-shaped units called osteons. The osteocytes (bone cells) are in tiny chambers called *lacunae* that occur between concentric layers of matrix called *lamellae*. The matrix contains collagenous protein fibers and mineral deposits, primarily of calcium and phosphorus salts.

In each osteon, the lamellae and lacunae surround a single central canal. Blood vessels and nerves from the periosteum enter the central canal. The osteocytes have extensions that extend into passageways called *canaliculi*, and thereby the osteocytes are connected to each other and to the central canal.

Spongy Bone

Spongy bone, or cancellous bone, contains numerous bony bars and plates, called *trabeculae*. Although lighter than compact bone, spongy bone is still designed for strength. Like braces used for support in buildings, the trabeculae of spongy bone follow lines of stress.

In infants, **red bone marrow**, a specialized tissue that produces blood cells, is found in the cavities of most bones. In adults, red blood cell formation, called **hematopoiesis**, occurs in the spongy bone of the skull, ribs, sternum (breastbone), and vertebrae, and in the ends of the long bones.

Figure 6.2 Anatomy of a long bone. **a.** A long bone is encased by the periosteum except at the epiphyses, which are covered by articular cartilage. Spongy bone of the epiphyses contains red bone marrow. The diaphysis contains yellow bone marrow and is bordered by compact bone. **b.** The detailed anatomy of spongy bone and compact bone is shown in the enlargement, along with a blowup of an osteocyte in a lacuna.

Epiphysis

epiphyseal plates

articular cartilage

spongy bone (contains red bone marrow)

compact bone

periosteum

endosteum

medullary cavity (contains yellow bone marrow)

blood vessel

Diaphysis

trabeculae

Spongy Bone

osteon

lamella

canaliculi

osteocyte within lacuna

b.

a.

Humerus

central canal

blood vessels

Compact Bone

Bone Growth and Repair

Bones are composed of living tissues, as exemplified by their ability to grow and undergo repair. Several different types of cells are involved in bone growth and repair:

Osteoprogenitor cells are unspecialized cells present in the inner portion of the periosteum, in the endosteum, and in the central canal of compact bone.

Osteoblasts are bone-forming cells derived from osteoprogenitor cells. They are responsible for secreting the matrix characteristic of bone.

Osteocytes are mature bone cells derived from osteoblasts. Once the osteoblasts are surrounded by matrix, they become the osteocytes in bone.

Osteoclasts are thought to be derived from monocytes, a type of white blood cell present in red bone marrow. Osteoclasts perform bone resorption; that is, they break down bone and assist in depositing calcium and phosphate in the blood. The work of osteoclasts is important to the growth and repair of bone.

Bone Development and Growth

The term **ossification** refers to the formation of bone. The bones of the skeleton form during embryonic development in two distinctive ways—intramembranous ossification and endochondral ossification.

In **intramembranous ossification,** bone develops between sheets of fibrous connective tissue. Cells derived from connective tissue become osteoblasts that form a matrix resembling the trabeculae of spongy bone. Other osteoblasts associated with a periosteum lay down compact bone over the surface of the spongy bone. The osteoblasts become osteocytes when they are surrounded by a mineralized matrix. The bones of the skull develop in this manner.

Most of the bones of the human skeleton form by **endochondral ossification.** Hyaline cartilage models, which appear during fetal development, are replaced by bone as development continues. During endochondral ossification of a long bone, the cartilage begins to break down in the center of the diaphysis, which is now covered by a periosteum (Fig. 6.3). Osteoblasts invade the region and begin to lay down spongy bone in what is called a primary ossification center. Other osteoblasts lay down compact bone beneath the periosteum. As the compact bone thickens, the spongy bone of the diaphysis is broken down by osteoclasts, and the cavity created becomes the medullary cavity.

After birth, the epiphyses of a long bone continue to grow, but soon secondary ossification centers appear in these regions. Here spongy bone forms and does not break down. A band of cartilage called an **epiphyseal plate** remains between the primary ossification center and each secondary center. The limbs keep increasing in length and width as long as epiphyseal plates are still present. The rate of growth is controlled by hormones, such as growth hormones and the sex hormones. Eventually, the epiphyseal plates become ossified, and the bone stops growing.

Figure 6.3 Endochondral ossification of a long bone. **a.** A cartilaginous model develops during fetal development. **b.** A periosteum develops. **c.** A primary ossification center contains spongy bone surrounded by compact bone. **d.** The medullary cavity forms in the diaphysis, and secondary ossification centers develop in the epiphyses. **e.** After birth, growth is still possible as long as cartilage remains at the epiphyseal plates. **f.** When the bone is fully formed, the remnants of the epiphyseal plates become a thin line.

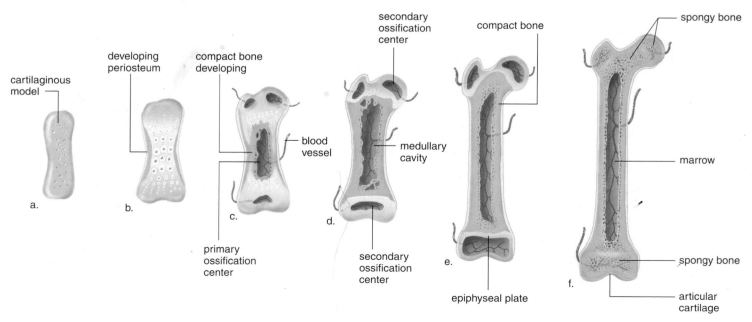

Remodeling of Bones

In the adult, bone is continually being broken down and built up again. Osteoclasts derived from monocytes in red bone marrow break down bone, remove worn cells, and assist in depositing calcium in the blood. After a period of about three weeks, the osteoclasts disappear, and the bone is repaired by the work of osteoblasts. As they form new bone, osteoblasts take calcium from the blood. Eventually some of these cells get caught in the mineralized matrix they secrete and are converted to osteocytes, the cells found within the lacunae of osteons.

Strange as it may seem, adults apparently require more calcium in the diet (about 1,000 to 1,500 mg daily) than do children in order to promote the work of osteoblasts. Otherwise, osteoporosis, a condition in which weak and thin bones easily fracture, may develop. Osteoporosis is discussed in the Medical Focus on page 88.

Bone Repair

Repair of a bone is required after it breaks, or **fractures**. Bone repair occurs in a series of four steps:

1. *Hematoma.* Within six to eight hours after a fracture, blood escapes from ruptured blood vessels and forms a hematoma (mass of clotted blood) in the space between the broken bones.

2. *Fibrocartilaginous callus.* Tissue repair begins, and fibrocartilage fills the space between the ends of the broken bone for about three weeks.
3. *Bony callus.* Osteoblasts produce trabeculae of spongy bone and convert the fibrocartilaginous callus to a bony callus that joins the broken bones together and lasts about three to four months.
4. *Remodeling.* Osteoblasts build new compact bone at the periphery, and osteoclasts reabsorb the spongy bone, creating a new medullary cavity.

In some ways, bone repair parallels the development of a bone except that the first step, hematoma, indicates that injury has occurred, and then fibrocartilage instead of hyaline cartilage precedes the production of compact bone.

The naming of fractures describes what kind of break occurred. A fracture is *complete* if the bone is broken clear through and *incomplete* if the bone is not separated into two parts. A fracture is *simple* if it does not pierce the skin and *compound* if it does pierce the skin. *Impacted* means that the broken ends are wedged into each other, and a *spiral fracture* occurs when the break is ragged due to twisting of a bone.

Surface Features of Bones

As we study the various bones of the skeleton, refer to Table 6.1, which lists and explains the surface features of bones.

Table 6.1	**Surface Features of Bones**	
PROCESSES		
Term	**Definition**	**Example**
Articulating Surfaces		
Condyle (kon'dīl)	A large, rounded, articulating knob	Mandibular condyle of the mandible (Fig 6.6b)
Head	A prominent, rounded, articulating proximal end of a bone	Head of the femur (Fig. 6.16)
Projections for Muscle Attachment		
Crest	A narrow, ridgelike projection	Iliac crest of the coxal bone (Fig. 6.15)
Spine	A sharp, slender process	Spine of the scapula (Fig. 6.11b)
Trochanter (tro-kan'ter)	A massive process found only on the femur	Greater trochanter and lesser trochanter of the femur (Fig. 6.16)
Tubercle (tu'ber-kl)	A small, rounded process	Greater tubercle of the humerus (Fig. 6.12)
Tuberosity (tu"bĕ-ros'ĭ-te)	A large, roughened process	Radial tuberosity of the radius (Fig. 6.13)
DEPRESSIONS AND OPENINGS		
Foramen (fo-ra'men)	A rounded opening through a bone	Foramen magnum of the occipital bone (Fig. 6.7a)
Fossa (fos'uh)	A flattened or shallow surface	Mandibular fossa of the temporal bone (Fig. 6.7a)
Meatus (me-a'tus)	A tubelike passageway through a bone	External auditory meatus of the temporal bone (Fig. 6.6b)
Sinus (si'nus)	A cavity or hollow space in a bone	Frontal sinus of the frontal bone (Fig. 6.5)

Source: Data from Kent M. Van De Graaff and Stuart Ira Fox, *Concepts of Human Anatomy and Physiology,* 5th ed., 1999, p. 187.

Medical Focus

Osteoporosis

Osteoporosis is a condition in which the bones are weakened due to a decrease in the bone mass that makes up the skeleton. Throughout life, bones are continuously remodeled. While a child is growing, the rate of bone formation is greater than the rate of bone breakdown. The skeletal mass continues to increase until ages 20 to 30. After that, the rates of formation and breakdown of bone mass are equal until ages 40 to 50. Then, reabsorption begins to exceed formation, and the total bone mass slowly decreases.

Over time, men are apt to lose 25% and women 35% of their bone mass. But we have to consider that men tend to have denser bones than women anyway, and their testosterone (male sex hormone) level generally does not begin to decline significantly until after age 65. In contrast, the estrogen (female sex hormone) level in women begins to decline at about age 45. Because sex hormones play an important role in maintaining bone strength, this difference means that women are more likely than men to suffer fractures, involving especially the hip, vertebrae, long bones, and pelvis. Although osteoporosis may at times be the result of various disease processes, it is essentially a disease of aging.

Everyone can take measures to avoid having osteoporosis when they get older. Adequate dietary calcium throughout life is an important protection against osteoporosis. The U.S. National Institutes of Health recommend a calcium intake of 1,200–1,500 mg per day during puberty. Males and females require 1,000 mg per day until age 65 and 1,500 mg per day after age 65, because the intestinal tract has fewer vitamin D receptors in the elderly.

A small daily amount of vitamin D is also necessary to absorb calcium from the digestive tract. Exposure to sunlight is required to allow skin to synthesize vitamin D. If you reside on or north of a "line" drawn from Boston to Milwaukee, to Minneapolis, to Boise, chances are, you're not getting enough vitamin D during the winter months. Therefore, you should avail yourself of the vitamin D in fortified foods such as low-fat milk and cereal.

Postmenopausal women should have an evaluation of their bone density. Presently, bone density is measured by a method called dual energy X-ray absorptiometry (DEXA). This test measures bone density based on the absorption of photons generated by an X-ray tube. Soon, a blood and urine test may be able to detect the biochemical markers of bone loss, making it possible for physicians to screen all older women and at-risk men for osteoporosis.

If the bones are thin, it is worthwhile to take measures to gain bone density because even a slight increase can significantly reduce fracture risk. Regular, moderate, weight-bearing exercise such as walking or jogging is a good way to maintain bone strength (Fig. 6A). A combination of exercise and drug treatment, as recommended by a physician, may yield the best results.

A wide variety of prescribed drugs that have different modes of action are available. Hormone therapy includes black cohosh, which is a phytoestrogen (estrogen made by a plant as opposed to an animal). Calcitonin is a naturally occurring hormone whose main site of action is the skeleton where it inhibits the action of osteoclasts, the cells that break down bone. Promising new drugs include slow-release fluoride therapy and certain growth hormones. These medications stimulate the formation of new bone.

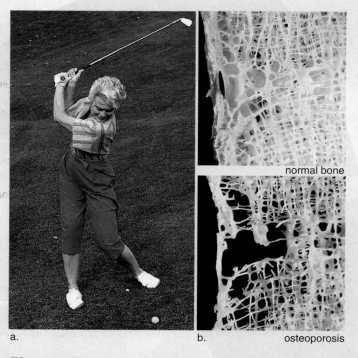

normal bone

a.   b.   osteoporosis

Figure 6A Preventing osteoporosis. **a.** Exercise can help prevent osteoporosis, but when playing golf, you should carry your own clubs and walk instead of using a golf cart. **b.** Normal bone growth compared to bone from a person with osteoporosis.

6.2 Axial Skeleton

The skeleton is divided into the axial skeleton and the appendicular skeleton. The tissues of the axial and appendicular skeletons are bone (both compact and spongy), cartilage (hyaline, fibrocartilage, and elastic cartilage), and dense connective tissue, a type of fibrous connective tissue. (The various types of connective tissues were extensively discussed in Chapter 3.)

In Figure 6.4, the bones of the axial skeleton are colored orange, and the bones of the appendicular skeleton are colored yellow for easy distinction. Notice that the **axial skeleton** lies in the midline of the body and contains the bones of the skull, the hyoid bone, the vertebral column, and the thoracic cage. Six tiny middle ear bones (three in each ear) are also in the axial skeleton; we will study them in Chapter 9 in connection with the ear.

Figure 6.4 Major bones of the skeleton. **a.** Anterior view. **b.** Posterior view. The bones of the axial skeleton are shown in orange, and those of the appendicular skeleton are shown in yellow.

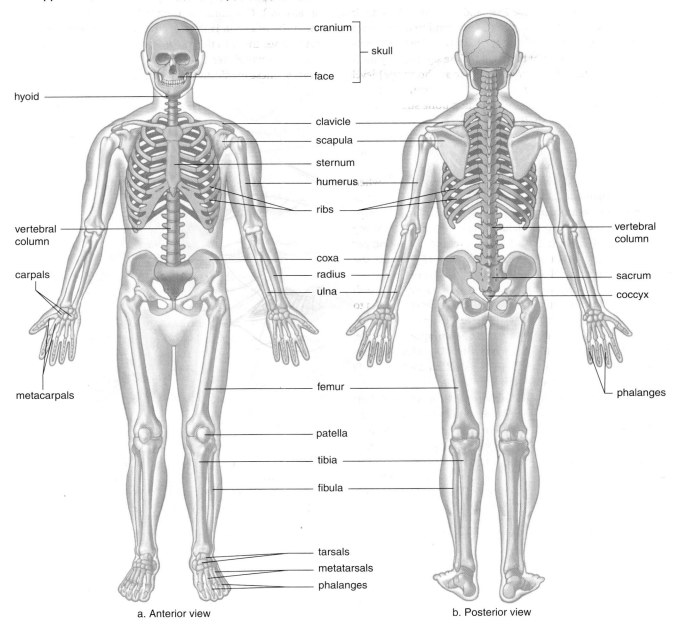

a. Anterior view b. Posterior view

Figure 6.5 Sagittal section of the skull.

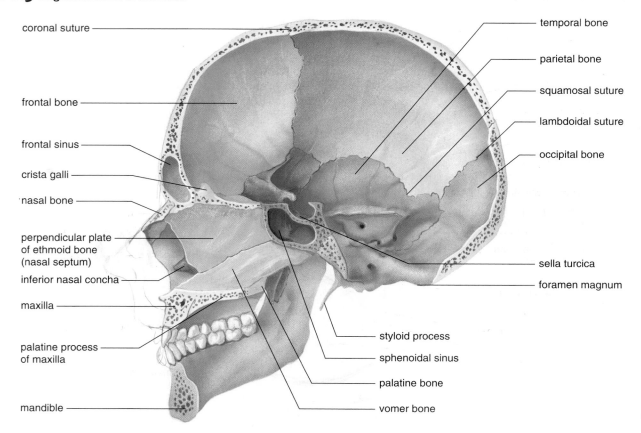

coronal suture

frontal bone

frontal sinus

crista galli

nasal bone

perpendicular plate
of ethmoid bone
(nasal septum)

inferior nasal concha

maxilla

palatine process
of maxilla

mandible

temporal bone

parietal bone

squamosal suture

lambdoidal suture

occipital bone

sella turcica

foramen magnum

styloid process

sphenoidal sinus

palatine bone

vomer bone

Skull

The skull is formed by the cranium and the facial bones. These bones contain **sinuses** (Fig. 6.5), air spaces lined by mucous membranes, that reduce the weight of the skull and give the voice a resonant sound. The paranasal sinuses empty into the nose and are named for their locations. They include the maxillary, frontal, sphenoidal, and ethmoidal sinuses. The two mastoid sinuses drain into the middle ear. **Mastoiditis,** a condition that can lead to deafness, is an inflammation of these sinuses.

Bones of the Cranium

The cranium protects the brain and is composed of eight bones. These bones are separated from each other by immovable joints called **sutures.** Newborns have membranous regions called **fontanels,** where more than two bones meet. The largest of these is the anterior fontanel, which is located where the two parietal bones meet the two parts of the frontal bone. The fontanels permit the bones of the skull to shift during birth as the head passes through the birth canal. The anterior fontanel (often called the "soft spot") usually closes by the age of two years. Besides the frontal bone, the cranium is composed of two parietal bones, one occipital bone, two temporal bones, one sphenoid bone, and one ethmoid bone (Figs. 6.6 and 6.7).

Frontal Bone One frontal bone forms the forehead, a portion of the nose, and the superior portions of the orbits (bony sockets of the eyes).

Parietal Bones Two parietal bones are just posterior to the frontal bone. They form the roof of the cranium and also help form its sides.

Occipital Bone One occipital bone forms the most posterior part of the skull and the base of the cranium. The spinal cord joins the brain by passing through a large opening in the occipital bone called the foramen magnum. The **occipital condyles** (Fig. 6.7a) are rounded processes on either side of the foramen magnum that articulate with the first vertebra of the spinal column.

Figure 6.6 Skull anatomy. **a.** Anterior view. **b.** Lateral view.

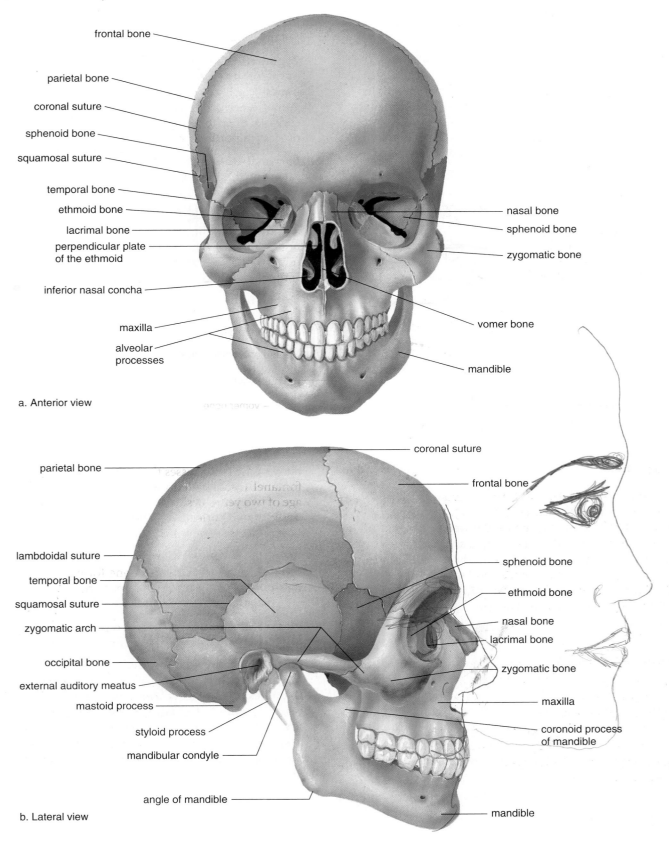

frontal bone

parietal bone

coronal suture

sphenoid bone

squamosal suture

temporal bone

ethmoid bone

lacrimal bone

perpendicular plate of the ethmoid

inferior nasal concha

maxilla

alveolar processes

nasal bone

sphenoid bone

zygomatic bone

vomer bone

mandible

a. Anterior view

coronal suture

parietal bone

frontal bone

lambdoidal suture

temporal bone

squamosal suture

zygomatic arch

occipital bone

external auditory meatus

mastoid process

styloid process

mandibular condyle

angle of mandible

sphenoid bone

ethmoid bone

nasal bone

lacrimal bone

zygomatic bone

maxilla

coronoid process of mandible

mandible

b. Lateral view

Temporal Bones Two temporal bones are just inferior to the parietal bones on the sides of the cranium. They also help form the base of the cranium (Figs. 6.6b and 6.7a). Each temporal bone has the following:

external auditory meatus, a canal that leads to the middle ear;
mandibular fossa, which articulates with the mandible;
mastoid process, which provides a place of attachment for certain neck muscles;
styloid process, which provides a place of attachment for muscles associated with the tongue and larynx;
zygomatic process, which projects anteriorly and helps form the cheekbone.

Sphenoid Bone The sphenoid bone helps form the sides and floor of the cranium and the rear wall of the orbits. The sphenoid bone has the shape of a bat and this shape means that it articulates with and holds together the other cranial bones (Fig. 6.7). Within the cranial cavity, the sphenoid bone has a saddle-shaped midportion called the **sella turcica** (Fig. 6.7b), which houses the pituitary gland in a depression.

Ethmoid Bone The ethmoid bone is anterior to the sphenoid bone and helps form the floor of the cranium. It contributes to the medial sides of the orbits and forms the roof and sides of the nasal cavity (Figs. 6.6 and 6.7b). The ethmoid bone contains the following:

crista galli (cock's comb), a triangular process that serves as an attachment for membranes that enclose the brain;
cribriform plate with tiny holes that serve as passageways for nerve fibers from the olfactory receptors;
perpendicular plate (Fig. 6.5), which projects downward to form the nasal septum;
superior and middle nasal conchae, which project toward the perpendicular plate. These projections support mucous membranes that line the nasal cavity.

Bones of the Face

Maxillae The two maxillae form the upper jaw. Aside from contributing to the floors of the orbits and to the sides of the floor of the nasal cavity, each maxilla has the following processes:

alveolar process (Fig. 6.6a). The alveolar processes contain the tooth sockets for teeth: incisors, canines, premolars, and molars.
palatine process (Fig. 6.7a). The left and right palatine processes form the anterior portion of the **hard palate** (roof of the mouth).

Palatine Bones The two palatine bones contribute to the floor and lateral wall of the nasal cavity (Fig. 6.5). The horizontal plates of the palatine bones form the posterior portion of the hard palate (Fig. 6.7a).

Notice that the hard palate consists of (1) portions of the maxillae (i.e., the palatine processes) and (2) horizontal plates of the palatine bones. A cleft palate results when either (1) or (2) have failed to fuse.

Zygomatic Bones The two zygomatic bones form the sides of the orbits (Fig. 6.7a). They also contribute to the "cheekbones." Each zygomatic bone has a **temporal process.** A **zygomatic arch,** the most prominent feature of a cheekbone consists of a temporal process connected to a zygomatic process (a portion of the temporal bone).

Lacrimal Bones The two small, thin lacrimal bones are located on the medial walls of the orbits (Fig. 6.6). A small opening between the orbit and the nasal cavity serves as a pathway for a duct that carries tears from the eyes to the nose.

Nasal Bones The two nasal bones are small, rectangular bones that form the bridge of the nose (Fig. 6.5). The ventral portion of the nose is cartilage, which explains why the nose is not seen on a skull.

Vomer Bone The vomer bone joins with the perpendicular plate of the ethmoid bone to form the nasal septum (Figs. 6.5 and 6.6a).

Inferior Nasal Conchae The two inferior nasal conchae are thin, curved bones that form a part of the inferior lateral wall of the nasal cavity (Fig. 6.6a). Like the superior and middle nasal conchae, they project into the nasal cavity and support the mucous membranes that line the nasal cavity.

Mandible The mandible, or lower jaw, is the only movable portion of the skull. The horseshoe-shaped front and horizontal sides of the mandible, referred to as the *body*, form the chin. The body has an **alveolar process** (Fig. 6.6a), which contains tooth sockets for 16 teeth. Superior to the left and right angle of the mandible are upright projections called *rami*. Each ramus has the following:

mandibular condyle (Fig. 6.6b), which articulates with a temporal bone;
coronoid process (Fig. 6.6b), which serves as a place of attachment for the muscles used for chewing.

Hyoid Bone

The U-shaped hyoid bone (Fig. 6.4) is located superior to the larynx (voice box) in the neck. It is the only bone in the body that does not articulate with another bone. Instead, it is suspended from the styloid processes of the temporal bones by the stylohyoid muscles and ligaments. It anchors the tongue and serves as the site for the attachment of several muscles associated with swallowing.

Figure 6.7 Skull anatomy continued. **a.** Inferior view. **b.** Superior view.

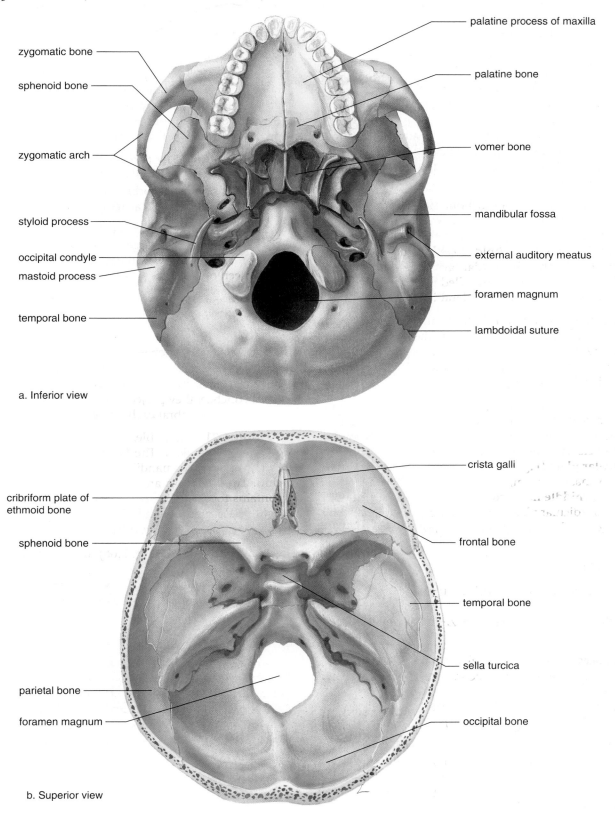

zygomatic bone

sphenoid bone

zygomatic arch

styloid process

occipital condyle

mastoid process

temporal bone

palatine process of maxilla

palatine bone

vomer bone

mandibular fossa

external auditory meatus

foramen magnum

lambdoidal suture

a. Inferior view

cribriform plate of
ethmoid bone

sphenoid bone

parietal bone

foramen magnum

crista galli

frontal bone

temporal bone

sella turcica

occipital bone

b. Superior view

Vertebral Column (Spine)

The **vertebral column** extends from the skull to the pelvis. It consists of a series of separate bones, the **vertebrae,** separated by pads of fibrocartilage called the **intervertebral disks** (Fig. 6.8). The vertebral column is located in the middorsal region and forms the vertical axis. The skull rests on the superior end of the vertebral column, which also supports the rib cage and serves as a point of attachment for the pelvic girdle. The vertebral column also protects the spinal cord, which passes through a vertebral canal formed by the vertebrae. The vertebrae are named according to their location: seven *cervical* (neck) *vertebrae,* twelve *thoracic* (chest) *vertebrae,* five *lumbar* (lower back) *vertebrae,* five *sacral vertebrae* fused to form the sacrum, and three to five *coccygeal vertebrae* fused into one coccyx.

When viewed from the side, the vertebral column has four normal curvatures, named for their location (Fig. 6.8). The cervical and lumbar curvatures are convex anteriorly, and the thoracic and sacral curvatures are concave anteriorly. In the fetus, the vertebral column has but one curve, and it is concave anteriorly. The cervical curve develops three to four months after birth, when the child begins to hold the head up. The lumbar curvature develops when a child begins to stand and walk, around one year of age. The curvatures of the vertebral column provide more support than a straight column would, and they also provide the balance needed to walk upright.

The curvatures of the vertebral column are subject to abnormalities. An abnormally exaggerated lumbar curvature is called **lordosis,** or "swayback." People who are balancing a heavy midsection, such as pregnant women or men with "potbellies," may have swayback. An increased roundness of the thoracic curvature is **kyphosis,** or "hunchback." This abnormality sometimes develops in older people. An abnormal lateral (side-to-side) curvature is called **scoliosis.** Occurring most often in the thoracic region, scoliosis is usually first seen during late childhood.

Intervertebral Disks

The fibrocartilaginous intervertebral disks located between the vertebrae act as a cushion. They prevent the vertebrae from grinding against one another and absorb shock caused by such movements as running, jumping, and even walking. The disks also allow motion between the vertebrae so that a person can bend forward, backward, and from side to side. Unfortunately, these disks become weakened with age, and can slip or even rupture (called a **herniated disk**). A damaged disk pressing against the spinal cord or the spinal nerves causes pain. Such a disk may need to be removed surgically. If a disk is removed, the vertebrae are fused together, limiting the body's flexibility.

Figure 6.8 Curvatures of the spine. The vertebrae are named for their location in the body. Note the presence of the coccyx, also called the tailbone.

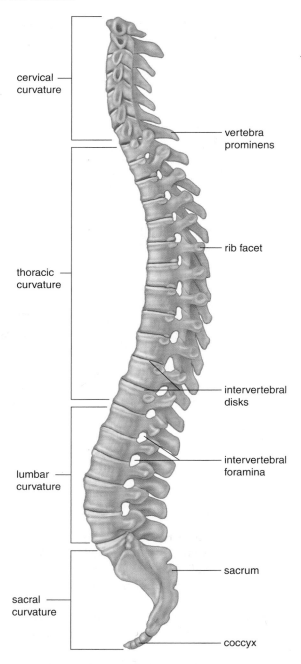

cervical curvature

vertebra prominens

rib facet

thoracic curvature

intervertebral disks

intervertebral foramina

lumbar curvature

sacrum

sacral curvature

coccyx

Figure 6.9 Vertebrae. **a.** A typical vertebra in articular position. The vertebral canal where the spinal cord is found is formed by adjacent vertebral foramina. **b.** Atlas and axis, showing how they articulate with one another. The odontoid process of the axis is the pivot around which the atlas turns, as when the head is shaken "no."

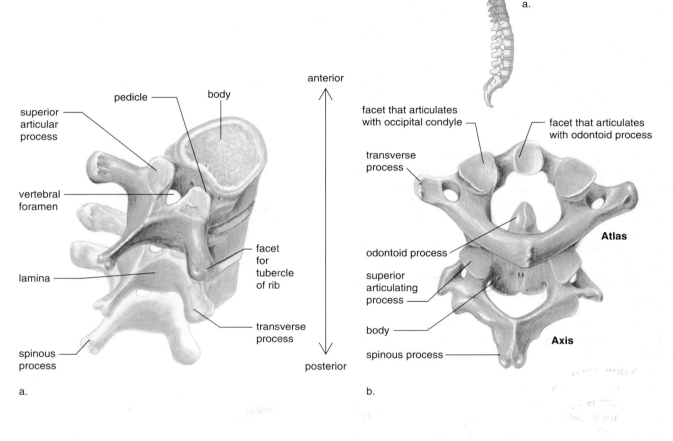

Vertebrae

Figure 6.9*a* shows that a typical vertebra has an anteriorly placed *body* and a posteriorly placed vertebral *arch*. The vertebral arch forms the wall of a *vertebral foramen* (pl., *foramina*). The foramina become a canal through which the spinal cord passes.

The vertebral *spinous process (spine)* occurs where two thin plates of bone called *laminae* meet. A transverse process is located where a pedicle joins a lamina. These processes serve for the attachment of muscles and ligaments. Articular processes (superior and inferior) serve for the joining of vertebrae.

The vertebrae have regional differences. For example, as the vertebral column descends, the bodies get bigger and are better able to carry more weight. In the cervical region, the spines are short and tend to have a split, or bifurcation. The thoracic spines are long and slender and project downward. The lumbar spines are massive and square and project posteriorly. The transverse processes of thoracic vertebrae have articular facets for connecting to ribs.

Atlas and Axis The first two cervical vertebrae are not typical (Fig. 6.9*b*). The **atlas** supports and balances the head. It has two depressions that articulate with the occipital condyles, allowing movement of the head forward and back. The **axis** has an *odontoid process* (also called the dens) that projects into the ring of the atlas. When the head moves from side to side, the atlas pivots around the odontoid process.

Sacrum and Coccyx The five sacral vertebrae are fused to form the **sacrum**. The sacrum articulates with the pelvic girdle and forms the posterior wall of the pelvic cavity (see Fig. 6.15). The **coccyx,** or tailbone, is the last part of the vertebral column. It is formed from a fusion of three to five vertebrae.

Figure 6.10 The rib cage. This structure includes the thoracic vertebrae, the ribs, and the sternum. The three bones that make up the sternum are the manubrium, body, and xiphoid process. The ribs numbered 1–7 are true ribs; those numbered 8–12 are false ribs.

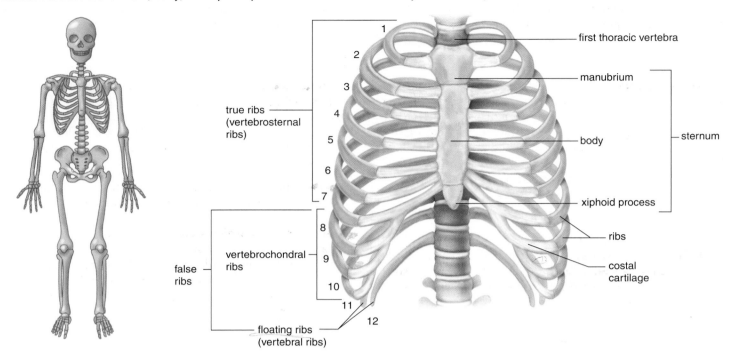

The Rib Cage

The **rib cage** (Fig. 6.10), sometimes called the thoracic cage, is composed of the thoracic vertebrae, ribs and associated cartilages, and sternum.

The rib cage demonstrates how the skeleton is protective but also flexible. The rib cage protects the heart and lungs; yet it swings outward and upward upon inspiration and then downward and inward upon expiration. The rib cage also provides support for the bones of the pectoral girdle (see page 97).

The Ribs

There are twelve pairs of ribs. All twelve pairs connect directly to the thoracic vertebrae in the back. After connecting with thoracic vertebrae, each rib first curves outward and then forward and downward. A rib articulates with the body of one vertebra and the transverse processes of two adjoining thoracic vertebra (called facet for tubercle of rib) (see Fig. 6.9).

The upper seven pairs of ribs connect directly to the sternum by means of costal cartilages. These are called the "true ribs," or the vertebrosternal ribs. The next three pairs of ribs are called the "false ribs," or vertebrochondral ribs, because they attach to the sternum by means of a common cartilage. The last two pairs are called "floating ribs," or vertebral ribs, because they do not attach to the sternum at all.

The Sternum

The **sternum**, or breastbone, is a flat bone that has the shape of a blade. The sternum, along with the ribs, helps protect the heart and lungs. During surgery the sternum may be split to allow access to the organs of the thoracic cavity.

The sternum is composed of three bones that fuse during fetal development. These bones are the manubrium, the body, and the xiphoid process. The *manubrium* is the superior portion of the sternum. The *body* is the middle and largest part of the sternum, and the *xiphoid process* is the inferior and smallest portion of the sternum. The manubrium joins with the body of the sternum at an angle. This joint is an important anatomical landmark because it occurs at the level of the second rib, and therefore allows the ribs to be counted. Counting the ribs is sometimes done to determine where the apex of the heart is located—usually between the fifth and sixth ribs.

The manubrium articulates with the costal cartilages of the first and second ribs; the body articulates costal cartilages of the second through tenth ribs; and the xiphoid process doesn't articulate with any ribs.

The xiphoid process is the third part of the sternum. Composed of hyaline cartilage in the child, it becomes ossified in the adult. The variably shaped xiphoid process serves as an attachment site for the diaphragm, which separates the thoracic cavity from the abdominal cavity.

6.3 Appendicular Skeleton

The **appendicular skeleton** contains the bones of the pectoral girdle, upper limbs, pelvic girdle, and lower limbs.

Pectoral Girdle

The **pectoral girdle** (shoulder girdle) contains four bones: two clavicles and two scapulae (Fig. 6.11). It supports the arms and serves as a place of attachment for muscles that move the arms. The bones of this girdle are not held tightly together; rather, they are weakly attached and held in place by ligaments and muscles. This arrangement allows great flexibility but means that the pectoral girdle is prone to dislocation.

Clavicles

The **clavicles** (collarbones) are slender and S-shaped. Each clavicle articulates medially with the manubrium of the sternum. This is the only place where the pectoral girdle is attached to the axial skeleton.

Each clavicle also articulates with a scapula. The clavicle serves as a brace for the scapula and helps stabilize the shoulder. It is structurally weak, however, and if undue force is applied to the shoulder, the clavicle will fracture.

Scapulae

The **scapulae** (sing., scapula), also called the shoulder blades, are broad bones that somewhat resemble triangles (Fig. 6.11b). One reason for the pectoral girdle's flexibility is that the scapulae are not joined to each other (see Fig. 6.4).

Each scapula has a spine, as well as the following features:

- **acromion process**, which articulates with a clavicle and provides a place of attachment for arm and chest muscles;
- **coracoid process**, which serves as a place of attachment for arm and chest muscles;
- **glenoid cavity**, which articulates with the head of the arm bone (humerus). The pectoral girdle's flexibility is also a result of the glenoid cavity being smaller than the head of the humerus.

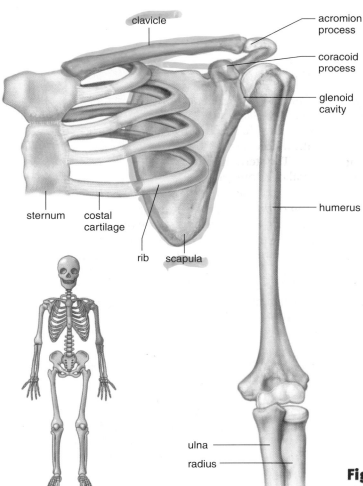

a. Pectoral girdle, frontal view

b. Scapula, posterior view

Figure 6.11 The pectoral girdle. **a.** Frontal view of the pectoral girdle (left side) with the upper limb attached. **b.** Posterior view the right scapula.

Figure 6.12 Left humerus. **a.** Posterior surface view. **b.** Anterior surface view.

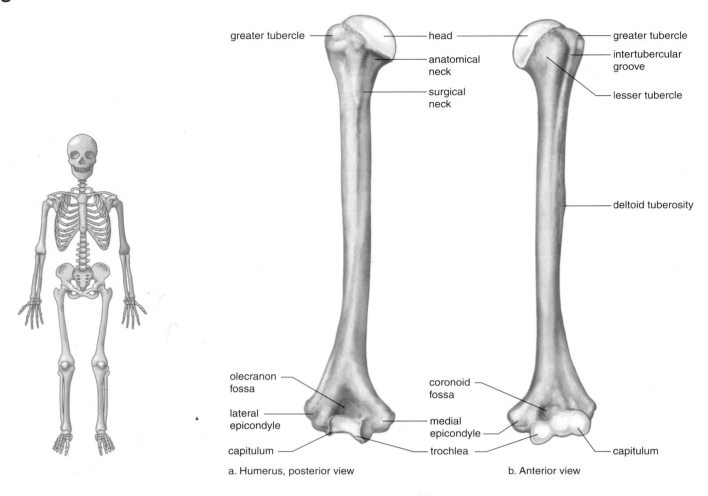

a. Humerus, posterior view
b. Anterior view

Upper Limb

The upper limb includes the bones of the arm (humerus), the forearm (radius and ulna), and the hand (carpals, metacarpals, and phalanges).[1]

Humerus

The **humerus** (Fig. 6.12) is the bone of the arm. It is a long bone with the following features at the proximal end:

head, which articulates with the glenoid cavity of the scapula;

greater and **lesser tubercles,** which provide attachments for muscles that move the arm and shoulder;

intertubercular groove, which holds a tendon from the biceps brachii, a muscle of the arm;

deltoid tuberosity, which provides an attachment for the deltoid, a muscle that covers the shoulder joint.

The humerus has the following features at the distal end:

capitulum, a lateral condyle that articulates with the head of the radius;

trochlea, a spool-shaped condyle that articulates with the ulna;

coronoid fossa, a depression for a process of the ulna when the elbow is flexed;

olecranon fossa, a depression for a process of the ulna when the elbow is extended.

---

[1]The term *upper extremity* is used to include a clavicle and scapula (of the pectoral girdle), an arm, forearm, wrist, and hand.

Figure 6.13 Right radius and ulna. **a.** The head of the radius articulates with the radial notch of the ulna. The head of the ulna articulates with the ulnar notch of the radius. **b.** Lateral view of the proximal end of the ulna.

- trochlear notch
- coronoid process
- head of radius
- radial tuberosity
- radius
- ulna
- head of ulna
- styloid process
- ulnar notch of radius
- styloid process
- olecranon process

a. Radius and ulna

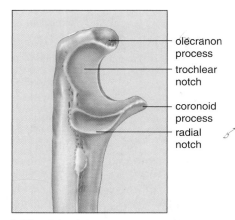

- olecranon process
- trochlear notch
- coronoid process
- radial notch

b. Ulna, lateral view

Radius

The **radius** and **ulna** (see Figs. 6.11*a* and 6.13) are the bones of the forearm. The radius is on the lateral side of the forearm (the thumb side). When you turn your hand from the "palms up" position to the "palms down" position, the radius crosses over the ulna, so the two bones are crisscrossed. Proximally, the radius has the following features:

head, which articulates with the capitulum of the humerus and fits into the radial notch of the ulna;
radial tuberosity, which serves as a place of attachment for a tendon from the biceps brachii;

Distally, the radius has the following features:

ulnar notch, which articulates with the head of the ulna;
styloid process, which serves as a place of attachment for ligaments that run to the wrist.

Ulna

The ulna is the longer bone of the forearm. Proximally, the ulna has the following features:

coronoid process, which articulates with the coronoid fossa of the humerus when the elbow is flexed;
olecranon process, the point of the elbow, articulates with the olecranon fossa of the humerus when the elbow is extended;
trochlear notch, which articulates with the trochlea of the humerus at the elbow joint;
radial notch, which articulates with head of the radius.

Distally, the ulna has the following features:

head, which articulates with the ulnar notch of the radius;
styloid process, which serves as a place of attachment for ligaments that run to the wrist.

Figure 6.14 Right wrist and hand. **a.** Anterior view. **b.** Posterior view.

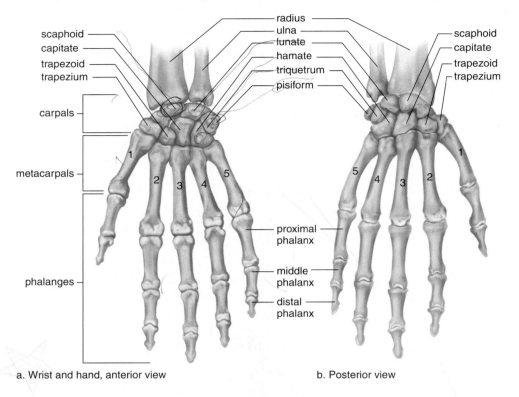

a. Wrist and hand, anterior view

b. Posterior view

Hand

Each hand (Fig. 6.14) has a wrist, a palm, and five fingers, or digits.

The wrist, or carpus, contains eight small carpal bones, tightly bound by ligaments in two rows of four each. Where we wear a "wrist watch" is the distal forearm—the true wrist is the proximal part of what we generally call the hand. Only two of the carpals (the scaphoid and lunate) articulate with the radius. Anteriorly, the concave region of the wrist is covered by a ligament, forming the so-called carpal tunnel. Inflammation of the tendons running though this area causes them to compress a nerve and the result is a numbness known as carpal tunnel syndrome.

Five metacarpal bones, numbered 1 to 5 from the thumb side of the hand toward the little finger, fan out to form the palm. When the fist is clenched, the heads of the metacarpals, which articulate with the phalanges, become obvious. The first metacarpal is more anterior than the others, and this allows the thumb to touch each of the other fingers.

The fingers, including the thumb, contain bones called the *phalanges*. The thumb has only two phalanges (proximal and distal), but the other fingers have three each (proximal, middle, and distal).

Pelvic Girdle

The **pelvic girdle** contains two coxal bones (hipbones), as well as the sacrum and coccyx (Fig. 6.15*a,b;* see Fig. 6.8). The strong bones of the pelvic girdle are firmly attached to one another and bear the weight of the body. The pelvis also serves as the place of attachment for the lower limbs and protects the urinary bladder, the internal reproductive organs, and a portion of the large intestine.

Coxal Bones

Each **coxal bone** has the following three parts:

1. **ilium** (Fig. 6.15). The ilium, the largest part of a coxal bone, flares outward to give the hip prominence. The margin of the ilium is called the iliac crest. Each ilium connects posteriorly with the sacrum at a **sacroiliac joint.**
2. **ischium** (Fig. 6.15*c*). The ischium is the most inferior part of a coxal bone. Its posterior region, the *ischial tuberosity*, allows a person to sit. Near the junction of the ilium and ischium is the **ischial spine**, which projects into the pelvic cavity. The distance between the ischial spines tells the size of the pelvic cavity. The **greater sciatic notch** is the site where blood vessels and the large sciatic nerve pass posteriorly into the lower leg.

Figure 6.15 The female pelvis is usually wider in all diameters and roomier than that of the male. **a.** Female pelvis. **b.** Male pelvis. **c.** Left coxal bone, lateral view.

a. Female pelvis

b. Male pelvis

c. Coxal bone

3. **pubis** (Fig. 6.15). The pubis is the anterior part of a coxal bone. The two pubic bones join together at the *pubic symphysis.* Posterior to where the pubis and the ischium join together is a large opening, the *obturator foramen,* through which blood vessels and nerves pass anteriorly into the leg.

Where the three parts of each coxal bone meet is a depression called the **acetabulum,** which receives the rounded head of the femur.

False and True Pelvises

The false pelvis is the portion of the trunk bounded laterally by the flared parts of the ilium. This space is much larger than that of the true pelvis. The true pelvis, which is inferior to the false pelvis, is the portion of the trunk bounded by the sacrum, lower ilium, ischium, and pubic bones. The true pelvis is said to have an upper inlet and a lower outlet. The dimensions of these outlets are important for females because

the outlets must be large enough to allow a baby to pass through during the birth process.

Sex Differences

Female and male pelvises (Fig. 6.15) usually differ in several ways, including the following:

1. Female iliac bones are more flared than those of the male; therefore, the female has broader hips.
2. The female pelvis is wider between the ischial spines and the ischial tuberosities.
3. The female inlet and outlet of the true pelvis are wider.
4. The female pelvic cavity is more shallow, while the male pelvic cavity is more funnel shaped.
5. Female bones are lighter and thinner.
6. The female pubic arch (angle at the pubic symphysis) is wider.

In addition to these differences in pelvic structure, male pelvic bones are larger and heavier, the articular ends are thicker, and the points of muscle attachment may be larger.

Figure 6.16 Right femur. **a.** Anterior view. **b.** Posterior view.

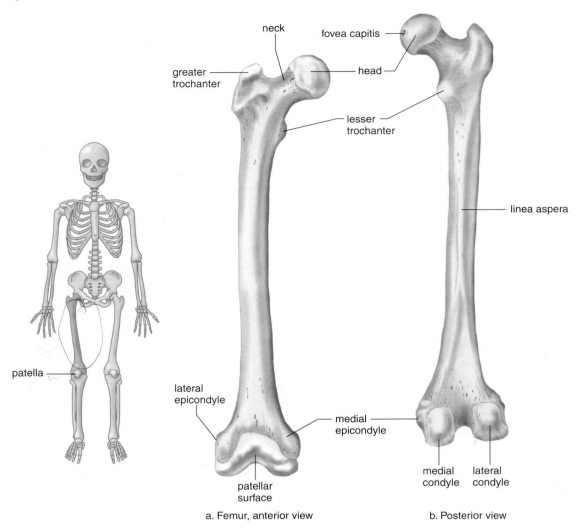

neck

fovea capitis

greater trochanter

head

lesser trochanter

linea aspera

lateral epicondyle

medial epicondyle

patella

medial condyle

lateral condyle

patellar surface

a. Femur, anterior view

b. Posterior view

Lower Limb

The lower limb includes the bones of the thigh (femur), the kneecap (patella), the leg (tibia and fibula), and the foot (tarsals, metatarsals, and phalanges).[2]

Femur

The **femur** (Fig. 6.16), or thighbone, is the longest and strongest bone in the body. Proximally, the femur has the following features:

head, which fits into the acetabulum of the coxal bone;
greater and **lesser trochanters,** which provide a place of attachment for the muscles of the thighs and buttocks;

linea aspera, a crest that serves as a place of attachment for several muscles.

Distally, the femur has the following features:

medial and **lateral epicondyles** that serve as sites of attachment for muscles and ligaments;
lateral and **medial condyles** that articulate with the tibia;
patellar surface, which is located between the condyles on the anterior surface, articulates with the **patella,** a small triangular bone that protects the knee joint.

Tibia

The **tibia** and **fibula** (Fig. 6.17) are the bones of the leg. The tibia, or shinbone, is medial to the fibula. It is thicker than the fibula and bears the weight from the femur, with which it articulates. It has the following features:

---

[2]The term *lower extremity* is used to include a coxal bone (of the pelvic girdle), the thigh, kneecap, leg, ankle, and foot.

Figure 6.17 Bones of the right leg, viewed anteriorly.

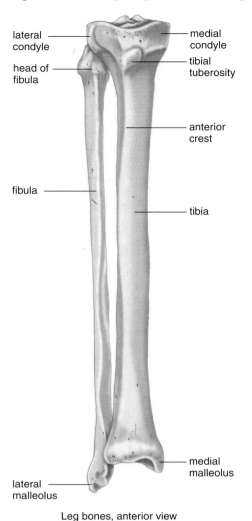

lateral condyle

medial condyle

head of fibula

tibial tuberosity

anterior crest

fibula

tibia

medial malleolus

lateral malleolus

Leg bones, anterior view

Figure 6.18 The right foot, viewed superiorly.

calcaneus

talus

navicular

cuboid

lateral cuneiform

intermediate cuneiform

medial cuneiform

tarsal bones

5
4
3
2
1

metatarsal bones

proximal phalanx

middle phalanx

distal phalanx

phalanges

Right foot, superior view

medial and **lateral condyles,** which articulate with the femur;

tibial tuberosity, where the patellar (kneecap) ligaments attach;

anterior crest, commonly called the shin;

medial malleolus, the bulge of the inner ankle, articulates with the talus in the foot.

Fibula

The fibula is lateral to the tibia and is more slender. It has a head that articulates with the tibia just below the lateral condyle. Distally, the **lateral malleolus** articulates with the talus and forms the outer bulge of the ankle. Its role is to stabilize the ankle.

Foot

Each foot (Fig. 6.18) has an ankle, an instep, and five toes (also called digits).

The ankle has seven **tarsal bones;** together, they are called the tarsus. Only one of the seven bones, the **talus,** can move freely where it joins the tibia and fibula. The largest of the ankle bones is the **calcaneus,** or heel bone. Along with the talus, it supports the weight of the body.

The instep has five elongated **metatarsal bones.** The distal ends of the metatarsals form the ball of the foot. Along with the tarsals, these bones form the arches of the foot (longitudinal and transverse), which give spring to a person's step. If the ligaments and tendons holding these bones together weaken, fallen arches, or "flat feet," can result.

The toes contain the **phalanges.** The big toe has only two phalanges, but the other toes have three each.

6.4 Joints (Articulations)

Bones articulate at the **joints**, which are often classified according to the amount of movement they allow:

Fibrous joints are immovable. Fibrous connective tissue joins bone to bone.

Cartilaginous joints are slightly movable. Fibrocartilage is located between two bones.

Synovial joints are freely movable. In these joints, the bones do not come in contact with each other.

Fibrous Joints

Some bones, such as those that make up the cranium, are sutured together by a thin layer of fibrous connective tissue and are *immovable*. Review Figures 6.6 and 6.7, and note the following immovable sutures:

coronal suture, between the parietal bones and the frontal bone;

lambdoidal suture, between the parietal bones and the occipital bone;

squamosal suture, between each parietal bone and each temporal bone;

sagittal suture, between the parietal bones (not shown).

Cartilaginous Joints

Slightly movable joints are those in which the bones are joined by fibrocartilage. The ribs are joined to the sternum by costal cartilages (see Fig. 6.10). The *bodies* of adjacent vertebrae are separated by intervertebral disks (see Fig. 6.8) that increase vertebral flexibility. The **pubic symphysis,** which occurs between the pubic bones (see Fig. 6.15), consists largely of fibrocartilage. Due to hormonal changes, this joint becomes more flexible during late pregnancy, which allows the pelvis to expand during childbirth.

Synovial Joints

All synovial joints are freely movable because, unlike the joints discussed so far, the two bones are separated by a *joint cavity* (Figs. 6.19 and 6.20). The cavity is lined by a **synovial membrane,** which produces **synovial fluid,** a lubricant for the joint. The absence of tissue between the articulating bones allows them to be freely movable but means that the joint has to be stabilized in some way.

The joint is stabilized by the joint capsule, a sleevelike extension of the periosteum of each articulating bone. **Ligaments,** which are composed of dense regular connective tissue, bind the two bones to one another and add even more stability. Tendons, which are cords of dense fibrous connective tissue that connect muscle to bone, also help stabilize a synovial joint.

The articulating surfaces of the bones are protected in several ways. The bones are covered by a layer of articular (hyaline) cartilage. In addition, the joint, such as the knee, contains **menisci** (sing., *meniscus*), crescent-shaped pieces of cartilage and fluid-filled sacs called **bursae,** which ease friction between all parts of the joint. Inflammation of the bursae is called **bursitis.** Tennis elbow is a form of bursitis.

Figure 6.19 Generalized anatomy of a synovial joint.

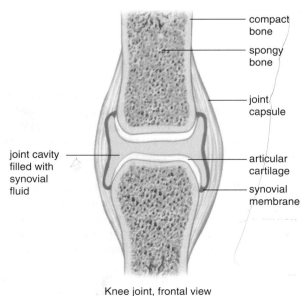

compact bone
spongy bone
joint capsule
joint cavity filled with synovial fluid
articular cartilage
synovial membrane

Knee joint, frontal view

Figure 6.20 The knee joint. Notice the menisci and bursae associated with the knee joint.

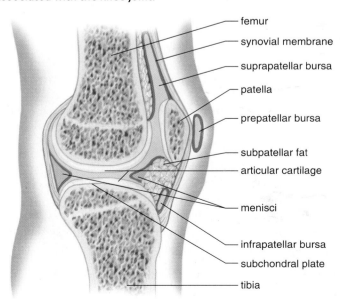

femur
synovial membrane
suprapatellar bursa
patella
prepatellar bursa
subpatellar fat
articular cartilage
menisci
infrapatellar bursa
subchondral plate
tibia

Knee joint, lateral view

Figure 6.21 Types of synovial joints.

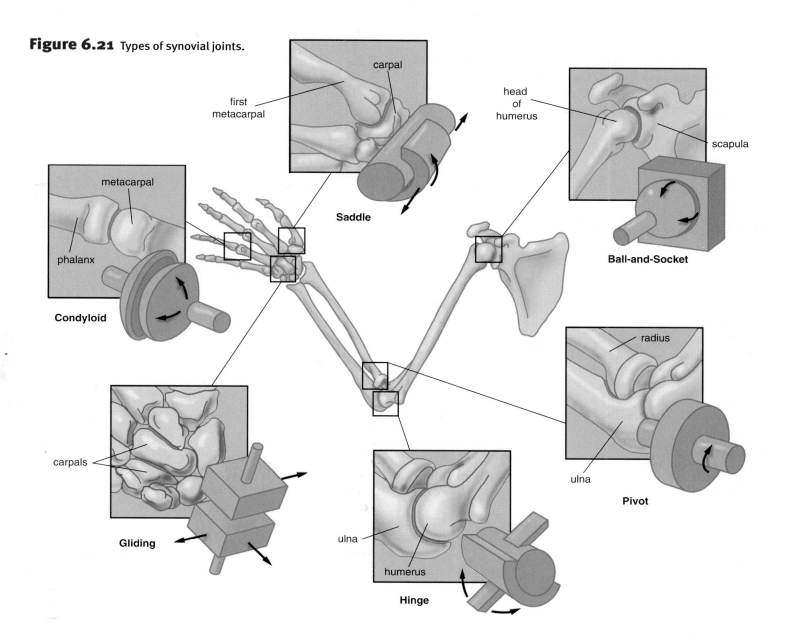

Types of Synovial Joints

Different types of freely movable joints are listed here and depicted in Figure 6.21.

Saddle joint. Each bone is saddle-shaped and fits into the complementary regions of the other. A variety of movements are possible. *Example*: the joint between the carpal and metacarpal bones of the thumb.

Ball-and-socket joint. The ball-shaped head of one bone fits into the cup-shaped socket of another. Movement in all planes, as well as rotation, are possible. *Examples*: the shoulder and hip joints.

Pivot joint. A small, cylindrical projection of one bone pivots within the ring formed of bone and ligament of another bone. Only rotation is possible. *Examples*: the joint between the proximal ends of the radius and ulna, and the joint between the atlas and axis.

Hinge joint. The convex surface of one bone articulates with the concave surface of another. Up-and-down motion in one plane is possible. *Examples*: the elbow and knee joints.

Gliding joint. Flat or slightly curved surfaces of bones articulate. Sliding or twisting in various planes is possible. *Examples*: the joints between the bones of the wrist and between the bones of the ankle.

Condyloid joint. The oval-shaped condyle of one bone fits into the elliptical cavity of another. Movement in different planes is possible, but rotation is not. *Examples*: the joints between the metacarpals and phalanges.

Figure 6.22 Joint movements. **a.** Angular movements increase or decrease the angle between the bones of a joint. **b.** Circular movements describe a circle or part of a circle. **c.** Special movements are unique to certain joints.

flexion of leg   extension of leg   adduction of thigh   abduction of thigh

a. Angular movements

rotation of arm   supination / pronation of hand   inversion   eversion

b. Circular movements   c. Special movements

Movements Permitted by Synovial Joints

Skeletal muscles are attached to bones by tendons that cross joints. When a muscle contracts, one bone moves in relation to another bone. The more common types of movements are described here.

Angular Movements (Fig. 6.22*a*):

Flexion decreases the joint angle. Flexion of the elbow moves the forearm toward the arm; flexion of the knee moves the leg toward the thigh. *Dorsiflexion* is flexion of the foot upward, as when you stand on your heels; *plantar flexion* is flexion of the foot downward, as when you stand on your toes.

Extension increases the joint angle. Extension of the flexed elbow straightens the upper limb. Hyperextension occurs when a portion of the body part is extended beyond 180°. It is possible to hyperextend the head and the trunk of the body, and also the shoulder and wrist (arm and hand).

Adduction is the movement of a body part toward the midline. For example, adduction of the arms or legs moves them back to the sides, toward the body.

Abduction is the movement of a body part laterally, away from the midline. Abduction of the arms or legs moves them laterally, away from the body.

Circular Movements (Fig. 6.22*b*):

Circumduction is the movement of a body part in a wide circle, as when a person makes arm circles. Careful observation of the motion reveals that, because the proximal end of the arm is stationary, the shape outlined by the arm is actually a cone.

Rotation is the movement of a body part around its own axis, as when the head is turned to answer "no" or when the arm is twisted toward the trunk (medial rotation) and away from the trunk (lateral rotation).

Supination is the rotation of the forearm so that the palm is upward; **pronation** is the opposite—the movement of the forearm so that the palm is downward.

Special movements (Fig. 6.22*c*):

Inversion and **eversion** apply only to the feet. Inversion is turning the foot so that the sole faces inward, and eversion is turning the foot so that the sole faces outward.

Elevation and **depression** refer to the lifting up and down, respectively, of a body part, as when you shrug your shoulders or move your jaw up and down.

Human Systems Work Together

Integumentary System

Bones provide support for skin.

Skin protects bones; helps provide vitamin D for Ca^{2+} absorption.

Muscular System

Bones provide attachment sites for muscles; store Ca^{2+} for muscle function.

Muscular contraction causes bones to move joints; muscles help protect bones.

Nervous System

Bones protect sense organs, brain, and spinal cord; store Ca^{2+} for nerve function.

Receptors send sensory input from bones to joints.

Endocrine System

Bones provide protection for glands; store Ca^{2+} used as second messenger.

Growth hormone regulates bone development; parathyroid hormone and calcitonin regulate Ca^{2+} content.

Cardiovascular System

Rib cage protects heart; red bone marrow produces blood cells; bones store Ca^{2+} for blood clotting.

Blood vessels deliver nutrients and oxygen to bones, carry away wastes.

How the Skeletal System works with other body systems

Lymphatic System/Immunity

Red bone marrow produces white blood cells involved in immunity.

Lymphatic vessels pick up excess tissue fluid; immune system protects against infections.

Respiratory System

Rib cage protects lungs and assists breathing; bones provide attachment sites for muscles involved in breathing.

Gas exchange in lungs provides oxygen and rids body of carbon dioxide.

Digestive System

Jaws contain teeth that chew food; hyoid bone assists swallowing.

Digestive tract provides Ca^{2+} and other nutrients for bone growth and repair.

Urinary System

Bones provide support and protection.

Kidneys provide active vitamin D for Ca^{2+} absorption and help maintain blood level of Ca^{2+}, needed for bone growth and repair.

Reproductive System

Bones provide support and protection of reproductive organs.

Sex hormones influence bone growth and density in males and females.

Selected New Terms

Basic Key Terms

abduction (ab-duk'shun), p. 106

adduction (uh-duk'shun), p. 106

appendicular skeleton (ap"en-dik'yŭ-ler skel'ĕ-ton), p. 97

articular cartilage (ar-tik'yŭ-ler kar'tĭ-lij), p. 84

articulation (ar-tik"yŭ-la'shun), p. 84

axial skeleton (ak'se-al skel'ĕ-ton), p. 89

bursa (bur'suh), p. 104

circumduction (ser"kum-duk'shun), p. 106

compact bone (kom'pakt bōn), p. 84

diaphysis (di-af'ĭ-sis), p. 84

epiphyseal plate (ep"ĭ-fiz'e-al plāt), p. 86

epiphysis (ĕ-pif'ĭ-sis), p. 84

eversion (e-ver'zhun), p. 106

extension (ek-sten'shun), p. 106

flexion (flek'shun), p. 106

fontanel (fon"tuh-nel'), p. 90

hematopoiesis (hem"ah-to-poi-e'sis), p. 84

intervertebral disk (in"ter-ver'tĕ-bral disk), p. 94

inversion (in-ver'zhun), p. 106

ligament (lig'uh-ment), p. 104

medullary cavity (med'u-lār"e kav'ĭ-te), p. 84

meniscus (mĕ-nis'kus), p. 104

ossification (os'-ĭ-fĭ-ka'shun), p. 86

osteoblast (os'te-o-blast"), p. 86

osteoclast (os'te-o-klast"), p. 86

osteocyte (os'te-o-sīt), p. 86

pectoral girdle (pek'tor-al ger'dl), p. 97

pelvic girdle (pel'vik ger'dl), p. 100

periosteum (per"e-os'te-um), p. 84

pronation (pro-na'shun), p. 106

red bone marrow (red bōn mār'o), p. 84

rotation (ro-ta'shun), p. 106

sinus (si'nus), p. 90

spongy bone (spunj'e bōn), p. 84

supination (su"pĭ-na'shun), p. 106

suture (su'cher), p. 90

synovial fluid (si-no've-al flu'id), p. 104

synovial joint (si-no've-al joint), p. 104

synovial membrane (si-no've-al mem'brān), p. 104

vertebral column (ver'tĕ-bral kah'lum), p. 94

Clinical Key Terms

bursitis (ber-si'tis), p. 104

fracture (frak'cher), p. 87

herniated disk (her'ne-a-ted disk), p. 94

kyphosis (ki-fo'sis), p. 94

lordosis (lor-do'sis), p. 94

mastoiditis (mas"toi-di'tis), p. 90

osteoarthritis (os"te-o-ar-thri'tis), p. 107

osteoporosis (os"te-o-po-ro'sis), p. 107

rheumatoid arthritis (ru'muh-toid ar-thri'tis), p. 107

scoliosis (sko"le-o'sis), p. 94

Summary

6.1 Skeleton: Overview

A. The skeleton supports and protects the body; produces red blood cells; serves as a storehouse for inorganic calcium and phosphate ions and fat; and permits flexible movement.

B. A long bone has a shaft (diaphysis) and two ends (epiphyses), which are covered by articular cartilage. The diaphysis contains a medullary cavity with yellow marrow and is bounded by compact bone. The epiphyses contain spongy bone with red bone marrow that produces red blood cells.

C. Bone is a living tissue. It develops, grows, remodels, and repairs itself. In all these processes, osteoclasts break down bone, and osteoblasts build bone.

D. Fractures are of various types, but repair requires four steps: (1) hematoma, (2) fibrocartilaginous callus, (3) bony callus, and (4) remodeling.

6.2 Axial Skeleton

The axial skeleton lies in the midline of the body and consists of the skull, the hyoid bone, the vertebral column, and the thoracic cage.

A. The skull is formed by the cranium and the facial bones. The cranium includes the frontal bone, two parietal bones, one occipital bone, two temporal bones, one sphenoid bone, and one ethmoid bone. The facial bones include two maxillae, two palatine bones, two zygomatic bones, two lacrimal bones, two nasal bones, the vomer bone, two inferior nasal conchae, and the mandible.

B. The U-shaped hyoid bone is located in the neck. It anchors the tongue and does not articulate with any other bone.

C. The typical vertebra has a body, a vertebral arch surrounding the vertebral foramen, and a spinous process. The first two vertebrae are the atlas and axis. The vertebral column has four curvatures and contains the cervical, thoracic, lumbar, sacral, and coccygeal vertebrae, which are separated by intervertebral disks.

D. The rib cage contains the thoracic vertebrae, ribs and associated cartilages, and the sternum.

6.3 Appendicular Skeleton

The appendicular skeleton consists of the bones of the pectoral girdle, upper limbs, pelvic girdle, and lower limbs.

A. The pectoral (shoulder) girdle contains two clavicles and two scapulae.

B. The upper limb contains the humerus, the radius, the ulna, and the bones of the hand (the carpals, metacarpals, and phalanges).

C. The pelvic girdle contains two coxal bones, as well as the sacrum and coccyx. The female pelvis is generally wider and more shallow than the male pelvis.

D. The lower limb contains the femur, the patella, the tibia, the fibula, and the bones of the foot (the tarsals, metatarsals, and phalanges).

6.4 Joints (Articulations)

A. Joints are regions of articulation between bones. They are classified according to their degree of movement. Some joints are immovable, some are slightly movable, and some are freely movable (synovial). The different kinds of synovial joints are ball-and-socket, hinge, condyloid, pivot, gliding, and saddle.

B. Movements at joints are broadly classified as angular (flexion, extension, adduction, abduction); circular (circumduction, rotation, supination, and pronation); and special (inversion, eversion, elevation, and depression).

6.5 Effects of Aging

Two fairly common effects of aging on the skeletal system are arthritis and osteoporosis.

6.6 Homeostasis

A. The bones protect the internal organs: The rib cage protects the heart and lungs; the skull protects the brain; and the vertebrae protect the spinal cord.

B. The bones assist all phases of respiration. The rib cage assists the breathing process, and red bone marrow produces the red blood cells that transport oxygen.

C. The bones store and release calcium. Calcium ions play a major role in muscle contraction and nerve conduction. Calcium ions also help regulate cellular metabolism.

D. The bones assist the lymphatic system and immunity. Red bone marrow produces not only the red blood cells but also the white blood cells.

E. The bones assist digestion. The jaws contain sockets for the teeth, which chew food, and a place of attachment for the muscles that move the jaws.

F. The skeleton is necessary for locomotion. Locomotion is efficient in human beings because they have a jointed skeleton for the attachment of muscles that move the bones.

Study Questions

1. What are five functions of the skeleton? (p. 84)

2. What are five major categories of bones based on their shapes? (p. 84)

3. What are the parts of a long bone? What are some differences between compact bone and spongy bone? (pp. 84–85)

4. How does bone grow in children, and how is it remodeled in all age groups? (pp. 86–87)

5. What are the various types of fractures? What four steps are required for fracture repair? (p. 87)

6. List the bones of the axial and appendicular skeletons. (Fig. 6.4, p. 89)

7. What are the bones of the cranium and the face? What are the special features of the temporal bones, sphenoid bone, and ethmoid bone? (pp. 90–93)

8. What are the parts of the vertebral column, and what are its curvatures? Distinguish between the atlas, axis, sacrum, and coccyx. (pp. 94–95)

9. What are the bones of the rib cage, and what are several of its functions? (p. 96)

10. What are the bones of the pectoral girdle? Give examples to demonstrate the flexibility of the pectoral girdle. What are the special features of a scapula? (p. 97)

11. What are the bones of the upper limb? What are the special features of these bones? (pp. 98–100)

12. What are the bones of the pelvic girdle, and what are their functions? (pp. 100–101)

13. What are the false and true pelvises, and what are several differences between the male and female pelvises? (p. 101)

14. What are the bones of the lower limb? Describe the special features of these bones. (pp. 102–3)

15. How are joints classified? Give examples of each type of joint. (p. 104)

16. How can joint movements permitted by synovial joints be categorized? Give an example of each category. (p. 106)

17. How does aging affect the skeletal system? (p. 107)

18. What functions of the skeletal system are particularly helpful in maintaining homeostasis? (pp. 108–9)

Objective Questions

I. Match the items in the key to the bones listed in questions 1–6.
   Key:
   a. forehead
   b. chin
   c. cheekbone
   d. elbow
   e. shoulder blade
   f. hip
   g. ankle
   1. temporal and zygomatic bones
   2. tibia and fibula
   3. frontal bone
   4. ulna
   5. coxal bone
   6. scapula

II. Match the items in the key to the bones listed in questions 7–13.

Key:
   a. external auditory meatus
   b. cribriform plate
   c. xiphoid process
   d. glenoid cavity
   e. olecranon process
   f. acetabulum
   g. greater and lesser trochanters
   7. scapula
   8. sternum
   9. femur
   10. temporal bone
   11. coxal bone
   12. ethmoid bone
   13. ulna

III. Fill in the blanks.
   14. Long bones are _____ than they are wide.
   15. The epiphysis of a long bone contains _____ bone, where red blood cells are produced.
   16. The _____ are the air-filled spaces in the cranium.
   17. The sacrum is a part of the _____ , and the sternum is a part of the _____ .
   18. The pectoral girdle is specialized for _____ , while the pelvic girdle is specialized for _____ .
   19. The term *phalanges* is used for the bones of both the _____ and the _____ .
   20. The knee is a freely movable (synovial) joint of the _____ type.

Medical Terminology Reinforcement Exercise

Consult Appendix B for help in pronouncing and analyzing the meaning of the terms that follow.

1. chondromalacia (kon″dro-muh-la′she-uh)
2. osteomyelitis (os″te-o-mi″e-li′tis)
3. craniosynostosis (kra″ne-o-sin″os-to′sis)
4. myelography (mi″ĕ-log′ruh-fe)
5. acrocyanosis (ak″ro-si″uh-no′sis)
6. syndactylism (sin-dak′tĭ-lizm)
7. orthopedist (or″tho-pe′dist)
8. prognathism (prog′nah-thizm)
9. micropodia (mi″kro-po′de-uh)
10. arthroscopic (ar″thro-skop′ik)
11. bursectomy (ber-sek′to-me)
12. synovitis (sin-o-vi′tis)
13. acephaly (a-sef′uh-le)
14. sphenoidostomy (sfe-noy-dos′to-me)
15. acetabuloplasty (as-ĕ-tab′yū-lo-plas-te)

Website Link

Visit the Student Edition of the Online Learning Center at http://www.mhhe.com/maderap5 for additional quizzes, interactive learning exercises, and other study tools.

The Muscular System

chapter 7

Scanning electron micrograph of motor neurons terminating at muscle fibers. A muscle fiber receives the stimulus to contract at a neuromuscular junction.

chapter outline & learning objectives

After you have studied this chapter, you should be able to:

7.1 Functions and Types of Muscles (p. 114)
- Distinguish between the three types of muscles, and tell where they are located in the body.
- Describe the connective tissues of a skeletal muscle.
- Name and discuss five functions of skeletal muscles.

7.2 Microscopic Anatomy and Contraction of Skeletal Muscle (p. 116)
- Name the components of a skeletal muscle fiber, and describe the function of each.
- Explain how skeletal muscle fibers are innervated and how they contract.
- Describe how ATP is made available for muscle contraction.

7.3 Muscle Responses (p. 122)
- Contrast the responses of a muscle fiber and whole muscle in the laboratory with their responses in the body.
- Contrast slow-twitch and fast-twitch muscle fibers.

7.4 Skeletal Muscles of the Body (p. 124)
- Discuss how muscles work together to achieve the movement of a bone.
- Give examples to show how muscles are named.
- Describe the locations and actions of the major skeletal muscles of each body region.

7.5 Effects of Aging (p. 134)
- Describe the anatomical and physiological changes that occur in the muscular system as we age.

7.6 Homeostasis (p. 136)
- Describe how the muscular system works with other systems of the body to maintain homeostasis.
- Describe some common muscle disorders and some of the serious diseases that can affect muscles.

Visual Focus
Anatomy of a Muscle Fiber (p. 117)

Medical Focus
Benefits of Exercise (p. 135)

7.1 Functions and Types of Muscles

All muscles, regardless of the particular type, can contract—that is, shorten. When muscles contract, some part of the body or the entire body moves. Humans have three types of muscles: smooth, cardiac, and skeletal (Fig. 7.1). The contractile cells of these tissues are elongated and therefore are called **muscle fibers**.

Smooth Muscle

Smooth muscle is located in the walls of hollow internal organs, and its involuntary contraction moves materials through an organ. Smooth muscle fibers are spindle-shaped cells, each with a single nucleus (uninucleated). The cells are usually arranged in parallel lines, forming sheets. Smooth muscle does not have the striations (bands of light and dark) seen in cardiac and skeletal muscle. Although smooth muscle is slower to contract than skeletal muscle, it can sustain prolonged contractions and does not fatigue easily.

Cardiac Muscle

Cardiac muscle forms the heart wall. Its fibers are uninucleated, striated, tubular, and branched, which allows the fibers to interlock at intercalated disks. Intercalated disks permit contractions to spread quickly throughout the heart. Cardiac fibers relax completely between contractions, which prevents fatigue. Contraction of cardiac muscle fibers is rhythmical; it occurs without outside nervous stimulation or control. Thus, cardiac muscle contraction is involuntary.

Skeletal Muscle

Skeletal muscle fibers are tubular, multinucleated, and striated. They make up the skeletal muscles attached to the skeleton. Skeletal muscle fibers can run the length of a muscle and therefore can be quite long. Skeletal muscle is voluntary because its contraction is always stimulated and controlled by the nervous system. In this chapter, we will explore why skeletal muscle (and cardiac muscle) is striated.

Connective Tissue Coverings

Muscles are organs, and as such they contain other types of tissues, such as nervous tissue, blood vessels, and connective tissue. Connective tissue is essential to the organization of the fibers within a muscle (Fig. 7.2). First, each fiber is surrounded by a thin layer of areolar connective tissue called the *endomysium*. Blood capillaries and nerve fibers reach each muscle fiber by way of the endomysium. Second, the muscle fibers are grouped into bundles called *fascicles*. The fascicles have a sheath of connective tissue called the *perimysium*. Finally, the

Figure 7.1 Types of muscles. The three types of muscles in the body have the appearance and characteristics shown here.

Smooth muscle
- has spindle-shaped, nonstriated, uninucleated fibers.
- occurs in walls of internal organs.
- is involuntary.

Cardiac muscle
- has striated, tubular, branched, uninucleated fibers.
- occurs in walls of heart.
- is involuntary.

Skeletal muscle
- has striated, tubular, multinucleated fibers.
- is usually attached to skeleton.
- is voluntary.

muscle itself is covered by a connective tissue layer called the *epimysium*. The epimysium becomes a part of the *fascia*, a layer of fibrous tissue that separates muscles from each other (deep fascia) and from the skin (superficial fascia). Collagen fibers of the epimysium continue as a strong, fibrous **tendon** that attaches the muscle to a bone. The epimysium merges with the periosteum of the bone.

Functions of Skeletal Muscles

This chapter concerns the skeletal muscles, and therefore it is fitting to consider their functions independent of the other types of muscles:

Skeletal muscles support the body. Skeletal muscle contraction opposes the force of gravity and allows us to remain upright. Some skeletal muscles are serving this purpose even when you think you are relaxed.

Skeletal muscles make bones and other body parts move. Muscle contraction accounts not only for the movement of limbs but also for eye movements, facial expressions, and breathing.

Skeletal muscles help maintain a constant body temperature. Skeletal muscle contraction causes ATP to break down, releasing heat that is distributed about the body.

Skeletal muscle contraction assists movement in cardiovascular and lymphatic vessels. The pressure of skeletal muscle contraction keeps blood moving in cardiovascular veins and lymph moving in lymphatic vessels.

Skeletal muscles help protect internal organs and stabilize joints. Muscles pad the bones that protect organs, and they have tendons that help hold bones together at joints.

Figure 7.2 Connective tissue of a skeletal muscle. **a.** Trace the connective tissue of a muscle from the endomysium to the perimysium to the epimysium, which becomes a part of the deep fascia and from which the tendon extends to attach a muscle to the periosteum of a bone. **b.** Cross section of the arm showing the arrangement of the muscles, which are separated from the skin by fascia. The superficial fascia contains adipose tissue. **c.** Photomicrograph of muscle fascicles from the tongue where the fascicles run in different directions. (c.s. = cross section; l.s. = longitudinal section.)

7.2 Microscopic Anatomy and Contraction of Skeletal Muscle

We have already examined the structure of skeletal muscle as seen with the light microscope. As you know, skeletal muscle tissue has alternating light and dark bands, giving it a striated appearance. The electron microscope shows that these bands are due to the arrangement of myofilaments in a muscle fiber.

Muscle Fiber

A muscle fiber contains the usual cellular components, but special names have been assigned to some of these components (Table 7.1 and Figure 7.3). The plasma membrane is called the *sarcolemma*; the cytoplasm is the sarcoplasm; and the endoplasmic reticulum is the *sarcoplasmic reticulum*. A muscle fiber also has some unique anatomical characteristics. One feature is its T (for transverse) system; the sarcolemma forms **T (transverse) tubules** that penetrate, or dip down, into the cell so that they come into contact—but do not fuse—with expanded portions of the sarcoplasmic reticulum. The expanded portions of the sarcoplasmic reticulum are calcium storage sites. Calcium ions (Ca^{2+}), as we shall see, are essential for muscle contraction.

The sarcoplasmic reticulum encases hundreds and sometimes even thousands of **myofibrils**, each about 1 μm in diameter, which are the contractile portions of the muscle fibers. Any other organelles, such as mitochondria, are located in the sarcoplasm between the myofibrils. The sarcoplasm also contains glycogen, which provides stored energy for muscle contraction, and the red pigment **myoglobin**, which binds oxygen until it is needed for muscle contraction.

Myofibrils and Sarcomeres

Myofibrils are cylindrical in shape and run the length of the muscle fiber. The striations of skeletal muscle fibers are formed by the placement of myofilaments within units of myofibrils called **sarcomeres.** A sarcomere extends between two dark lines called the Z lines. A sarcomere contains two types of protein myofilaments. The thick filaments are made up of a protein called **myosin,** and the thin filaments are made up of a protein called **actin.** Other proteins are also present. The I band is light colored because it contains only actin filaments attached to a Z line. The dark regions of the A band contain overlapping actin and myosin filaments, and its H zone has only myosin filaments.

Myofilaments

The thick and thin filaments differ in the following ways:

Thick Filaments   A thick filament is composed of several hundred molecules of the protein myosin. Each myosin molecule is shaped like a golf club, with the straight portion of the molecule ending in a double globular head, or *crossbridge*. Cross-bridges are slanted away from the middle of a sarcomere.

Thin Filaments   Primarily, a thin filament consists of two intertwining strands of the protein actin. Two other proteins, called tropomyosin and troponin, are also present, as we will discuss later in this section.

Sliding Filaments   We will also see that when muscles are innervated, impulses travel down a T tubule, and calcium is released from the sarcoplasmic reticulum. Now the muscle fiber contracts as the sarcomeres within the myofibrils shorten. When a sarcomere shortens, the actin (thin) filaments slide past the myosin (thick) filaments and approach one another. This causes the I band to shorten and the H zone to almost or completely disappear. The movement of actin filaments in relation to myosin filaments is called the **sliding filament theory** of muscle contraction. During the sliding process, the sarcomere shortens even though the filaments themselves remain the same length. ATP supplies the energy for muscle contraction. Although the actin filaments slide past the myosin filaments, it is the myosin filaments that do the work. Myosin filaments break down ATP and have cross-bridges that pull the actin filaments toward the center of the sarcomere.

Table 7.1	Microscopic Anatomy of a Muscle
Name	**Function**
Sarcolemma	Plasma membrane of a muscle fiber that forms T tubules
Sarcoplasm	Cytoplasm of a muscle fiber that contains organelles, including myofibrils
Glycogen	A polysaccharide that stores energy for muscle contraction
Myoglobin	A red pigment that stores oxygen for muscle contraction
T tubule	Extension of the sarcolemma that extends into the muscle fiber and conveys impulses that cause Ca^{2+} to be released into the sarcoplasmic reticulum
Sarcoplasmic reticulum	The smooth ER of a muscle fiber that stores Ca^{2+}
Myofibril	A bundle of myofilaments that contracts
Myofilament	Actin filaments and myosin filaments whose structure and functions account for muscle striations and contractions

visual focus

bundle of muscle fibers

muscle fiber

T tubules

nucleus

sarcoplasm

sarcoplasmic reticulum

calcium storage sites

skeletal muscle fiber

Muscle fiber has many myofibrils.

one myofibril

one sarcomere

Z line

Z line

sarcolemma

Myofibril has many sarcomeres.

cross-bridge

Sarcomere is relaxed.

myosin

actin

H zone

Z line

A band

I band

Sarcomere is contracted.

Figure 7.3 Anatomy of a muscle fiber. A muscle fiber contains many myofibrils with the components shown. A myofibril has many sarcomeres that contain myosin and actin filaments whose arrangement gives rise to the striations so characteristic of skeletal muscle. Muscle contraction occurs when sarcomeres contract and actin filaments slide past myosin filaments.

Skeletal Muscle Contraction

Muscle fibers are innervated—that is, they are stimulated to contract by motor neurons whose axons are found in nerves. The axon of one motor neuron has several branches and can stimulate from a few to several muscle fibers of a particular muscle. Each branch of the axon ends in an axon terminal that lies in close proximity to the sarcolemma of a muscle fiber. A small gap, called a synaptic cleft, separates the axon bulb from the sarcolemma. This entire region is called a **neuromuscular junction** (Fig. 7.4).

Axon terminals contain synaptic vesicles that are filled with the neurotransmitter acetylcholine (ACh). When nerve impulses traveling down a motor neuron arrive at an axon terminal, the synaptic vesicles release a neurotransmitter into the synaptic cleft. It quickly diffuses across the cleft and binds to receptors in the sarcolemma. Now the sarcolemma generates impulses that spread over the sarcolemma and down T tubules to the sarcoplasmic reticulum. The release of calcium from the sarcoplasmic reticulum causes the filaments within the sarcomeres to slide past one another. Sarcomere contraction results in myofibril contraction, which in turn results in muscle fiber, and finally muscle, contraction.

Figure 7.4 Neuromuscular junction. The branch of an axon ends in an axon terminal that meets but does not touch a muscle fiber. A synaptic cleft separates the axon terminal from the sarcolemma of the muscle fiber. Nerve impulses traveling down an axon cause synaptic vesicles to discharge acetylcholine, which diffuses across the synaptic cleft. When the neurotransmitter is received by the sarcolemma of a muscle fiber, impulses begin and lead to muscle fiber contractions.

The Role of Actin and Myosin

Figure 7.5 shows the placement of two other proteins associated with an actin filament, which you will recall is composed of a double row of twisted actin molecules. Threads of *tropomyosin* wind about an actin filament, and *troponin* occurs at intervals along the threads. Calcium ions (Ca^{2+}) that have been released from the sarcoplasmic reticulum combine with troponin. After binding occurs, the tropomyosin threads shift their position, and myosin binding sites are exposed.

The double globular heads of a myosin filament have ATP binding sites. The heads function as ATPase enzymes, splitting ATP into ADP and Ⓟ. This reaction activates the head so that it will bind to actin. The ADP and Ⓟ remain on the myosin heads until the heads attach to actin, forming a cross-bridge. Now, ADP and Ⓟ are released, and this causes the cross-bridges to change their positions. This is the power stroke that pulls the thin filaments toward the middle of the sarcomere. When another ATP molecule binds to a myosin head, the cross-bridge is broken as the head detaches from actin. The cycle begins again; the actin filaments move nearer the center of the sarcomere each time the cycle is repeated.

Contraction continues until nerve impulses cease and calcium ions are returned to their storage sites. The membranes of the sarcoplasmic reticulum contain active transport proteins that pump calcium ions back into the sarcoplasmic reticulum.

Figure 7.5 The role of calcium and myosin in muscle contraction. **a.** Upon release, calcium binds to troponin, exposing myosin binding sites. **b.** After breaking down ATP, myosin heads bind to an actin filament, and later, a power stroke causes the actin filament to move.

a.

actin filament — troponin — myosin binding sites — Ca^{2+}

tropomyosin

Ca^{2+}

Troponin-Ca^{2+} complex pulls tropomyosin away, exposing myosin binding sites.

b.

actin filament

myosin filament

Ⓟ — ADP

1. ATP is hydrolyzed when myosin head is unattached.

cross-bridge — myosin head

2. ADP+Ⓟ are bound to myosin as myosin head attaches to actin.

3. ADP+Ⓟ release causes head to change position and actin filament to move.

4. Binding of ATP causes myosin head to return to resting position.

ATP

Energy for Muscle Contraction

ATP produced previous to strenuous exercise lasts a few seconds, and then muscles acquire new ATP in three different ways: creatine phosphate breakdown, cellular respiration, and fermentation (Fig. 7.6). Creatine phosphate breakdown and fermentation are anaerobic, meaning that they do not require oxygen.

Creatine Phosphate Breakdown

Creatine phosphate is a high-energy compound built up when a muscle is resting. Creatine phosphate cannot participate directly in muscle contraction. Instead, it can regenerate ATP by the following reaction:

This reaction occurs in the midst of sliding filaments, and therefore is the speediest way to make ATP available to muscles. Creatine phosphate provides enough energy for only about eight seconds of intense activity, and then it is spent. Creatine phosphate is rebuilt when a muscle is resting by transferring a phosphate group from ATP to creatine.

Cellular Respiration

Cellular respiration completed in mitochondria usually provides most of a muscle's ATP. Glycogen and fat are stored in muscle cells. Therefore, a muscle cell can use glucose from glycogen and fatty acids from fat as fuel to produce ATP if oxygen is available:

Myoglobin, an oxygen carrier similar to hemoglobin, is synthesized in muscle cells, and its presence accounts for the reddish-brown color of skeletal muscle fibers. Myoglobin has a higher affinity for oxygen than does hemoglobin. Therefore, myoglobin can pull oxygen out of blood and make it available to muscle mitochondria that are carrying on cellular respiration. Then, too, the ability of myoglobin to temporarily store oxygen reduces a muscle's immediate need for oxygen when cellular respiration begins. The end products (carbon dioxide and water) are usually no problem. Carbon dioxide leaves the body at the lungs, and water simply enters the extracellular space. The by-product, heat, keeps the entire body warm.

Fermentation

Fermentation, like creatine phosphate breakdown, supplies ATP without consuming oxygen. During fermentation, glucose is broken down to lactate (lactic acid):

The accumulation of lactate in a muscle fiber makes the cytoplasm more acidic, and eventually enzymes cease to function well. If fermentation continues longer than two or three minutes, cramping and fatigue set in. Cramping seems to be due to lack of the ATP needed to pump calcium ions back into the sarcoplasmic reticulum and to break the linkages between the actin and myosin filaments so that muscle fibers can relax.

Oxygen Deficit

When a muscle uses fermentation to supply its energy needs, it incurs an **oxygen deficit**. Oxygen deficit is obvious when a person continues to breathe heavily after exercising. The ability to run up an oxygen deficit is one of muscle tissue's greatest assets. Brain tissue cannot last nearly as long without oxygen as muscles can.

Repaying an oxygen deficit requires replenishing creatine phosphate supplies and disposing of lactic acid. Lactic acid can be changed back to pyruvic acid and metabolized completely in mitochondria, or it can be sent to the liver to reconstruct glycogen. A marathon runner who has just crossed the finish line is not exhausted due to oxygen deficit. Instead, the runner has used up all the muscles', and probably the liver's, glycogen supply. It takes about two days to replace glycogen stores on a high-carbohydrate diet.

People who train rely more heavily on cellular respiration than do people who do not train. In people who train, the number of muscle mitochondria increases, and so fermentation is not needed to produce ATP. Their mitochondria can start consuming oxygen as soon as the ADP concentration starts rising during muscle contraction. Because mitochondria can break down fatty acid, instead of glucose, blood glucose is spared for the activity of the brain. (The brain, unlike other organs, can only utilize glucose to produce ATP.) Because less lactate is produced in people who train, the pH of the blood remains steady, and there is less of an oxygen deficit.

Figure 7.6 Energy sources for muscle contraction.

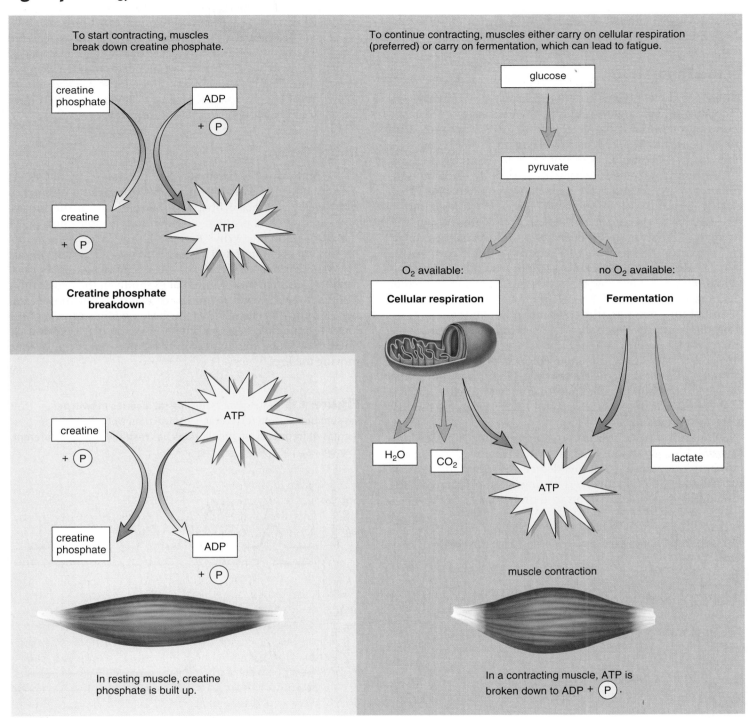

To start contracting, muscles break down creatine phosphate.

creatine phosphate

ADP + P

creatine + P

ATP

Creatine phosphate breakdown

ATP

creatine + P

creatine phosphate

ADP + P

In resting muscle, creatine phosphate is built up.

To continue contracting, muscles either carry on cellular respiration (preferred) or carry on fermentation, which can lead to fatigue.

glucose

pyruvate

O_2 available:

Cellular respiration

no O_2 available:

Fermentation

H_2O

CO_2

lactate

ATP

muscle contraction

In a contracting muscle, ATP is broken down to ADP + P.

7.3 Muscle Responses

Muscles can be studied in the laboratory in an effort to understand how they respond when in the body.

In the Laboratory

When a muscle fiber is isolated, placed on a microscope slide, and provided with ATP plus the various electrolytes it requires, it contracts completely along its entire length. This observation has resulted in the **all-or-none law:** A muscle fiber contracts completely or not at all. In contrast, a whole muscle shows degrees of contraction. To study whole muscle contraction in the laboratory, an isolated muscle is stimulated electrically, and the mechanical force of contraction is recorded as a visual pattern called a *myogram*. When the strength of the stimulus is above a threshold level, the muscle contracts and then relaxes. This action—a single contraction that lasts only a fraction of a second—is called a **muscle twitch.** Figure 7.7 is a myogram of a muscle twitch, which is customarily divided into three stages: the latent period, or the period of time between stimulation and initiation of contraction; the contraction period, when the muscle shortens; and the relaxation period, when the muscle returns to its former length. It's interesting to use our knowledge of muscle fiber contraction to understand these events. From our study thus far, we know that a muscle fiber in an intact muscle contracts when calcium leaves storage sacs and relaxes when calcium returns to storage sacs.

But unlike the contraction of a muscle fiber, a muscle has degrees of contraction, and a twitch can vary in height (strength) depending on the degree of stimulation. Why should that be? Obviously, a stronger stimulation causes more individual fibers to contract than before.

If a whole muscle is given a rapid series of stimuli, it can respond to the next stimulus without relaxing completely. **Summation** is increased muscle contraction until maximal sustained contraction, called a **tetanic contraction,** is achieved (Fig. 7.8). The myogram no longer shows individual twitches; rather, the twitches are fused and blended completely into a straight line. Tetanus continues until the muscle *fatigues* due to depletion of energy reserves. Fatigue is apparent when a muscle relaxes even though stimulation continues.

In the Body

In the body, muscles are innervated to contract by nerves. As mentioned, each axon within a nerve stimulates a number of muscle fibers. A nerve fiber together with all of the muscle fibers it innervates is called a **motor unit.** A motor unit obeys the all-or-none law. Why? Because all the muscle fibers in a motor unit are stimulated at once, and they all either contract or do not contract. A variable of interest is the number of muscle fibers within a motor unit. For example, in the ocular muscles that move the eyes, the innervation ratio is one motor axon per 23 muscle fibers, while in the gastrocnemius muscle of the lower leg, the ratio is about one motor axon per 1,000 muscle fibers. No doubt, moving the eyes requires finer control than moving the legs.

Figure 7.8 Myograms showing **(a)** a series of twitches, **(b)** summation, and **(c)** a tetanic contraction. Note that an increased frequency of stimulations has resulted in these different responses.

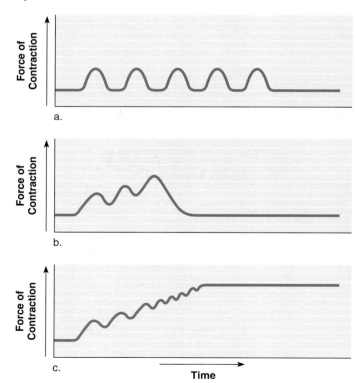

Figure 7.7 A myogram showing a single muscle twitch.

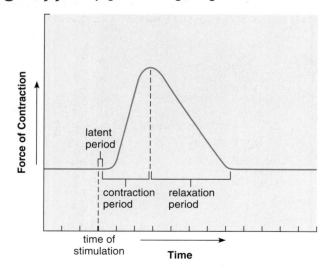

Tetanic contractions ordinarily occur in the body because, as the intensity of nervous stimulation increases, more and more motor units are activated. This phenomenon, known as **recruitment,** results in stronger and stronger muscle contractions. But while some muscle fibers are contracting, others are relaxing. Because of this, intact muscles rarely fatigue completely. Even when muscles appear to be at rest, they exhibit **tone,** in which some of their fibers are always contracting. Muscle tone is particularly important in maintaining posture. If all the fibers within the muscles of the neck, trunk, and legs were to suddenly relax, the body would collapse.

Athletics and Muscle Contraction

Athletes who excel in a particular sport, and much of the general public as well, are interested in staying fit by exercising. The Medical Focus on page 135 gives suggestions for exercise programs according to age.

Exercise and Size of Muscles Muscles that are not used or that are used for only very weak contractions decrease in size, or atrophy. **Atrophy** can occur when a limb is placed in a cast or when the nerve serving a muscle is damaged. If nerve stimulation is not restored, muscle fibers are gradually replaced by fat and fibrous tissue. Unfortunately, atrophy can cause muscle fibers to shorten progressively, leaving body parts contracted in contorted positions.

Forceful muscular activity over a prolonged period causes muscle to increase in size as the number of myofibrils within the muscle fibers increases. Increase in muscle size, called **hypertrophy,** occurs only if the muscle contracts to at least 75% of its maximum tension.

Some athletes take anabolic steroids, either testosterone or related chemicals, to promote muscle growth. This practice has many undesirable side effects as discussed in the Medical Focus on page 199.

Slow-Twitch and Fast-Twitch Muscle Fibers We have seen that all muscle fibers metabolize both aerobically and anaerobically. Some muscle fibers, however, utilize one method more than the other to provide myofibrils with ATP. Slow-twitch fibers tend to be aerobic, and fast-twitch fibers tend to be anaerobic (Fig. 7.9).

Slow-twitch fibers have a steadier tug and more endurance, despite having motor units with a smaller number of fibers. These muscle fibers are most helpful in sports such as long-distance running, biking, jogging, and swimming. Because they produce most of their energy aerobically, they tire only when their fuel supply is gone. Slow-twitch fibers have many mitochondria and are dark in color because they contain myoglobin, the respiratory pigment found in muscles. They are also surrounded by dense capillary beds and draw more blood and oxygen than fast-twitch fibers. Slow-twitch fibers have a low maximum tension, which develops slowly, but these muscle fibers are highly resistant to fatigue. Because slow-twitch fibers have a substantial reserve of glycogen and fat, their abundant mitochondria can maintain a steady, prolonged production of ATP when oxygen is available.

Fast-twitch fibers tend to be anaerobic and seem to be designed for strength because their motor units contain many fibers. They provide explosions of energy and are most helpful in sports activities such as sprinting, weight lifting, swinging a golf club, or throwing a shot. Fast-twitch fibers are light in color because they have fewer mitochondria, little or no myoglobin, and fewer blood vessels than slow-twitch fibers do. Fast-twitch fibers can develop maximum tension more rapidly than slow-twitch fibers can, and their maximum tension is greater. However, their dependence on anaerobic energy leaves them vulnerable to an accumulation of lactic acid that causes them to fatigue quickly.

Figure 7.9 Slow- and fast-twitch fibers. If your muscles contain many slow-twitch fibers (dark color), you would probably do better at a sport like cross-country running. But if your muscles contain many fast-twitch fibers (light color), you would probably do better at a sport like weight lifting.

slow-twitch fibers

fast-twitch fibers

Slow-twitch muscle fiber
• is aerobic
• has steady power
• has endurance

Fast-twitch muscle fiber
• is anaerobic
• has explosive power
• fatigues easily

7.4 Skeletal Muscles of the Body

The human body has some 600 skeletal muscles, but this text will discuss only some of the most significant of these. First, let us consider certain basic principles of muscle contraction.

Basic Principles

When a muscle contracts, one bone remains fairly stationary, and the other one moves. The **origin** of a muscle is on the stationary bone, and the **insertion** of a muscle is on the bone that moves.

Frequently, a body part is moved by a group of muscles working together. Even so, one muscle does most of the work, and this muscle is called the **prime mover.** For example, in flexing the elbow, the prime mover is the biceps brachii (Fig. 7.10) The assisting muscles are called the **synergists.** The brachialis (see Fig. 7.12) is a synergist that helps the biceps brachii flex the elbow. A prime mover can have several synergists.

When muscles contract, they shorten. Therefore, muscles can only pull; they cannot push. However, muscles have **antagonists,** and antagonistic pairs work opposite one another to bring about movement in opposite directions. For example, the biceps brachii and the triceps brachii are antagonists; one flexes the forearm, and the other extends the forearm (Fig. 7.10). Later on in our discussion, we will encounter other antagonistic pairs.

Naming Muscles

When learning the names of muscles, considering what the name means will help you remember it. The names of the various skeletal muscles are often combinations of the following terms used to characterize muscles:

1. **Size.** For example, the *gluteus maximus* is the largest muscle that makes up the buttocks. The *gluteus minimus* is the smallest of the gluteal muscles. Other terms used to indicate size are vastus (huge), longus (long), and brevis (short).
2. **Shape.** For example, the *deltoid* is shaped like a delta, or triangle, while the *trapezius* is shaped like a trapezoid. Other terms used to indicate shape are latissimus (wide) and teres (round).
3. **Direction of fibers.** For example, the *rectus abdominis* is a longitudinal muscle of the abdomen (*rectus* means straight). The *orbicularis* is a circular muscle around the eye. Other terms used to indicate direction are transverse (across) and oblique (diagonal).
4. **Location.** For example, the *frontalis* overlies the frontal bone. The *external obliques* are located outside the internal obliques. Other terms used to indicate location are pectoralis (chest), gluteus (buttock), brachii (arm), and sub (beneath). You should also review these directional terms: anterior, posterior, lateral, medial, proximal, distal, superficial, and deep.

Figure 7.10 The origin of a muscle is on a bone that remains stationary, and the insertion of a muscle is on a bone that moves when a muscle contracts. Two of the muscles shown here are antagonistic. **a.** When the biceps brachii contracts, the lower arm flexes. **b.** When the triceps brachii contracts, the lower arm extends.

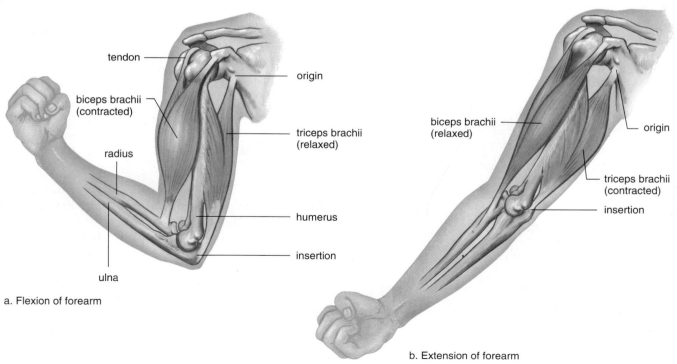

tendon — biceps brachii (contracted) — radius — ulna
origin — triceps brachii (relaxed) — humerus — insertion

a. Flexion of forearm

biceps brachii (relaxed) — origin — triceps brachii (contracted) — insertion

b. Extension of forearm

Figure 7.11 Anterior view of the body's superficial skeletal muscles.

- frontalis
- orbicularis oculi
- zygomaticus
- masseter
- orbicularis oris
- trapezius
- sternocleido-mastoid
- deltoid
- pectoralis major
- serratus anterior
- biceps brachii
- brachialis
- external oblique
- rectus abdominis
- sartorius
- rectus femoris
- quadriceps femoris group
- vastus medialis
- vastus lateralis
- pectineus
- adductor longus
- gracilis
- adductor group
- peroneus longus
- tibialis anterior
- extensor digitorum
- gastrocnemius

Figure 7.12 Posterior view of the body's superficial skeletal muscles.

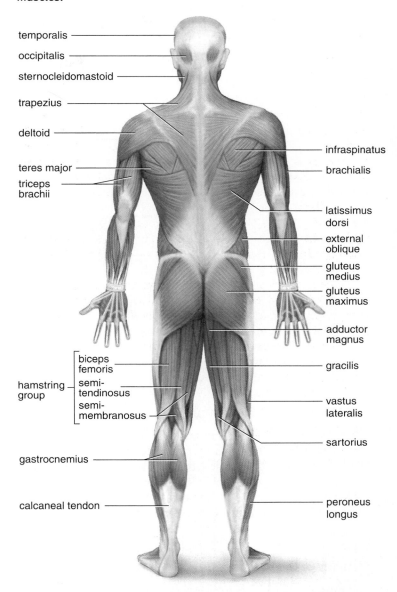

- temporalis
- occipitalis
- sternocleidomastoid
- trapezius
- deltoid
- teres major
- triceps brachii
- infraspinatus
- brachialis
- latissimus dorsi
- external oblique
- gluteus medius
- gluteus maximus
- adductor magnus
- biceps femoris
- hamstring group
- semi-tendinosus
- semi-membranosus
- gracilis
- vastus lateralis
- sartorius
- gastrocnemius
- calcaneal tendon
- peroneus longus

5. **Attachment.** For example, the *sternocleidomastoid* is attached to the sternum, clavicle, and mastoid process. The *brachioradialis* is attached to the brachium (arm) and the radius.

6. **Number of attachments.** For example, the biceps brachii has two attachments, or origins (and is located on the arm). The quadriceps femoris has four origins (and is located on the anterior femur).

7. **Action.** For example, the *extensor digitorum* extends the fingers or digits. The *adductor magnus* is a large muscle that adducts the thigh. Other terms used to indicate action are flexor (to flex), masseter (to chew), and levator (to lift).

With every muscle you learn, try to understand its name.

Skeletal Muscle Groups

In our discussion, the muscles of the body (Figs. 7.11 and 7.12) will be grouped according to their location and their action. After you understand the meaning of a muscle's name, try to correlate its name with the muscle's location and the action it performs. Knowing the origin and insertion will also help you remember what the muscle does. Why? Because the insertion is on the bone that moves. You should review the various body movements listed and illustrated in Chapter 6 (see page 106). Only then will you be able to understand the actions of the muscles listed in Tables 7.2–7.5. Scientific terminology is necessary because it allows all persons to know the exact action being described for that muscle. Also review the meaning of the terms *arm* and *leg*.

Figure 7.13 Muscles of the head and neck. Some of these muscles account for our facial expressions and the ability to chew our food; others move the head.

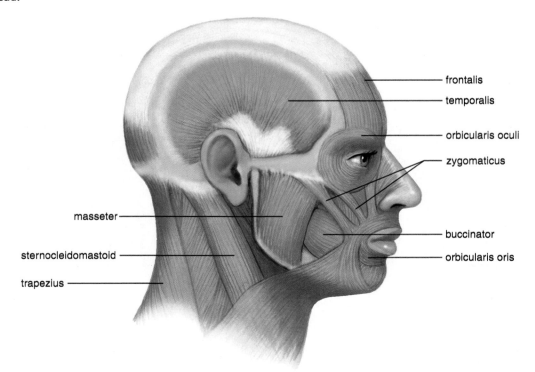

frontalis

temporalis

orbicularis oculi

zygomaticus

buccinator

orbicularis oris

masseter

sternocleidomastoid

trapezius

Muscles of the Head

The muscles of the head and neck are the first group of muscles we will study. The muscles of the head and neck are illustrated in Figure 7.13 and listed in Table 7.2. The muscles of the head are responsible for facial expression and mastication (chewing). One muscle of the head and several muscles of the neck allow us to swallow. The muscles of the neck also move the head.

Muscles of Facial Expression

The muscles of facial expression are located on the scalp and face. These muscles are unusual in that they insert into and move the skin. Therefore, we expect them to move the skin and not a bone. The use of these muscles communicates to others whether we are surprised, angry, fearful, happy, and so forth.

Frontalis lies over the frontal bone; it raises the eyebrows and wrinkles the brow. Frequent use results in furrowing of the forehead.

Orbicularis oculi is a ringlike band of muscle that encircles (forms an orbit about) the eye. It causes the eye to close or blink, and is responsible for "crow's feet" at the eye corners.

Orbicularis oris encircles the mouth and is used to pucker the lips, as in forming a kiss. Frequent use results in lines about the mouth.

Buccinator muscles are located in the cheek areas. When a buccinator contracts, the cheek is compressed, as when a person whistles or blows out air. Therefore, this muscle is called the "trumpeter's muscle." Important to everyday life, the buccinator helps hold food in contact with the teeth during chewing. It is also used in swallowing, as discussed next.

Zygomaticus extends from each zygomatic arch (cheekbone) to the corners of the mouth. It raises the corners of the mouth when a person smiles.

Muscles of Mastication

The muscles of mastication are used when we chew food or bite something. Although there are four pairs of muscles for chewing, only two pairs are superficial and shown in Figure 7.13. As you might expect, both of these muscles insert on the mandible.

Each **masseter** has its origin on the zygomatic arch and its insertion on the mandible. The masseter is a muscle of mastication (chewing) because it is a prime mover for elevating the mandible.

Each **temporalis** is a fan-shaped muscle that overlies the temporal bone. It is also a prime mover for elevating the mandible. The masseter and temporalis are synergists.

Table 7.2   Muscles of the Head and Neck

Name	Function	Origin/Insertion
Muscles of Facial Expression		
Frontalis (frun-ta'lis)	Raises eyebrows	Cranial fascia/skin and muscles around eye
Orbicularis oculi (or-bik'yū-lā-ris ok'yū-li)	Closes eye	Maxillary and frontal bones/skin around eye
Orbicularis oris (or-bik'yū-lā-ris o'ris)	Closes and protrudes lips	Muscles near the mouth/skin around mouth
Buccinator (buk'si-na"tor)	Compresses cheeks inward	Outer surfaces of maxilla and mandible/orbicularis oris
Zygomaticus (zi"go-mat'ik-us)	Raises corner of mouth	Zygomatic bone/skin and muscle around mouth
Muscles of Mastication		
Masseter (mas-se'ter)	Closes jaw	Zygomatic arch/mandible
Temporalis (tem-po-ra'lis)	Closes jaw	Temporal bone/mandibular coronoid process
Muscles That Move the Head		
Sternocleidomastoid (ster"no-kli"do-mas'toid)	Flexes head and rotates head	Sternum and clavicle/mastoid process of temporal bone
Trapezius (truh-pe'ze-us)	Extends head and adducts scapula	Occipital bone and all cervical and thoracic vertebrae/spine of scapula and clavicle

Muscles of the Neck

Deep muscles of the neck (not illustrated) are responsible for swallowing. Superficial muscles of the neck move the head (see Table 7.2 and Figure 7.13).

Swallowing

Swallowing is an important activity that begins after we chew our food. First, the tongue (a muscle) and the buccinators squeeze the food back along the roof of the mouth toward the pharynx. An important bone that functions in swallowing is the hyoid (see page 92). The hyoid is the only bone in the body that does not articulate with another bone.

Muscles that lie superior to the hyoid, called the suprahyoid muscles, and muscles that lie inferior to the hyoid, called the infrahyoid muscles, move the hyoid. These muscles lie deep in the neck and are not illustrated in Figure 7.13. The suprahyoid muscles pull the hyoid forward and upward toward the mandible. Because the hyoid is attached to the larynx, this pulls the larynx upward and forward. The epiglottis now lies over the glottis and closes the respiratory passages. Small palatini muscles (not illustrated) pull the soft palate backward, closing off the nasal passages. Pharyngeal constrictor muscles (not illustrated) push the bolus of food into the pharynx, which widens when the suprahyoid muscles move the hyoid. The hyoid bone and larynx are returned to their original positions by the infrahyoid muscles. Notice that the suprahyoid and infrahyoid muscles are antagonists.

Muscles That Move the Head

Two muscles in the neck are of particular interest: The sternocleidomastoid and the trapezius are listed in Table 7.2 and illustrated in Figure 7.13. Recall that *flexion* is a movement that closes the angle at a joint and *extension* is a movement that increases the angle at a joint. Recall that *abduction* is a movement away from the midline of the body, while *adduction* is a movement toward the midline. Also, *rotation* is the movement of a part around its own axis.

Sternocleidomastoid muscles ascend obliquely from their origin on the sternum and clavicle to their insertion on the mastoid process of the temporal bone. Which part of the body do you expect them to move? When both sternocleidomastoid muscles contract, flexion of the head occurs. When only one contracts, the head turns to the opposite side. If you turn your head to the right, you can see how the left sternocleidomastoid shortens, pulling the head to the right.

Each **trapezius** muscle is triangular, but together, they take on a diamond or trapezoid shape. The origin of a trapezius is at the base of the skull. Its insertion is on a clavicle and scapula. You would expect the trapezius muscles to move the scapulae, and they do. They adduct the scapulae when the shoulders are shrugged or pulled back. The trapezius muscles also help extend the head, however. The prime movers for head extension are actually deep to the trapezius and not illustrated in Figure 7.13.

Figure 7.14 Muscles of the anterior shoulder and trunk. The right pectoralis major is removed to show the deep muscles of the chest.

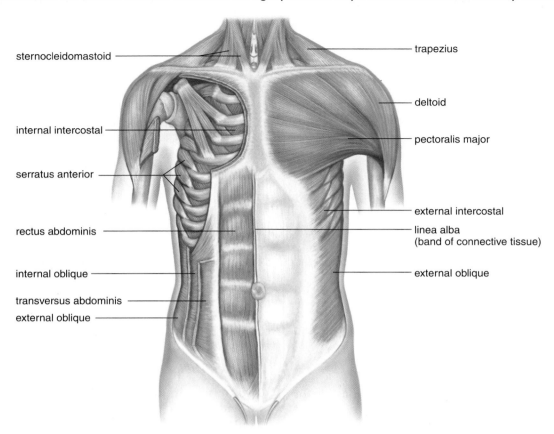

sternocleidomastoid

trapezius

internal intercostal

deltoid

serratus anterior

pectoralis major

rectus abdominis

external intercostal

linea alba
(band of connective tissue)

internal oblique

external oblique

transversus abdominis

external oblique

Table 7.3	Muscles of the Trunk	
Name	**Function**	**Origin/Insertion**
Muscles of the Trunk		
External intercostals	Elevate rib cage for inspiration	Superior rib/inferior rib
Internal intercostals	Depress rib cage for expiration	Inferior rib/superior rib
External oblique	Tenses abdominal wall; lateral rotation of trunk	Lower eight ribs/iliac crest
Internal oblique	Tenses abdominal wall; lateral rotation of trunk	Iliac crest/lower three ribs
Transversus abdominis	Tenses abdominal wall	Lower six ribs/pubis
Rectus abdominis	Flexes and rotates the vertebral column	Pubis, pubic symphysis/xiphoid process of sternum, fifth to seventh costal cartilages

Muscles of the Trunk

The muscles of the trunk are listed in Table 7.3 and illustrated in Figure 7.14. The muscles of the thoracic wall are primarily involved in breathing. The muscles of the abdominal wall protect and support the organs within the abdominal cavity.

Muscles of the Thoracic Wall

External intercostal muscles occur between the ribs; they originate on a superior rib and insert on an inferior rib.

These muscles elevate the rib cage during the inspiration phase of breathing.

The **diaphragm** is a dome-shaped muscle that, as you know, separates the thoracic cavity from the abdominal cavity (see Fig. 1.5). Contraction of the diaphragm also assists inspiration.

Internal intercostal muscles originate on an inferior rib and insert on a superior rib. These muscles depress the rib cage and contract only during a forced expiration. Normal expiration does not require muscular action.

Figure 7.15 Muscles of the posterior shoulder. The right trapezius is removed to show deep muscles that move the scapula and the rotator cuff muscles.

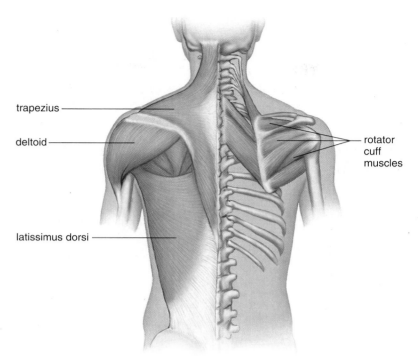

trapezius

deltoid

rotator cuff muscles

latissimus dorsi

Muscles of the Abdominal Wall

The abdominal wall has no bony reinforcement (Fig. 7.14). The wall is strengthened by four pairs of muscles that run at angles to one another. The external and internal obliques and the transversus abdominis occur laterally, but the fasciae of these muscle pairs meet at the midline of the body, forming a tendinous area called the linea alba. The rectus abdominis is a superficial medial pair of muscles.

All of the muscle pairs of the abdominal wall compress the abdominal cavity and support and protect the organs within the abdominal cavity.

External and **internal obliques** occur on a slant and are at right angles to one another between the lower ribs and the pelvic girdle. The external obliques are superior to the internal obliques. These muscles also aid trunk rotation and lateral flexion.

Transversus abdominis, deep to the obliques, extends horizontally across the abdomen. The obliques and the transversus abdominis are synergistic muscles.

Rectus abdominis has a straplike appearance but takes its name from the fact that it runs straight (*rectus* means straight) up from the pubic bones to the ribs and sternum. These muscles also help flex and rotate the lumbar portion of the vertebral column.

Muscles of the Shoulder

Muscles of the shoulder are shown in Figures 7.14 and 7.15. They are also listed in Table 7.4 on page 130. The muscles of the shoulder attach the scapula to the thorax and move the scapula; they also attach the humerus to the scapula and move the arm.

Muscles That Move the Scapula

Of the muscles that move the scapula, we have already discussed the trapezius (see page 127).

Serratus anterior is located below the axilla (armpit) on the lateral chest. It runs between the upper ribs and the scapula. It depresses the scapula and pulls it forward, as when we push something. It also helps to elevate the arm above the horizontal level.

Muscles That Move the Arm

Deltoid is a large, fleshy, triangular muscle (*deltoid* in Greek means triangular) that covers the shoulder and causes a bulge in the arm where it meets the shoulder. It runs from both the clavicle and the scapula of the pectoral girdle to the humerus. This muscle abducts the arm to the horizontal position.

Table 7.4   Muscles of the Shoulder and Upper Limb

Name	Function	Origin/Insertion
Muscles That Move the Scapula and Arm		
Serratus anterior	Depresses scapula and pulls it forward; elevates arm above horizontal	Upper nine ribs/vertebral border of scapula
Deltoid	Abducts arm to horizontal	Acromion process, spine of scapula, and clavicle/deltoid tuberosity of humerus
Pectoralis major	Flexes and adducts arm	Clavicle, sternum, second to sixth costal cartilages/intertubular groove of humerus
Latissmus dorsi	Extends or adducts arm	Iliac crest/intertubular groove of humerus
Rotator cuff	Angular and rotational movements of arm	Scapula/humerus
Muscles That Move the Forearm		
Biceps brachii	Flexes forearm, and supinates hand	Scapula/radial tuberosity
Triceps brachii	Extends forearm	Scapula, proximal humerus/olecranon process of ulna
Brachialis	Flexes forearm	Anterior humerus/coronoid process of ulna
Muscles That Move the Hand and Fingers		
Flexor carpi and extensor carpi	Move wrist and hand	Humerus/carpals and metacarpals
Flexor digitorum and extensor digitorum	Move fingers	Humerus, radius, ulna/phalanges

Pectoralis major (Fig. 7.14) is a large anterior muscle of the upper chest. It originates from a clavicle, but also from the sternum and ribs. It inserts on the humerus. The pectoralis major flexes the arm (raises it anteriorly) and adducts the arm, pulling it toward the chest.

Latissimus dorsi (Fig. 7.15) is a large, wide, triangular muscle of the back. This muscle originates from the lower spine and sweeps upward to insert on the humerus. The latissimus dorsi extends and adducts the arm (brings it down from a raised position). This muscle is very important for swimming, rowing, and climbing a rope.

Rotator cuff (Fig. 7.15). This group of muscles is so named because their tendons help form a cuff over the proximal humerus. These muscles lie deep to those already mentioned, and they are synergists to them.

Muscles of the Arm

The muscles of the arm move the forearm. They are illustrated in Figure 7.16 and listed in Table 7.4.

Biceps brachii is a muscle of the proximal anterior arm (Fig. 7.16a) that is familiar because it bulges when the forearm is flexed. It also supinates the hand when a doorknob is turned or the cap of a jar is unscrewed. The name of the muscle refers to its two heads that attach to the scapula, where it originates. The biceps brachii inserts on the radius.

Brachialis originates on the humerus and inserts on the ulna. It is a muscle of the distal anterior humerus and lies deep to the biceps brachii. It is synergistic to the biceps brachii in flexing the forearm.

Triceps brachii is the only muscle of the posterior arm (Fig. 7.16b). It has three heads that attach to the scapula and humerus, and it inserts on the ulna. The triceps extends the forearm. It is sometimes called the "boxer's muscle" because it extends the elbow when a punch is thrown. The triceps is also used in tennis to do a backhand volley.

Muscles of the Forearm

The muscles of the forearm move the hand and fingers. They are illustrated in Figure 7.16c,d and listed in Table 7.4. Note that extensors of the wrists and fingers are on the lateral forearm and flexors are on the medial forearm.

Flexor carpi and **extensor carpi** muscles originate on the bones of the forearm and insert on the bones of the hand. The flexor carpi flex the wrists and hands, and the extensor carpi extend the wrists and hands.

Flexor digitorum and **extensor digitorum** muscles also originate on the bones of the forearm and insert on the bones of the hand. The flexor digitorum flexes the wrist and fingers, and the extensor digitorum extends the wrist and fingers (i.e., the digits).

Figure 7.16 **a.** Muscles of the anterior arm and shoulder. **b.** Muscles of the posterior arm and shoulder. **c.** Muscles of the anterior forearm. **d.** Muscles of the posterior forearm.

trapezius

clavicle

deltoid

medial border of scapula

short head of biceps brachii

long head of biceps brachii

brachialis

a.

rotator cuff muscle

spine of scapula

deltoid

rotator cuff muscles

long head of triceps brachii

lateral head of triceps brachii

b.

biceps brachii

brachialis

extensor carpi

flexor carpi

c.

triceps brachii

flexor carpi

extensor carpi

extensor digitorum

d.

Table 7.5 — Muscles of the Hip and Lower Limb

Name	Function	Origin/Insertion
Muscles That Move the Thigh		
Iliopsoas (il'e-o-so'us)	Flexes thigh	Lumbar vertebrae, ilium/lesser trochanter of femur
Gluteus maximus	Extends thigh	Posterior ilium, sacrum/proximal femur
Gluteus medius	Abducts thigh	Ilium/greater trochanter of femur
Adductor group	Adducts thigh	Pubis, ischium/femur and tibia
Muscles That Move the Leg		
Quadriceps femoris group	Extends leg	Ilium, femur/patellar tendon that continues as a ligament to tibial tuberosity
Sartorius	Flexes, abducts, and rotates leg laterally	Ilium/medial tibia
Hamstring group	Flexes and rotates leg medially, and extends thigh	Ischial tuberosity/lateral and medial tibia
Muscles That Move the Ankle and Foot		
Gastrocnemius (gas"trok-ne'me-us)	Plantar flexion and eversion of foot	Condyles of femur/calcaneus by way of Achilles tendon
Tibialis anterior (tib"e-a'lis an-te're-or)	Dorsiflexion and inversion of foot	Condyles of tibia/tarsal and metatarsal bones
Peroneus group (per"o-ne-us)	Plantar flexion and eversion of foot	Fibula/tarsal and metatarsal bones
Flexor and extensor digitorum longus	Moves toes	Tibia, fibula/phalanges

Muscles of the Hip and Lower Limb

The muscles of the hip and lower limb are listed in Table 7.5 and shown in Figures 7.17 to 7.20. These muscles, particularly those of the hips and thigh, tend to be large and heavy because they are used to move the entire weight of the body and to resist the force of gravity. Therefore, they are important for movement and balance.

Muscles That Move the Thigh

The muscles that move the thigh have at least one origin on the pelvic girdle and insert on the femur. Notice that the iliopsoas is an anterior muscle that moves the thigh, while the gluteal muscles ("gluts") are posterior muscles that move the thigh. The adductor muscles are medial muscles (Fig. 7.17 and Fig. 7.18). Before studying the action of these muscles, review the movement of the hip joint when the thigh flexes, extends, abducts, and adducts.

Iliopsoas (includes psoas major and iliacus) originates at the ilium and the bodies of the lumbar vertebrae, and inserts on the femur anteriorly (Fig. 7.17). This muscle is the prime mover for flexing the thigh and also the trunk, as when we bow. As the major flexor of the thigh, the iliopsoas is important to the process of walking. It also helps prevent the trunk from falling backward when a person is standing erect.

The gluteal muscles form the buttocks. We will consider only the gluteus maximus and the gluteus medius, both of which are illustrated in Figure 7.18.

Gluteus maximus is the largest muscle in the body and covers a large part of the buttock (*gluteus* means buttocks in Greek). It originates at the ilium and sacrum, and inserts on the femur. The gluteus maximus is a prime mover of thigh extension, as when a person is walking, climbing stairs, or jumping from a crouched position. Notice that the iliopsoas and the gluteus maximus are antagonistic muscles.

Gluteus medius lies partly behind the gluteus maximus (Fig. 7.18). It runs between the ilium and the femur, and functions to abduct the thigh. The gluteus maximus assists the gluteus medius in this function. Therefore, they are synergistic muscles.

Adductor group muscles (pectineus, adductor longus, adductor magnus, gracilis) are located on the medial thigh (Fig. 7.17). All of these muscles originate from the pubis and ischium, and insert on the femur; the deep adductor magnus is shown in Figure 7.17. Adductor muscles adduct the thigh—that is, they lower the thigh sideways from a horizontal position. Because they press the thighs inward, these are the muscles that keep a rider on a horse. Notice that the gluts and the adductor group are antagonistic muscles.

Figure 7.17 Muscles of the anterior right hip and thigh.

- iliopsoas
  - psoas major
  - iliacus
- sartorius
- quadriceps femoris group
  - rectus femoris
  - vastus lateralis
  - vastus medialis
- patella
- pectineus
- adductor longus
- adductor magnus
- gracilis
- adductor group

Figure 7.18 Muscles of the posterior right hip and thigh.

- gluteus medius
- gluteus maximus
- adductor magnus
- gracilis
- vastus lateralis covered by fascia
- hamstring group
  - semi-tendinosus
  - biceps femoris
  - semimem-branosus
- sartorius
- gastrocnemius

Muscles That Move the Leg

The muscles that move the leg originate from the pelvic girdle or femur and insert on the tibia. They are listed in Table 7.5 and illustrated in Figures 7.17 and 7.18. Before studying these muscles, review the movement of the knee when the leg extends and when it flexes.

Quadriceps femoris group (rectus femoris, vastus lateralis, vastus medialis, vastus intermedius), also known as the "quads," is found on the anterior and medial thigh. The rectus femoris, which originates from the ilium, is external to the vastus intermedius, and therefore the vastus intermedius is not shown in Figure 7.17. These muscles are the primary extensors of the leg, as when you kick a ball by straightening your knee.

Sartorius is a long, straplike muscle that has its origin on the iliac spine and then goes across the anterior thigh to insert on the medial side of the knee (Fig. 7.17). Because this muscle crosses both the hip and knee joint, it acts on the thigh in addition to the leg. The insertion of the sartorius is such that it flexes both the leg and the thigh. It also rotates the thigh laterally, enabling us to sit cross-legged, as tailors were accustomed to do in another era. Therefore, it is sometimes called the "tailor's muscle," and in fact, *sartor* means tailor in Latin.

Hamstring group (biceps femoris, semimembranosus, semitendinosus) is located on the posterior thigh (Fig. 7.18). Notice that these muscles also cross the hip and knee joint because they have origins on the ischium and insert on the tibia. They flex and rotate the leg medially, but they also extend the thigh. Their strong tendons can be felt behind the knee. These same tendons are present in hogs and were used by butchers as strings to hang up hams for smoking—hence, the name. Notice that the quadriceps femoris group and the hamstring group are antagonistic muscles in that the quads extend the leg and the hamstrings flex the leg.

Figure 7.19 Muscles of the anterior right leg.

patella

patellar ligament

tibialis anterior

peroneus longus

extensor digitorum longus

peroneus brevis

gastrocnemius

tibia

Muscles That Move the Ankle and Foot

Muscles that move the ankle and foot are shown in Figures 7.19 and 7.20.

Gastrocnemius is a muscle of the posterior leg, where it forms a large part of the calf. It arises from the femur; distally, the muscle joins the strong calcaneal tendon, which attaches to the calcaneus bone (heel). The gastrocnemius is a powerful plantar flexor of the foot that aids in pushing the body forward during walking or running. It is sometimes called the "toe dancer's muscle" because it allows a person to stand on tiptoe.

Tibialis anterior is a long, spindle-shaped muscle of the anterior leg. It arises from the surface of the tibia and attaches to the bones of the ankle and foot. Contraction of this muscle causes dorsiflexion and inversion of the foot.

Peroneus muscles (peroneus longus, peroneus brevis) are found on the lateral side of the leg, connecting the fibula to the metatarsal bones of the foot. These muscles evert the foot and also help bring about plantar flexion.

Figure 7.20 Muscles of the lateral right leg.

biceps femoris

vastus lateralis

gastrocnemius

head of fibula

tibialis anterior

peroneus longus

extensor digitorum longus

peroneus brevis

calcaneal tendon

peroneus tertius

Flexor (not shown) and **extensor digitorum longus** muscles are found on the lateral and posterior portion of the leg. They arise mostly from the tibia and insert on the toes. They flex and extend the toes, respectively, and assist in other movements of the feet.

7.5 Effects of Aging

Muscle mass and strength tend to decrease as people age. How much of this is due to lack of exercise and a poor diet has yet to be determined. Deteriorated muscle elements are replaced initially by connective tissue and, eventually, by fat. With age, degenerative changes take place in the mitochondria, and endurance decreases. Also, changes in the nervous and cardiovascular systems adversely affect the structure and function of muscles.

Muscle mass and strength can improve remarkably if elderly people undergo a training program. Exercise at any age appears to stimulate muscle buildup. As discussed in the Medical Focus on page 135, exercise has many other benefits as well. For example, exercise improves the cardiovascular system and reduces the risk of diabetes and glycation. During glycation, excess glucose molecules stick to body proteins so that the proteins no longer have their normal structure and cannot function properly. Exercise burns glucose and, in this way, helps prevent muscle deterioration.

Benefits of Exercise

Exercise programs improve muscular strength, muscular endurance, and flexibility. Muscular strength is the force a muscle group (or muscle) can exert against a resistance in one maximal effort. Muscular endurance is judged by the ability of a muscle to contract repeatedly or to sustain a contraction for an extended period. Flexibility is tested by observing the range of motion about a joint.

As muscular strength improves, the overall size of the muscle, as well as the number of muscle fibers and myofibrils in the muscle, increases. The total amount of protein, the number of capillaries, and the amounts of connective tissue, including tissue found in tendons and ligaments, also increase. Physical training with weights can improve muscular strength and endurance in all adults, regardless of their age. Over time, increased muscle strength promotes strong bones.

A surprising finding, however, is that health benefits also accompany less strenuous programs, such as those described in Table 7A. A study of 12,000 men by Dr. Arthur Leon at the University of Minnesota showed that even moderate exercise lowered the risk of a heart attack by one-third. People with arthritis reported much less pain, swelling, fatigue, and depression after only four months of attending a twice-weekly, low-impact aerobics class. Increasing daily activity by walking to the corner store instead of driving and by taking the stairs instead of the elevator can improve a person's health.

The benefits of exercise are most apparent with regard to cardiovascular health. Brisk walking for 2.5–4 hours a week can raise the blood levels of high-density lipoprotein (HDL), a chemical that promotes healthy blood vessels (see Chapter 12). Exercise also helps prevent osteoporosis, a condition in which the bones are weak and tend to break. The stronger the bones are when a person is young, the less chance of osteoporosis as a person ages. Exercise promotes the activity of osteoblasts (as opposed to osteocytes) in young people, as well as older people. An increased activity level can also keep off unwanted pounds, which is a worthwhile goal because added body weight contributes to numerous conditions, such as type II diabetes (see page 197). Increased muscle activity is also helpful by causing glucose to be transported into muscle cells and making the body less dependent on the presence of insulin.

People in chronic pain are often diagnosed as having **fibromyalgia**, characterized by achy pain, tenderness, and stiffness of muscles. Substance P has been found in the bloodstream of these patients. Exercise (more frequent and longer periods of exercise, not increased intensity) decreases the concentration of substance P. Stretching exercises, such as yoga, and massages (two to three a week) also decrease the amount of substance P. More information on this subject is currently being sought.

Cancer prevention and early detection involve eating properly, not smoking, avoiding cancer-causing chemicals and radiation, undergoing appropriate medical screening tests, and knowing the early warning signs of cancer. However, evidence indicates that exercise also helps prevent certain kinds of cancer. Studies show that people who exercise are less likely to develop colon, breast, cervical, uterine, and ovarian cancer.

Table 7A A Checklist for Staying Fit

Children, 7–12	Teenagers, 13–18	Adults, 19–55	Seniors, 56 and Up
Vigorous activity 1–2 hours daily	Vigorous activity 1 hour 3–5 days a week; otherwise, $\frac{1}{2}$ hour daily moderate activity	Vigorous activity 1 hour 3 days a week; otherwise, $\frac{1}{2}$ hour daily moderate activity	Moderate exercise 1 hour daily 3 days a week; otherwise, $\frac{1}{2}$ hour daily moderate activity
Free play	Build muscle with calisthenics	Exercise to prevent lower back pain: aerobics, stretching, yoga	Take a daily walk
Build motor skills through team sports, dance, swimming	Do aerobic exercise to control buildup of fat cells	Take active vacations: hike, bicycle, cross-country ski	Do daily stretching exercises
Encourage more exercise outside of physical education classes	Pursue tennis, swimming, horseback riding—sports that can be enjoyed for a lifetime	Find exercise partners: join a running club, bicycle club, outing group	Learn a new sport or activity: golf, fishing, ballroom dancing
Initiate family outings: bowling, boating, camping, hiking	Continue team sports, dancing, hiking, swimming		Try low-impact aerobics. Before undertaking new exercises, consult your doctor

7.6 Homeostasis

The illustration in Human Systems Work Together on page 137 tells how the muscular system works with other systems of the body to maintain homeostasis.

Cardiac muscle contraction accounts for the heartbeat, which creates blood pressure, the force that propels blood in the arteries and arterioles. The walls of the arteries and arterioles contain smooth muscle. Constriction of arteriole walls is regulated to help maintain blood pressure. Arterioles branch into the capillaries where exchange takes place that creates and cleanses tissue fluid. Blood and tissue fluid are the internal environment of the body, and without cardiac and smooth muscle contraction, blood would never reach the capillaries for exchange to take place. Blood is returned to the heart in cardiovascular veins, and excess tissue fluid is returned to the cardiovascular system within lymphatic vessels. Skeletal muscle contraction presses on the cardiovascular veins and lymphatic vessels, and this creates the pressure that moves fluids in both types of vessels. Without the return of blood to the heart, circulation would stop, and without the return of lymph to the blood vessels, normal blood pressure could not be maintained.

The contraction of sphincters composed of smooth muscle fibers temporarily prevents the flow of blood into a capillary. This is an important homeostatic mechanism because in times of emergency it is more important, for example, for blood to be directed to the skeletal muscles than to the tissues of the digestive tract. Smooth muscle contraction also accounts for peristalsis, the process that moves food along the digestive tract. Without this action, food would never reach all the organs of the digestive tract where digestion releases nutrients that enter the bloodstream. Smooth muscle contraction assists the voiding of urine, which is necessary for ridding the body of metabolic wastes and for regulating the blood volume, salt concentration, and pH of internal fluids.

Skeletal muscles protect internal organs, and their strength protects joints by stabilizing their movements. Skeletal muscle contraction raises the rib cage and lowers the diaphragm during the active phase of breathing. As we breathe, oxygen enters the blood and is delivered to the tissues, including the muscles, where ATP is produced in mitochondria with heat as a by-product. The heat produced by skeletal muscle contraction allows the body temperature to remain within the normal range for human beings.

Finally, skeletal muscle contraction moves bones and allows us to perform those daily activities necessary to our health and benefit. Although it may seem as if movement of our limbs does not affect homeostasis, it does so by allowing us to relocate our bodies to keep the external environment within favorable limits for our existence.

Muscular Disorders

When spasms or injuries occur, homeostasis is challenged, and when disease is present, homeostasis may be overcome to the point of death.

Spasms and Injuries

Spasms are sudden and involuntary muscular contractions, most often accompanied by pain. Spasms can occur in both smooth and skeletal muscles. A spasm of the intestinal tract is a type of colic sometimes called a "bellyache." Multiple spasms of skeletal muscles are called a seizure or convulsion. Cramps are strong painful spasms, especially of the leg and foot, usually due to strenuous activity. Cramps can even occur when sleeping after a strenuous workout. Facial tics, such as periodic eye blinking, head turning, or grimacing, are spasms that can be controlled voluntarily but only with great effort.

A **strain** is the overstretching of a muscle near a joint. A **sprain** is the twisting of a joint, leading to swelling and to injury not only of muscles but also of ligaments, tendons, blood vessels, and nerves. The ankle is often subject to sprains.

Myalgia refers to inflammation of muscle tissue. **Tendinitis** is inflammation of a tendon due to the strain of repeated athletic activity. The tendons most commonly affected are those associated with the shoulder, elbow, hip, and knee.

Diseases

In persons who have not been properly immunized, the toxin of the tetanus bacterium can cause muscles to lock in a tetanic contraction. A rigidly locked jaw is one of the first signs of an infection known as **tetanus.** Like other bacterial infections, tetanus is curable with the administration of an antibiotic.

Muscular dystrophy is a broad term applied to a group of disorders characterized by progressive degeneration and weakening of muscles. As muscle fibers die, fat and connective tissue take their place. Duchenne muscular dystrophy, the most common type, is inherited through a flawed gene carried by the mother. It is now known that the lack of a protein called dystrophin causes the condition. When dystrophin is absent, calcium leaks into the cell and activates an enzyme that dissolves muscle fibers. In an attempt to treat the condition, muscles have been injected with immature muscle cells that do produce dystrophin.

Myasthenia gravis is an autoimmune disease characterized by weakness that especially affects the muscles of the eyelids, face, neck, and extremities. Muscle contraction is impaired because the immune system mistakenly produces antibodies that destroy acetylcholine receptors. In many cases, the first signs of the disease are drooping eyelids and double vision. Treatment includes drugs that are antagonistic to the enzyme acetylcholinesterase.

Human Systems Work Together

Integumentary System

Muscle contraction provides heat to warm skin. Muscle moves skin of face.

Skin protects muscles; rids the body of heat produced by muscle contraction.

How the Muscular System works with other body systems

Lymphatic System/Immunity

Skeletal muscle contraction moves lymph; physical exercise enhances immunity.

Lymphatic vessels pick up excess tissue fluid; immune system protects against infections.

Skeletal System

Muscle contraction causes bones to move joints; muscles help protect bones.

Bones provide attachment sites for muscles; store Ca^{2+} for muscle function.

Respiratory System

Muscle contraction assists breathing; physical exercise increases respiratory capacity.

Lungs provide oxygen for, and rid the body of, carbon dioxide from contracting muscles.

Nervous System

Muscle contraction moves eyes, permits speech, creates facial expressions.

Brain controls nerves that innervate muscles; receptors send sensory input from muscles to brain.

Digestive System

Smooth muscle contraction accounts for peristalsis; skeletal muscles support and help protect abdominal organs.

Digestive tract provides glucose for muscle activity; liver metabolizes lactic acid following anaerobic muscle activity.

Endocrine System

Muscles help protect glands.

Androgens promote growth of skeletal muscle; epinephrine stimulates heart and constricts blood vessels.

Urinary System

Smooth muscle contraction assists voiding of urine; skeletal muscles support and help protect urinary organs.

Kidneys maintain blood levels of Na^+, K^+, and Ca^{2+}, which are needed for muscle innervation, and eliminate creatinine, a muscle waste.

Cardiovascular System

Muscle contraction keeps blood moving in heart and blood vessels.

Blood vessels deliver nutrients and oxygen to muscles, carry away wastes.

Reproductive System

Muscle contraction occurs during orgasm and moves gametes; abdominal and uterine muscle contraction occurs during childbirth.

Androgens promote growth of skeletal muscle.

Selected New Terms

Basic Key Terms

actin (ak'tin), p. 116

all-or-none law, p. 122

antagonist (an-tag'o-nist), p. 124

cardiac muscle (kar'de-ak mus'el), p. 114

creatine phosphate (kre'uh-tin fos'fāt), p. 120

insertion (in-ser'shun), p. 124

motor unit (mo'tor yū'nit), p. 122

muscle fiber (mus'el fi'ber), p. 114

muscle twitch (mus'el twich), p. 122

myofibril (mi"o-fi'bril), p. 116

myoglobin (mi"o-glo'bin), p. 116

myosin (mi'o-sin), p. 116

neuromuscular junction (nu"ro-mus'kyū-ler junk'shun), p. 118

origin (or'ĭ-jin), p. 124

oxygen deficit (ok'sĭ-jen def'ĭ-sit), p. 120

prime mover (prīm mu'ver), p. 124

recruitment (re-krūt'ment), p. 123

sarcomere (sar'ko-mēr), p. 116

skeletal muscle (skel'ĕ-tal mus'el), p. 114

sliding filament theory (sli'ding fil'uh-ment the'o-re), p. 116

smooth muscle (smūth mus'el), p. 114

synergist (sin'er-jist), p. 124

T (transverse) tubules (tranz-vers' tu'byūl), p. 116

tendon (ten'don), p. 115

tone (tōn), p. 123

Clinical Key Terms

atrophy (at'ro-fe), p. 123

hypertrophy (hi-per'tro-fe), p. 123

lockjaw (lok'jaw), p. 136

muscular dystrophy (mus'kyū-ler dis'trĕ-fe), p. 136

myalgia (mi-al'juh), p. 136

myasthenia gravis (mi"as-the'ne-uh grah'vis), p. 136

spasm (spazm), p. 136

sprain (sprān), p. 136

strain (strān), p. 136

tendinitis (ten"dĕ-ni'tis), p. 136

tetanus (tet'uh-nus), p. 136

Summary

7.1 Functions and Types of Muscles

A. Muscular tissue is either smooth, cardiac, or skeletal. Skeletal muscles have tubular, multinucleated, and striated fibers that contract voluntarily.

B. Skeletal muscles support the body, make bones move, help maintain a constant body temperature, assist movement in cardiovascular and lymphatic vessels, and help protect internal organs and stabilize joints.

7.2 Microscopic Anatomy and Contraction of Skeletal Muscle

A. The sarcolemma, which extends into a muscle fiber, forms T tubules; the sarcoplasmic reticulum has calcium storage sites. The placement of actin and myosin in the contractile myofibrils accounts for the striations of skeletal muscle fibers.

B. Skeletal muscle innervation occurs at neuromuscular junctions. Impulses travel down the tubules of the T system and cause the release of calcium from calcium storage sites.

The presence of calcium and ATP in muscle cells prompts actin myofilaments to slide past myosin myofilaments, shortening the length of the sarcomere.

C. ATP, required for muscle contraction, can be generated by way of creatine phosphate breakdown and fermentation. Lactic acid from fermentation represents an oxygen deficit, because oxygen is required to metabolize this product. Cellular respiration, an aerobic process, is the best source of ATP.

7.3 Muscle Responses

A. In the laboratory, muscle fibers obey the all-or-none law, but whole muscles do not. The occurrence of a muscle twitch, summation, or tetanic contraction depends on the frequency with which a muscle is stimulated.

B. In the body, muscle fibers belong to motor units that obey the all-or-none law. The strength of muscle contraction depends on the

recruitment of motor units. A muscle has tone because some fibers are always contracting.

7.4 Skeletal Muscles of the Body

A. When muscles cooperate to achieve movement, some act as prime movers, others as synergists, and still others as antagonists.

B. The skeletal muscles of the body are divided into those that move: the head and neck (see Table 7.2); the trunk (see Table 7.3); the shoulder and arm (see Table 7.4); the forearm (see Table 7.4); the hand and fingers (see Table 7.4); the thigh (see Table 7.5); the leg (see Table 7.5); and the ankle and foot (see Table 7.5).

7.5 Effects of Aging

As we age, muscles become weaker, but exercise can help retain vigor.

7.6 Homeostasis

Smooth muscle contraction helps move the blood; cardiac muscle contraction pumps the blood. Skeletal muscle contraction produces heat and is needed for breathing.

1. Name and describe the three types of muscles, and give a general location for each type. (p. 114)
2. List and discuss five functions of muscles. (p. 115)
3. Describe the anatomy of a muscle, from the whole muscle to the myofilaments within a sarcomere. Name the layers of fascia that cover a skeletal muscle and divide the muscle interior. (pp. 116–17)
4. List the sequential events that occur after a nerve impulse reaches a muscle. (pp. 118–19)
5. How is ATP supplied to muscles? What is oxygen deficit? (pp. 120–21)
6. What is the all-or-none law? What is the difference between a single muscle twitch, summation, and a tetanic contraction? (p. 122)
7. What is muscle tone? How does muscle contraction affect muscle size? (p. 123)
8. Describe how muscles are attached to bones. Define the terms prime mover, synergist, and antagonist. (p. 124)
9. How do muscles get their names? Give an example for each characteristic used in naming muscles. (pp. 124–25)
10. Which of the muscles of the head are used for facial expression? Which are used for chewing? (p. 126)
11. Which muscles of the neck flex and extend the head? (p. 127)
12. What are the muscles of the thoracic wall? What are the muscles of the abdominal wall? (pp. 128–29)
13. Which of the muscles of the shoulder and upper limb move the arm and forearm, and what are their actions? Name the muscles that move the hand and fingers. (p. 130)
14. Which of the muscles of the hip move the thigh, and what are their actions? Which of the muscles of the thigh move the leg, and what are their actions? Which of the muscles of the leg move the feet? (pp. 132–34)

I. Fill in the blanks.

1. _____ muscle is uninucleated, nonstriated, and located in the walls of internal organs.
2. The fascia called _____ separates muscle fibers from one another within a fascicle.
3. When a muscle fiber contracts, an _____ myofilament slides past a myosin myofilament.
4. The energy molecule _____ is needed for muscle fiber contraction.
5. Whole muscles have _____, a condition in which some fibers are always contracted.
6. When muscles contract, the _____ does most of the work, but the _____ help.
7. The _____ is a muscle in the arm that has two origins.
8. The _____ acts as the origin of the latissimus dorsi, and the _____ acts as the insertion during most activities.

II. For questions 9–12, name the muscle indicated by the combination of origin and insertion shown.

	Origin	Insertion
9.	temporal bone	mandibular coronoid process
10.	scapula, clavicle	humerus
11.	scapula, proximal humerus	olecranon process of ulna
12.	posterior ilium, sacrum	proximal femur

III. Match the muscles in the key to the actions listed in questions 13–20.

Key:
   a. orbicularis oculi
   b. zygomaticus
   c. deltoid
   d. serratus anterior
   e. rectus abdominis
   f. iliopsoas
   g. gluteus maximus
   h. gastrocnemius

13. Allows a person to stand on tiptoe
14. Tenses abdominal wall
15. Abducts arm
16. Flexes thigh
17. Raises corner of mouth
18. Closes eyes

Consult Appendix B for help in pronouncing and analyzing the meaning of the terms that follow.

1. hyperkinesis (hi″per-ki-ne′sis)
2. dystrophy (dis′tro-fe)
3. electromyogram (e-lek″tro-mi′-o-gram)
4. menisectomy (men″i-sek′to-me)
5. tenorrhaphy (te-nor′uh-fe)
6. myatrophy (mi-at′ro-fe)
7. leiomyoma (li″o-mi-o′muh)
8. kinesiotherapy (ki-ne″se-o-thĕr′uh-pe)
9. myocardiopathy (mi″o-kar″de-op′ uh-the)
10. myasthenia (mi″as-the′ne-uh)

Visit the Student Edition of the Online Learning Center at http://www.mhhe.com/maderap5 for additional quizzes, interactive learning exercises, and other study tools.

The Nervous System

Autonomic neurons located within close proximity to the digestive tract.

chapter outline & learning objectives

After you have studied this chapter, you should be able to:

Part III

8.1 Nervous System

The nervous system has three specific functions:

1. *Sensory input.* Sensory receptors present in skin and organs respond to external and internal stimuli by generating nerve impulses that travel to the brain and spinal cord.
2. *Integration.* The brain and spinal cord sum up the data received from all over the body and send out nerve impulses.
3. *Motor output.* The nerve impulses from the brain and spinal cord go to the effectors, which are muscles and glands. Muscle contractions and gland secretions are responses to stimuli received by sensory receptors.

Divisions of the Nervous System

The nervous system has two major divisions: the central nervous system and the peripheral nervous system (Fig. 8.1). The **central nervous system (CNS)** includes the brain and spinal cord, which have a *central* location—they lie in the midline of the body. The **peripheral nervous system (PNS)**, which is further divided into the somatic division and the autonomic division, includes all the cranial and spinal nerves. Nerves have a *peripheral* location in the body, meaning that they project out from the central nervous system. The division between the central nervous system and the peripheral nervous system is arbitrary; the two systems work together, as we shall see.

Figure 8.1 Organization of the nervous system in humans. **a.** This pictorial representation shows the central nervous system (CNS, composed of brain and spinal cord) and some of the nerves of the peripheral nervous system (PNS). **b.** The CNS communicates with the PNS. In the somatic system, nerves conduct impulses from sensory receptors located in the skin and internal organs to the CNS; nerves also conduct motor impulses from the CNS to the skeletal muscles. In the autonomic system, consisting of the sympathetic and parasympathetic divisions, motor impulses travel to smooth muscle, cardiac muscle, and glands.

a.

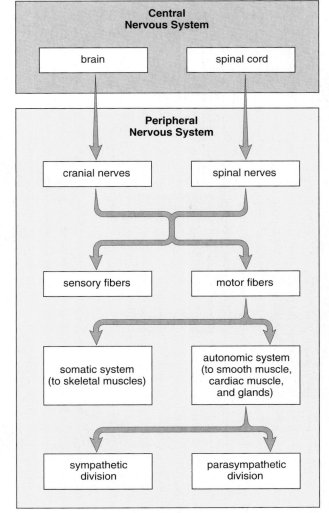

b.

Nervous Tissue

Although exceedingly complex, nervous tissue is made up of just two principal types of cells: (1) **neurons,** also called nerve cells, which transmit nerve impulses; and (2) **neuroglia,** which supports and nourishes neurons (see Chapter 4, page 64).

Neuron Structure

Neurons vary in appearance, but all of them have just three parts: a cell body, dendrite(s), and an axon. In Figure 8.2a, the **cell body** contains the nucleus as well as other organelles.

In motor neurons, the **dendrites** are the many short extensions that receive signals from sensory receptors or other neurons. At the dendrites, signals can result in nerve impulses that are then conducted by an axon. The **axon** is the portion of a neuron that conducts nerve impulses.

Any long axon is also called a **nerve fiber.** Long axons are covered by a white **myelin sheath** formed from the membranes of tightly spiraled neuroglia. In the PNS, a neuroglial cell called a **neurolemmocyte** (Schwann cell) performs this function, leaving gaps called neurofibril nodes (nodes of Ranvier). Another type of neuroglial cell performs a similar function in the CNS.

Types of Neurons

Neurons can be classified according to their function and shape. **Motor neurons** take nerve impulses from the CNS to muscles or glands. Motor neurons are said to be multipolar because they have many dendrites and a single axon (Fig. 8.2a). Motor neurons cause muscle fibers to contract or glands to secrete, and therefore they are said to *innervate* these structures.

Sensory neurons take nerve impulses from sensory receptors to the CNS. The sensory receptor, which is the distal end of the long axon of a sensory neuron, may be as simple as a naked nerve ending (a pain receptor), or it may be a part of a highly complex organ, such as the eye or ear. Almost all sensory neurons have a structure that is termed unipolar (Fig. 8.2b). In unipolar neurons, the extension from the cell body divides into a branch that comes to the periphery and another that goes to the CNS. Because both branches are long and myelinated and transmit nerve impulses, it is now generally accepted to refer to them collectively as an axon.

Interneurons, also known as association neurons, occur entirely within the CNS. Interneurons, which are typically multipolar (Fig. 8.2c), convey nerve impulses between various parts of the CNS. Some lie between sensory neurons and motor neurons, and some take messages from one side of the spinal cord to the other or from the brain to the cord, and vice versa. They also form complex pathways in the brain where processes accounting for thinking, memory, and language occur.

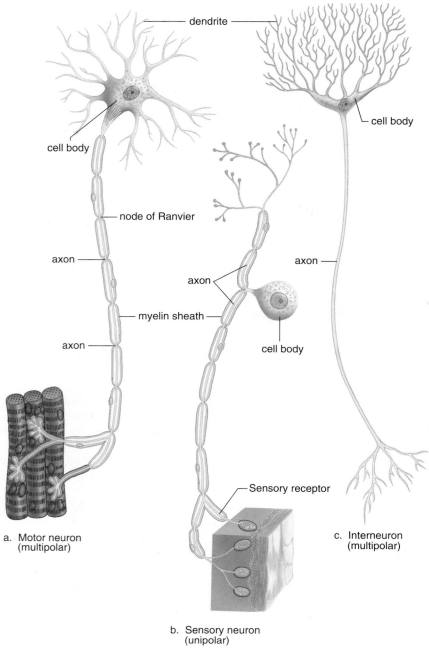

a. Motor neuron (multipolar)

b. Sensory neuron (unipolar)

c. Interneuron (multipolar)

Figure 8.2 Neuron anatomy. **a.** Motor neuron. Note the branched dendrites and the single, long axon, which branches only near its tip. **b.** Sensory neuron with dendritelike structures projecting from the peripheral end of the axon. **c.** Interneuron (from the cortex of the cerebellum) with highly branched dendrites.

Figure 8.3 Resting and action potentials in a nonmyelinated axon. **a.** Resting potential. There are many more Na$^+$ ions outside the axon and many more K$^+$ ions inside the axon. Also, the inside is negative compared to the outside. **b.** Action potential. First, Na$^+$ gates open, and Na$^+$ ions move to the inside of an axon. This causes the inside to become positive. Second, K$^+$ gates open, and K$^+$ ions move to the outside. This causes the inside to become negative again.

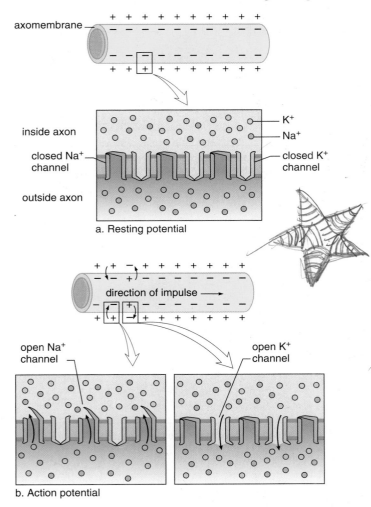

a. Resting potential

b. Action potential

Nerve Impulses

When axons are resting, they are not conducting nerve impulses. When they are active, axons are conducting **nerve impulses,** also called **action potentials.**

Resting Potential

When an axon is resting, its membrane is polarized; that is, the outside is positive compared to the inside, which is negative. A protein carrier in the membrane, called the sodium-potassium pump, pumps sodium (Na$^+$) out of the axon and potassium (K$^+$) into the axon. Another factor that causes the inside of the axon to be negative compared to the outside is the presence of large, negatively charged protein ions inside an axon. The polarity across an axon that is not conducting nerve impulses is called the *resting potential* (Fig. 8.3*a*).

Figure 8.4 Conduction of an action potential in a myelinated axon. The action potential jumps from one neurofibril node to the next along the axon. This makes the speed of a nerve impulse much faster than in unmyelinated axons. Almost all axons are myelinated in humans.

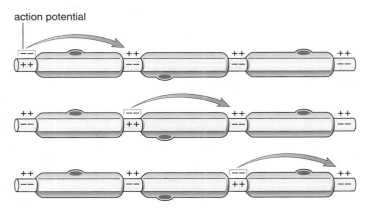

action potential

Action Potential

When the nerve fiber is conducting a nerve impulse (action potential), a change in polarity occurs across the axon's membrane (Fig. 8.3*b*). First, the inside of an axon becomes positive compared to the outside (this is called **depolarization**), and then the inside becomes negative again (this is called **repolarization**). An action potential requires two types of channels in the membrane: One channel can allow Na$^+$ ions to pass through the membrane, and the other can allow K$^+$ ions to pass through the membrane. During depolarization, Na$^+$ ions move to the inside of the axon, and during repolarization, K$^+$ ions move to the outside.

Conduction of Action Potentials

If an axon is unmyelinated, an action potential at one locale stimulates an adjacent part of the axomembrane to produce an action potential. In myelinated fibers, an action potential at one node of Ranvier causes an action potential at the next node (Fig. 8.4). This type of conduction, called *saltatory conduction*, is much faster than otherwise. In thin, unmyelinated axons, the action potential travels about 1.0 m/sec, and in thick, myelinated fibers, the rate is more than 100 m/sec.

The conduction of a nerve impulse (action potential) is an all-or-none event; that is, either an axon conducts a nerve impulse or it does not. The intensity of a message is determined by how many nerve impulses are generated within a given time span. A fiber can conduct a volley of nerve impulses because only a small number of ions are exchanged with each impulse. As soon as an impulse has passed by each successive portion of an axon, it undergoes a short refractory period during which it is unable to conduct an impulse. This ensures the one-way direction of an impulse from cell body to axon terminal.

It is interesting to observe that all functions of the nervous system, from our deepest emotions to our highest reasoning abilities, are dependent on the conduction of nerve impulses.

visual focus

axon branches of other neurons

cell body

axon terminals

dendrites

axon

cell body of postsynaptic cell

axon terminals

Many axons synapse with each cell body.

path of action potential

synaptic vesicles

axon terminal

dendrite

synaptic cleft

postsynaptic neuron

After an action potential arrives at an axon terminal, synaptic vesicles fuse with the presynaptic membrane.

neurotransmitter

synaptic vesicle

presynaptic membrane

synaptic cleft

postsynaptic membrane

receptor

Neurotransmitter molecules are released and bind to receptors on the postsynaptic membrane.

Na$^+$

neurotransmitter

When a stimulatory neurotransmitter binds to a receptor, Na$^+$ diffuses into the postsynaptic neuron.

Figure 8.5 Synapse structure and function. Transmission across a synapse from one neuron to another occurs when a neurotransmitter is released at the presynaptic membrane, diffuses across a synaptic cleft, and binds to a receptor in the postsynaptic membrane.

Transmission Across a Synapse

Every axon branches into many fine endings, each tipped by a small swelling called an **axon terminal.** Each swelling lies very close to either the dendrite or the cell body of another neuron. This region of close proximity is called a **synapse** (Fig. 8.5). At a synapse, the membrane of the first neuron is called the *pre*synaptic membrane, and the membrane of the next neuron is called the *post*synaptic membrane. The small gap between is the **synaptic cleft.**

Transmission across a synapse is carried out by molecules called **neurotransmitters,** which are stored in synaptic vesicles in the axon terminals. When nerve impulses traveling along an axon reach an axon terminal, channels for calcium ions (Ca^{2+}) open, and calcium enters the terminal. This sudden rise in Ca^{2+} stimulates synaptic vesicles to merge with the presynaptic membrane, and neurotransmitter molecules are released into the synaptic cleft. They diffuse across the cleft to the postsynaptic membrane, where they bind with specific receptor proteins.

Depending on the type of neurotransmitter and the type of receptor, the response of the postsynaptic neuron can be toward excitation or toward inhibition. After excitatory neurotransmitters combine with a receptor, a sodium ion channel opens, and Na^+ enters the neuron (Fig. 8.5). Other neurotransmitters have an inhibitory effect as described in the next section.

Synaptic Integration

A single neuron can have many dendrites plus the cell body, and both can synapse with many other neurons. Typically, a neuron is on the receiving end of many excitatory and inhibitory signals. An excitatory neurotransmitter produces a potential change called a *signal* that drives the polarity of a neuron closer to an action potential; an inhibitory neurotransmitter produces a signal that drives the polarity of a neuron farther from an action potential. Excitatory signals have a depolarizing effect, and inhibitory signals have a hyperpolarizing effect.

Neurons integrate these incoming signals. **Integration** is the summing up of excitatory and inhibitory signals. If a neuron receives many excitatory signals (either from different synapses or at a rapid rate from one synapse), chances are, the axon will transmit a nerve impulse. On the other hand, if a neuron receives both inhibitory and excitatory signals, the summing up of these signals may prohibit the axon from firing.

Neurotransmitter Molecules

At least 25 different neurotransmitters have been identified, but two very well-known ones are **acetylcholine (ACh)** and **norepinephrine (NE).**

Once a neurotransmitter has been released into a synaptic cleft and has initiated a response, it is removed from the cleft. In some synapses, the postsynaptic membrane contains enzymes that rapidly inactivate the neurotransmitter. For example, the enzyme **acetylcholinesterase (AChE)** breaks down acetylcholine. In other synapses, the presynaptic membrane rapidly reabsorbs the neurotransmitter, possibly for repackaging in synaptic vesicles or for molecular breakdown. The short existence of neurotransmitters at a synapse prevents continuous stimulation (or inhibition) of postsynaptic membranes.

The Medical Focus on this page discusses Alzheimer disease, which may be due in part to a lack of ACh in the brain. It is also of interest to note that many drugs are available that enhance or block the release of a neurotransmitter, mimic the action of a neurotransmitter or block the receptor, or interfere with the removal of a neurotransmitter from a synaptic cleft.

Medical Focus

Alzheimer Disease

Alzheimer disease (AD) is a disorder characterized by a gradual loss of reason that begins with memory lapses and ends with the inability to perform any type of daily activity. Personality changes signal the onset of AD. A normal 50- to 60-year-old might forget the name of a friend not seen for years. People with AD, however, forget the name of a neighbor who visits daily. People afflicted with AD become confused and tend to repeat the same question. Signs of mental disturbance eventually appear, and patients gradually become bedridden and die of a complication, such as pneumonia.

Researchers have discovered that in some families whose members have a 50% chance of AD, a genetic defect exists on chromosome 21. This is of extreme interest because Down syndrome, as you know, results from the inheritance of three copies of chromosome 21, and people with Down syndrome tend to develop AD.

AD is characterized by the presence of abnormally structured neurons and a reduced amount of ACh. The AD neuron has two features: (1) Bundles of fibrous protein, called neurofibrillary tangles, surround the nucleus in the cells, and (2) Protein-rich accumulations, called amyloid plaques, envelop the axon branches. These abnormal neurons are especially seen in the portions of the brain involved in reason and memory. Drugs that enhance acetylcholine production are currently being tested in AD patients. Experimental drugs that prevent neuron degeneration are also being tested. For example, it is possible that nerve growth factor, a substance that is made by the body and that promotes the growth of neurons, will one day be tested in AD patients.

8.2 Central Nervous System

The CNS, consisting of the brain and spinal cord, is composed of gray matter and white matter. **Gray matter** is gray because it contains cell bodies and short, nonmyelinated fibers. **White matter** is white because it contains myelinated axons that run together in bundles called **tracts**.

Meninges and Cerebrospinal Fluid

Both the spinal cord and the brain are wrapped in protective membranes known as **meninges** (sing., meninx). The outer meninx, the **dura mater**, is tough, white, fibrous connective tissue that lies next to the skull and vertebrae. The dural sinuses collect venous blood before it returns to the cardiovascular system. Bleeding into the space between the dura mater and bone is called an **epidural hematoma**. The presence of blood between the dura mater and the next meninx, the arachnoid, is called a **subdural hematoma**. The **arachnoid** consists of weblike connective tissue with thin strands that attach it to the **pia mater**, the deepest meninx. The subarachnoid space is filled with **cerebrospinal fluid**, a clear tissue fluid that forms a protective cushion around and within the CNS. The pia mater is very thin and closely follows the contours of the brain and spinal cord (Fig. 8.6).

Cerebrospinal fluid is stored within the central canal of the spinal cord and in the brain's **ventricles**, which are interconnecting chambers that also produce cerebrospinal fluid. Normally, any excess cerebrospinal fluid drains away into the cardiovascular system. However, blockages can occur. In an infant, the brain can enlarge due to cerebrospinal fluid accumulation, resulting in a condition called **hydrocephalus** ("water on the brain").

The Spinal Cord

The **spinal cord** is a cylinder of nervous tissue that begins at the base of the brain and extends through a large opening in the skull called the foramen magnum. The spinal cord is protected by the vertebral column, which is composed of individual vertebrae. The cord passes through the vertebral canal formed by openings in the vertebrae. It ends at the first lumbar vertebra (see Fig. 6.8).

Structure of the Spinal Cord

Figure 8.7*a* shows how an individual vertebra protects the spinal cord. The spinal nerves extend from the cord between the vertebrae. Intervertebral disks separate the vertebrae, and if a disk slips a bit and presses on the spinal cord, pain results.

A cross section of the spinal cord shows a central canal, gray matter, and white matter (Fig. 8.7*b,c*). The central canal contains cerebrospinal fluid, as do the meninges that protect the spinal cord. The gray matter is centrally located and shaped like the letter H. Portions of sensory neurons and motor neurons are found there, as are interneurons that communicate with these two types of neurons. The posterior (dorsal) root of a spinal nerve contains sensory fibers entering the gray matter, and the anterior (ventral) root of a spinal nerve contains motor fibers exiting the gray matter. The posterior and anterior roots join, forming a spinal nerve that leaves the vertebral canal. Spinal nerves are a part of the PNS.

The white matter of the spinal cord contains ascending tracts taking information to the brain (primarily located posteriorly) and descending tracts taking information from the brain (primarily located anteriorly). Because the tracts cross just after they enter and exit the brain, the left side of the brain controls the right side of the body, and the right side of the brain controls the left side of the body.

Figure 8.6 Meninges. a. Meninges are protective membranes that enclose the brain and spinal cord. b. The meninges include three layers: the dura mater, the arachnoid, and the pia mater.

a.

b.

Functions of the Spinal Cord

The spinal cord provides a means of communication between the brain and the peripheral nerves that leave the cord.

When someone touches your hand, sensory receptors generate nerve impulses that pass through sensory fibers to the spinal cord and up one of several ascending tracts to a sensory area of the brain. When you voluntarily move your limbs, motor impulses originating in the brain pass down one of several descending tracts to the spinal cord and out to your muscles by way of motor fibers. The Medical Focus on this page discusses what happens if the spinal cord is injured.

We will see that the spinal cord is also the center for thousands of reflex arcs (see Fig. 8.13): A stimulus causes sensory receptors to generate nerve impulses that travel in sensory neurons to the spinal cord. Interneurons integrate the incoming data and relay signals to motor neurons. A response to the stimulus occurs when motor axons cause skeletal muscles to contract. Each interneuron in the spinal cord has synapses with many other neurons, and therefore they send signals to several other interneurons in addition to motor neurons.

Medical Focus

Spinal Cord Injuries

Spinal cord injuries may result from accidents or other trauma. The cord may be completely cut across (transection) or only partially severed (partial section). The location and extent of the damage produce a variety of effects, depending on the partial or complete stoppage of impulses passing up and down the spinal cord. If the spinal cord is completely transected, no sensations or somatic motor impulses traveling in the cord will be able to pass the point where the cord is cut. If the injury is between the first thoracic vertebra (T1) and the second lumbar vertebra (L2), paralysis of the lower body and legs occurs. This condition is known as **paraplegia**. If the injury is between the fourth cervical vertebra (C4) and the first thoracic vertebra (T1), the entire body and all four limbs are usually affected. This condition is called **quadriplegia**. If the injury is a unilateral hemisection (half cut), motor loss will occur on the same side as the injury because motor neuron crossover occurs in the medulla oblongata. At the same time, loss of sensation will vary, and the pattern and type of such loss can be analyzed to locate the lesion.

Figure 8.7 Spinal cord. **a.** The spinal cord passes through the vertebral canal formed by the vertebrae. It gives off spinal nerves that project through openings between the vertebrae. **b.** The spinal cord has a central canal filled with cerebrospinal fluid, gray matter in an H-shaped configuration, and white matter elsewhere. The white matter contains tracts that take nerve impulses to and from the brain. **c.** Photomicrograph of a cross section of the spinal cord.

a.

b.

c.

The Brain

We will discuss the parts of the brain with reference to the cerebrum, the diencephalon, the cerebellum, and the brain stem. The brain's four ventricles are called, in turn, the two lateral ventricles, the third ventricle, and the fourth ventricle. It will be helpful for you to associate the cerebrum with the two lateral ventricles, the diencephalon with the third ventricle, and the brain stem and the cerebellum with the fourth ventricle (Fig. 8.8a).

The electrical activity of the brain can be recorded in the form of an **electroencephalogram (EEG).** Electrodes are taped to different parts of the scalp, and an instrument records the so-called brain waves. The EEG is a diagnostic tool; for example, an irregular pattern can signify epilepsy or a brain tumor. A flat EEG signifies brain death.

The Cerebrum

The **cerebrum** is the largest portion of the brain in humans. The cerebrum is the last center to receive sensory input and carry out integration before commanding voluntary motor responses. It communicates with and coordinates the activities of the other parts of the brain. The cerebrum carries out the higher thought processes required for learning and memory and for language and speech.

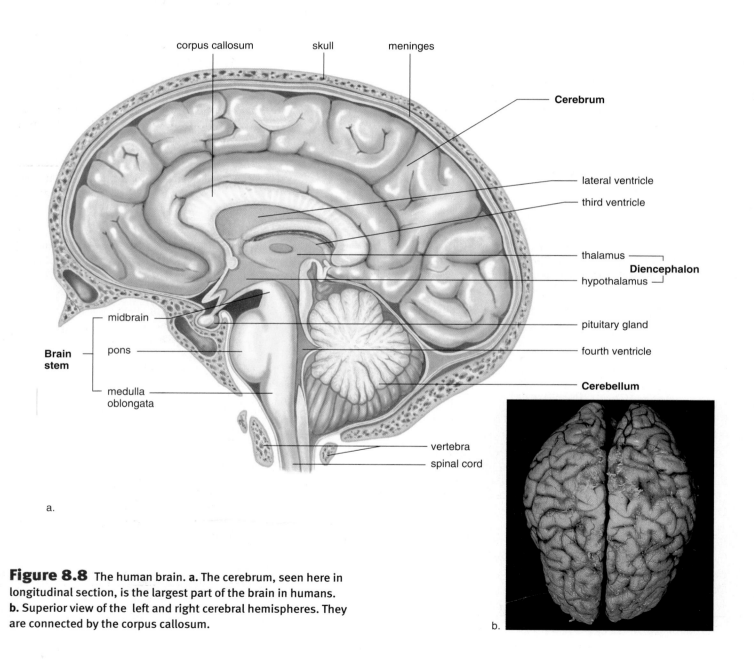

Figure 8.8 The human brain. **a.** The cerebrum, seen here in longitudinal section, is the largest part of the brain in humans. **b.** Superior view of the left and right cerebral hemispheres. They are connected by the corpus callosum.

The Cerebral Hemispheres   The cerebrum has two halves called the left and right **cerebral hemispheres** (Fig. 8.8b). A deep groove, the longitudinal *fissure,* divides the left and right cerebral hemispheres. Still, the two cerebral hemispheres are connected by a bridge of white matter within the **corpus callosum.**

Convolutions called *gyri* are separated by shallow grooves called *sulci* (sing., sulcus). The sulci divide each hemisphere into lobes (Fig. 8.9). The *frontal lobe* is anterior to the *parietal lobe,* which is anterior to the *occipital lobe.* The *temporal lobe* is the lateral portion of the cerebral hemisphere.

The **cerebral cortex** is a thin but highly convoluted outer layer of gray matter that covers the cerebral hemispheres. The cerebral cortex contains over one billion cell bodies and is the region of the brain that accounts for sensation, voluntary movement, and all the thought processes we associate with consciousness.

Motor and Sensory Areas of the Cortex   The **primary motor area** is in the frontal lobe just anterior to the central sulcus. Voluntary commands to skeletal muscles begin in the primary motor area, and each part of the body is controlled by a certain section (see Fig. 8.10a).

The **primary somatosensory area** is just posterior to the central sulcus in the parietal lobe. Sensory information from the skin and skeletal muscles arrives here, where each part of

the body is sequentially represented (see Fig. 8.10b). A primary taste area, also in the parietal lobe, accounts for taste sensations. A primary visual area in the occipital lobe receives information from our eyes, and a primary auditory area in the temporal lobe receives information from our ears.

Association areas   Association areas are places where integration occurs. Anterior to the primary motor area is a premotor area. The premotor area organizes motor functions for skilled motor activities, and then the primary motor area sends signals to the cerebellum, which integrates them. A momentary lack of oxygen during birth can damage the motor areas of the cerebral cortex so that **cerebral palsy,** a condition characterized by a spastic weakness of the arms and legs, develops.

The somatosensory association area, located just posterior to the primary somatosensory area, processes and analyzes sensory information from the skin and muscles. The visual association area associates new visual information with previously received visual information. It might "decide", for example, whether we have seen this face, tool, or whatever before. The auditory association area performs the same functions with regard to sounds.

Processing Centers   There are a few areas of the cortex that receive information from the other association areas and perform higher-level analytical functions. The **prefrontal area,** a

Figure 8.9   The lobes of a cerebral hemisphere. Each cerebral hemisphere is divided into four lobes: frontal, parietal, temporal, and occipital. These lobes contain centers for reasoning and movement (frontal lobe), somatic sensing including taste (parietal lobe), hearing (temporal lobe), and vision (occipital lobe). Broca's area is only in the left lobe.

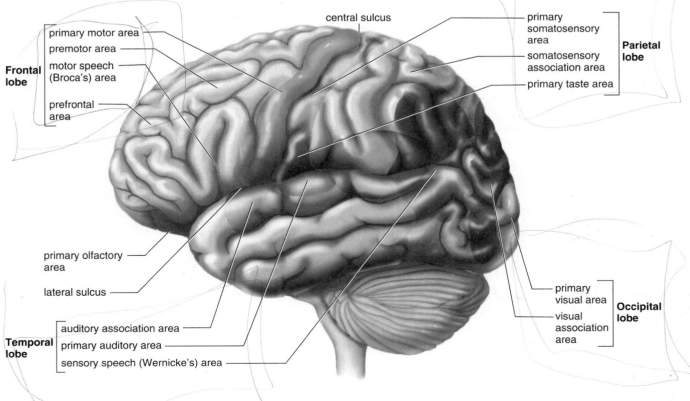

Figure 8.10 Portions of the body controlled by the primary motor area and the primary somatosensory area of the cerebrum. Notice that the size of the body part in the diagram reflects the amount of cerebral cortex devoted to that body part.

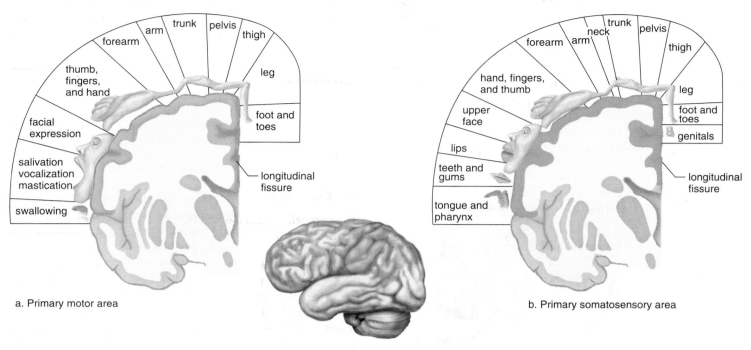

a. Primary motor area

b. Primary somatosensory area

Medical Focus

Left and Right Brain

Current research indicates that the right side of the cerebral hemisphere handles emotion and holistic thoughts ("the big picture"), and is more intuitive than the left side. The left side appears to handle language, math, and music, and is said to be the "rational" side of the brain. Brain imaging techniques illustrate more activity in the right hemisphere for artists and navigators. The motor cortex, cerebellum, and basal ganglia are more organized in dancers and other athletes, while individuals who work with people, such as psychologists, use their limbic system more efficiently.

From ages 7–10 years to adulthood, males are observed to excel at visual-spatial skills, whereas females during the same time period are more generalists. In general, males use the left hemisphere (including Broca's area) more while females use both hemispheres equally. This explains why males tend to have more speaking difficulties after a stroke affects the brain's left side than females in the same situation. Females have an analogous region to Broca's area in their right side that can take over speech functions.

processing area in the frontal lobe, receives information from the other association areas and uses this information to reason and plan our actions. Integration in this area accounts for our most cherished human abilities to think critically and to formulate appropriate behaviors.

The unique ability of humans to speak is partially dependent upon *Broca's area,* a processing area in the left frontal lobe. Signals originating here pass to the premotor area before reaching the primary motor area. Damage to this area can interfere with a person's ability to understand words (written or spoken) and to communicate with others.

Wernicke's area, also called the general interpretive area, receives information from all the other sensory association areas. Damage to this area hinders the ability to interpret written and spoken messages even though the words are understood.

Central White Matter Much of the rest of the cerebrum beneath the cerebral cortex is composed of white matter. Tracts within the cerebrum take information between the different sensory, motor, and association areas pictured in Figure 8.9. The corpus callosum, previously mentioned, contains tracts that join the two cerebral hemispheres. Descending tracts from the primary motor area communicate with various parts of the brain, and ascending tracts from lower brain centers send sensory information up to the primary somatosensory area (Fig. 8.10).

Basal Nuclei While the bulk of the cerebrum is composed of tracts, there are masses of gray matter located deep within the white matter. These so-called **basal nuclei** (formerly termed basal ganglia) integrate motor commands, ensuring that proper muscle groups are activated or inhibited. Huntington disease and Parkinson disease, which are both characterized by uncontrollable movements, are believed to be due to an imbalance of neurotransmitters in the basal nuclei.

Limbic System The **limbic system** (blue in figure) lies just inferior to the cerebral cortex and contains neural pathways that connect portions of the cerebral cortex and the temporal lobes with the thalamus and the hypothalamus:

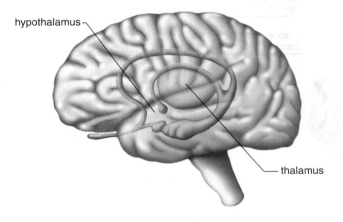

hypothalamus

thalamus

Stimulation of different areas of the limbic system causes the subject to experience rage, pain, pleasure, or sorrow. By causing pleasant or unpleasant feelings about experiences, the limbic system apparently guides the individual into behavior that is likely to increase the chance of survival.

The limbic system is also involved in learning and memory. Learning requires memory, and memory is stored in the sensory regions of the cerebrum, but just what permits memory development is not definitely known. The involvement of the limbic system in memory explains why emotionally charged events result in our most vivid memories. The fact that the limbic system communicates with the sensory areas for touch, smell, vision, and so forth accounts for the ability of any particular sensory stimulus to awaken a complex memory.

The Diencephalon

The hypothalamus and the thalamus are in the **diencephalon,** a region that encircles the third ventricle (see Fig. 8.8a). The **hypothalamus** forms the floor of the third ventricle. The hypothalamus is an integrating center that helps maintain homeostasis by regulating hunger, sleep, thirst, body temperature, and water balance. The hypothalamus produces the hormones secreted by the posterior pituitary gland and secretes hormones that control the anterior pituitary. Therefore, it is a link between the nervous and endocrine systems.

The **thalamus** consists of two masses of gray matter located in the sides and roof of the third ventricle. The thalamus is on the receiving end for all sensory input except smell. Visual, auditory, and somatosensory information arrives at the thalamus via the cranial nerves and tracts from the spinal cord. The thalamus integrates this information and sends it on to the appropriate portions of the cerebrum. The thalamus is involved in arousal of the cerebrum, and it also participates in higher mental functions such as memory and emotions.

The pineal gland, which secretes the hormone melatonin and regulates our body's daily rhythms, is located in the diencephalon.

The Cerebellum

The **cerebellum** is separated from the brain stem by the fourth ventricle (see Fig. 8.8a). The cerebellum has two portions that are joined by a narrow median portion. Each portion is primarily composed of white matter, which in longitudinal section has a treelike pattern. Overlying the white matter is a thin layer of gray matter that forms a series of complex folds.

The cerebellum receives sensory input from the eyes, ears, joints, and muscles about the present position of body parts. It also receives motor output from the cerebral cortex about where these parts should be located. After integrating this information, the cerebellum sends motor impulses by way of the brain stem to the skeletal muscles. In this way, the cerebellum maintains posture and balance. It also ensures that all of the muscles work together to produce smooth, coordinated voluntary movements. In addition, the cerebellum assists the learning of new motor skills, such as playing the piano or hitting a baseball.

The Brain Stem

The **brain stem** contains the midbrain, the pons, and the medulla oblongata (see Fig. 8.8a). The **midbrain** acts as a relay station for tracts passing between the cerebrum and the spinal cord or cerebellum. It also has reflex centers for visual, auditory, and tactile responses. The word *pons* means "bridge" in Latin, and true to its name, the **pons** contains bundles of axons traveling between the cerebellum and the rest of the CNS. In addition, the pons functions with the medulla oblongata to regulate breathing rate and has reflex centers concerned with head movements in response to visual and auditory stimuli.

The **medulla oblongata** contains a number of reflex centers for regulating heartbeat, breathing, and vasoconstriction. It also contains the reflex centers for vomiting, coughing, sneezing, hiccuping, and swallowing. The medulla oblongata lies just superior to the spinal cord, and it contains tracts that ascend or descend between the spinal cord and higher brain centers.

8.3 Peripheral Nervous System

The peripheral nervous system (PNS) lies outside the central nervous system and is composed of nerves and ganglia. **Nerves** are bundles of myelinated axons. Ganglia (sing., **ganglion**) are swellings associated with nerves that contain collections of cell bodies. As with muscles, connective tissue separates axons at various levels of organization:

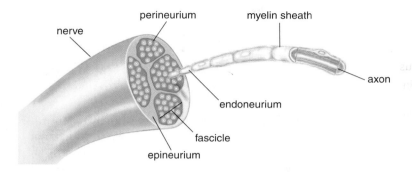

The PNS is subdivided into the somatic system and the autonomic system. The **somatic system** serves the skin, skeletal muscles, and tendons. It includes nerves that take sensory information from external sensory receptors to the CNS and motor commands away from the CNS to the skeletal muscles. The **autonomic system**, with a few exceptions, regulates the activity of cardiac and smooth muscles and glands.

Types of Nerves

The **cranial nerves** are attached to the brain, and the **spinal nerves** are attached to the spinal cord.

Cranial Nerves

Humans have 12 pairs of cranial nerves (Table 8.1). By convention, the pairs of cranial nerves are referred to by roman numerals (Fig. 8.11a). Most of the cranial nerves belong to the somatic system. Some of these are sensory nerves—that is, they contain only sensory fibers; some are *motor nerves*, containing only motor fibers; and others are mixed nerves, so called because they contain both sensory and motor fibers. Cranial nerves are largely concerned with the head, neck, and facial regions of the body. However, the *vagus nerve (X)*, which has branches to most of the internal organs, is a part of the autonomic system.

Figure 8.11 Cranial and spinal nerves. **a.** Ventral surface of the brain showing the attachment of the 12 pairs of cranial nerves. **b.** Cross section of the spinal cord, showing 3 pairs of spinal nerves. Each spinal nerve has a posterior root and an anterior root that join shortly beyond the cord.

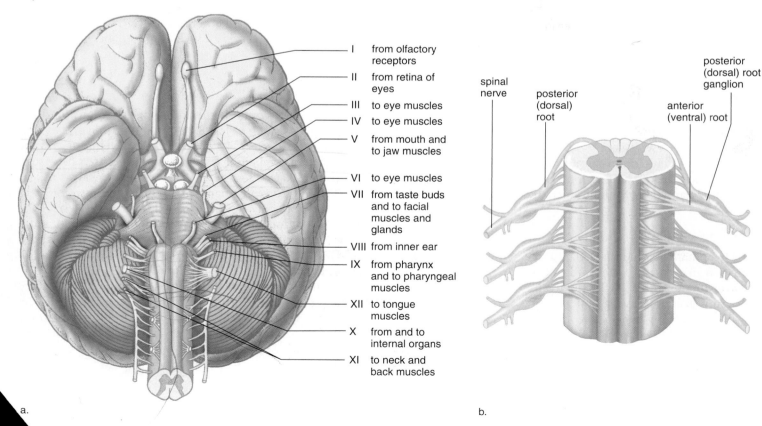

Spinal Nerves

Humans have 31 pairs of spinal nerves; one of each pair is on either side of the spinal cord (Fig. 8.11*b*). The spinal nerves are grouped as shown in Table 8.2 because they are at either the cervical, thoracic, or lumbar regions of the vertebral column. The spinal nerves are designated according to their location in relation to the vertebrae because each passes through an intervertebral foramen as it leaves the spinal cord. This organizational principle is illustrated in Figure 8.12.

Table 8.1 Cranial Nerves

Nerve	Type		Brain Location	Transmits Nerve Impulses to (Motor) or from (Sensory)
Olfactory (I)	Sensory		Olfactory bulb	Olfactory receptors for sense of smell
Optic (II)	Sensory		Thalamus	Retina for sense of sight
Oculomotor (III)	Motor		Midbrain	Eye muscles (including eyelids and lens); pupil (parasympathetic division)
Trochlear (IV)	Motor		Midbrain	Eye muscles
Trigeminal (V)	Mixed	Sensory	Pons	Teeth, eyes, skin, and tongue
		Motor		Jaw muscles (chewing)
Abducens (VI)	Motor		Pons	Eye muscles
Facial (VII)	Mixed	Sensory	Pons	Taste buds of anterior tongue
		Motor		Facial muscles (facial expression) and glands (tear and salivary)
Vestibulocochlear (VIII)	Sensory		Pons	Inner ear for sense of balance and hearing
Glossopharyngeal (IX)	Mixed	Sensory	Medulla oblongata	Pharynx
		Motor		Pharyngeal muscles (swallowing)
Vagus (X)	Sensory		Medulla oblongata	Internal organs
	Motor			Internal organs (parasympathetic division)
Spinal accessory (XI)	Motor		Medulla oblongata	Neck and back muscles
Hypoglossal (XII)	Motor		Medulla oblongata	Tongue muscles

Table 8.2 Spinal Nerves

Name	Spinal Nerves Involved*	Function
Musculocutaneous nerves	C5–T1	Supply muscles of the arms on the anterior sides, and skin of the forearms
Radial nerves	C5–T1	Supply muscles of the arms on the posterior sides, and skin of the forearms and hands
Median nerves	C5–T1	Supply muscles of the forearms, and muscles and skin of the hands
Ulnar nerves	C5–T1	Supply muscles of the forearms and hands, and skin of the hands
Phrenic nerves	C3–C5	Supply the diaphragm
Intercostal nerves	T2–T12	Supply intercostal muscles, abdominal muscles, and skin of the trunk
Femoral nerves	L2–L4	Supply muscles and skin of the thighs and legs
Sciatic nerves	L4–S3	Supply muscles and skin of the thighs, legs, and feet

*C = cervical; T = thoracic; L = lumbar

Many spinal nerves carry fibers that belong to either the somatic or the autonomic system. However, the spinal nerves are called mixed nerves because they contain both sensory fibers that conduct impulses to the spinal cord from sensory receptors and motor fibers that conduct impulses away from the cord to effectors. The sensory fibers enter the cord via the posterior root, and the motor fibers exit by way of the anterior root. The cell body of a sensory neuron is in a **posterior (dorsal)-root ganglion.** Each spinal nerve serves the particular region of the body in which it is located.

Somatic Nervous System

Many actions in the somatic nervous system are voluntary, and these always originate in the cerebral cortex, as when we decide to move a limb. Other actions in the somatic nervous system are due to **reflexes,** automatic involuntary responses to changes occurring inside or outside the body. A reflex occurs quickly, without our even having to think about it.

Some reflexes, called *cranial reflexes*, involve the brain, as when we automatically blink our eyes when an object nears

Figure 8.12 Spinal nerves. The number and kinds of spinal nerves are given on the right. The location of major peripheral nerves is given on the left. Table 8.2 lists the functions of these nerves.

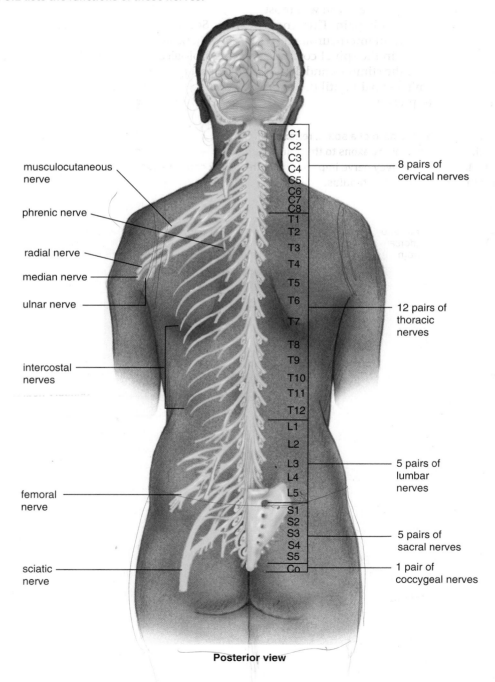

musculocutaneous nerve

phrenic nerve

radial nerve

median nerve

ulnar nerve

intercostal nerves

femoral nerve

sciatic nerve

C1
C2
C3
C4
C5
C6
C7
C8 — 8 pairs of cervical nerves

T1
T2
T3
T4
T5
T6
T7
T8
T9
T10
T11
T12 — 12 pairs of thoracic nerves

L1
L2
L3
L4
L5 — 5 pairs of lumbar nerves

S1
S2
S3
S4
S5 — 5 pairs of sacral nerves

Co — 1 pair of coccygeal nerves

Posterior view

the eye suddenly. Figure 8.13 illustrates the path of a reflex within the somatic nervous system that involves only the spinal cord (called a spinal reflex). If your hand touches a sharp pin, a sensory receptor in the skin generates nerve impulses that move along a sensory fiber through the posterior-root ganglia toward the spinal cord. Sensory neurons enter the cord posteriorly and pass signals on to many interneurons. Some of these interneurons synapse with motor neurons whose short dendrites and cell bodies are in the spinal cord. Nerve impulses travel along a motor fiber to an effector, which brings about a response to the stimulus. In this case, the effector is a skeletal muscle, which contracts so that you withdraw your hand from the pin.

Various other reactions are also possible—you will most likely look at the pin, wince, and cry out in pain. This whole series of responses occurs because certain interneurons carry nerve impulses to the brain via tracts in the spinal cord and brain. The brain makes you aware of the stimulus and directs your other reactions to it. You don't feel pain until the brain receives the information and interprets it.

Reflexes are essential to homeostasis. They keep the internal organs functioning within normal bounds and protect the body from external harm. Reflexes can also be used to determine if the nervous system is reacting properly. Two of these types of reflexes are:

knee-jerk reflex (patellar reflex), initiated by striking the patellar ligament just below the patella. The response is contraction of the quadriceps femoris muscles, which causes the lower leg to extend;

ankle-jerk reflex, initiated by tapping the Achilles tendon just above its insertion on the calcaneus. The response is plantar flexion due to contraction of the gastrocnemius and soleus muscles.

Some reflexes are important for avoiding injury, but the knee-jerk and ankle-jerk reflexes are important for normal physiological functions. For example, the knee-jerk reflex helps a person stand erect. If the knee begins to bend slightly when a person stands still, the quadriceps femoris is stretched, and the leg straightens.

Figure 8.13 A reflex arc showing the path of a spinal reflex. A stimulus (e.g., a pinprick) causes sensory receptors in the skin to generate nerve impulses that travel in sensory axons to the spinal cord. Interneurons integrate data from sensory neurons and then relay signals to motor neurons. Motor axons convey nerve impulses from the spinal cord to a skeletal muscle, which contracts. Movement of the hand away from the pin is the response to the stimulus.

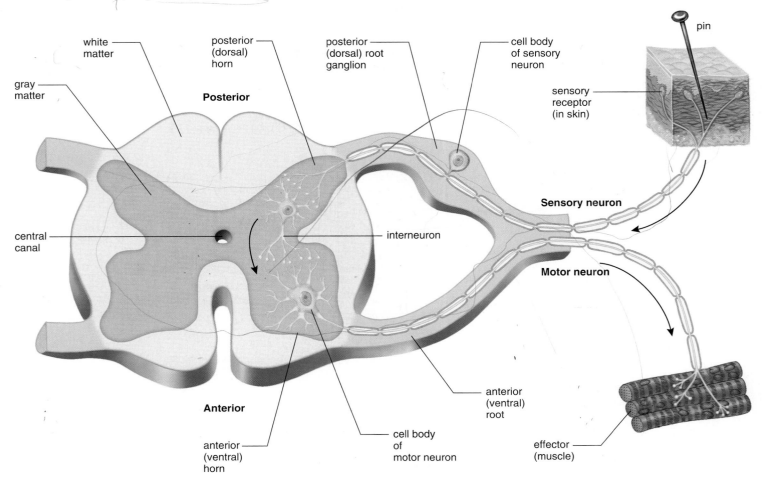

visual focus

Sympathetic division

Parasympathetic division

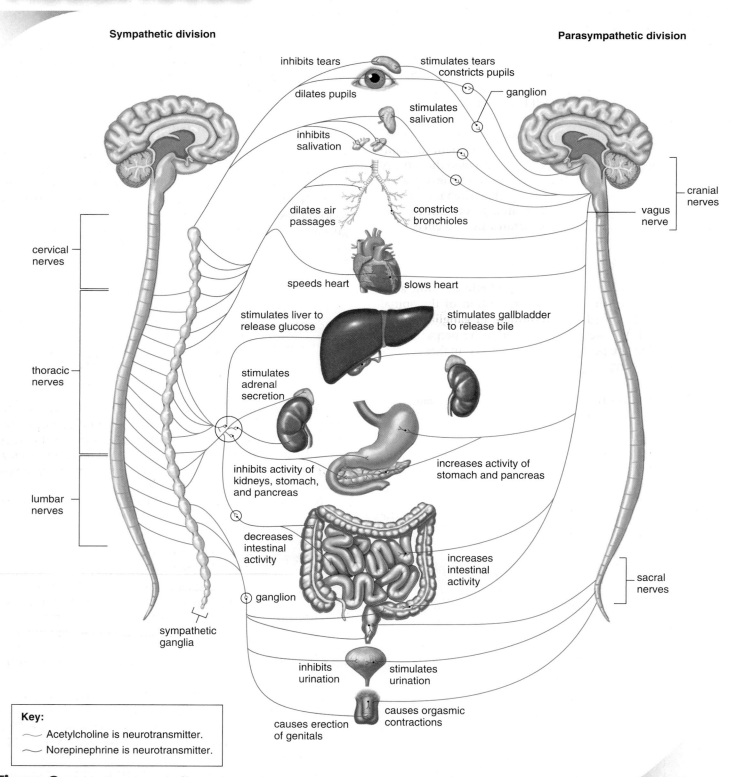

inhibits tears

stimulates tears
constricts pupils

dilates pupils

ganglion

stimulates
salivation

inhibits
salivation

cranial
nerves

cervical
nerves

dilates air
passages

constricts
bronchioles

vagus
nerve

speeds heart

slows heart

stimulates liver to
release glucose

stimulates gallbladder
to release bile

thoracic
nerves

stimulates
adrenal
secretion

inhibits activity of
kidneys, stomach,
and pancreas

increases activity of
stomach and pancreas

lumbar
nerves

decreases
intestinal
activity

increases
intestinal
activity

ganglion

sacral
nerves

sympathetic
ganglia

inhibits
urination

stimulates
urination

causes orgasmic
contractions

causes erection
of genitals

Key:

⌒ Acetylcholine is neurotransmitter.

⌒ Norepinephrine is neurotransmitter.

Figure 8.14 Autonomic system structure and function. Sympathetic preganglionic fibers (*left*) arise from the cervical, thoracic, and lumbar portions of the spinal cord; parasympathetic preganglionic fibers (*right*) arise from the cranial and sacral portions of the spinal cord. Each system innervates the same organs but has contrary effects.

Autonomic Nervous System

The autonomic nervous system (ANS) is composed of the sympathetic and parasympathetic divisions (Fig. 8.14). These two divisions have several features in common: (1) They function automatically and usually in an involuntary manner; (2) they innervate all internal organs; and (3) they utilize two motor neurons and one ganglion for each impulse. The first neuron has a cell body within the CNS and a preganglionic fiber. The second neuron has a cell body within the ganglion and a postganglionic fiber.

Visceral reflex actions, such as those that regulate blood pressure and breathing rate, are especially important to maintenance of homeostasis. These reflexes begin when the sensory neurons in contact with internal organs send messages via spinal nerves to the CNS. They are completed when motor neurons within the autonomic system stimulate smooth muscle, cardiac muscle, or a gland. These structures are also effectors.

Sympathetic Division

Most preganglionic fibers of the **sympathetic division** arise from the middle, or thoracic-lumbar, portion of the spinal cord and almost immediately terminate in ganglia that lie near the cord. Therefore, in this division, the preganglionic fiber is short, but the postganglionic fiber that makes contact with an organ is long:

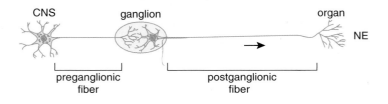

The sympathetic division is especially important during emergency situations when a person might be required to fight or take flight. It accelerates the heartbeat and dilates the bronchi—active muscles, after all, require a ready supply of glucose and oxygen. On the other hand, the sympathetic division inhibits the digestive tract—digestion is not an immediate necessity if you are under attack. The neurotransmitter released by the postganglionic axon is primarily norepinephrine (NE). The structure of NE is like that of epinephrine (adrenaline), an adrenal medulla hormone that usually increases heart rate and contractility.

Parasympathetic Division

The **parasympathetic division** includes a few cranial nerves (e.g., the vagus nerve) as well as fibers that arise from the sacral (bottom) portion of the spinal cord. Therefore, this division is often referred to as the craniosacral portion of the autonomic system. In the parasympathetic division, the preganglionic fiber is long, and the postganglionic fiber is short because the ganglia lie near or within the organ:

The parasympathetic division, sometimes called the housekeeper division, promotes all the internal responses we associate with a relaxed state; for example, it causes the pupil of the eye to contract, promotes digestion of food, and retards the heartbeat. The neurotransmitter utilized by the parasympathetic division is acetylcholine (ACh).

Table 8.3 contrasts the two divisions of the autonomic system.

8.4 Effects of Aging

After age 60, the brain begins to lose thousands of neurons a day. When these cells die, they are not replaced. By age 80, the brain weighs about 10% less than when the person was a young adult. The cerebral cortex shrinks more than other areas of the brain, losing as much as 45% of its cells. Therefore, such mental activities as learning, memory, and reasoning decline.

Neurotransmitter production also decreases, resulting in slower synaptic transmission. As a person ages, thought processing and translating a thought into action take longer. This partly explains why younger athletes tend to outshine older athletes in sports.

Neurological disorders, especially Alzheimer disease which is discussed in the Medical Focus on page 145, are, more apt to occur in the elderly. The What's New reading on page 158 describes a new procedure for the treatment of Parkinson disease.

Table 8.3	Autonomic Motor Pathways	
	Sympathetic	**Parasympathetic**
Type of control	Involuntary	Involuntary
Number of neurons per message	Two (preganglionic shorter than postganglionic)	Two (preganglionic longer than postganglionic)
Location of motor fiber	Thoracolumbar spinal nerves	Cranial (e.g., vagus) and sacral spinal nerves
Neurotransmitter	Norepinephrine	Acetylcholine
Effectors	Smooth and cardiac muscle, glands	Smooth and cardiac muscle, glands

8.5 Homeostasis

The nervous system detects, interprets, and responds to changes in internal and external conditions to keep the internal environment relatively constant. Together with the endocrine system, it coordinates and regulates the functioning of the other systems in the body to maintain homeostasis.

The everyday regulation of internal organs that maintains the composition of blood and tissue fluid usually takes place below the level of consciousness. Subconscious control is dependent on reflex actions that involve the hypothalamus and the medulla oblongata. The hypothalamus and the medulla oblongata act through the autonomic nervous system to control such important parameters as the heart rate, the constriction of the blood vessels, and the breathing rate.

The illustration in Human Systems Work Together on page 159 tells how the nervous system works with other systems in the body to maintain homeostasis. The hypothalamus works closely with the endocrine system and even produces the hormone ADH, which causes the kidneys to reabsorb water. Other hormones also influence the work of the kidneys in maintaining blood volume and pressure.

Because the nervous system stimulates skeletal muscles to contract, it controls the major movements of the body. When when we are in a "fight-or-flight" mode, the nervous system stimulates the adrenal glands and voluntarily controls the skeletal muscles to keep us from danger. On a daily basis, you might think that voluntary movements don't play a role in homeostasis, but actually we usually take all necessary actions to stay in as moderate an environment as possible. Otherwise, we are testing the ability of the nervous system to maintain homeostasis despite extreme conditions.

What's New

Pacemakers for Parkinson Disease

"My body is completely out of control. That's the hardest thing about this disease. Sometimes I can't move at all, or I move so slowly that it takes forever just to cross the room. Next thing you know, I'm jerking around like a puppet."

Your patient has just described the classic symptoms of **Parkinson disease,** a progressive central nervous system disorder. The Parkinson patient is usually a person age 60 or older. However, the disease is seen increasingly in younger people as well, making headlines when 38-year-old actor Michael J. Fox announced publicly in 1999 that he suffered from Parkinson disease. If the facial muscles are involved, the person's face may not be able to show emotion, resulting in a fixed, masklike appearance. Routine tasks such as dressing and bathing become very difficult. The sufferer has an increased risk of falling and injuring himself because balance and coordination are also affected. The disease takes its toll on the patient psychologically; most suffer depression as their activities and independence become more and more limited.

Parkinson disease is caused by destruction of specific areas of the brain called the basal nuclei (see page 151). Researchers have determined that these basal nuclei nerve cells produce the neurotransmitter dopamine. The lack of this neurotransmitter seems to cause the signs and symptoms of the disorder. Treatment for the disease has, until recently, focused on ways to replace dopamine in the brain. Drug treatment produces temporary dopamine replacement and relieves the symptoms completely for a few weeks to months. However, as the disease progresses, patients need increasingly stronger medications in higher dosages to relieve the symptoms. These stronger medications produce undesirable side effects, such as dizziness, sleepiness, and memory loss.

Implants of dopamine-producing cells have also been placed into the brain. These implants have had low to moderate success rates in relieving symptoms. Because the cells are often obtained from human embryos, scientists have also raised ethical concerns about the source of the implanted cells.

A novel approach to therapy involves the use of deep-brain stimulation. Similar to a cardiac pacemaker, this "pacemaker for the brain" consists of a set of electrodes implanted into precise centers in the brain. The electrodes are connected to a wire extension, threaded under the skin from the head to the upper chest. The extension is connected to an electrical neurostimulator implanted into the chest near the clavicle, or collarbone. The stimulator delivers continuous electrical signals into the patient's brain. The electrical impulses block the signals that cause Parkinsonian movement. Once implanted, the stimulator can be adjusted from outside the patient's body. Using radio waves, the stimulator can be set to achieve maximum control and symptom relief. Additional surgery is only necessary to replace the stimulator after its three-year life span. The "brain pacemaker" can achieve up to 85% improvement in symptoms and may allow patients to resume normal activities.

Human Systems Work Together

Integumentary System

Brain controls nerves that regulate size of cutaneous blood vessels, activate sweat glands and arrector pili muscles.

Skin protects nerves, helps regulate body temperature; skin receptors send sensory input to brain.

Skeletal System

Receptors send sensory input from bones and joints to brain.

Bones protect sense organs, brain, and spinal cord; store Ca^{2+} for nerve function.

Muscular System

Brain controls nerves that innervate muscles; receptors send sensory input from muscles to brain.

Muscle contraction moves eyes, permits speech, and creates facial expressions.

Endocrine System

Hypothalamus is part of endocrine system; nerves innervate certain glands of secretion.

Sex hormones affect development of brain.

Cardiovascular System

Brain controls nerves that regulate the heart and dilation of blood vessels.

Blood vessels deliver nutrients and oxygen to neurons, carry away wastes.

How the Nervous System works with other body systems

Lymphatic System/Immunity

Microglial cells engulf and destroy pathogens.

Lymphatic vessels pick up excess tissue fluid; immune system protects against infections of nerves.

Respiratory System

Respiratory centers in brain regulate breathing rate.

Lungs provide oxygen for neurons and rid the body of carbon dioxide produced by neurons.

Digestive System

Brain controls nerves that innervate smooth muscle and permit digestive tract movements.

Digestive tract provides nutrients for growth, maintenance, and repair of neurons and neuroglial cells.

Urinary System

Brain controls nerves that innervate muscles that permit urination.

Kidneys maintain blood levels of Na^+, K^+, and Ca^{2+}, which are needed for nerve conduction.

Reproductive System

Brain controls onset of puberty; nerves are involved in erection of penis and clitoris, contraction of ducts that carry gametes, and contraction of uterus.

Sex hormones masculinize or feminize the brain, exert feedback control over the hypothalamus, and influence sexual behavior.

Basic Key Terms

acetylcholine (as″ē-til-ko′lēn), p. 145

acetylcholinesterase (as″ē-til-ko″lin-es′ter-ās), p. 145

action potential (ak′-shun po-ten′shul), p. 143

arachnoid membrane (uh-rak′noyd mem′brān), p. 146

association area (uh-so″se-a′shun a′re-uh), p. 149

autonomic system (aw″to-nom′ik sis′tem), p. 152

axon (ak′son), p. 142

basal nuclei (bas′al nu′kle-i), p. 151

cell body (sel bod′e), p. 142

central nervous system (sen′tral ner′vus sis′tem), p. 141

cerebellum (sĕr″ĕ-bel′um), p. 151

cerebral cortex (sĕr′ĕ-bral kor′teks), p. 149

cerebral hemisphere (sĕr′ĕ-bral hem′ĭ-sfēr), p. 149

cerebrospinal fluid (sĕr″e-bro-spi′nal flu′id), p. 146

cerebrum (sĕr′ĕ-brum), p. 148

cranial nerve (kra′ne-al nerve), p. 152

dendrite (den′drīt), p. 142

diencephalon (di″en-sef′uh-lon), p. 151

ganglion (gang′gle-on), p. 152

gray matter (grā mat′er), p. 146

hypothalamus (hi″po-thal′uh-mus), p. 151

interneuron (in″ter-nu′ron), p. 142

limbic system (lim′bik sis′tem), p. 151

meninges (mĕ-nin′jez), p. 146

midbrain (mid′brān), p. 151

nerve (nerv), p. 152

nerve impulse (nerv im′puls), p. 143

neuron (nu′ron), p. 142

neurotransmitter (nu″ro-trans′mit-er), p. 145

norepinephrine (nor″ep-ĭ-nef′rin), p. 145

parasympathetic division (pār″uh-sim″puh-thet′ik dĭ-vizh′un), p. 157

peripheral nervous system (pĕ-rif′er-al ner′vus sis′tem), p. 141

pons (ponz), p. 151

posterior-root ganglion (pos-tēr′e-or-rut gang′gle-on), p. 154

primary motor area (pri′ma-re mo′tor a′re-uh), p. 149

primary somatosensory area (pri′ma-re so″mă-to-sen′so-re a′re-uh), p. 149

reflex (re′fleks), p. 154

somatic system (so-mat′ik sis′tem), p. 152

spinal cord (spi′nal kord), p. 146

spinal nerve (spi′nal nerv), p. 152

sympathetic division (sim″puh-thet′ik dĭ-vizh′un), p. 157

synapse (sin′aps), p. 145

synaptic cleft (sĭ-nap′tik kleft), p. 145

thalamus (thal′uh-mus), p. 151

tract (trakt), p. 146

ventricle (ven′trĭ-kl), p. 146

white matter (whīt mat′er), p. 146

Clinical Key Terms

Alzheimer disease (altz′hi-mer dĭ-zēz′), p. 145

ankle-jerk reflex (an′kl-jerk re′fleks), p. 155

cerebral palsy (sĕr′ĕ-bral pal′ze), p. 149

electroencephalogram (e-lek″tro-en-sef′uh-lo-gram), p. 151

epidural hematoma (ep″ĭ-du′ral he″muh-to′muh), p. 146

hydrocephalus (hi″dro-sĕ′fuh-lus), p. 146

knee-jerk reflex (ne′jerk re′fleks), p. 155

paraplegia (par-uh-ple′je-uh), p. 147

Parkinson disease (par′kin-sun dĭ-zēz′), p. 158

quadriplegia (kwah-druh-ple′je-uh), p. 147

stroke (strōk), p. 149

subdural hematoma (sub″du′ral he″muh-to′muh), p. 146

8.1 Nervous System

A. The nervous system permits sensory input, performs integration, and stimulates motor output.

B. The nervous system is divided into the central nervous system (brain and spinal cord) and the peripheral nervous system (somatic and autonomic nervous systems). The CNS lies in the midline of the body, and the PNS is located peripherally to the CNS.

C. Nervous tissue contains neurons and neuroglia. Each type of neuron (motor, sensory, and interneuron) has three parts (dendrites, cell body, and axon). Neuroglia support, protect, and nourish the neurons.

D. All axons transmit the same type of nerve impulse: a change in polarity (called an action potential) that moves along the membrane of a nerve fiber. Saltatory conduction in myelinated axons is a faster type of conduction.

E. Transmission of a nerve impulse across a synapse is dependent on the release of a neurotransmitter into a synaptic cleft.

8.2 Central Nervous System

A. The CNS, consisting of the spinal cord and brain, is protected by the meninges and the cerebrospinal fluid.

B. The spinal cord, located in the vertebral column, is composed of white matter and gray matter. White matter contains bundles of nerve fibers, called tracts, that conduct nerve impulses to and from the higher centers of the brain. Gray matter is mainly made up of short fibers and cell bodies. The spinal cord is a center for reflex action and allows communication between the brain and the peripheral nerves leaving the spinal cord.

C. The brain has four ventricles. The lateral ventricles are found in the left and right cerebral hemispheres. The third ventricle is found in the diencephalon. The fourth ventricle is found in the brain stem.

D. The cerebrum is divided into the left and right hemispheres. The cerebral cortex, a thin layer of gray matter, has four lobes in each hemisphere. The frontal lobe initiates motor output. The parietal lobe is the final receptor for sensory input from the skin and muscles. The other lobes receive specific sensory input.

Various association areas integrate sensory data. Processing centers integrate data from other association areas: The prefrontal area carries out higher mental processes; Broca's area and Wernicke's area are concerned with speech.

E. The limbic system includes portions of the cerebrum, the thalamus, and the hypothalamus. It is involved in learning and memory and in causing the emotions that guide behavior.

F. The hypothalamus helps control the functioning of most internal organs and controls the secretions of the pituitary gland. The thalamus receives sensory impulses from all parts of the body and channels them to the cerebrum.

G. The cerebellum controls balance and complex muscular movements.

H. The brain stem contains the medulla oblongata, pons, and midbrain. The medulla oblongata contains vital centers for regulating heartbeat, breathing, and blood pressure. The pons assists the medulla oblongata in regulating the breathing rate. The midbrain contains tracts that conduct impulses to and from the higher parts of the brain.

8.3 Peripheral Nervous System

A. A nerve contains bundles of long fibers covered by fibrous connective tissue layers.

B. In the somatic nervous system, cranial nerves take impulses to and/or from the brain. Spinal nerves take impulses to and from the spinal cord.

C. Reflexes (automatic reactions to internal and external stimuli) depend on the reflex arc. Some reflexes are important for avoiding injury, and others are necessary for normal physiological functions.

D. The autonomic nervous system controls the functioning of internal organs.

1. The divisions of the autonomic nervous system: (1) function automatically and usually subconsciously in an involuntary manner; (2) innervate all internal organs; and (3) utilize two motor neurons and one ganglion for each impulse.

2. The sympathetic division brings about the responses associated with the "fight-or-flight" response.

3. The parasympathetic division brings about the responses associated with normally restful activities.

8.4 Effects of Aging

A. The brain loses nerve cells, and this affects learning, memory, and reasoning.

B. Alzheimer disease is more often seen among the elderly.

8.5 Homeostasis

A. The nervous system, along with the endocrine system, regulates and coordinates the other systems to maintain homeostasis.

B. Skeletal muscle contraction also plays a role because movement helps us take precautions or stay in a moderate environment.

Study Questions

1. What are the functions of the nervous system? (p. 141)
2. What are the two main divisions of the nervous system? How are these divisions subdivided? (p. 141)
3. What is the general structure of a neuron, and what are the functions of three different types of neurons? (p. 142)
4. What constitutes a nerve impulse (action potential)? Describe the resting potential. Why do myelinated fibers have a faster speed of conduction? (p. 143)
5. How is the nerve impulse transmitted across a synapse? Name two well-known neurotransmitters. (p. 145)
6. Name the meninges, and describe their locations. Where do you find cerebrospinal fluid? (p. 146)
7. Describe the structure and function of the spinal cord. (pp. 146–47)
8. What is the difference between the cerebrum and the cerebral cortex? Name the lobes of the cerebral cortex, and state their function. Describe the primary motor area and the primary somatosensory area. (pp. 148–49)
9. What is the limbic system, and what is its function? (p. 151)
10. Name the other parts of the brain, and give a location and function for each part. (p. 151)
11. Describe the structure of a nerve. In general, discuss the location and function of the cranial nerves and the spinal nerves. (pp. 152–54)
12. Describe a spinal reflex, including the role played by a sensory nerve fiber, interneurons, and a motor fiber. (pp. 154–55)
13. Contrast the actions of the sympathetic and the parasympathetic divisions of the autonomic system. (pp. 156–57)
14. What role does the nervous system play in homeostasis? (pp. 158–59)

Objective Questions

Fill in the blanks.

1. A(n) _____ carries nerve impulses away from the cell body.

2. During the depolarization portion of an action potential, _____ ions are moving to the _____ of the nerve fiber.

3. The space between the axon ending of one neuron and the dendrite of another is called the _____ .

4. ACh is broken down by the enzyme _____ after it has initiated an action potential on a neighboring neuron.

5. Motor nerves stimulate _____ .

6. In a reflex arc, only the _____ is completely within the CNS.

7. The _____ is the part of the brain responsible for coordinating body movements.

8. The _____ is the part of the brain responsible for consciousness.

9. The brain and spinal cord are covered by protective layers called _____ .

10. The vagus nerve is a _____ nerve that controls _____ .

11. Whereas the central nervous system is composed of the _____ and _____, the peripheral nervous system is composed of the _____ .

12. The limbic system records emotions and also is involved in _____ and _____ .

13. Whereas the _____ division of the autonomic nervous system brings about organ responses that are part of the "fight-or-flight" response, the _____ division brings about responses associated with normal restful conditions.

14. The electrical activity of the brain can be recorded in the form of a(n) _____ .

15. Label the following diagram.

a. _____
b. _____
c. _____
d. _____
e. _____
f. _____
g. _____
h. _____
i. _____
j. _____

Medical Terminology Reinforcement Exercise

Consult Appendix B for help in pronouncing and analyzing the meaning of the terms that follow.

1. neuropathogenesis (nu"ro-path"o-jen'ĕ-sis)
2. anesthesia (an"es-the'ze-uh)
3. encephalomyeloneuropathy (en-sef"uh-lo-mi"ĕ-lo-nu-rop'uh-the)
4. hemiplegia (hem"ĭ-ple'je-uh)
5. glioblastoma (gli"o-blas-to'muh)
6. subdural hemorrhage (sub-du'ral hem'or-ij)
7. cephalometer (sef"uh-lom'ĕ-ter)
8. meningoencephalocele (me-ning"go-en-sef"uh-lo-sēl)
9. neurorrhaphy (nu-rōr'uh-fe)
10. ataxiaphasia (uh-tak"se-uh-fa'ze-uh)
11. cerebrovascular accident (sĕr'-e-bro'-vas-kyū-ler ak'suh-dent)
12. duraplasty (du'ruh-plas-te)
13. brachycephalic (brak'e-sef-al'ik)
14. arachnoiditis (uh-rak"noy-di'tis)

Website Link

Visit the Student Edition of the Online Learning Center at http://www.mhhe.com/maderap5 **for additional quizzes, interactive learning exercises, and other study tools.**

The Sensory System

The activity of the brain's temporal lobe as a subject hears sound is detected (red and yellow) in this positron emission tomography (PET) scan.

chapter outline & learning objectives

After you have studied this chapter, you should be able to:

9.1 General Senses (p. 164)
- Categorize sensory receptors according to five types of stimuli.
- Discuss the function of proprioceptors.
- Relate specific sensory receptors in the skin to particular senses of the skin.
- Discuss the phenomenon of referred pain.

9.2 Senses of Taste and Smell (p. 166)
- Name the chemoreceptors, and state their location, anatomy, and mechanism of action.

9.3 Sense of Vision (p. 168)
- Describe the anatomy and function of the accessory organs of the eye.

- Describe the anatomy of the eye, and give a function of each part.
- Describe the sensory receptors for sight, their mechanism of action, and the mechanism for stereoscopic vision.
- Describe some common disorders of sight.

9.4 Sense of Hearing (p. 178)
- Describe the anatomy of the ear, and give a function of each part.
- Describe the sensory receptors for hearing and their mechanism of action.

9.5 Sense of Equilibrium (p. 181)
- Describe the sensory receptors for equilibrium and their mechanism of action.

9.6 Effects of Aging (p. 181)
- Describe the anatomical and physiological changes that occur in the sensory system as we age.

Medical Focus
Corrective Lenses (p. 172)
Hearing Damage and Deafness (p. 182)

What's New
A Bionic Cure for Macular Degeneration (pp. 176–77)

When a sensory receptor is stimulated, it generates nerve impulses that travel to your brain. Interpretation of these impulses is the function of the brain, which has a special region for receiving information from each of the sense organs. Impulses arriving at a particular sensory area of the brain can be interpreted in only one way; for example, those arriving at the olfactory area result in smell sensation, and those arriving at the visual area result in sight sensation. The brain integrates data from various sensory receptors in order to perceive whatever caused the stimulation of olfactory and visual receptors—for example, a flower.

Sensory receptors may be categorized into five types based on their stimuli:

Mechanoreceptors, such as proprioceptors in muscles and pressure receptors in the skin, are stimulated by changes in pressure or movement.
Thermoreceptors, such as the temperature receptors in the skin, are stimulated by changes in temperature.
Pain receptors, such as those in skin, are stimulated by tissue damage.
Chemoreceptors, such as those for taste and smell, are stimulated by changes in the chemical concentration of substances.
Photoreceptors, which are only located in the eye, are stimulated by light energy.

9.1 General Senses

Sensory receptors in the muscles, joints and tendons, other internal organs, and skin send nerve impulses to the spinal cord. From there, they travel up the spinal cord in tracts to the somatosensory areas of the cerebral cortex. These general sensory receptors can be categorized into three types: proprioceptors, cutaneous receptors, and pain receptors.

Proprioceptors

Proprioceptors are mechanoreceptors involved in reflex actions that maintain muscle tone and thereby the body's equilibrium and posture. They help us know the position of our limbs in space by detecting the degree of muscle relaxation, the stretch of tendons, and the movement of ligaments. Muscle spindles act to increase the degree of muscle contraction, and Golgi tendon organs act to decrease it. The result is a muscle that has the proper length and tension, or muscle tone.

Figure 9.1 illustrates the activity of a muscle spindle. In a muscle spindle, sensory nerve endings are wrapped around thin muscle cells within a connective tissue sheath. When the muscle relaxes and undue stretching of the muscle spindle occurs, nerve impulses are generated. The rapidity of the nerve impulses generated by the muscle spindle is proportional to the stretching of a muscle. A reflex action then occurs, which results in contraction of muscle fibers adjoining the muscle spindle. The knee-jerk reflex, which involves muscle spindles, offers an opportunity for physicians to test a reflex action.

The information sent by muscle spindles to the CNS is used to maintain the body's equilibrium and posture despite the force of gravity always acting upon the skeleton and muscles.

Cutaneous Receptors

The skin is composed of two layers: the epidermis and the dermis. In Figure 9.2, the artist has dramatically indicated these two layers by separating the epidermis from the dermis in one location. The epidermis is stratified squamous epithelium in which cells become keratinized as they rise to the surface where they are sloughed off. The dermis is a thick connective tissue layer. The dermis contains **cutaneous receptors,** which make the skin sensitive to touch, pressure, pain, and temperature (warmth and cold). The dermis is a mosaic of these tiny sensory receptors, as you can determine by slowly passing a metal probe over your skin. At certain points, you will feel touch or pressure, and at others, you will feel heat or cold (depending on the probe's temperature).

Figure 9.1 Muscle spindle. When a muscle is stretched, a muscle spindle sends sensory nerve impulses to the spinal cord. Motor nerve impulses from the spinal cord result in muscle fiber contraction so that muscle tone is maintained.

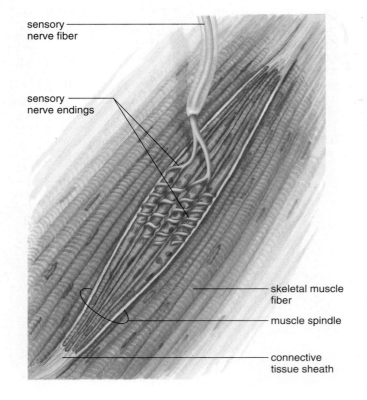

sensory nerve fiber

sensory nerve endings

skeletal muscle fiber

muscle spindle

connective tissue sheath

Three types of cutaneous receptors are sensitive to fine touch. *Meissner corpuscles* are concentrated in the fingertips, the palms, the lips, the tongue, the nipples, the penis, and the clitoris. *Merkel disks* are found where the epidermis meets the dermis. A free nerve ending called a *root hair plexus* winds around the base of a hair follicle and fires if the hair is touched.

The three different types of cutaneous receptors that are sensitive to pressure are Pacinian corpuscles, Ruffini endings, and Krause end bulbs. *Pacinian corpuscles* are onion-shaped sensory receptors that lie deep inside the dermis. *Ruffini endings* and *Krause end bulbs* are encapsulated by sheaths of connective tissue and contain lacy networks of nerve fibers.

Temperature receptors are simply free nerve endings in the epidermis. Some free nerve endings are responsive to cold; others are responsive to warmth. Cold receptors are far more numerous than warmth receptors, but the two types have no known structural differences.

Pain Receptors

Like the skin, many internal organs have pain receptors, also called *nociceptors*, which are sensitive to chemicals released by damaged tissues. When inflammation occurs due to mechanical, thermal, electrical, or toxic substances, cells release chemicals that stimulate pain receptors. Aspirin and ibuprofen reduce pain by inhibiting the synthesis of one class of these chemicals.

Sometimes, stimulation of internal pain receptors is felt as pain from the skin as well as the internal organs. This is called **referred pain**. Some internal organs have a referred pain relationship with areas located in the skin of the back, groin, and abdomen; for example, pain from the heart is felt in the left shoulder and arm. This most likely happens when nerve impulses from the pain receptors of internal organs travel to the spinal cord and synapse with neurons also receiving impulses from the skin.

Figure 9.2 Sensory receptors in human skin. The classical view is that each sensory receptor has the main function shown here. However, investigators report that matters are not so clear-cut. For example, microscopic examination of the skin of the ear shows only free nerve endings (pain receptors), and yet the skin of the ear is sensitive to all sensations. Therefore, it appears that the receptors of the skin are somewhat, but not completely, specialized.

free nerve endings (pain, heat, cold)

Merkel disks (touch)

Krause end bulbs (touch)

root hair plexus (touch)

epidermis

Meissner corpuscles (touch)

Pacinian corpuscles (pressure)

dermis

Ruffini endings (pressure)

9.2 Senses of Taste and Smell

Taste and smell are called chemical senses because their receptors are sensitive to molecules in the food we eat and the air we breathe. The body also has other chemoreceptors.

Chemoreceptors in the carotid arteries and in the aorta are primarily sensitive to the pH of the blood. These bodies communicate via sensory nerve fibers with the respiratory center in the medulla oblongata. When the pH drops, they signal this center, and immediately thereafter the breathing rate increases. The expiration of CO_2 raises the pH of the blood.

Sense of Taste

The sensory receptors for the sense of taste are located in **taste buds**. Taste buds are embedded in epithelium primarily on the tongue (Fig. 9.3). Many lie along the walls of the papillae, the small elevations on the tongue that are visible to the naked eye. Isolated taste buds are also present on the hard palate, the pharynx, and the epiglottis. We have at least four primary types of taste, but the taste buds for each are located throughout the tongue (Fig. 9.3a). Even so, certain regions of the tongue are most sensitive to particular tastes: The tip of the tongue is most sensitive to sweet tastes; the margins to salty and sour tastes; and the rear of the tongue to bitter tastes.

How the Brain Receives Taste Information

Taste buds open at a taste pore. They have supporting cells and a number of elongated taste cells that end in microvilli. The microvilli of taste cells project through the taste pore. These microvilli have receptor proteins for molecules that cause the brain to distinguish between sweet, sour, salty, and bitter tastes. When these molecules bind to receptor proteins, nerve impulses are generated in associated sensory nerve fibers. These nerve impulses go to the brain, including the cortical areas, which interpret them as tastes.

Since we can respond to a range of sweet, sour, salty, and bitter tastes, the brain appears to survey the overall pattern of incoming sensory impulses and to take a "weighted average" of their taste messages as the perceived taste. Again, we can note that even though our senses are dependent on sensory receptors, the brain integrates the incoming information and gives us our sense perceptions.

Figure 9.3 Taste buds. **a.** Papillae on the tongue contain taste buds that are sensitive to sweet, sour, salty, and bitter tastes. **b.** Enlargement of papillae. **c.** Taste buds occur along the walls of the papillae. **d.** Taste cells end in microvilli that bear receptor proteins for certain molecules. When molecules bind to the receptor proteins, nerve impulses are generated that go to the brain, where the sensation of taste occurs.

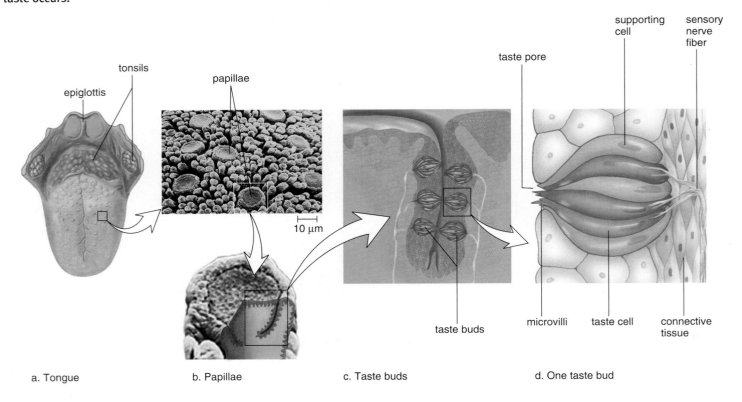

a. Tongue
b. Papillae
c. Taste buds
d. One taste bud

Sense of Smell

Our sense of smell is dependent on **olfactory cells** located within olfactory epithelium high in the roof of the nasal cavity (Fig. 9.4). Olfactory cells are modified neurons. Each cell ends in a tuft of about five olfactory cilia, which bear receptor proteins for odor molecules. The brain distinguishes odors after odor molecules bind to the receptor proteins.

How the Brain Receives Odor Information

Each olfactory cell has only one type out of 1,000 different types of receptor proteins. Nerve fibers from like olfactory cells lead to the same neuron in the olfactory bulb, an extension of the brain. An odor contains many odor molecules, which activate a characteristic combination of receptor proteins. For example, a rose might stimulate olfactory cells, designated by purple and green in Figure 9.4, while a hyacinth might stimulate a different combination. An odor's signature in the olfactory bulb is determined by which neurons are stimulated. When the neurons communicate this information via the olfactory tract to the olfactory areas of the cerebral cortex, we know we have smelled a rose or a hyacinth.

Have you ever noticed that a certain aroma vividly brings to mind a certain person or place? A person's perfume may remind you of someone else, or the smell of boxwood may remind you of your grandfather's farm. The olfactory bulbs have direct connections with the limbic system and its centers for emotions and memory. One investigator showed that when subjects smelled an orange while viewing a painting, they not only remembered the painting when asked about it later, but they also had many deep feelings about it.

Sense of Taste and Sense of Smell

Actually, the sense of taste and the sense of smell work together to create a combined effect when interpreted by the cerebral cortex. For example, when you have a cold, you think food has lost its taste, but most likely you have lost the ability to sense its smell. This method works in reverse also. When you smell something, some of the molecules move from the nose down into the mouth region and stimulate the taste buds there. Therefore, part of what we refer to as smell may in fact be taste.

Figure 9.4 Olfactory cell location and anatomy. **a.** The olfactory epithelium in humans is located in the nasal cavity. **b.** Olfactory cells end in cilia that bear receptor proteins for specific odor molecules. The cilia of each olfactory cell can bind to only one type of odor molecule (signified here by color). For example, if a rose causes olfactory cells sensitive to "purple" and "green" odor molecules to be stimulated, then neurons designated by purple and green in the olfactory bulb are activated. The primary olfactory area of the cerebral cortex interprets the pattern of stimulation as the scent of a rose.

a.

b.

Figure 9.5 Accessory structures of the orbit. **a.** Sagittal section of the eye and orbit. **b.** The lacrimal apparatus.

a.

b.

9.3 Sense of Vision

The photoreceptors for sight are in the eyes. The eyes are located in orbits formed by seven of the skull's bones (frontal, lacrimal, ethmoid, zygomatic, maxilla, sphenoid, and palatine). The bony ridge superior to the orbits, called the *supraorbital ridge,* protects the eye from blows, and serves as a location for the eyebrows. The eye has certain accessory organs.

Accessory Organs of the Eye

Accessory organs of the eye include: (1) the eyebrows, eyelids, and eyelashes; (2) the lacrimal apparatus, which produces tears; and (3) the extrinsic muscles that move the eye.

Eyebrows, Eyelids, and Eyelashes

Eyebrows have short, thick hairs positioned transversely above the eye along the supraorbital ridge (Fig. 9.5a). Eyebrows shade the eyes from the sun and prevent perspiration or debris from falling into the eye.

Eyelids are a continuation of the skin. The eyelashes of the eye can trap debris and keep it from entering the eyes.

Sebaceous glands associated with each eyelash produce an oily secretion that lubricates the eye. Inflammation of one of the glands is called a sty.

Blinking of eyelids keeps the eye lubricated and free of debris. The eyelids are operated by the orbicularis oculi muscle which closes the lid, and by the levator palpebrae superioris muscle which raises the lid. A person with myasthenia gravis has weakness in these muscles due to an inability to respond to acetylcholine, and the eyelids often have to be taped open.

The inner surface of an eyelid is lined by a transparent mucous membrane, called the **conjunctiva.** The conjunctiva folds back to cover the anterior of the eye, except for the cornea which is covered by a delicate epithelium.

Lacrimal Apparatus

A **lacrimal apparatus** consists of the lacrimal gland and the lacrimal sac with its ducts (Fig. 9.5b). The lacrimal gland, which lies in the orbit above the eye, produces tears that flow over the eye when the eyelids are blinked. The tears, collected by two small ducts, pass into the lacrimal sac before draining into the nose by way of the nasolacrimal duct.

Figure 9.6 Extrinsic muscles of the eye, along with the anatomy of the eyelids and eyelashes.

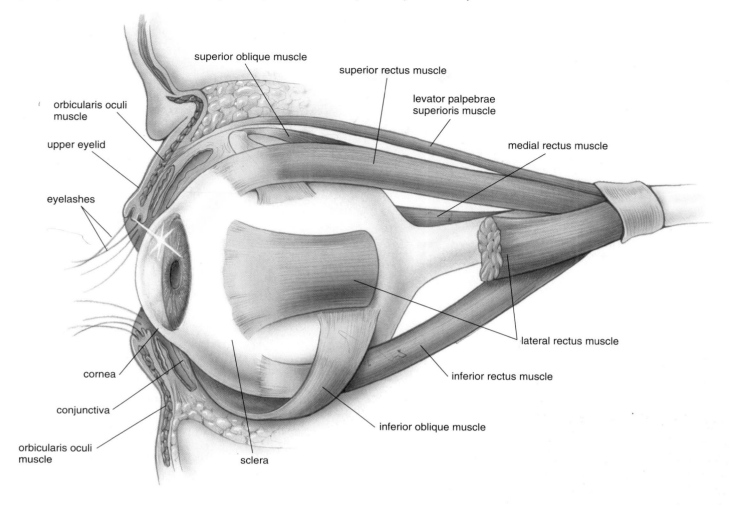

- superior oblique muscle
- superior rectus muscle
- orbicularis oculi muscle
- levator palpebrae superioris muscle
- upper eyelid
- medial rectus muscle
- eyelashes
- cornea
- conjunctiva
- orbicularis oculi muscle
- sclera
- inferior oblique muscle
- inferior rectus muscle
- lateral rectus muscle

Extrinsic Muscles

Within an orbit, the eye is anchored in place by the **extrinsic muscles,** whose contractions move the eyes. Each of these muscles originates from the bony orbit and inserts by tendons to the outer layer of the eyeball. There are three pairs of antagonistic extrinsic muscles (Fig. 9.6):

First pair:

Superior rectus	Rolls eye upward
Inferior rectus	Rolls eye downward

Second pair:

Lateral rectus	Turns eye outward, away from mid-line
Medial rectus	Turns eye inward, toward midline

Third pair:

Superior oblique	Rotates eye counterclockwise
Inferior oblique	Rotates eye clockwise

Although stimulation of each muscle causes a precise movement of the eyeball, most movements of the eyeball involve the combined contraction of two or more muscles. For example, if your left eye is directed upward toward your nose, which muscles are required? The answer is the superior and medial rectus muscles.

Three cranial nerves—the oculomotor, abducens, and trochlear nerves—control these muscles. The oculomotor nerve innervates the superior, inferior, and medial rectus muscles, as well as the inferior oblique muscles; the abducens nerve innervates the lateral rectus muscle; and the trochlear nerve innervates the superior oblique muscle. The motor units of these muscles are the smallest in the body. A single motor axon serves only about 10 muscle fibers, allowing eyeball movements to be very precise.

Figure 9.7 Anatomy of the human eye. Notice that the sclera, the outer layer of the eye, becomes the cornea and that the choroid, the middle layer, is continuous with the ciliary body and the iris. The retina, the inner layer, contains the photoreceptors for vision; the fovea centralis is the region where vision is most acute.

Anatomy and Physiology of the Eye

The eyeball, which is an elongated sphere about 2.5 cm in diameter, has three layers, or coats: the sclera, the choroid, and the retina (Fig. 9.7). Only the retina contains photoreceptors for light energy. Table 9.1 gives the functions of the parts of the eye.

The outer layer, the **sclera,** is white and fibrous except for the **cornea,** which is made of transparent collagen fibers. The cornea is the window of the eye. The middle, thin, darkly pigmented layer, the **choroid,** is vascular and absorbs stray light rays that photoreceptors have not absorbed. Toward the front, the choroid becomes the donut-shaped **iris.** The iris regulates the size of the **pupil,** a hole in the center of the iris through which light enters the eyeball. The color of the iris (and therefore the color of your eyes) correlates with its pigmentation. Heavily pigmented eyes are brown, while lightly pigmented eyes are green or blue. Behind the iris, the choroid thickens and forms the circular ciliary body. The **ciliary body** contains the **ciliary muscle,** which controls the shape of the lens for near and far vision.

The **lens,** attached to the ciliary body by ligaments, divides the eye into two compartments; the one in front of the lens is the anterior compartment, and the one behind the lens

Table 9.1	Functions of the Parts of the Eye
Part	**Function**
Sclera	Protects and supports eyeball
Cornea	Refracts light rays
Pupil	Admits light
Choroid	Absorbs stray light
Ciliary body	Holds lens in place, accommodation
Iris	Regulates light entrance
Retina	Contains sensory receptors for sight
Rods	Make black-and-white vision possible
Cones	Make color vision possible
Fovea centralis	Makes acute vision possible
Other	
Lens	Refracts and focuses light rays
Humors	Transmit light rays and support eyeball
Optic nerve	Transmits impulse to brain

is the posterior compartment. The anterior compartment is filled with a clear, watery fluid called the **aqueous humor.** A small amount of aqueous humor is continually produced each day. Normally, it leaves the anterior compartment by way of tiny ducts. When a person has **glaucoma,** these drainage ducts are blocked, and aqueous humor builds up. If glaucoma is not treated, the resulting pressure compresses the arteries that serve the nerve fibers of the retina, where photoreceptors are located. The nerve fibers begin to die due to lack of nutrients, and the person becomes partially blind. Eventually, total blindness can result.

The third layer of the eye, the **retina,** is located in the posterior compartment, which is filled with a clear, gelatinous material called the **vitreous humor.** The retina contains photoreceptors called rod cells and cone cells. The rods are very sensitive to light, but they do not see color; therefore, at night or in a darkened room, we see only shades of gray. The cones, which require bright light, are sensitive to different wavelengths of light, and therefore we have the ability to distinguish colors. The retina has a very special region called the **fovea centralis** where cone cells are densely packed. Light is normally focused on the fovea when we look directly at an object. This is helpful because vision is most acute in the fovea centralis. Sensory fibers from the retina form the **optic nerve,** which takes nerve impulses to the brain.

Function of the Lens

The lens, assisted by the cornea and the humors, focuses images on the retina (Fig. 9.8*a*). Focusing starts with the cornea and continues as the rays pass through the lens and the humor. The image produced is much smaller than the object because light rays are bent (refracted) when they are brought into focus. Notice that the image on the retina is inverted (upside down) and reversed from left to right.

The shape of the lens is controlled by the ciliary muscle within the ciliary body. When we view a distant object, the ciliary muscle is relaxed, causing the suspensory ligaments attached to the ciliary body to be taut; therefore, the lens remains relatively flat (Fig. 9.8*b*). When we view a near object, the ciliary muscle contracts, releasing the tension on the suspensory ligaments, and the lens rounds up due to its natural elasticity (Fig. 9.8*c*). As discussed in the Medical Focus on page 172, if the eyeball is too long or too short, the person may need corrective lenses to **focus** the image on the retina.

Figure 9.8 Focusing. **a.** Light rays from each point on an object are bent by the cornea and the lens in such a way that an inverted and reversed image of the object forms on the retina. **b.** When focusing on a distant object, the lens is flat because the ciliary muscle is relaxed and the suspensory ligament is taut. **c.** When focusing on a near object, the lens accommodates; it becomes rounded because the ciliary muscle contracts, causing the suspensory ligament to relax.

a. Focusing

b. Focusing on distant object

c. Focusing on near object

Accommodation It is said that **visual accommodation** must occur for close vision. Because close work requires contraction of the ciliary muscle, it very often causes muscle fatigue, known as eyestrain.

Usually after the age of 40, the lens loses some of its elasticity and is unable to accommodate. Bifocal lenses may then be necessary for those who already have corrective lenses.

Corrective Lenses

The majority of people can see what is designated as a size 20 letter 20 feet away, and so are said to have 20/20 vision. Persons who can see close objects but cannot see the letters from this distance have **myopia**—that is, nearsightedness. Nearsighted people can see close objects better than they can see objects at a distance. These individuals have an elongated eyeball, and when they attempt to look at a distant object, the image is brought to focus in front of the retina (Fig. 9A*a*). They can see close objects because they can adjust the lens to allow the image to focus on the retina, but to see distant objects, these people must wear concave lenses, which diverge the light rays so that the image can be focused on the retina.

Rather than wear glasses or contact lenses, many nearsighted people are now choosing to undergo laser surgery. First, specialists determine how much the cornea needs to be flattened to achieve visual acuity. Controlled by a computer, the laser then removes this amount of the cornea. Most patients achieve at least 20/40 vision, but a few complain of glare and varying visual acuity.

Persons who can easily see the optometrist's chart but cannot see close objects well have **hyperopia**—that is, farsightedness. These individuals can see distant objects better than they can see close objects. They have a shortened eyeball, and when they try to see close objects, the image is focused behind the retina (Fig. 9A*b*). When the object is distant, the lens can compensate for the short eyeball, but when the object is close, these persons must wear a convex lens to increase the bending of light rays so that the image can be focused on the retina.

When the cornea or lens is uneven, the image is fuzzy. The light rays cannot be evenly focused on the retina. This condition, called **astigmatism,** can be corrected by an unevenly ground lens to compensate for the uneven cornea (Fig. 9A*c*).

Figure 9A Common abnormalities of the eye, with possible corrective lenses. **a.** A concave lens in nearsighted persons focuses light rays on the retina. **b.** A convex lens in farsighted persons focuses light rays on the retina. **c.** An uneven lens in persons with astigmatism focuses light rays on the retina.

Light rays from far object

normal eyeball

Long eyeball; rays focus in front of retina when viewing distant objects.

Concave lens allows subject to see distant objects.

a. Nearsightedness

Light rays from near object

normal eyeball

Short eyeball; rays focus behind retina when viewing close objects.

Convex lens allows subject to see close objects.

b. Farsightedness

Light rays from far object

Uneven cornea; rays do not focus evenly.

Uneven lens allows subject to see objects clearly.

c. Astigmatism

Figure 9.9 Photoreceptors in the eye. The outer segment of rods and cones contains stacks of membranous disks, which contain visual pigments. In rods, the membrane of each disk contains rhodopsin, a complex molecule containing the protein opsin and the pigment retinal. When retinal absorbs light energy, it splits, releasing opsin, which sets in motion a cascade of reactions that cause ion channels in the plasma membrane to close. Thereafter, nerve impulses go to the brain.

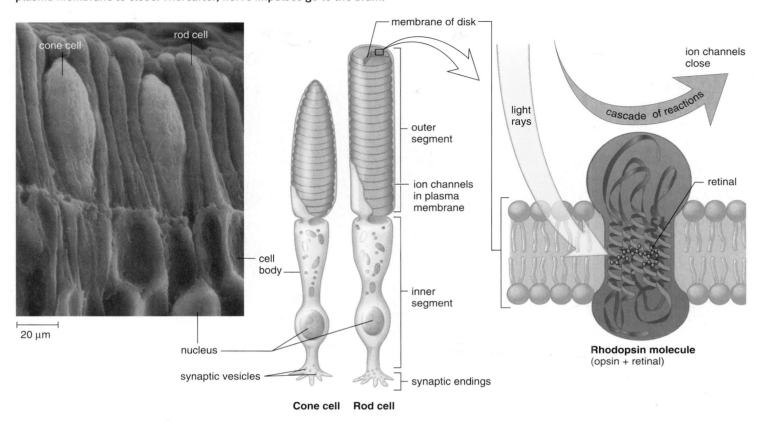

Cone cell   Rod cell

Rhodopsin molecule
(opsin + retinal)

Vision Pathway

The pathway for vision begins once light has been focused on the photoreceptors in the retina. Some integration occurs in the retina where nerve impulses begin before the optic nerve transmits them to the brain.

Function of Photoreceptors Figure 9.9 illustrates the structure of the photoreceptors called **rod cells** and **cone cells.** Both rods and cones have an outer segment joined to an inner segment by a stalk. Pigment molecules are embedded in the membrane of the many disks present in the outer segment. Synaptic vesicles are located at the synaptic endings of the inner segment.

The visual pigment in rods is a deep purple pigment called rhodopsin. **Rhodopsin** is a complex molecule made up of the protein opsin and a light-absorbing molecule called **retinal,** which is a derivative of vitamin A. When a rod absorbs light, rhodopsin splits into opsin and retinal, leading to a cascade of reactions and the closure of ion channels in the rod cell's plasma membrane. The release of inhibitory transmitter molecules from the rod's synaptic vesicles ceases.

Thereafter, nerve impulses go to the visual area of the cerebral cortex. Rods are very sensitive to light and therefore are suited to night vision. (Because carrots are rich in vitamin A, it is true that eating carrots can improve your night vision.) Rod cells are plentiful throughout the entire retina; therefore, they also provide us with peripheral vision and perception of motion.

The cones, on the other hand, are located primarily in the fovea and are activated by bright light. They allow us to detect the fine detail and the color of an object. Therefore, the condition called macular degeneration, which affects the fovea, is particularly devastating. The What's New reading on page 176 describes the condition and tells of a promising treatment that may soon be available.

Color vision depends on three different kinds of cones, which contain pigments called the B (blue), G (green), and R (red) pigments. Each pigment is made up of retinal and opsin, but there is a slight difference in the opsin structure of each, which accounts for their individual absorption patterns. Various combinations of cones are believed to be stimulated by in-between shades of color.

Figure 9.10 Structure and function of the retina. **a.** The retina is the inner layer of the eyeball. Rod cells and cone cells, located at the back of the retina nearest the choroid, synapse with bipolar cells, which synapse with ganglion cells. Integration of signals occurs at these synapses; therefore, much processing occurs in bipolar and ganglion cells. Further, notice that many rod cells share one bipolar cell, but cone cells do not. Certain cone cells synapse with only one bipolar cell. Cone cells, in general, distinguish more detail than do rod cells. **b.** This micrograph shows that the sclera and choroid are relatively thin compared to the retina, which is composed of several layers of cells.

a. Drawing of retina

b. Micrograph of retina

Function of the Retina The retina has three layers of neurons (Fig. 9.10). The layer closest to the choroid contains the rod cells and cone cells; the middle layer contains bipolar cells; and the innermost layer contains ganglion cells, whose sensory fibers become the *optic nerve*. Only the rod cells and the cone cells are sensitive to light, and therefore light must penetrate to the back of the retina before they are stimulated.

The rod cells and the cone cells synapse with the bipolar cells, which in turn synapse with ganglion cells that initiate nerve impulses. Notice in Figure 9.10 that there are many more rod cells and cone cells than ganglion cells. In fact, the retina has as many as 150 million rod cells and 6 million cone cells but only one million ganglion cells. The sensitivity of cones versus rods is mirrored by how directly they connect to ganglion cells. As many as 150 rods may activate the same ganglion cell. No wonder stimulation of rods results in vision that is blurred and indistinct. In contrast, some cone cells in the fovea centralis activate only one ganglion cell. This explains why cones, especially in the fovea, provide us with a sharper, more detailed image of an object.

As signals pass to bipolar cells and ganglion cells, integration occurs. Each ganglion cell receives signals from rod cells covering about one square millimeter of retina (about the size of a thumbtack hole). This region is the ganglion cell's receptive field. Some time ago, scientists discovered that a ganglion cell is stimulated only by nerve impulses received from the center of its receptive field; otherwise, it is inhibited. If all the rod cells in the receptive field receive light, the ganglion cell responds in a neutral way—that is, it reacts only weakly or perhaps not at all. This supports the hypothesis that considerable processing occurs in the retina before nerve impulses are sent to the brain. Additional integration occurs in the visual areas of the cerebral cortex.

Blind Spot Figure 9.10 provides an opportunity to point out that there are no rods and cones where the optic nerve exits the retina. Therefore, no vision is possible in this area. You can prove this to yourself by putting a dot to the right of center on a piece of paper. Use your right hand to move the paper slowly toward your right eye while you look straight ahead. The dot will disappear at one point—this is your **blind spot**.

From the Retina to the Visual Cortex As stated, sensory fibers from the ganglion cells in the retina assemble to form the optic nerves. The **optic nerves** carry nerve impulses from the eyes to the optic chiasma. The **optic chiasma** has an X-shape formed by a crossing over of some of the optic nerve fibers. At the chiasma, fibers from the right half of each retina converge and continue on together in the *right optic tract*, and fibers from the left half of each retina converge and continue on together in the *left optic tract*.

The optic tracts sweep around the hypothalamus, and most fibers synapse with neurons in nuclei (masses of neuron cell bodies) in the thalamus. Axons from the thalamic nuclei form optic radiations that take nerve impulses to the primary visual areas of the occipital lobes (Fig. 9.11). The occipital lobes are a part of the cerebral cortex (see Fig. 8.9).

The *visual cortex* consists of the primary visual area and the visual association areas of the occipital lobes. Notice that the image arriving at the thalamus, and therefore the primary visual areas, has been split because the left optic tract carries information about the right portion of the visual field and the right optic tract carries information about the left portion of the visual field. Therefore, the right and left visual cortex must communicate with each other for us to see the entire visual field. Also, because the image is inverted and reversed (see Figs. 9.8 and 9.11) it must be righted for us to correctly perceive the visual field.

The most surprising finding has been that each primary visual area of the cerebral cortex acts like a post office, parceling out information regarding color, form, motion, and possibly other attributes to different portions of the adjoining visual association areas. In other words, the visual field has been taken apart even though we see a unified field. The visual association areas are believed to rebuild the field and give us an understanding of it.

Figure 9.11 Optic chiasma. Both eyes "see" the entire visual field. Because of the optic chiasma, data from the right half of each retina go to the right visual area of the cerebral cortex, and data from the left half of the retina go to the left visual area of the cerebral cortex. These data are then combined to allow us to see the entire visual field. Note that the visual pathway to the brain includes the thalamus, which has the ability to filter sensory stimuli.

primary visual area of occipital lobe

thalamic nucleus

optic tract

optic chiasma

optic nerve

Right visual field

Left visual field

A Bionic Cure for Macular Degeneration

As described in Figure 9.10, the retina is a three-layered tissue. The ganglion cells are the outermost layer, and light passing through the eye strikes these retinal cells first. The axons of ganglion cells form the optic nerve. Ganglion cells connect to the middle layer of bipolar cells. Bipolar cells then connect to rod and cone cells. The rod and cone cells are the actual photoreceptor cells, forming the deepest layer of the retina. When light enters the eye, it must penetrate the three layers—ganglion cells, bipolar cells, and finally the rods and cones. Recall that rods and cones contain the photochemicals that can respond to light. Rods respond to movement and changes in light intensity, and cones can respond to color. Once the rods or cones have responded, the nerve signal is sent backward through the retinal layers: from rod or cone, to bipolar cell, to ganglion cell, to the optic nerve, and from there to the visual cortex of the brain.

Macular Degeneration

If the photoreceptors—rods or cones—are destroyed, the individual will be blind, even if the rest of the visual pathway is undamaged. The most common cause of blindness in the Western world is age-related **macular degeneration,** which results in destruction of the macula lutea, a yellowish area in the central region of the retina. The macula lutea contains a concentration of cones, especially in the fovea centralis. Individuals with this condition have a distorted visual field: Blurriness or a blind spot is present, straight lines may look wavy, objects may appear larger or smaller than they are, and colors may look faded (Fig. 9B).

There are two main forms of age-related macular degeneration. "Wet" macular degeneration means that abnormal growth of new blood vessels is evident in the region of the macula. The blood vessels leak serum and blood, and the retina becomes distorted, leading to severe scarring that completely destroys the macula. "Dry" macular degeneration is not accompanied by the growth of blood vessels, and visual loss is less dramatic.

Heredity plays a role in the development of age-related macular degeneration: 15% of people with a family history of the condition develop the disease after age 60. Also, light-eyed people tend to be afflicted more frequently than dark-eyed people. Smoking, hypertension, and excessive sun exposure are possible contributing factors.

A yearly eye examination assists in the early detection of many eye diseases, including macular degeneration, cataracts, and glaucoma. When an ophthalmologist presents an Amsler grid (a crosshatched pattern of straight lines) to someone with macular degeneration, the grid looks blurred, distorted, or discolored. Signs of the "wet" form can be detected by an examination of the retina and confirmed by a fluorescein angiogram. In this test, a number of pictures are taken of the macula lutea after an orange dye has been injected into a vein in the patient's arm.

Currently, the treatment for the "dry" form of macular degeneration is the use of vitamin and mineral supplements, which may help stem the disease. For example, research indicates that consumption of zinc may prevent further loss of vision. On the other hand, when the "wet" form of the disease is diagnosed early, laser treatment can sometimes stop the growth of blood vessels.

Although people with age-related macular degeneration are classified as blind, they still have normal peripheral vision (outside the macula), which they can learn to use effectively. Because the periphery of the retina contains a high concentration of rods, vision there is less acute, and colors are not detected. But high-powered eyeglasses, magnifying devices, closed-circuit television, and special lamps can help patients see details more clearly.

Accumulating evidence suggests that both macular degeneration and cataracts, which tend to occur in the elderly, are caused by long-term exposure to the ultraviolet rays of the sun. Therefore, everyone—especially people who live in sunny climates or work outdoors—should wear sunglasses that absorb ultraviolet light. Large lenses worn close to the eyes offer further protection. The Sunglass Association of America has devised a system for categorizing sunglasses, which is helpful.

Figure 9B Macular degeneration. When a person with macular degeneration looks at a clump of trees, the trees may appear larger or smaller than they really are, the trunks may look wavy, details may be absent, and the colors may be dim.

Beginnings for Bionic Eyes

Science fiction often borrows heavily from science fact. The science fiction television classic "Six Million Dollar Man" of the late 1970s featured a "bionic" man with an implanted, telescopic eye that could zoom in and change focus. Fans of the 1990-era science fiction classic "Star Trek: The Next Generation" will certainly remember the character of Geordi LaForge, played by actor LeVar Burton. The character of Geordi was blind from birth. In the series, Geordi was equipped with special goggles that gave him vision superior to that of the average person. While these two sci-fi examples may have seemed far-fetched at the time, actual pioneering studies of retinal implant prosthetic devices began in the early 1990s and continue to the present.

The devices show some promise of being able to restore limited vision to individuals with retinal destruction. Although the cone cells are useless, the ganglion cells in the retinas of these patients can still send nerve signals. Two types of "bionic eyes" are currently being studied: a *subretinal implant* and an *epiretinal implant*. Both devices are designed to directly stimulate the ganglion cells of the retina. The subretinal system is surgically placed below the retina. It is a simple and very tiny, solar-powered silicon chip. Electricity from the solar chip produces nerve signals in ganglion cells. The epiretinal implant, which sits on top of the ganglion cells of the retina, consists of several parts. A miniature digital camera and computer are mounted in special glasses worn by the user. The glasses can transmit information to a silicon microchip placed on top of the ganglion cells. A battery pack worn at the belt transmits power to the implanted microchip.

Currently, clinical research has shown that subretinal implanted silicon chips do indeed stimulate the ganglion cells. Blind human volunteers have reported return of some vision after receiving these implants. In the most remarkable case, a totally blind patient was able to see his wife's face for the first time in decades. Epiretinal implants have also triggered visual sensations in blind human volunteers. More important, these tiny silicon chips seem to be stable after surgery. They do not cause infection, irritation, or breakdown of the retinal tissue.

Neither the subretinal implant nor the epiretinal implant is currently approved by the Food and Drug Administration for widespread use in patients. Both require further study and experimentation to ensure that they are totally safe and effective for use in humans. It is also important to note that these implants can't restore perfect vision at present. However, as the technology allowing miniaturization of electronics continues to improve, the blind may soon be able to obtain a device that restores some useful vision. Future research may result in even better vision.

9.4 Sense of Hearing

The ear has two sensory functions: hearing and equilibrium (balance). The sensory receptors for both of these are located in the inner ear, and each consists of **hair cells** with stereocilia (long microvilli) that are sensitive to mechanical stimulation. The hair cells are mechanoreceptors.

Anatomy of the Ear

Figure 9.12 shows that the ear has three divisions: outer, middle, and inner. The **outer ear** consists of the **pinna** (external flap) and the **auditory canal.** The opening of the auditory canal is lined with fine hairs and sweat glands. Modified sweat glands are located in the upper wall of the canal; they secrete earwax, a substance that helps guard the ear against the entrance of foreign materials, such as air pollutants.

The **middle ear** begins at the **tympanic membrane** (eardrum) and ends at a bony wall containing two small openings covered by membranes. These openings are called the **oval window** and the **round window.** Three small bones are found between the tympanic membrane and the oval window. Collectively called the **ossicles,** individually they are the **malleus** (hammer), the **incus** (anvil), and the **stapes** (stirrup) because their shapes resemble these objects. The malleus adheres to the tympanic membrane, and the stapes touches the

oval window. An **auditory tube** (eustachian tube), which extends from each middle ear to the nasopharynx, permits equalization of air pressure. Chewing gum, yawning, and swallowing in elevators and airplanes help move air through the auditory tubes upon ascent and descent. As this occurs, we often hear the ears "pop."

Whereas the outer ear and the middle ear contain air, the inner ear is filled with fluid. Anatomically speaking, the **inner ear** has three areas: The **semicircular canals** and the **vestibule** are both concerned with equilibrium; the **cochlea** is concerned with hearing. The cochlea resembles the shell of a snail because it spirals.

Sound Pathway

Sound waves pass through the auditory canal and middle ear to the spiral organ in the inner ear, which transforms them into nerve impulses conducted in the auditory nerve to the brain.

Through the Auditory Canal and Middle Ear The process of hearing begins when sound waves enter the auditory canal. Just as ripples travel across the surface of a pond, sound waves travel by the successive vibrations of molecules. Sound waves do not carry much energy, but when a large number of waves strike the tympanic membrane, it moves back and forth (vibrates)

Figure 9.12 Anatomy of the human ear. In the middle ear, the malleus (hammer), the incus (anvil), and the stapes (stirrup) amplify sound waves. In the inner ear, the mechanoreceptors for equilibrium are in the semicircular canals and the vestibule, and the mechanoreceptors for hearing are in the cochlea.

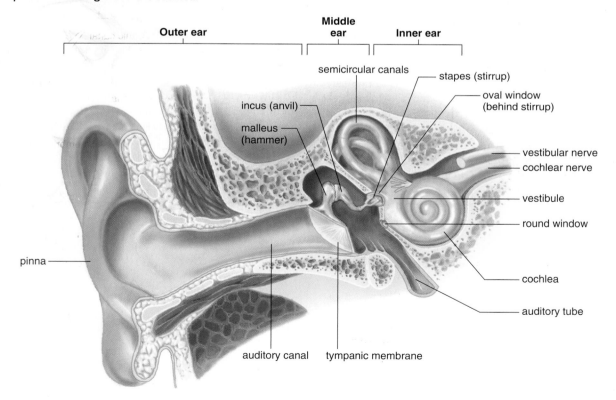

ever so slightly. The malleus then takes the pressure from the inner surface of the tympanic membrane and passes it by means of the incus to the stapes in such a way that the pressure is multiplied about 20 times as it moves. The stapes strikes the membrane of the oval window, causing it to vibrate, and in this way, the pressure is passed to the fluid within the cochlea of the inner ear.

From the Cochlea to the Auditory Cortex If the cochlea is unwound and examined in cross section (Fig. 9.13), you can see that it has three canals: the vestibular canal, the **cochlear canal**, and the tympanic canal. The sense organ for hearing, called the **spiral organ** (organ of Corti), is located in the cochlear canal. The spiral organ consists of little hair cells and a gelatinous material called the tectorial membrane. The hair cells sit on the basilar membrane and their stereocilia are embedded in the tectorial membrane.

When the stapes strikes the membrane of the oval window, pressure waves move from the vestibular canal to the tympanic canal across the basilar membrane. The basilar membrane moves up and down, and the stereocilia of the hair cells embedded in the tectorial membrane bend. Then nerve impulses begin in the cochlear nerve and travel to the brain stem. When they reach the auditory cortex of the cerebral cortex, they are interpreted as a sound.

Each part of the spiral organ is sensitive to different wave frequencies, or pitch. Near the tip, the spiral organ responds to low pitches, such as a tuba, and near the base, it responds to higher pitches, such as a bell or a whistle. The nerve fibers from each region along the length of the spiral organ lead to slightly different areas in the brain. The pitch sensation we experience depends upon which region of the basilar membrane vibrates and which area of the brain is stimulated.

Volume is a function of the amplitude of sound waves. Loud noises cause the fluid within the vestibular canal to exert more pressure and the basilar membrane to vibrate to a greater extent. The resulting increased stimulation is interpreted by the brain as volume. It is believed that the brain interprets the tone of a sound based on the distribution of the hair cells stimulated.

Cochlea uncoiling

tectorial membrane

vestibular canal

cochlear canal

tympanic canal

basilar membrane

cochlear nerve

Cochlea cross section

stereocilia

2 μm

tectorial membrane

hair cell

microvilli

cochlear nerve

basilar membrane

tympanic canal

Spiral organ

Figure 9.13 Mechanoreceptors for hearing. The spiral organ (organ of Corti) is located within the cochlea. In the uncoiled cochlea, note that the spiral organ consists of hair cells (resting on the basilar membrane), and the tectorial membrane above the hair cells. Pressure waves move from the vestibular canal to the tympanic canal, causing the basilar membrane to vibrate. This causes the stereocilia (of at least a portion of the more than 20,000 hair cells) embedded in the tectorial membrane to bend. Nerve impulses traveling in the cochlear nerve result in hearing.

Table 9.2   Functions of the Parts of the Ear

Part	Medium	Function	Mechanoreceptor
Outer Ear	Air		
Pinna		Collects sound waves	—
Auditory canal		Filters air	—
Middle Ear	Air		
Tympanic membrane and ossicles		Amplify sound waves	—
Auditory tube		Equalizes air pressure	—
Inner Ear	Fluid		
Cochlea (contains spiral organ)		Hearing	Stereocilia embedded in tectorial membrane
Semicircular canals		Rotational equilibrium	Stereocilia embedded in cupula
Vestibule (contains utricle and saccule)		Gravitational equilibrium	Stereocilia embedded in otolithic membrane

Figure 9.14 Mechanoreceptors for equilibrium. **a.** Rotational equilibrium. The ampullae of the semicircular canals contain hair cells with stereocilia embedded in a cupula. When the head rotates, the cupula is displaced, bending the stereocilia. Thereafter, nerve impulses travel in the vestibular nerve to the brain. **b.** Gravitational equilibrium. The utricle and the saccule contain hair cells with stereocilia embedded in an otolithic membrane. When the head bends, otoliths are displaced, causing the membrane to sag and the stereocilia to bend. If the stereocilia bend toward the kinocilium, the longest of the stereocilia, nerve impulses increase in the vestibular nerve. If the stereocilia bend away from the kinocilium, nerve impulses decrease in the vestibular nerve. The difference tells the brain in which direction the head moved.

a. Rotational equilibrium: receptors in ampullae of semicircular canal.

b. Gravitational equilibrium: receptors in utricle and saccule of vestibule.

9.5 Sense of Equilibrium

Mechanoreceptors in the semicircular canals detect rotational and/or angular movement of the head (**rotational equilibrium**), while mechanoreceptors in the utricle and saccule detect movement of the head in the vertical or horizontal planes (**gravitational equilibrium**) (Fig. 9.14).

Through their communication with the brain, these mechanoreceptors help us achieve equilibrium, but other structures in the body are also involved. For example, we already mentioned that proprioceptors are necessary for maintaining our equilibrium. Vision, if available, provides extremely helpful input the brain can act upon.

Rotational Equilibrium Pathway

Rotational equilibrium involves the three semicircular canals, which are arranged so that there is one in each dimension of space. The base of each of the three canals, called the **ampulla,** is slightly enlarged. Little hair cells, whose stereocilia are embedded within a gelatinous material called a cupula, are found within the ampullae. Because of the way the semicircular canals are arranged, each ampulla responds to head rotation in a different plane of space. As fluid within a semicircular canal flows over and displaces a cupula, the stereocilia of the hair cells bend, and the pattern of impulses carried by the vestibular nerve to the brain changes. The brain uses information from the hair cells within ampulla of the semicircular canals to maintain rotational equilibrium through appropriate motor output to various skeletal muscles that can right our present position in space as need be.

Sometimes data regarding rotational equilibrium bring about unfortunate circumstances. For example, continuous movement of fluid in the semicircular canals causes one form of motion sickness. **Vertigo** is dizziness and a sensation of rotation. It is possible to simulate a feeling of vertigo by spinning rapidly and stopping suddenly. When the eyes are rapidly jerked back to a midline position, the person feels like the room is spinning. This shows that the eyes are also involved in our sense of equilibrium.

Gravitational Equilibrium Pathway

Gravitational equilibrium depends on the **utricle** and **saccule,** two membranous sacs located in the vestibule. Both of these sacs contain little hair cells, whose stereocilia are embedded within a gelatinous material called an otolithic membrane. Calcium carbonate ($CaCO_3$) granules, or **otoliths,** rest on this membrane. The utricle is especially sensitive to horizontal (back–forth) movements and the bending of the head, while the saccule responds best to vertical (up-down) movements.

When the body is still, the otoliths in the utricle and the saccule rest on the otolithic membrane above the hair cells. When the head bends or the body moves in the horizontal and vertical planes, the otoliths are displaced and the otolithic membrane sags, bending the stereocilia of the hair cells beneath. If the stereocilia move toward the largest stereocilium, called the kinocilium, nerve impulses increase in the vestibular nerve. If the stereocilia move away from the kinocilium, nerve impulses decrease in the vestibular nerve. If you are upside down, nerve impulses in the vestibular nerve cease. These data tell the brain the direction of the movement of the head at the moment. The brain uses this information to maintain gravitational equilibrium through appropriate motor output to various skeletal muscles that can right our present position in space as need be.

Table 9.2 summarizes the functions of the parts of the ear.

9.6 Effects of Aging

As we age, assistance is likely required to improve our sight and hearing. The lens of the eye does not accommodate as well, and therefore, eyeglasses, contact lenses, or corrective surgery will most likely be needed to improve vision. Also, three serious visual disorders are seen more frequently in older persons: (1) Possibly due to exposure to the sun, the lens is subject to **cataracts.** The lens becomes opaque and therefore incapable of transmitting rays of light. Today, the lens is usually surgically replaced with an artificial lens. In the future, it may be possible to restore the original configuration of the proteins making up the lens. (2) Age-related macular degeneration (see the What's New reading on page 176) is the most frequent cause of blindness in older people. (3) Glaucoma is more likely to develop because the anterior compartment of the eye (see Fig. 9.7) undergoes a reduction in size.

The need for a hearing aid also increases with age. Atrophy of the organ of Corti can lead to **presbycusis** (age-related hearing decline). First, people tend to lose the ability to detect high-frequency tones, and later the lower tones are affected. Eventually, they can hear speech but cannot detect the words being said.

Otosclerosis, an overgrowth of bone that causes the stapes to adhere to the oval window, is the most frequent cause of conduction deafness in adults (see the Medical Focus on page 182). The condition actually begins during youth but may not become evident until later in life. Dizziness and the inability to maintain balance may also occur in older people due to changes in the inner ear.

Medical Focus

Hearing Damage and Deafness

Two major types of deafness are conduction deafness and nerve deafness. In **conduction deafness,** the ossicles tend to fuse together, restricting their ability to magnify sound waves. Conduction deafness can be caused by a congenital defect, particularly when a pregnant woman contracts German measles (rubella) during the first trimester of pregnancy. (For this reason, every female should be immunized against rubella before the childbearing years.) Conduction deafness can also be due to repeated infections or otosclerosis. With **otosclerosis,** the normal bone of the middle ear is replaced by vascular spongy bone.

Nerve deafness most often occurs when cilia on the receptors within the cochlea have worn away. Because this may happen with normal aging, older people are more likely to have trouble hearing. However, studies also suggest that age-associated hearing loss can be prevented if ears are protected from loud noises, starting even during infancy. Hospitals are now aware of the problem and are taking steps to ensure that neonatal intensive care units and nurseries are as quiet as possible.

In today's society, exposure to the types of noises listed in Table 9A is common. Everyone should consider three aspects of noise to prevent hearing loss: (1) how loud is the noise, (2) how long is the noise heard, and (3) how close is the noise to the ear. Loudness is measured in decibels, and any level above 80 decibels could damage the hair cells of the organ of Corti. Exposure to intense sounds of short duration, such as a burst of gunfire, can result in an immediate hearing loss. Since the butt of a rifle offers some protection, hunters may have a significant hearing reduc-

tion in the ear opposite the shoulder they use for support while firing their gun. Because even listening to city traffic for extended periods can damage hearing, frequent attendance at rock concerts and constant listening to loud music from a stereo are obviously dangerous. Noisy indoor or outdoor equipment, such as a rug-cleaning machine or a chain saw, is also troublesome. Even motorcycles and recreational vehicles, such as snowmobiles and motocross bikes, can contribute to a gradual hearing loss.

The first hint of a problem could be temporary hearing loss, a "full" feeling in the ears, muffled hearing, or tinnitus (ringing in the ears). If you have any of these symptoms, modify your listening habits immediately to prevent further damage. If exposure to noise is unavoidable, use specially designed noise-reduction earmuffs or purchase earplugs made from a compressible, sponge-like material at a drugstore or sporting goods store. These earplugs are not the same as those worn for swimming, and they should not be used interchangeably.

Finally, people need to be aware that some medicines are **ototoxic** (damaging to any of the elements of hearing or balance). Anticancer drugs—most notably, cisplatin—and certain antibiotics (for example, streptomycin, kanamycin, and gentamicin) make the ears especially susceptible to a hearing loss. People taking such medications should protect their ears from any excessive noises.

Cochlear implants that directly stimulate the auditory nerve are available for persons with nerve deafness. However, they are costly, and people wearing these electronic devices report that the speech they hear is like that of a robot.

Table 9A	Sound Intensity and Hearing Damage	
Type of Noise	**Sound Level (decibels)**	**Effect**
Rock concert, shotgun, jet engine	Over 125	Beyond threshold of pain; potential for hearing loss is high.
Nightclub, boom box, thunderclap	Over 120	Hearing loss is likely.
Chain saw, pneumatic drill, jackhammer, symphony orchestra, snowmobile, garbage truck, cement mixer	100–200	Regular exposure of longer than 1 minute risks permanent hearing loss.
Farm tractor, newspaper press, subway, motorcycle	90–100	Fifteen minutes of unprotected exposure is potentially harmful.
Lawnmower, food blender	85–90	Continuous daily exposure for more than 8 hours can cause hearing damage.
Diesel truck, average city traffic noise	80–85	Annoying; constant exposure may cause hearing damage.

Source: National Institute on Deafness and Other Communication Disorders, National Institutes of Health, January 1990.

Selected New Terms

Basic Key Terms

ampulla (am-pul'uh), p. 181
aqueous humor (a'kwe-us hyū'mer), p. 171
auditory canal (aw'dĭ-to"re kuh-nal'), p. 178
auditory tube (aw'dĭ-to"re tūb), p. 178
blind spot (blīnd spot), p. 174
choroid (ko'royd), p. 170
ciliary muscle (sil'e-ĕr"e mus'l), p. 170
cochlea (kōk'le-uh), p. 178
cochlear canal (kōk'le-er kuh-nal'), p. 179
cone cell (kōn sel), p. 173
cornea (kor'ne-uh), p. 170
incus (ing'kus), p. 178
iris (i'ris), p. 170
lacrimal apparatus (lak'rĭ-mul ap"uh-ră'tus), p. 168
lens (lenz), p. 170
malleus (mal'e-us), p. 178
olfactory cell (ol-fak'to-re sel), p. 167
optic nerve (op'tik nerv), p. 171
ossicle (os'ĭ-kl), p. 178
otolith (ō'tō-lith), p. 181
pinna (pin'uh), p. 178
proprioceptor (pro"pre-o-sep'tor), p. 164
pupil (pyū'pl), p. 170
retina (ret'ĭ-nuh), p. 171
rod cell (rod sel), p. 173

saccule (sak'yūl), p. 181
sclera (sklēr'uh), p. 170
semicircular canal (sem"e-ser'kyū-ler kuh-nal'), p. 178
spiral organ (spi'rul or'gun), p. 179
stapes (sta'pēz), p. 178
taste bud (tāst bud), p. 166
tympanic membrane (tim-pan'ik mem'brān), p. 178
utricle (u'trĭ-kl), p. 181
visual accommodation (vizh'ū-ul uh-kom"o-da'shun), p. 171
vitreous humor (vit're-us hyū'mor), p. 171

Clinical Key Terms

cataract (kat'uh-rakt), p. 181
cochlear implant (kōk'le-er im'plant), p. 182
conduction deafness (kon-duk'shun def'nes), p. 182
glaucoma (glaw-ko'muh), p. 171
hyperopia (hi"per-o'pe-uh), p. 172
macular degeneration (mă'kyū-ler de"jen-er-a'shun), p. 176
myasthenia gravis (mi"as-the'ne-uh grah'vis), p. 168
myopia (mi-o'pe-uh), p. 172
nerve deafness (nerv def'nes), p. 182
otosclerosis (ō"tō-sklĕ-ro'sis), p. 182
ototoxic (ō"tō-tok'sik), p. 182
presbycusis (prez"be-ku'sis), p. 181
sty (sti), p. 168

Summary

9.1 General Senses
Each type of sensory receptor detects a particular kind of stimulus. When stimulation occurs, sensory receptors initiate nerve impulses that are transmitted to the spinal cord and/or brain. Sensation occurs when nerve impulses reach the cerebral cortex. Perception is an interpretation of the meaning of sensations.

9.2 Senses of Taste and Smell
A. Taste and smell are due to chemoreceptors that are stimulated by molecules in the environment. The taste buds contain taste cells that communicate with sensory fibers, while the chemoreceptors for smell are neurons.
B. After molecules bind to plasma membrane receptor proteins on the microvilli of taste cells and the cilia

of olfactory cells, nerve impulses eventually reach the cerebral cortex, which determines the taste and odor according to the pattern of stimulation.

9.3 Sense of Vision
A. Vision is dependent on the eye, the optic nerves, and the visual areas of the cerebral cortex. The eye has three layers. The outer layer, the sclera, can be seen as the white of the eye; it also becomes the transparent bulge in the front of the eye called the cornea. The middle pigmented layer, called the choroid, absorbs stray light rays. The rod cells (sensory receptors for dim light) and the cone cells (sensory receptors for bright light and color) are located in the retina, the inner layer of the eyeball. The cornea, the humors, and especially the lens bring

the light rays to focus on the retina. To see a close object, accommodation occurs as the lens rounds up.
B. When light strikes rhodopsin within the membranous disks of rod cells, rhodopsin splits into opsin and retinal. A cascade of reactions leads to the closing of ion channels in a rod cell's plasma membrane. Inhibitory transmitter molecules are no longer released, and nerve impulses are carried in the optic nerve to the brain.
C. Integration occurs in the retina, which is composed of three layers of cells: the rod and cone layer, the bipolar cell layer, and the ganglion cell layer. Integration also occurs in the brain. The visual field is taken apart by the optic chiasma and by the primary visual area in the cerebral cortex, which parcels out

signals for color, form, and motion to the visual association area. Then the cortex rebuilds the field.

9.4 Sense of Hearing
A. Hearing is dependent on the ear, the cochlear nerve, and the auditory areas of the cerebral cortex.
B. The ear is divided into three parts: outer, middle, and inner. The outer ear consists of the pinna and the auditory canal, which direct sound waves to the middle ear. The middle ear begins with the tympanic membrane and contains the ossicles (malleus, incus, and stapes). The malleus is attached to the tympanic membrane, and the stapes is attached to the oval window, which is covered by a membrane. The inner ear contains the cochlea and the semicircular canals, plus the utricle and the saccule.
C. Hearing begins when the outer ear receives and the middle ear amplifies the sound waves that then strike the oval window membrane. Its vibrations set up pressure waves across the cochlear canal, which contains the spiral organ, consisting of hair cells whose stereocilia are embedded within the tectorial membrane. When the basilar membrane vibrates, the stereocilia of the hair cells bend. Nerve impulses begin in the cochlear nerve and are carried to the brain.

9.5 Sense of Equilibrium
The ear also contains mechano-receptors for our sense of equilibrium. Rotational equilibrium is dependent on the stimulation of hair cells within the ampullae of the semicircular canals. Gravitational equilibrium relies on the stimulation of hair cells within the utricle and the saccule.

9.6 Effects of Aging
As we age, assistance is likely needed to improve our failing senses of sight and hearing. Three more serious visual disorders—cataracts, age-related macular degeneration, and glaucoma—may occur, making medical intervention necessary.

Study Questions

1. What type of sensory receptors are categorized as general? (pp. 164–65)
2. Discuss the senses of taste and sound. (pp. 166–67)
3. Describe the anatomy of the eye. (pp. 168–71)
4. Explain focusing and accommodation. (p. 171)
5. Describe sight in dim light. What chemical reaction is responsible for vision in dim light? Explain color vision. (p. 173)
6. How does the retina integrate and the brain process visual information? (pp. 174, 175)
7. Describe the anatomy of the ear and how a person hears. (pp. 178–79)
8. Describe the role of the utricle, saccule, and semicircular canals in balance. (p. 181)
9. Discuss the two major causes of deafness, including why young people frequently suffer loss of hearing. (p. 182)

Objective Questions

Fill in the blanks.

1. The sensory organs for position and movement are called _____.
2. Taste buds and olfactory cells are termed _____ because they are sensitive to chemicals in the air and food.
3. The sensory receptors for sight, the _____ and _____, are located in the _____, the inner layer of the eye.
4. The cones give us _____ vision and work best in _____ light.
5. The lens _____ for viewing close objects.
6. People who are nearsighted cannot see objects that are _____. A _____ lens will restore this ability.
7. The ossicles are the _____, _____ , and _____.
8. The semicircular canals are involved in the sense of _____.
9. The spiral organ is located in the _____ canal of the _____.
10. Vision, hearing, taste, and smell do not occur unless nerve impulses reach the proper portion of the _____.

Medical Terminology Reinforcement Exercise

Consult Appendix B for help in pronouncing and analyzing the meaning of the terms that follow.

1. ophthalmologist (of″thal-mol′o-jist)
2. presbyopia (pres″be-o′pe-uh)
3. blepharoptosis (blef″uh-ro-to′sis)
4. keratoplasty (ker′uh-to-plas″te)
5. optometrist (op-tom′ĕ-trist)
6. lacrimator (lak′rĭ-ma″tor)
7. otitis media (o-ti′tis me′de-uh)
8. tympanocentesis (tim″puh-no-sen-te′sis)
9. microtia (mi″kro′she-uh)
10. myringotome (mi-ring′go-tōm)
11. iridomalacia (ir′ĭ-do-muh′la′she-uh)
12. hypogeusia (hi-po′go′se-uh)

Website Link

Visit the Student Edition of the Online Learning Center at http://www.mhhe.com/maderap5 for additional quizzes, interactive learning exercises, and other study tools.

The Endocrine System

Pancreatic islets (light pink areas) are shown in this photomicrograph of the pancreas.

chapter outline & learning objectives
After you have studied this chapter, you should be able to:

10.1 Endocrine Glands

The endocrine system consists of glands and tissues that secrete hormones. This chapter will give many examples of the close association between the endocrine and nervous systems. Like the nervous system, the endocrine system is intimately involved in homeostasis.

Hormones are chemical signals that affect the behavior of other glands or tissues. Hormones influence the metabolism of cells, the growth and development of body parts, and homeostasis. **Endocrine glands** are ductless; they secrete their hormones into tissue fluid. From there, they diffuse into the bloodstream for distribution throughout the body. Endocrine glands can be contrasted with exocrine glands, which have ducts and secrete their products into these ducts. For example, the salivary glands send saliva into the mouth by way of the salivary ducts.

Figure 10.1 depicts the locations of the major endocrine glands in the body, and Table 10.1 lists the hormones they release. Each type of hormone has a different composition. Even so, hormones can be categorized as either peptides (which include proteins, glycoproteins, and modified amino acids) or steroids. Protein hormones, such as insulin, must be administered by injection. If these hormones were taken orally, they would be acted on by digestive enzymes. Steroid hormones, such as those in birth control pills, can be taken orally because they can pass through the plasma membrane without prior digestion.

Hormones and Homeostasis

The effect of hormones is usually controlled in two ways: (1) Negative feedback opposes their release, and (2) antagonistic hormones oppose each other's actions. Notice in Table 10.1 that several hormones directly affect the blood glucose, calcium, and sodium levels. Other hormones are involved in the function of various organs, including the reproductive organs.

Some hormones or their effects are controlled by a negative feedback system. The result is that the activity of the hormone is maintained within normal limits. The negative feedback system can be sensitive to either a resulting condition or to the blood level of a hormone. For example, when the blood glucose level rises, the pancreas secretes insulin, which causes the liver to store glucose and the cells to take it up. When blood glucose lowers, the secretion of insulin is inhibited, and the pancreas stops producing insulin. On the other hand, when the blood level of thyroid hormones rises, the anterior pituitary stops secreting thyroid-stimulating hormones. These examples illustrate regulation by negative feedback.

The actions of a hormone can also be controlled by the presence of an antagonistic hormone. The effect of insulin, for example, is offset by the production of glucagon by the pancreas. Insulin lowers the blood glucose level, while glucagon raises it. Also, the thyroid lowers the blood calcium level, but the parathyroids raise the blood calcium level. In subsequent sections of this chapter, we will point out other instances in which hormones work opposite to one another, and thereby bring about the regulation of a substance in the blood.

Figure 10.1 The endocrine system. Anatomical location of major endocrine glands in the body. The hypothalamus and pituitary gland are in the brain, the thyroid and parathyroids are in the neck, and the adrenal glands and pancreas are in the pelvic cavity. The gonads include the ovaries in females, located in the pelvic cavity, and the testes in males, located outside this cavity in the scrotum. Also shown are the pineal gland, located in the brain, and the thymus gland, which lies within the thoracic cavity.

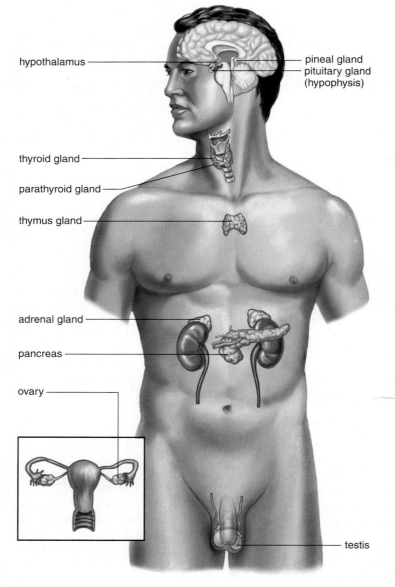

hypothalamus

pineal gland
pituitary gland (hypophysis)

thyroid gland

parathyroid gland

thymus gland

adrenal gland

pancreas

ovary

testis

Table 10.1 Principal Endocrine Glands and Hormones

Endocrine Gland	Hormone Released	Chemical Class	Target Tissues/Organs	Chief Function(s) of Hormone
Hypothalamus	Hypothalamic-releasing and -inhibiting hormones	Peptide	Anterior pituitary	Regulate anterior pituitary hormones
Pituitary gland				
Posterior pituitary	Antidiuretic (ADH)	Peptide	Kidneys	Stimulates water reabsorption by kidneys
	Oxytocin	Peptide	Uterus, mammary glands	Stimulates uterine muscle contraction, release of milk by mammary glands
Anterior pituitary	Thyroid-stimulating (TSH)	Glycoprotein	Thyroid	Stimulates thyroid
	Adrenocorticotropic (ACTH)	Peptide	Adrenal cortex	Stimulates adrenal cortex
	Gonadotropic	Glycoprotein	Gonads	Egg and sperm production; sex hormone production
	Prolactin (PRL)	Protein	Mammary glands	Milk production
	Growth (GH)	Protein	Soft tissues, bones	Cell division, protein synthesis, and bone growth
	Melanocyte-stimulating (MSH)	Peptide	Melanocytes in skin	Unknown function in humans; regulates skin color in lower vertebrates
Thyroid	Thyroxine (T_4) and triiodothyronine (T_3)	Iodinated amino acid	All tissues	Increases metabolic rate; regulates growth and development
	Calcitonin	Peptide	Bones, kidneys, intestine	Lowers blood calcium level
Parathyroids	Parathyroid (PTH)	Peptide	Bones, kidneys, intestine	Raises blood calcium level
Adrenal gland				
Adrenal cortex	Glucocorticoids (cortisol)	Steroid	All tissues	Raise blood glucose level; stimulate breakdown of protein
	Mineralocorticoids (aldosterone)	Steroid	Kidneys	Reabsorb sodium and excrete potassium
	Sex hormones	Steroid	Gonads, skin, muscles, bones	Stimulate reproductive organs and bring about sex characteristics
Adrenal medulla	Epinephrine and norepinephrine	Modified amino acid	Cardiac and other muscles	Released in emergency situations; raise blood glucose level
Pancreas	Insulin	Protein	Liver, muscles, adipose tissue	Lowers blood glucose level; promotes formation of glycogen
	Glucagon	Protein	Liver, muscles, adipose tissue	Raises blood glucose level
Gonads				
Testes	Androgens (testosterone)	Steroid	Gonads, skin, muscles, bones	Stimulate male sex characteristics
Ovaries	Estrogens and progesterone	Steroid	Gonads, skin, muscles, bones	Stimulate female sex characteristics
Thymus	Thymosins	Peptide	T lymphocytes	Stimulate production and maturation of T lymphocytes
Pineal gland	Melatonin	Modified amino acid	Brain	Controls circadian and circannual rhythms; possibly involved in maturation of sexual organs

10.2 Hypothalamus and Pituitary Gland

The **hypothalamus** regulates the internal environment. For example, through the autonomic system, it helps control heartbeat, body temperature, and water balance (by creating thirst). The hypothalamus also controls the glandular secretions of the **pituitary gland (hypophysis).** The pituitary, a small gland about 1 cm in diameter, is connected to the hypothalamus by a stalklike structure. The pituitary has two portions: the **posterior pituitary (neurohypophysis)** and the **anterior pituitary (adrenohypophysis).**

Posterior Pituitary

Neurons in the hypothalamus called neurosecretory cells produce the hormones antidiuretic hormone (ADH) and oxytocin (Fig. 10.2, *left*). These hormones pass through axons into the posterior pituitary where they are stored in axon endings.

Antidiuretic Hormone and Oxytocin

Certain neurons in the hypothalamus are sensitive to the water–salt balance of the blood. When these cells determine that the blood is too concentrated, **antidiuretic hormone (ADH)** is released from the posterior pituitary. Upon reaching the kidneys, ADH causes more water to be reabsorbed into kidney capillaries. As the blood becomes dilute, ADH is no longer released. This is an example of control by negative feedback because the effect of the hormone (to dilute blood) acts to shut down the release of the hormone. Negative feedback maintains stable conditions and homeostasis.

Inability to produce ADH causes **diabetes insipidus** (watery urine), in which a person produces copious amounts of urine with a resultant loss of ions from the blood. The condition can be corrected by the administration of ADH.

Oxytocin, the other hormone made in the hypothalamus, causes uterine contraction during childbirth and milk letdown when a baby is nursing. The more the uterus contracts during labor, the more nerve impulses reach the hypothalamus, causing oxytocin to be released. Similarly, the more a baby suckles, the more oxytocin is released. In both instances, the release of oxytocin from the posterior pituitary is controlled by **positive feedback**—that is, the stimulus continues to bring about an effect that ever increases in intensity. Positive feedback is not a way to maintain stable conditions and homeostasis.

Anterior Pituitary

A portal system, consisting of two capillary systems connected by a vein, lies between the hypothalamus and the anterior pituitary (Fig. 10.2, *right*). The hypothalamus controls the anterior pituitary by producing **hypothalamic-releasing hormones** and **hypothalamic-inhibiting hormones.** For example, there is a thyrotropin-releasing hormone (TRH) and a prolactin-inhibiting hormone (PIH). TRH stimulates the anterior pituitary to secrete thyroid-stimulating hormone, and PIH inhibits the pituitary from secreting prolactin.

Hormones That Affect Other Glands

Three of the hormones produced by the anterior pituitary have an effect on other glands: **Thyroid-stimulating hormone (TSH)** stimulates the thyroid to produce the thyroid hormones; **adrenocorticotropic hormone (ACTH)** stimulates the adrenal cortex to produce its hormones; and **gonadotropic hormones** stimulate the gonads—the testes in males and the ovaries in females—to produce gametes and sex hormones. The hypothalamus, the anterior pituitary, and other glands controlled by the anterior pituitary are all involved in self-regulating negative feedback mechanisms that maintain stable conditions. In each instance, the blood level of the last hormone in the sequence exerts negative feedback control over the secretion of the first two hormones:

Effects of Other Hormones

Other hormones produced by the anterior pituitary do not affect other endocrine glands. **Prolactin (PRL)** is produced in quantity after childbirth. It causes the mammary glands in the breasts to develop and produce milk. It also plays a role in carbohydrate and fat metabolism.

Growth hormone (GH), or somatotropic hormone, stimulates protein synthesis within cartilage, bone, and muscle. It stimulates the rate at which amino acids enter cells and protein synthesis occurs. It also promotes fat metabolism as opposed to glucose metabolism.

visual focus

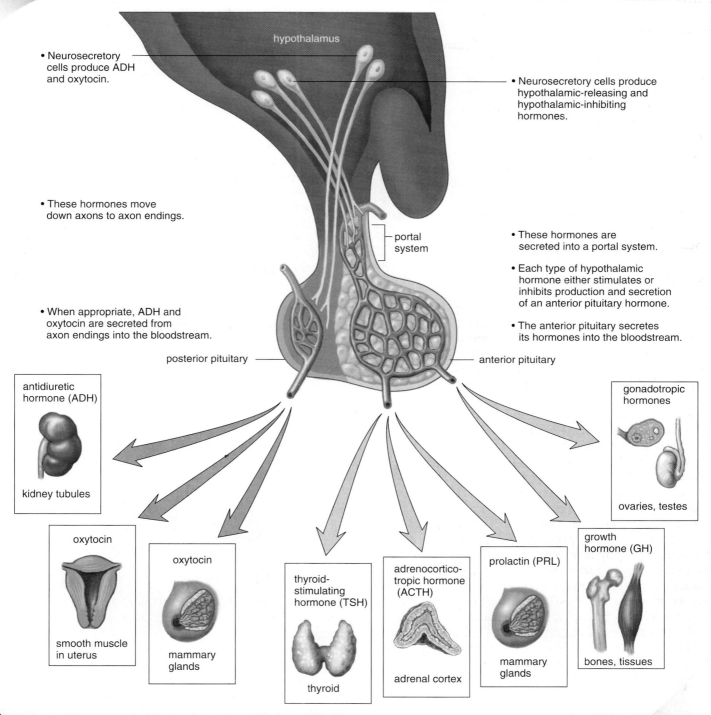

hypothalamus

• Neurosecretory cells produce ADH and oxytocin.

• Neurosecretory cells produce hypothalamic-releasing and hypothalamic-inhibiting hormones.

• These hormones move down axons to axon endings.

portal system

• These hormones are secreted into a portal system.

• Each type of hypothalamic hormone either stimulates or inhibits production and secretion of an anterior pituitary hormone.

• When appropriate, ADH and oxytocin are secreted from axon endings into the bloodstream.

• The anterior pituitary secretes its hormones into the bloodstream.

posterior pituitary

anterior pituitary

antidiuretic hormone (ADH)

kidney tubules

gonadotropic hormones

ovaries, testes

oxytocin

smooth muscle in uterus

oxytocin

mammary glands

thyroid-stimulating hormone (TSH)

thyroid

adrenocortico-tropic hormone (ACTH)

adrenal cortex

prolactin (PRL)

mammary glands

growth hormone (GH)

bones, tissues

Figure 10.2 The hypothalamus and the pituitary. *Left:* The hypothalamus produces two hormones, ADH and oxytocin, which are stored and secreted by the posterior pituitary. *Right:* The hypothalamus controls the secretions of the anterior pituitary, and the anterior pituitary controls the secretions of the thyroid, adrenal cortex, and gonads, which are also endocrine glands. It also secretes growth hormone and prolactin.

Effects of Growth Hormone

The amount of GH produced by the anterior pituitary affects the height of the individual. The quantity of GH produced is greatest during childhood and adolescence, when most body growth is occurring (Fig. 10.3*a*). If too little GH is produced during childhood, the individual has **pituitary dwarfism**, characterized by perfect proportions but small stature. If too much GH is secreted, a person can become a giant (Fig. 10.3*b*). Giants usually have poor health, primarily because GH has a secondary effect on the blood sugar level, promoting an illness called diabetes mellitus (see page 197).

On occasion, GH is overproduced in the adult, and a condition called **acromegaly** results. Because long bone growth is no longer possible in adults, only the feet, hands, and face (particularly the chin, nose, and eyebrow ridges) can respond, and these portions of the body become overly large (Fig. 10.4).

Figure 10.3 Effect of growth hormone. **a.** The amount of growth hormone produced by the anterior pituitary during childhood affects the height of an individual. Plentiful growth hormone produces very tall basketball players. **b.** Too much growth hormone can lead to giantism, while an insufficient amount results in limited stature and even pituitary dwarfism.

a.

b.

Figure 10.4 Acromegaly. Acromegaly is caused by overproduction of GH in the adult. It is characterized by enlargement of the bones in the face, the fingers, and the toes as a person ages.

Age 9   Age 16   Age 33   Age 52

10.3 Thyroid and Parathyroid Glands

The **thyroid gland** is a large gland located in the neck, where it is attached to the trachea just below the larynx (see Fig. 10.1). The parathyroid glands are embedded in the posterior surface of the thyroid gland.

Thyroid Gland

The thyroid gland is composed of a large number of follicles, each a small spherical structure made of thyroid cells filled with triiodothyronine (T_3), which contains three iodine atoms, and **thyroxine (T_4),** which contains four iodine atoms.

Effects of Thyroid Hormones

To produce triiodothyronine and thyroxine, the thyroid gland actively acquires iodine. The concentration of iodine in the thyroid gland can increase to as much as 25 times that of the blood. If iodine is lacking in the diet, the thyroid gland is unable to produce the thyroid hormones. In response to constant stimulation by the anterior pituitary, the thyroid enlarges, resulting in a **simple goiter** (Fig. 10.5). Some years ago, it was discovered that the use of iodized salt allows the thyroid to produce the thyroid hormones, and therefore helps prevent simple goiter.

Thyroid hormones increase the metabolic rate. They do not have a target organ; instead, they stimulate all cells of the body to metabolize at a faster rate. More glucose is broken down, and more energy is utilized.

If the thyroid fails to develop properly, a condition called **cretinism** results (Fig. 10.6). Individuals with this condition are short and stocky and have had extreme hypothyroidism (undersecretion of thyroid hormone) since infancy or childhood. Thyroid hormone therapy can initiate growth, but unless treatment is begun within the first two months of life, mental retardation results. The occurrence of hypothyroidism in adults produces the condition known as **myxedema,** which is characterized by lethargy, weight gain, loss of hair, slower pulse rate, lowered body temperature, and thickness and puffiness of the skin. The administration of adequate doses of thyroid hormones restores normal function and appearance.

In the case of hyperthyroidism (oversecretion of thyroid hormone), as seen in **Graves disease,** the thyroid gland is overactive, and a goiter forms. This type of goiter is called **exophthalmic goiter.** The eyes protrude because of edema in eye socket tissues and swelling of the muscles that move the eyes. The patient usually becomes hyperactive, nervous, and irritable, and suffers from insomnia. Removal or destruction of a portion of the thyroid by means of radioactive iodine is sometimes effective in curing the condition. Hyperthyroidism can also be caused by a thyroid tumor, which is usually detected as a lump during physical examination. Again, the treatment is surgery in combination with administration of radioactive iodine. The prognosis for most patients is excellent.

Figure 10.5 Simple goiter. An enlarged thyroid gland is often caused by a lack of iodine in the diet. Without iodine, the thyroid is unable to produce its hormones, and continued anterior pituitary stimulation causes the gland to enlarge.

Figure 10.6 Cretinism. Individuals who have hypothyroidism since infancy or childhood do not grow and develop as others do. Unless medical treatment is begun, the body is short and stocky; mental retardation is also likely.

Calcitonin

Calcium (Ca^{2+}) plays a significant role in both nervous conduction and muscle contraction. It is also necessary for coagulation (clotting) of blood. The blood calcium level is regulated in part by **calcitonin,** a hormone secreted by the thyroid gland when the blood calcium level rises (Fig. 10.7). The primary effect of calcitonin is to bring about the deposit of calcium in the bones. It does this by temporarily reducing the activity and number of osteoclasts. When the blood calcium lowers to normal, the release of calcitonin by the thyroid is inhibited, but a low calcium level stimulates the release of parathyroid hormone (PTH) by the parathyroid glands.

Parathyroid Glands

Parathyroid hormone (PTH), the hormone produced by the **parathyroid glands,** causes the blood phosphate (HPO_4^{2-}) level to decrease and the blood calcium (Ca^{2+}) level to increase. The antagonistic actions of calcitonin, from the thyroid gland, and parathyroid hormone, from the parathyroid glands, maintain the blood calcium level within normal limits.

Note in Figure 10.7 that after a low blood calcium level stimulates the release of PTH, it promotes release of calcium from the bones. (It does this by promoting the activity of osteoclasts.) PTH promotes the reabsorption of calcium by the kidneys, where it also activates vitamin D. Vitamin D, in turn, stimulates the absorption of calcium from the intestine. These effects bring the blood calcium level back to the normal range so that the parathyroid glands no longer secrete PTH.

Many years ago, the four parathyroid glands were sometimes mistakenly removed during thyroid surgery because of their size and location in the thyroid. When insufficient parathyroid hormone production leads to a dramatic drop in the blood calcium level, tetany results. In **tetany,** the body shakes from continuous muscle contraction. This effect is brought about by increased excitability of the nerves, which initiate nerve impulses spontaneously and without rest.

calcitonin

Thyroid gland secretes calcitonin into blood.

Bones take up Ca^{2+} from blood.

Blood Ca^{2+} lowers.

high blood Ca^{2+}

Homeostasis
normal blood Ca^{2+}

low blood Ca^{2+}

Blood Ca^{2+} rises.

Parathyroid glands release PTH into blood.

activated vitamin D

parathyroid hormone (PTH)

Intestines absorb Ca^{2+} from digestive tract.

Kidneys reabsorb Ca^{2+} from kidney tubules.

Bones release Ca^{2+} into blood.

Figure 10.7 Regulation of blood calcium level. *Top:* When the blood calcium (Ca^{2+}) level is high, the thyroid gland secretes calcitonin. Calcitonin promotes the uptake of Ca^{2+} by the bones, and therefore the blood Ca^{2+} level returns to normal. *Bottom:* When the blood Ca^{2+} level is low, the parathyroid glands release parathyroid hormone (PTH). PTH causes the bones to release Ca^{2+}. It also causes the kidneys to reabsorb Ca^{2+} and activate vitamin D; thereafter, the intestines absorb Ca^{2+}. Therefore, the blood Ca^{2+} level returns to normal.

10.4 Adrenal Glands

The **adrenal glands** sit atop the kidneys (see Fig. 10.1). Each adrenal gland consists of an inner portion called the **adrenal medulla** and an outer portion called the **adrenal cortex**. These portions, like the anterior pituitary and the posterior pituitary, have no physiological connection with one another. The adrenal medulla is under nervous control, and the adrenal cortex is under the control of ACTH, an anterior pituitary hormone. Stress of all types, including emotional and physical trauma, prompts the hypothalamus to stimulate the adrenal glands (Fig. 10.8).

Adrenal Medulla

The hypothalamus initiates nerve impulses that travel by way of the brain stem, spinal cord, and sympathetic nerve fibers to the adrenal medulla, which then secretes its hormones.

Epinephrine (adrenaline) and **norepinephrine** (noradrenaline) produced by the adrenal medulla rapidly bring about all the body changes that occur when an individual reacts to an emergency situation. The effects of these hormones provide a short-term response to stress.

Adrenal Cortex

In contrast, the hormones produced by the adrenal cortex provide a long-term response to stress (Fig. 10.8). The two major types of hormones produced by the adrenal cortex are the mineralocorticoids and the glucocorticoids. The **mineralocorticoids** regulate salt and water balance, leading to increases in blood volume and blood pressure. The **glucocorticoids** regulate carbohydrate, protein, and fat metabolism, leading to an increase in blood glucose level. Cortisone, the medication often administered for inflammation of joints, is a glucocorticoid.

The adrenal cortex also secretes a small amount of male sex hormones and a small amount of female sex hormones in both sexes. That is, in the male, both male and female sex hormones are produced by the adrenal cortex, and in the female, both male and female sex hormones are also produced by the adrenal cortex.

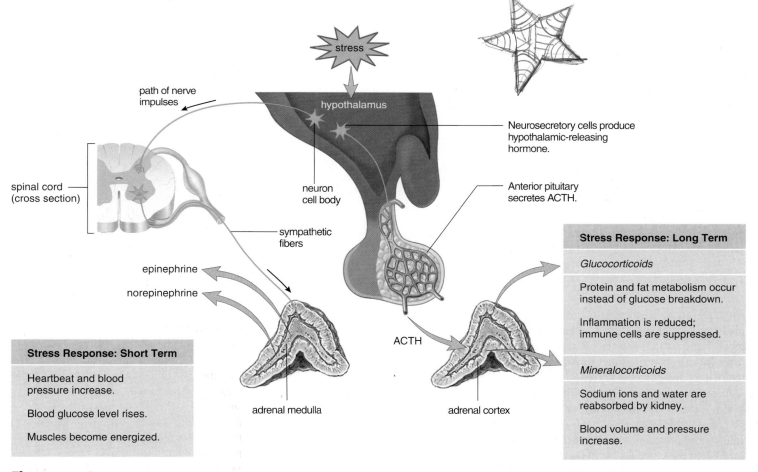

Figure 10.8 Adrenal glands. Both the adrenal medulla and the adrenal cortex are under the control of the hypothalamus when they help us respond to stress. *Left:* The adrenal medulla provides a rapid, but short-term, stress response. *Right:* The adrenal cortex provides a slower, but long-term, stress response.

Glucocorticoids

Cortisol is a biologically significant glucocorticoid produced by the adrenal cortex. Cortisol raises the blood glucose level in at least two ways: (1) It promotes the breakdown of muscle proteins to amino acids, which are taken up by the liver from the bloodstream. The liver then breaks down these excess amino acids to glucose, which enters the blood. (2) Cortisol promotes the metabolism of fatty acids rather than carbohydrates, and this spares glucose for the brain.

Cortisol also counteracts the inflammatory response that leads to the pain and swelling of joints in arthritis and bursitis. The administration of cortisol aids these conditions because it reduces inflammation. Very high levels of glucocorticoids in the blood can suppress the body's defense system, including the inflammatory response that occurs at infection sites. Cortisone and other glucocorticoids can relieve swelling and pain from inflammation, but by suppressing pain and immunity, they can also make a person highly susceptible to injury and infection.

Mineralocorticoids

Aldosterone is the most important of the mineralocorticoids. Aldosterone primarily targets the kidney where it promotes renal absorption of sodium (Na^+) and renal excretion of potassium (K^+).

The secretion of mineralocorticoids is not controlled by the anterior pituitary. When the blood sodium level and therefore the blood pressure are low, the kidneys secrete **renin** (Fig. 10.9). Renin is an enzyme that converts the plasma protein angiotensinogen to angiotensin I, which is changed to angiotensin II by a converting enzyme found in lung capillaries. Angiotensin II stimulates the adrenal cortex to release aldosterone. The

effect of this system, called the renin-angiotensin-aldosterone system, is to raise blood pressure in two ways: Angiotensin II constricts arterioles, and aldosterone causes the kidneys to reabsorb sodium. When the blood sodium level rises, water is reabsorbed in part because the hypothalamus secretes ADH (see page 188). Reabsorption means that water enters kidney capillaries and thus the blood. Then blood pressure increases to normal.

There is an antagonistic hormone to aldosterone, as you might suspect. When the atria of the heart are stretched due to increased blood volume, cardiac cells release a hormone called **atrial natriuretic hormone (ANH),** which inhibits the secretion of aldosterone from the adrenal cortex. The effect of ANH is the excretion of sodium—that is, *natriuresis.* When sodium is excreted, so is water, and therefore blood pressure lowers to normal.

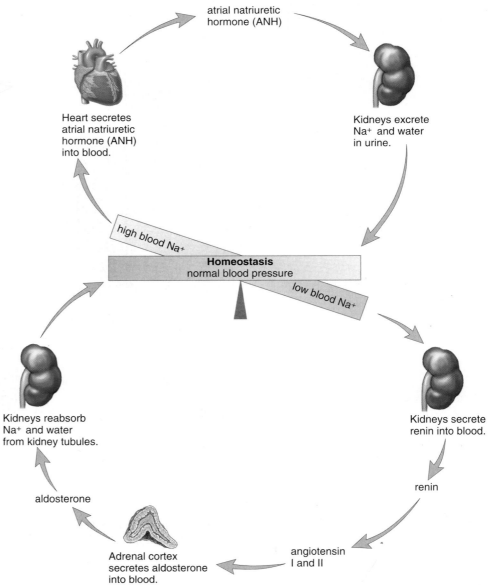

Figure 10.9 Regulation of blood pressure and volume. *Bottom:* When the blood sodium (Na^+) level is low, a low blood pressure causes the kidneys to secrete renin. Renin leads to the secretion of aldosterone from the adrenal cortex. Aldosterone causes the kidneys to reabsorb Na^+, and water follows, so that blood volume and pressure return to normal. *Top:* When the blood Na^+ is high, a high blood volume causes the heart to secrete atrial natriuretic hormone (ANH). ANH causes the kidneys to excrete Na^+, and water follows. The blood volume and pressure return to normal.

Labels within figure:
- atrial natriuretic hormone (ANH)
- Heart secretes atrial natriuretic hormone (ANH) into blood.
- Kidneys excrete Na+ and water in urine.
- high blood Na+
- **Homeostasis** normal blood pressure
- low blood Na+
- Kidneys reabsorb Na+ and water from kidney tubules.
- Kidneys secrete renin into blood.
- aldosterone
- renin
- Adrenal cortex secretes aldosterone into blood.
- angiotensin I and II

Malfunction of the Adrenal Cortex

Malfunction of the adrenal cortex can lead to a **syndrome,** a set of symptoms that occur together. The syndromes commonly associated with the adrenal cortex are Addison disease and Cushing syndrome.

Addison Disease and Cushing Syndrome

When the level of adrenal cortex hormones is low due to hyposecretion, a person develops **Addison disease.** The presence of excessive but ineffective ACTH causes a bronzing of the skin because ACTH can lead to a buildup of melanin (Fig. 10.10). Without cortisol, glucose cannot be replenished when a stressful situation arises. Even a mild infection can lead to death. The lack of aldosterone results in a loss of sodium and water, the development of low blood pressure, and possibly severe dehydration. Left untreated, Addison disease can be fatal.

When the level of adrenal cortex hormones is high due to hypersecretion, a person develops **Cushing syndrome** (Fig. 10.11). The excess cortisol results in a tendency toward diabetes mellitus as muscle protein is metabolized and subcutaneous fat is deposited in the midsection. The trunk is obese, while the arms and legs remain a normal size. An excess of aldosterone and reabsorption of sodium and water by the kidneys leads to a basic blood pH and hypertension. The face is moon-shaped due to edema. Masculinization may occur in women because of excess adrenal male sex hormones.

a.

b.

Figure 10.10 Addison disease. Addison disease is characterized by a peculiar bronzing of the skin, particularly noticeable in these light-skinned individuals. Note the color of **(a)** the face and **(b)** the hands compared to the hand of an individual without the disease.

Figure 10.11 Cushing syndrome. Cushing syndrome results from hypersecretion of adrenal cortex hormones. **a.** Patient first diagnosed with Cushing syndrome. **b.** Four months later, after therapy.

a.

b.

10.5 Pancreas

The **pancreas** is a long organ that lies transversely in the abdomen between the kidneys and near the duodenum of the small intestine. It is composed of two types of tissue. Exocrine tissue produces and secretes digestive juices that go by way of ducts to the small intestine. Endocrine tissue, called the **pancreatic islets** (islets of Langerhans), produces and secretes the hormones **insulin** and **glucagon** directly into the blood (Fig. 10.12).

The two antagonistic hormones insulin and glucagon, both produced by the pancreas, help maintain the normal level of glucose in the blood. Insulin is secreted when the blood glucose level is high, which usually occurs just after eating. Insulin stimulates the uptake of glucose by cells, especially liver cells, muscle cells, and adipose tissue cells. In liver and muscle cells, glucose is then stored as glycogen. In muscle cells, the glucose supplies energy for muscle contraction, and in fat cells, glucose enters the metabolic pool and thereby supplies glycerol for the formation of fat. In these ways, insulin lowers the blood glucose level. As discussed in the What's New reading on page 197, individuals who do not produce insulin have a condition called diabetes mellitus type I.

Glucagon is secreted from the pancreas, usually between meals, when the blood glucose level is low. The major target tissues of glucagon are the liver and adipose tissue. Glucagon stimulates the liver to break down glycogen to glucose and to use fat and protein in preference to glucose as energy sources. Adipose tissue cells break down fat to glycerol and fatty acids. The liver takes these up and uses them as substrates for glucose formation. In these ways, glucagon raises the blood glucose level.

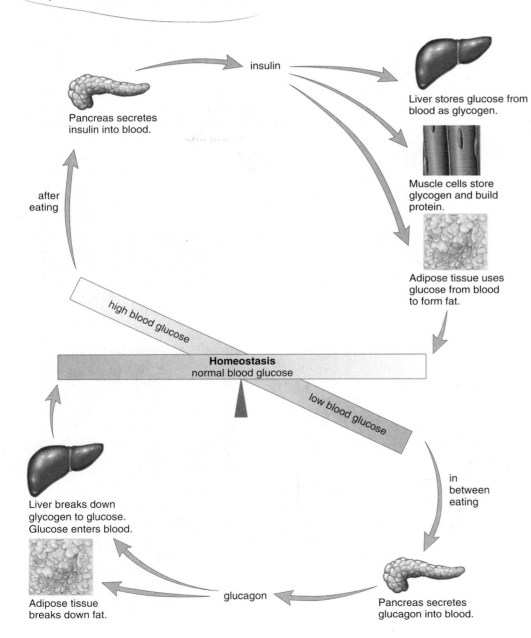

Figure 10.12 Regulation of blood glucose level. *Top:* When the blood glucose level is high, the pancreas secretes insulin. Insulin promotes the storage of glucose as glycogen in the liver and muscles and the use of glucose to form fat in adipose tissue. Therefore, insulin lowers the blood glucose level. *Bottom:* When the blood glucose level is low, the pancreas secretes glucagon. Glucagon acts opposite to insulin; therefore, glucagon raises the blood glucose level to normal.

Pancreatic Islet Cell Transplants

"I can remember getting sick with the flu just before I was diagnosed. I was eleven, and I was sick enough to miss two or three days of school. Then I just never got my strength back. I ate and drank constantly because I was thirsty and hungry all the time. I was always in the bathroom. It was so embarrassing. I started wetting the bed—can you imagine, at age 11? I fell asleep in school, and the teacher could barely get me to wake up. That's when my doctor diagnosed my diabetes for the first time."

The patient, age 25, is a typical type I, juvenile-onset or insulin-dependent diabetic. Her symptoms are classic for insulin-dependent diabetes mellitus (IDDM) (see page 198).

In insulin-dependent diabetes, the insulin-producing islet cells of the pancreas have been destroyed. Researchers think this is due to a malfunction of the immune system that causes the body's own immune cells to target the pancreas. Thus, insulin-dependent diabetes is considered an autoimmune disease. As the name suggests, insulin must be taken by injection. The diabetic patient's life then revolves around two to three daily insulin injections or monitoring by an insulin pump device that injects insulin automatically. Four or more daily blood tests are used to check blood glucose levels, and the patient must also monitor diet, activity level, exercise, and stress.

"My insulin pump saves me from those three-a-day shots, but boy, do I hate finger sticks to test my blood," the patient says with a wistful smile. "I know how carefully I have to manage this disease. Diabetics lose their sight, or go into kidney failure, or wind up having an early heart attack or stroke. I wish I could be placed on a transplant list for a pancreas, but everybody wants a pancreas. There aren't enough human donors to go around."

Pancreatic transplantation has been available to IDDM sufferers since 1966, but it suffers from the same limitations of all transplant technology. Transplanting an entire organ is major surgery, and there is always a shortage of available donors. Strong drugs must be taken for the rest of the patient's life in order to suppress the immune system. These antirejection drugs can have toxic effects on normal body cells. Moreover, with a weakened immune system, the patient has an increased risk of developing life-threatening infections or cancer.

The technique of *pancreatic islet cell transplantation* seems to hold promise for solving the problems of the traditional pancreas transplant. The islet cells are first isolated from a donor pancreas. The cells are then directly injected through the hepatic portal vein into the liver, where they form colonies and begin to produce insulin. This technique is much simpler than whole-pancreas transplantation and does not involve major surgery. In clinical studies, islet cells have been successfully implanted into human volunteers, who were then able to stop insulin injections.

It is estimated that 700,000 islets will be needed to produce enough insulin for an adult. Several donor pancreases are needed to harvest sufficient islet cells for a single transplant. If an animal cell source could be used, unlimited islet cells would be available. Heart valves from pigs have been used for decades, and insulin for injection into humans was first isolated from pigs. Tissue engineers are now experimenting with islet cells from pigs. These islet cells have been isolated and surrounded by a semipermeable plastic membrane, a process called microencapsulation. These capsules are so small that they can be placed into the abdomen, where they will float freely and produce insulin as needed (Fig. 10A). The membrane of the capsule contains pores large enough to allow oxygen and nutrients to flow in and wastes and insulin to flow out by diffusion. But the membrane prevents immune cells from coming into contact with the enclosed pancreatic cells. Unless immune cells actually come in contact with transplanted cells, they cannot destroy them. Therefore, the patient does not need to take harsh antirejection drugs, and the immune system can function normally to suppress infection and cancer. Researchers are optimistic that prepared microencapsulated islet cells could soon be available for clinical trials.

Figure 10A Encapsulated insulin-producing pancreatic islet cells from pigs can be transplanted into patients without the need for immune system-suppressing drugs.

Diabetes Mellitus

Diabetes mellitus is a fairly common hormonal disease in which liver cells, and indeed all body cells, are unable to take up and/or metabolize glucose. Therefore, the blood glucose level is elevated, called **hyperglycemia,** and the person becomes extremely hungry, called **polyphagia.** As the blood glucose level rises, glucose and water are excreted in excess, called **glycosuria** and **polyuria,** respectively. The loss of water in this way causes the diabetic to be extremely thirsty, called **polydipsia.** Since glucose is not being metabolized, the body turns to the breakdown of protein and fat for energy.

We now know that diabetes mellitus exists in two forms. In *type I,* more often called **insulin-dependent diabetes mellitus (IDDM),** the pancreas is not producing insulin. This condition is believed to be brought on, at least in part, by exposure to an environmental agent, most likely a virus, whose presence causes immune cells to destroy the pancreatic islets. The body turns to the metabolism of fat, which leads to the buildup of ketones in the blood, called **ketonuria,** and in turn to **acidosis** (acid blood), which can lead to coma and death. As a result, the individual must have daily insulin injections. These injections control the diabetic symptoms but can still cause inconveniences, because either an overdose of insulin or missing a meal can bring on the symptoms of **hypoglycemia** (low blood sugar). These symptoms include perspiration, pale skin, shallow breathing, and anxiety. The cure is quite simple: Immediate ingestion of a sugar cube or fruit juice can very quickly counteract hypoglycemia.

Of the 16 million people who now have diabetes in the United States, most have *type II,* more often called **noninsulin-dependent diabetes (NIDDM).** This type of diabetes mellitus usually occurs in people of any age who tend to be obese—adipose tissue produces a substance that interferes with the transport of glucose into cells. The amount of insulin in the blood is normal or elevated, but the insulin receptors on the cells do not respond to it. It is possible to prevent, or at least control, type II diabetes by adhering to a low-fat, low-sugar diet and exercising regularly. If this fails, oral drugs that stimulate the pancreas to secrete more insulin and enhance the metabolism of glucose in the liver and muscle cells are available. It's projected that as many as 7 million Americans may have type II diabetes without being aware of it. Yet, the effects of untreated type II diabetes are as serious as those of type I diabetes.

Long-term complications of both types of diabetes are blindness, kidney disease, and circulatory disorders, including atherosclerosis, heart disease, stroke, and reduced circulation. The latter can lead to gangrene in the arms and legs. Pregnancy carries an increased risk of diabetic coma, and the child of a diabetic is somewhat more likely to be stillborn or to die shortly after birth. However, these complications of diabetes are not expected to appear if the mother's blood glucose level is carefully regulated and kept within normal limits during the pregnancy.

10.6 Other Endocrine Glands

The body has a number of other endocrine glands, including the **gonads** (testes in males and the ovaries in females). Other lesser-known glands, such as the thymus gland and the pineal gland, also produce hormones. Some tissues within organs produce hormones and/or growth factors. Individual body cells produce prostaglandins.

Testes and Ovaries

The **testes** are located in the scrotum, and the **ovaries** are located in the pelvic cavity. The testes produce **androgens** (e.g., **testosterone**), which are the male sex hormones, and the ovaries produce **estrogens** and **progesterone,** the female sex hormones. The hypothalamus and the pituitary gland control the hormonal secretions of these organs in the manner previously described on page 188.

Androgens

Puberty is the time of life when sexual maturation occurs. Greatly increased testosterone secretion during puberty stimulates the growth of the penis and the testes. Testosterone also brings about and maintains the male secondary sex characteristics that develop during puberty, including the growth of a beard, axillary (underarm) hair, and pubic hair. It prompts the larynx and the vocal cords to enlarge, causing the voice to change. It is partially responsible for the muscular strength of males, and this is why some athletes take supplemental amounts of **anabolic steroids,** which are either testosterone or related chemicals. The contraindications of taking anabolic steroids are discussed in the Medical Focus on page 199. Testosterone also stimulates oil and sweat glands in the skin; therefore, it is largely responsible for acne and body odor. Another side effect of testosterone is baldness. Genes for baldness are probably inherited by both sexes, but baldness is seen more often in males because of the presence of testosterone.

Estrogen and Progesterone

The female sex hormones, estrogens and progesterone, have many effects on the body. In particular, estrogens secreted during puberty stimulate the growth of the uterus and the vagina. Estrogen is necessary for egg maturation and is largely responsible for the secondary sex characteristics in females, including female body hair and fat distribution. In general, females have a more rounded appearance than males because of a greater accumulation of fat beneath the skin. Also, the pelvic girdle is wider in females than in males, resulting in a larger pelvic cavity. Both estrogen and progesterone are required for breast development and for regulation of the uterine cycle, which includes monthly menstruation (discharge of blood and mucosal tissues from the uterus).

Medical Focus

Side Effects of Anabolic Steroids

Anabolic steroids are synthetic forms of the male sex hormone testosterone. Taking doses 10 to 100 times the amount prescribed by doctors for various illnesses promotes larger muscles when the person also exercises. Trainers may have been the first to acquire anabolic steroids for weight lifters, bodybuilders, and other athletes, such as professional football players. However, being a steroid user can have serious detrimental effects. Men often experience decreased sperm counts and decreased sexual desire due to atrophy of the testicles. Some develop an enlarged prostate gland or grow breasts. On the other hand, women can develop male sexual characteristics. They grow hair on their chests and faces, and lose hair from their heads; many experience abnormal enlargement of the clitoris. Some cease ovulating or menstruating, sometimes permanently.

Some researchers predict that two or three months of high-dosage use of anabolic steroids as a teen can cause death by age 30 or 40. Steroids have even been linked to heart disease in both sexes and implicated in the deaths of young athletes from liver cancer and one type of kidney tumor. Steroids can cause the body to retain fluid, which results in increased blood pressure. Users then try to get rid of "steroid bloat" by taking large doses of diuretics. A young California weight lifter had a fatal heart attack after using steroids, and the postmortem showed a lack of electrolytes, salts that help regulate the heart. Finally, steroid abuse has psychological effects, including depression, hostility, aggression, and eating disorders. Unfortunately, these drugs make a person feel invincible. One abuser even had his friend videotape him as he drove his car at 40 miles an hour into a tree!

The many harmful effects of anabolic steroids are given in Figure 10B. The Federal Food and Drug Administration now bans most steroids, and steroid use has also been banned by the National Collegiate Athletic Association (NCAA), the National Football League (NFL), and the International Olympic Committee (IOC). Of great concern is the increased use of steroids by teenagers wishing to build bulk quickly, possibly due to society's emphasis on physical appearance and adolescents' need to feel better about how they look.

balding in men and women; hair on face and chest in women

beard and deepening of voice in women

'roid mania– hostility and aggression; delusions and hallucinations; depression upon withdrawal

severe acne

breast enlargement in men and breast reduction in women

kidney disease and retention of fluids, called "steroid bloat"

reduced testicular size, low sperm count, and impotency

high blood cholesterol and atherosclerosis; high blood pressure and damage to heart

liver dysfunction and cancer

in women, increased size of ovaries; cessation of ovulation and menstruation

stunted growth in youngsters by prematurely halting activity of the epiphyseal plates

Figure 10B The effects of anabolic steroid use.

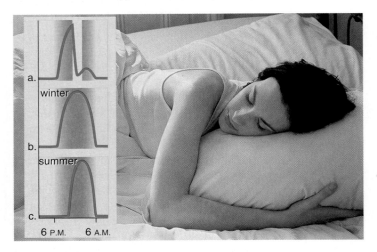

Figure 10.13 Melatonin production. Melatonin production is greatest at night when we are sleeping. Light suppresses melatonin production **(a)**, so its duration is longer in the winter **(b)** than in the summer **(c)**.

a.
winter

b.
summer

c.

6 P.M.   6 A.M.

Thymus Gland

The lobular **thymus gland**, which lies just beneath the sternum (see Fig. 10.1), reaches its largest size and is most active during childhood. Lymphocytes that originate in the bone marrow and then pass through the thymus are transformed into T lymphocytes. The lobules of the thymus are lined by epithelial cells that secrete hormones called **thymosins.** These hormones aid in the differentiation of lymphocytes packed inside the lobules. Although the hormones secreted by the thymus ordinarily work in the thymus, researchers hope that these hormones could be injected into AIDS or cancer patients where they would enhance T-lymphocyte function.

Pineal Gland

The **pineal gland,** which is located in the brain (see Fig. 10.1), produces the hormone **melatonin,** primarily at night. Melatonin is involved in our daily sleep-wake cycle; normally we grow sleepy at night when melatonin levels increase and awaken once daylight returns and melatonin levels are low (Fig. 10.13). Daily 24-hour cycles such as this are called **circadian rhythms**, and circadian rhythms are controlled by an internal timing mechanism called a biological clock.

Based on animal research, it appears that melatonin also regulates sexual development. It has also been noted that children whose pineal gland has been destroyed due to a brain tumor experience early puberty.

Hormones from Other Tissues

We have already mentioned that the heart produces atrial natriuretic hormone (see page 194). And you will see in Chapter 15 that the stomach and small intestine produce peptide hormones that regulate digestive secretions.

Leptin

Leptin is a protein hormone produced by adipose tissue. Leptin acts on the hypothalamus, where it signals satiety—that the individual has had enough to eat. Strange to say, the blood of obese individuals may be rich in leptin. It is possible that the leptin they produce is ineffective because of a genetic mutation, or else their hypothalamic cells lack a suitable number of receptors for leptin.

Growth Factors

A number of different types of organs and cells produce peptide **growth factors,** which stimulate cell division and mitosis. Some, such as lymphokines, are released into the blood; others diffuse to nearby cells. Growth factors of particular interest are the following:

Granulocyte and macrophage colony-stimulating factor (GM-CSF) is secreted by many different tissues. GM-CSF causes bone marrow stem cells to form either granulocyte or macrophage cells, depending on whether the concentration is low or high.

Platelet-derived growth factor is released from platelets and from many other cell types. It helps in wound healing and causes an increase in the number of fibroblasts, smooth muscle cells, and certain cells of the nervous system.

Epidermal growth factor and *nerve growth factor* stimulate the cells indicated by their names, as well as many others. These growth factors are also important in wound healing.

Tumor angiogenesis factor stimulates the formation of capillary networks and is released by tumor cells. One treatment for cancer is to prevent the activity of this growth factor.

Prostaglandins

Prostaglandins are potent chemical signals produced within cells from arachidonate, a fatty acid. Prostaglandins are not distributed in the blood; instead, they act locally, quite close to where they were produced. In the uterus, prostaglandins cause muscles to contract and may be involved in the pain and discomfort of menstruation. Also, prostaglandins mediate the effects of pyrogens, chemicals that are believed to reset the temperature regulatory center in the brain. For example, aspirin reduces body temperature and controls pain because of its effect on prostaglandins.

Certain prostaglandins reduce gastric secretion and have been used to treat ulcers; others lower blood pressure and have been used to treat hypertension; and still others inhibit platelet aggregation and have been used to prevent thrombosis. However, different prostaglandins have contrary effects, and it has been very difficult to successfully standardize their use.

10.7 Chemical Signals

Chemical signals are molecules that affect the behavior of those cells that have receptor proteins to receive them. For example, a hormone that binds to a receptor protein affects the metabolism of the cell.

Hormones fall into two basic chemical classes. As noted in Table 10.1, most are **peptide hormones,** a category that includes not only those that are peptides but also proteins, glycoproteins, or modified amino acids. The remainder are **steroid hormones,** each having the same four-carbon ring complex, but with different side chains.

How Hormones Function

Most peptide hormones bind to a receptor protein in the plasma membrane. This often leads to the conversion of ATP to **cyclic AMP** (cyclic adenosine monophosphate, abbreviated cAMP) (Fig. 10.14). In cAMP, one phosphate group is attached to the rest of the molecule at two spots. The peptide hormone is called the *first messenger,* and cAMP is called the *second messenger.* (Calcium is also a common second messenger, and this helps explain why calcium regulation in the body is so important.) The second messenger sets in motion an *enzyme cascade,* so called because each enzyme in turn activates several others next in line. The binding of a single peptide hormone can result in as much as a thousandfold response. The response can be an end product that leaves the cell.

Steroid hormones are lipids, and therefore they cross the plasma membrane and other cellular membranes (Fig. 10.15). Only after they are inside the cell do steroid hormones, such as estrogen and progesterone, bind to receptor proteins. The hormone-receptor complex then binds to DNA, activating particular genes. Activation leads to production of a cellular enzyme in multiple quantities.

The Importance of Chemical Signals

Cells, organs, and even individuals communicate with one another by using chemical signals.

We are most familiar with chemical signals, such as hormones, that are produced by organs some distance from one another in the body. Hormones produced by the anterior pituitary, for example, influence the function of numerous organs throughout the body. Insulin, produced by the pancreas, is transported in blood to the liver and also to all the cells. The nervous system at times utilizes chemical signals that are produced by an organ distant from the one being affected. For example, the hypothalamus produces releasing hormones that travel in a portal system to the anterior pituitary gland.

Many chemical signals act locally—that is, from cell to cell. Prostaglandins are local hormones, and certainly neurotransmitter substances released by one neuron affect a neuron nearby. Growth factors, which fall into this category, are very important regulators of cell division. Some growth factors are being used as medicines to promote the production of blood cells in AIDS and cancer patients. When a tumor develops, cell division occurs even when no stimulatory growth factor has been received. And the tumor produces a growth factor called tumor angiogenesis factor, which promotes the formation of capillary networks to service its cells.

Chemical Signals Between Individuals

Chemical signals that act between individuals are called pheromones. Pheromones are well exemplified in other animals, but they may also be effective between people. Humans produce airborne chemicals from a variety of areas, including the scalp, oral cavity, armpits, genital areas, and feet. For example, the armpit secretions of one woman could possibly affect the menstrual cycle of another woman. Women who live in the same household often have menstrual cycles in synchrony. Also, the cycle length becomes more normal when women with irregular cycles are exposed to extracts of male armpit secretions.

Figure 10.14 The binding of a peptide hormone leads to cAMP and then to activation of an enzyme cascade.

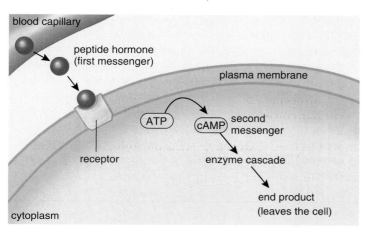

Figure 10.15 A steroid hormone results in a hormone-receptor complex that activates DNA and protein synthesis.

10.8 Effects of Aging

Thyroid disorders and diabetes are the most significant endocrine problems affecting health and function as we age. Both hypothyroidism and hyperthyroidism are seen in the elderly. Graves disease is an autoimmune disease that targets the thyroid, resulting in symptoms of cardiovascular disease, increased body temperature, and fatigue. In addition, a patient may experience weight loss of as much as 20 pounds, depression, and mental confusion. Hypothyroidism (myxedema) may fail to be diagnosed because the symptoms of hair loss, skin changes, and mental deterioration are attributed simply to the process of aging.

The true incidence of IDDM diabetes among the elderly is unknown. Its symptoms can be confused with those of other medical conditions that are present. As in all adults, NIDDM diabetes is associated with being overweight and often can be controlled by proper diet.

The effect of age on the sex organs is discussed in Chapter 17.

10.9 Homeostasis

The endocrine system and the nervous system work together to regulate the organs of the body and thereby maintain homeostasis. It is clear from reviewing the Human Systems Work Together illustration on page 203 that the endocrine system particularly influences the digestive, cardiovascular, and urinary systems in a way that maintains homeostasis.

The endocrine system helps regulate digestion. The digestive system adds nutrients to the blood, and hormones produced by the digestive system influence the gallbladder and pancreas to send their secretions to the digestive tract. Another hormone, gastrin, promotes the digestion of protein by the stomach. Through its influence on the digestive process, the endocrine system promotes the presence of nutrients in the blood.

The endocrine system helps regulate fuel metabolism. We often associate the level of glucose in the blood with insulin and glucagon. Just after eating, insulin encourages the uptake of glucose by cells and the storage of glucose as glycogen in the liver and muscles. In between eating, glucagon stimulates the liver to break down glycogen to glucose so that the blood level stays constant. Adrenaline from the adrenal medulla also stimulates the liver to release glucose. Glucagon (from the pancreas) and cortisol (from the adrenal cortex) promote the breakdown of protein to amino acids, which can be converted to glucose by the liver. They also promote the metabolism of fatty acids to conserve glucose, a process called **glucose sparing.**

The endocrine system helps regulate blood pressure and volume. ADH produced by the hypothalamus but secreted by the posterior pituitary promotes reabsorption of water by the kidneys, especially when we have not been drinking water that day. Aldosterone produced by the adrenal cortex causes the kidneys to reabsorb sodium, and when the level of sodium rises, water is automatically reabsorbed so that blood volume and pressure rise. Regulation by the endocrine system often involves antagonistic hormones; in this case, ANH produced by the heart causes sodium excretion.

The endocrine system helps regulate calcium balance. The concentration of calcium (Ca^{2+}) in the blood is critical because this ion is important to nervous conduction, muscle contraction, and the action of hormones. As you know, the bones serve as a reservoir for calcium. When the blood calcium concentration lowers, parathyroid hormone promotes the breakdown of bone and the reabsorption of calcium by the kidneys, and the absorption of calcium by the intestines. Opposing the action of parathyroid hormone, calcitonin secreted by the thyroid brings about the deposit of calcium in the bones.

The endocrine system helps regulate response to the external environment. In "fight-or-flight" situations, the nervous system stimulates the adrenal medulla to release epinephrine (adrenaline), which has a powerful effect on various organs. This, too, is important to homeostasis because it allows us to behave in a way that keeps us alive. Any damage due to stress is then repaired by the action of other hormones, including cortisol. As discussed in the Medical Focus on this page, glucocorticoid (e.g., cortisone) therapy is useful for its anti-inflammatory and immunosuppressive effects.

Medical Focus

Glucocorticoid Therapy

Glucocorticoids suppress the body's normal reaction to disease: the inflammatory reaction (see Fig. 13.4) and the immune process. Thus, glucocorticoid therapy is useful for treating autoimmune diseases such as rheumatoid arthritis, organ transplant rejection, allergies, and severe asthma. However, long-term administration of glucocorticoids for therapeutic purposes causes some degree of Cushing syndrome (see page 195). In addition, sudden withdrawal from glucocorticoid therapy causes symptoms of diminished secretory activity by the adrenal cortex. This occurs because glucocorticoids suppress the release of adrenocorticotropic hormone (ACTH) by the anterior pituitary and lead to a decrease in glucocorticoid production by the adrenal cortex. Therefore, withdrawal of glucocorticoids following long-term use must be tapered. During an alternate-day schedule, the dosage is gradually reduced and then finally discontinued as the patient's adrenal cortex resumes activity.

Human Systems Work Together

Integumentary System

Androgens activate sebaceous glands and help regulate hair growth.

Skin provides sensory input that results in the activation of certain endocrine glands.

Skeletal System

Growth hormone regulates bone development; parathyroid hormone and calcitonin regulate Ca^{2+} content.

Bones provide protection for glands; store Ca^{2+} used as second messenger.

Muscular System

Growth hormone and androgens promote growth of skeletal muscle; epinephrine stimulates heart and constricts blood vessels.

Muscles help protect glands.

Nervous System

Sex hormones affect development of brain.

Hypothalamus is part of endocrine system; nerves innervate glands of secretion.

Cardiovascular System

Epinephrine increases blood pressure; ADH, aldosterone, and atrial natriuretic hormone help regulate blood volume; growth factors control blood cell formation.

Blood vessels transport hormones from glands; blood services glands; heart produces atrial natriuretic hormones.

How the Endocrine System works with other body systems

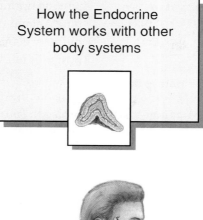

in female

Lymphatic System/Immunity

Thymus is necessary for maturity of T lymphocytes.

Lymphatic vessels pick up excess tissue fluid; immune system protects against infections.

Respiratory System

Epinephrine promotes ventilation by dilating bronchioles; growth factors control production of red blood cells that carry oxygen.

Gas exchange in lungs provides oxygen and rids body of carbon dioxide.

Digestive System

Hormones help control secretion of digestive glands and accessory organs; insulin and glucagon regulate glucose storage in liver.

Stomach and small intestine produce hormones.

Urinary System

ADH, aldosterone, and atrial natriuretic hormone regulate reabsorption of water and Na^+ by kidneys.

Kidneys keep blood values within normal limits so that transport of hormones continues.

Reproductive System

Hypothalamic, pituitary, and sex hormones control sex characteristics and regulate reproductive processes.

Gonads produce sex hormones.

Basic Key Terms

adrenal cortex (uh-dre′nul kor′teks), p. 193

adrenal gland (uh-dre′nul gland), p. 193

adrenal medulla (uh-dre′nul mĕ-dūl′uh), p. 193

adrenocorticotropic hormone (uh-dre′no-kor″ti-kō-trōp′ik hor′mōn), p. 188

aldosterone (al″dos′ter-ōn), p. 194

anabolic steroid (an″uh-bol′ik stĕ′royd), p. 198

androgen (an′dro-jen), p. 198

anterior pituitary (an-tēr′ē-or pĭ-tu′ĭ-tār″e), p. 188

antidiuretic hormone (an″tĭ-dī″yū-ret′ik hor′mōn), p. 188

atrial natriuretic hormone (ā′trē-al nā″trē-yū-ret′ik hor′mōn), p. 194

calcitonin (kal″sĭ-to′nin), p. 192

circadian rhythm (ser″ka′de-an rĭ′thm), p. 200

cortisol (kor′tĭ-sol), p. 194

cyclic AMP (sik′lik AMP), p. 201

endocrine gland (en′do-krin gland), p. 186

epinephrine (ep″ĭ-nef′rin), p. 193

estrogen (es′tro-jen), p. 198

glucagon (glu′kuh-gon), p. 196

glucocorticoid (glu″ko-kor′tĭ-koyd), p. 193

gonad (go′nad), p. 198

gonadotropic hormone (go″nad-o-trōp′ik hor′mōn), p. 188

growth factor (grōth fak′tor), p. 200

growth hormone (grōth hor′mōn), p. 188

hormone (hor′mōn), p. 186

hypothalamic-inhibiting hormone (hi″po-thĕ-lam′ik-in-hib′it-ing hor′mōn), p. 188

hypothalamic-releasing hormone (hi″po-thĕ-lam′ik-re-lēs′ing hor′mōn), p. 188

hypothalamus (hi″po-thal′uh-mus), p. 188

insulin (in′suh-lin), p. 196

leptin (lep′tin), p. 200

melatonin (mel″uh-to′nin), p. 200

mineralocorticoids (min″er-al-o-kor′tĭ-koyds), p. 193

norepinephrine (nor″ep-ĭ-nef′rin), p. 193

ovary (o′var-e), p. 198

oxytocin (ok″sĭ-to′sin), p. 188

pancreas (pan′kre-us), p. 196

pancreatic islets (of Langerhans) (pan″kre-at′ik ī′lets ov lahng′er-hanz), p. 196

parathyroid gland (pār″uh-thi′royd gland), p. 192

parathyroid hormone (pār″uh-thi′royd hor′mōn), p. 192

peptide hormone (pep′tid hor′mōn), p. 201

pineal gland (pin′e-ul gland), p. 200

pituitary gland (pĭ-tu′ĭ-tār″ē gland), p. 188

posterior pituitary (pōs-tēr′e-or pĭ-tū′ĭ-tār″ē), p. 188

positive feedback (poz′ĭ-tiv fēd′bak), p. 188

progesterone (pro-jes′ter-ōn), p. 198

prolactin (pro-lak′tin), p. 188

prostaglandins (pros″tuh-glan′dinz), p. 200

renin (re′nin), p. 194

steroid hormone (stēr′oyd hor′mōn), p. 201

testis (tes′tis), p. 198

testosterone (tes-tos′tĕ-rōn), p. 198

thymosin (thi′mo-sin), p. 200

thymus gland (thi′mus gland), p. 200

thyroid gland (thi′royd gland), p. 191

thyroid-stimulating hormone (thi′royd stim′yū-lāt-ing hor′mōn), p. 188

thyroxine (thī-rok′sin), p. 191

Clinical Key Terms

acidosis (as″ĭ-do′sis), p. 198

acromegaly (ak″ro-meg′uh-le), p. 190

Addison disease (ă′dĭ-son dĭ-zēz′), p. 195

cretinism (kre′tĭ-nizm), p. 191

Cushing syndrome (koosh′ing sin′drōm), p. 195

diabetes insipidus (dī″uh-be′tēz in-sip′ĭ-dus), p. 188

exophthalmic goiter (ek″sof-thal′mik goy′ter), p. 191

glycosuria (gli′ko-sūr′e-uh), p. 198

Graves disease (grāvz dĭ-zēz′), p. 191

hyperglycemia (hi″per-gli-se′me-uh), p. 198

hypoglycemia (hi″po-gli-se′me-uh), p. 198

insulin-dependent diabetes mellitus (in′sūl-in-de-pen′dent di″uh-be′tēz mĕ-li′tus), p. 198

ketonuria (ke″to-nū′re-uh), p. 198

myxedema (mik″sĕ-de′muh), p. 191

noninsulin-dependent diabetes (non′in′sūl-in-de-pen′dent di″uh-bē′tēz), p. 198

pituitary dwarfism (pĭ-tū′ĭ-tār″ē dwarf′-izm), p. 190

polydipsia (pol″e-dip′se-uh), p. 198

polyphagia (pol″e-fa-je-uh), p. 198

polyuria (pol″e-yū-re-uh), p. 198

simple goiter (sim′pl goy′ter), p. 191

tetany (tet′uh-ne), p. 192

Summary

10.1 Endocrine Glands
Endocrine glands secrete hormones into the bloodstream, and from there they are distributed to target organs or tissues. The major endocrine glands and hormones are listed in Table 10.1. Negative feedback controls the secretion of hormones, and antagonistic hormonal actions control the effect of hormones.

10.2 Hypothalamus and Pituitary Gland
A. Neurosecretory cells in the hypothalamus produce antidiuretic hormone (ADH) and oxytocin, which are stored in axon endings in the posterior pituitary until they are released.
B. The hypothalamus produces hypothalamic-releasing and hypothalamic-inhibiting hormones, which pass to the anterior pituitary by way of a portal system. The anterior pituitary produces at least six types of hormones, and some of these stimulate other hormonal glands to secrete hormones.

10.3 Thyroid and Parathyroid Glands
The thyroid gland requires iodine to produce triiodothyronine and thyroxine, which increase the metabolic rate. If iodine is available in limited quantities, a simple goiter develops; if the thyroid is overactive, an exophthalmic goiter develops. The thyroid gland also produces calcitonin, which helps lower the blood calcium level. The parathyroid glands secrete parathyroid hormone, which raises the blood calcium and decreases the blood phosphate levels.

10.4 Adrenal Glands
The adrenal glands respond to stress: Immediately, the adrenal medulla secretes epinephrine and norepinephrine, which bring about responses we associate with emergency situations. On a long-term basis, the adrenal cortex produces the glucocorticoids (e.g., cortisol) and the mineralocorticoids (e.g., aldosterone). Cortisol stimulates hydrolysis of proteins to amino acids that are converted to glucose; in this way, it raises the blood glucose level. Aldosterone causes the kidneys to reabsorb sodium ions (Na^+) and to excrete potassium ions (K^+). Addison disease develops when the adrenal cortex is underactive, and Cushing syndrome develops when the adrenal cortex is overactive.

10.5 Pancreas
The pancreatic islets secrete insulin, which lowers the blood glucose level, and glucagon, which has the opposite effect. The most common illness caused by hormonal imbalance is diabetes mellitus, which is due to the failure of the pancreas to produce insulin and/or the failure of the cells to take it up.

10.6 Other Endocrine Glands
A. The gonads produce the sex hormones. The thymus secretes thymosins, which stimulate T-lymphocyte production and maturation. The pineal gland produces melatonin, which may be involved in circadian rhythms and the development of the reproductive organs.

B. Tissues also produce hormones. Adipose tissue produces leptin, which acts on the hypothalamus, and various tissues produce growth factors. Prostaglandins are produced and act locally.

10.7 Chemical Signals
A. Hormones are either peptides or steroids. Reception of a peptide hormone at the plasma membrane activates an enzyme cascade inside the cell. Steroid hormones combine with a receptor in the cell, and the complex attaches to and activates DNA. Protein synthesis follows.
B. In the human body, some chemical signals, such as traditional endocrine hormones and secretions of neurosecretory cells, act at a distance. Others, such as prostaglandins, growth factors, and neurotransmitters, act locally. Whether humans have pheromones is under study.

10.8 Effects of Aging
Two concerns often seen in the elderly are thyroid malfunctioning and diabetes mellitus.

10.9 Homeostasis
Hormones particularly help maintain homeostasis in several ways: Hormones help maintain the level of nutrients (e.g., amino acids and glucose in blood); help maintain blood volume and pressure by regulating the sodium content of the blood; help maintain the blood calcium level; help regulate fuel metabolism; and help regulate our response to the external environment.

Study Questions

1. Describe a mechanism by which the secretion of a hormone is regulated and another by which the effect of a hormone is controlled. (p. 186)
2. Explain the relationship of the hypothalamus to the posterior pituitary gland and to the anterior pituitary gland. List the hormones secreted by the posterior and anterior pituitary glands. (pp. 187–88)
3. Give an example of the negative feedback relationship among the hypothalamus, the anterior pituitary, and other endocrine glands. (p. 188)
4. Discuss the effect of growth hormone on the body and the result of having too much or too little growth hormone when a young person is growing. What is the result if the anterior pituitary produces growth hormone in an adult? (p. 190)
5. What types of goiters are associated with a malfunctioning thyroid? Explain each type. (p. 191)
6. How do the thyroid and the parathyroid work together to control the blood calcium level? (p. 192)
7. How do the adrenal glands respond to stress? What hormones are secreted by the adrenal medulla, and what effects do these hormones have? (p. 193)
8. Name the most significant glucocorticoid and mineralocorticoid, and discuss their functions. Explain the symptoms of Addison disease and Cushing syndrome. (pp. 194–95)

9. Draw a diagram to explain how insulin and glucagon maintain the blood glucose level. Use your diagram to explain the major symptoms of type I diabetes mellitus. (pp. 196, 198)
10. Name the other endocrine glands discussed in this chapter, and discuss the functions of the hormones they secrete. (pp. 198, 200)
11. What are leptin, growth factors, and prostaglandins? How do these substances act? (p. 200)
12. Explain how peptide hormones and steroid hormones affect the metabolism of the cell. (p. 201)
13. Contrast hormonal and neural signals, and show that there is an overlap between the mode of operation of the nervous system and that of the endocrine system. (p. 201)
14. Discuss five ways the endocrine system helps maintain homeotasis. (p. 202)

Objective Questions

Fill in the blanks.

1. Generally, hormone production is self-regulated by a _____ mechanism.
2. The hypothalamus _____ the hormones _____ and _____ , released by the posterior pituitary.
3. The _____ secreted by the hypothalamus control the anterior pituitary.
4. Growth hormone is produced by the _____ pituitary.
5. Simple goiter occurs when the thyroid is producing _____ (too much or too little) _____ .

6. Parathyroid hormone increases the level of _____ in the blood.
7. Adrenocorticotropic hormone (ACTH), produced by the anterior pituitary, stimulates the _____ of the adrenal glands.
8. An overproductive adrenal cortex results in the condition called _____ .
9. Type I diabetes mellitus is due to a malfunctioning _____ , but type II diabetes is due to malfunctioning _____ .
10. Prostaglandins are not carried in the _____ as are hormones secreted by the endocrine glands.

11. Whereas _____ hormones are lipid soluble and bind to receptor proteins within the cytoplasm of target cells, _____ hormones bind to membrane-bound receptors, thereby activating second messengers.
12. Whereas the adrenal _____ is under the control of the autonomic nervous system, the adrenal _____ secretes its hormones in response to _____ from the anterior pituitary gland.

Medical Terminology Reinforcement Exercise

Consult Appendix B for help in pronouncing and analyzing the meaning of the terms that follow.

1. antidiuretic (an″tĭ-di″yū-ret′ik)
2. hypophysectomy (hi-pof″ĭ-sek′to-me)
3. gonadotropic (go″nad-o-trōp′ik)
4. hypokalemia (hi″po-kal″e′me-uh)
5. lactogenic (lak″to-jen′ik)
6. adrenopathy (ad″ren-op′uh-the)
7. adenomalacia (ad″ĕ-no-muh-la′she-uh)
8. parathyroidectomy (pār″uh-thi″roy-dek′to-me)
9. polydipsia (pol″e-dip′se-uh)
10. dyspituitarism (dis-pĭ-tu′ĭ-ter′izm)
11. ketoacidosis (ke′to-as′ĭ-do′sis)
12. thyroiditis (thi-roy-di′tis)
13. glucosuria (glu-co-su′re-uh)
14. microsomia (mi′kro-so′me-uh)
15. androgenic alopecia (an′dro-jen′ik al-o-pe′she-uh)

Website Link

Visit the Student Edition of the Online Learning Center at http://www.mhhe.com/maderap5 for additional quizzes, interactive learning exercises, and other study tools.

chapter

Blood

11

The formed elements of blood—red blood cells, white blood cells, and platelets—are shown in this colorized scanning electron micrograph.

chapter outline & learning objectives

After you have studied this chapter, you should be able to:

Part IV

FORMED ELEMENTS	Function and Description	Source
Red Blood Cells (erythrocytes) 4 million–6 million per mm³ blood	Transport O_2 and help transport CO_2 7–8 μm in diameter; bright-red to dark-purple biconcave disks without nuclei	Red bone marrow
White Blood Cells (leukocytes) 5,000–11,000 per mm³ blood	Fight infection	Red bone marrow
Granular leukocytes		
• Neutrophils 40–70%	Phagocytize pathogens. 10–14 μm in diameter; spherical cells with multilobed nuclei; fine, lilac granules in cytoplasm if Wright stained.	
• Eosinophils 1–4%	Phagocytize antigen-antibody complexes and allergens. 10–14 μm in diameter; spherical cells with bilobed nuclei; coarse, deep-red, uniformly sized granules in cytoplasm if Wright stained.	
• Basophils 0–1%	Release histamine and heparin, which promote blood flow to injured tissues. 10–12 μm in diameter; spherical cells with lobed nuclei; large, irregularly shaped, deep-blue granules in cytoplasm if Wright stained.	
Agranular leukocytes		
• Lymphocytes 20–45%	Responsible for specific immunity. 5–17 μm in diameter (average 9–10 μm); spherical cells with large, round nuclei.	
• Monocytes 4–8%	Become macrophages that phagocytize pathogens and cellular debris. 10–24 μm in diameter; large, spherical cells with kidney-shaped, round, or lobed nuclei.	
Platelets (thrombocytes) 150,000–300,000 per mm³ blood	Aid hemostasis. 2–4 μm in diameter; disk-shaped cell fragments with no nuclei; purple granules in cytoplasm.	Red bone marrow

Plasma 55%

Formed elements 45%

PLASMA	Function	Source
Water (90–92% of plasma)	Maintains blood volume; transports molecules	Absorbed from intestine
Plasma proteins (7–8% of plasma)	Maintain blood osmotic pressure and pH	Liver
Albumins	Maintain blood volume and pressure	
Globulins	Transport; fight infection	
Fibrinogen	Coagulation	
Salts (less than 1% of plasma)	Maintain blood osmotic pressure and pH; aid metabolism	Absorbed from intestine
Gases		
Oxygen	Cellular respiration	Lungs
Carbon dioxide	End product of metabolism	Tissues
Nutrients	Food for cells	Absorbed from intestine

Lipids
    Glucose
    Amino acids		

Nitrogenous wastes	Excretion by kidneys	Liver
Uric acid Urea		
Other		
Hormones, vitamins, etc.	Aid metabolism	Varied

• Appearance with Wright's stain.

Figure 11.1 Composition of blood. When a blood sample is prevented from clotting and spun in a centrifuge tube, it forms two layers. The lucent, yellow top layer is plasma, the liquid portion of blood. The formed elements are in the bottom layer. This table describes these components in detail.

11.1 The Composition and Functions of Blood

When a blood sample is prevented from clotting and spun in a centrifuge tube, it separates into two layers (Fig. 11.1). The lower layer consists of white blood cells (note the buffy layer), blood platelets, and red blood cells. Collectively, these are the **formed elements,** which make up about 45% of the total volume of whole blood; the percentage of blood attributed to red blood cells is called the **hematocrit.** The upper layer is plasma, which contains a variety of inorganic and organic molecules dissolved or suspended in water. Plasma accounts for about 55% of the total volume of whole blood.

Functions of Blood

The functions of blood fall into three categories: transport, defense, and regulation.

Transport

Blood moves from the heart to all the various organs, where exchange with tissues takes place across thin capillary walls. Blood picks up oxygen from the lungs and nutrients from the digestive tract and transports these to the tissues. It also picks up and transports cellular wastes, including carbon dioxide, away from the tissues to exchange surfaces, such as the lungs and kidneys. We will see that capillary exchanges keep the composition of tissue fluid within normal limits.

Various organs and tissues secrete hormones into the blood, and blood transports these to other organs and tissues, where they serve as signals that influence cellular metabolism.

Defense

Blood defends the body against invasion by **pathogens** (microscopic infectious agents, such as bacteria and viruses) in several ways. Certain blood cells are capable of engulfing and destroying pathogens, and others produce and secrete antibodies into the blood. Antibodies incapacitate pathogens, making them subject to destruction, sometimes by white blood cells.

When an injury occurs, blood forms a clot, and this prevents blood loss. Blood clotting involves platelets and the plasma protein fibrinogen. Without blood clotting, we could bleed to death even from a small cut.

Regulation

Blood helps regulate body temperature by picking up heat, mostly from active muscles, and transporting it about the body. If the blood is too warm, the heat dissipates from dilated blood vessels in the skin.

The salts and plasma proteins in blood act to keep the liquid content of blood high. In this way, blood plays a role in helping to maintain its own water-salt balance.

Because blood contains buffers, it also helps regulate body pH and keep it relatively constant.

Plasma

Plasma is the liquid portion of blood, and about 92% of plasma is water. The remaining 8% of plasma is composed of various salts (ions) and organic molecules (Table 11.1). The salts, which are simply dissolved in plasma, help maintain the pH of the blood. Small organic molecules such as glucose, amino acids, and urea are also dissolved in plasma. Glucose and amino acids are nutrients for cells; urea is a nitrogenous waste product on its way to the kidneys for excretion. The large organic molecules in plasma include hormones and the plasma proteins.

The Plasma Proteins

Three major types of plasma proteins are the albumins, the globulins, and fibrinogen. Most plasma proteins are made in the liver. An exception is the antibodies produced by B lymphocytes, which function in immunity. Certain hormones are plasma proteins made by various glands.

The plasma proteins have many functions that help maintain homeostasis. They are able to take up and release hydrogen ions; therefore, the plasma proteins help buffer the blood and keep its pH around 7.40. **Osmotic pressure** is a force caused by a difference in solute concentration on either side of a membrane. The plasma proteins, particularly the **albumins,** contribute to the osmotic pressure, which pulls water into the blood and helps keep it there.

There are three types of **globulins,** designated alpha, beta, and gamma globulins. The alpha and beta globulins, produced by the liver, bind to metal ions, to fat-soluble vitamins, and to lipids, forming the lipoproteins. Antibodies, which help fight infections by combining with antigens, are gamma globulins.

Both albumins and globulins combine with and transport large organic molecules. For example, albumin transports the molecule bilirubin, a breakdown product of hemoglobin. Lipoproteins, whose protein portion is a globulin, transport cholesterol.

Fibrinogen (and also a protein called prothrombin) are necessary to coagulation (blood clotting), which is discussed on page 215.

Table 11.1	Blood Plasma Solutes
Plasma proteins	Albumin, globulins, fibrinogen
Inorganic ions (salts)	Na^+, Ca^{2+}, K^+, Mg^{2+}, Cl^-, HCO_3^-, HPO_4^{2-}, SO_4^{2-}
Gases	O_2, CO_2
Organic nutrients	Glucose, fats, phospholipids, amino acids, etc.
Nitrogenous waste products	Urea, ammonia, uric acid
Regulatory substances	Hormones, enzymes

11.2 The Blood Cells

The formed elements contain blood cells and platelets. (Platelets are discussed in detail on page 215.) In the adult, the formed elements are produced continuously in the red bone marrow of the skull, ribs, and vertebrae, the iliac crests, and the ends of long bones.

The process by which formed elements are made is called **hematopoiesis** (Fig. 11.2). A **stem cell** is capable of dividing and producing new cells that go on to become particular types of cells. Stem cells in red bone marrow produce cells that ma-

ture into the various types of formed elements. At the top of Figure 11.2 is a multipotent stem cell that divides, producing two other types of stem cells. The myeloid stem cell gives rise to the cells that go through a number of stages to become red blood cells, platelets, granular leukocytes, and monocytes. The lymphatic stem cell produces the lymphocytes.

Many scientists are very interested in developing ways to use blood stem cells, as well as stem cells from other adult tissues, to regenerate the body's tissues in the laboratory. If all goes well, embryos will not be needed as a source of stem cells to generate tissues for various illnesses.

visual focus

Figure 11.2 Hematopoiesis. Multipotent stem cells give rise to two specialized stem cells. The myeloid stem cell gives rise to still other cells, which become red blood cells, platelets, and all the whole blood cells except lymphocytes. The lymphatic stem cell gives rise to lymphoblasts, which become lymphocytes.

Red Blood Cells

Red blood cells (RBCs, or **erythrocytes**) are small, biconcave disks that lack a nucleus when mature. They occur in great quantity; there are 4 to 6 million red blood cells per mm^3 of whole blood.

Red blood cells transport oxygen, and each contains about 200 million molecules of **hemoglobin,** the respiratory pigment. If this much hemoglobin were suspended within the plasma rather than enclosed within the cells, blood would be so viscous that the heart would have difficulty pumping it.

Hemoglobin

In a molecule of hemoglobin, each of four polypeptide chains making up globin has an iron-containing heme group in the center. Oxygen combines loosely with iron when hemoglobin is oxygenated:

$$Hb + O_2 \xrightleftharpoons[\text{tissues}]{\text{lungs}} HbO_2$$

In this equation, the hemoglobin on the right, which is combined with oxygen, is called oxyhemoglobin. Oxyhemoglobin forms in lung capillaries, and has a bright red color. The hemoglobin on the left, which is not combined with oxygen, is called deoxyhemoglobin. Deoxyhemoglobin forms in tissue capillaries, and has a dark maroon color.

Hemoglobin is remarkably adapted to its function of picking up oxygen in lung capillaries and releasing it in the tissues. As discussed in the What's New reading on page 212, hemoglobin alone can be used as a blood substitute. The higher concentration of oxygen, plus the slightly cooler temperature and slightly higher pH within lung capillaries, causes hemoglobin to take up oxygen. The lower concentration of oxygen, plus the slightly warmer temperature and slightly lower pH within tissue capillaries, causes hemoglobin to give up its oxygen.

Production of Red Blood Cells

Erythrocytes are formed from red bone marrow stem cells (see Fig. 11.2): A multipotent stem cell descendant, called a myeloid stem cell, gives rise to erythroblasts, which divide many times. During maturation, these cells lose their nucleus and other organelles. As they mature, they gain many molecules of hemoglobin and lose their nucleus and most of their organelles. Possibly because mature red blood cells lack a nucleus, they live only about 120 days. It is estimated that about 2 million red blood cells are destroyed per second; therefore, an equal number must be produced to keep the red blood cell count in balance.

Whenever blood carries a reduced amount of oxygen, as happens when an individual first takes up residence at a high altitude, loses red blood cells, or has impaired lung function, the kidneys accelerate their release of **erythropoietin** (Fig. 11.3).

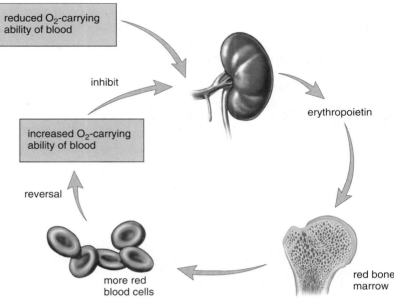

Figure 11.3 Action of erythropoietin. The kidneys release increased amounts of erythropoietin whenever the oxygen capacity of the blood is reduced. Erythropoietin stimulates the red bone marrow to speed up its production of red blood cells, which carry oxygen. Once the oxygen-carrying capacity of the blood is sufficient to support normal cellular activity, the kidneys cut back on their production of erythropoietin.

reduced O$_2$-carrying ability of blood

inhibit

increased O$_2$-carrying ability of blood

erythropoietin

reversal

more red blood cells

red bone marrow

This hormone stimulates stem cells and speeds up the maturation of red blood cells. The liver and other tissues also produce erythropoietin. Erythropoietin, now mass-produced through biotechnology, is sometimes abused by athletes in order to raise their red blood cell counts and thereby increase the oxygen-carrying capacity of their blood.

Destruction of Red Blood Cells

With age, red blood cells are destroyed in the liver and spleen, where they are engulfed by macrophages. When red blood cells are broken down, hemoglobin is released. The globin portion of the hemoglobin is broken down into its component amino acids, which are recycled by the body. The iron is recovered and returned to the bone marrow for reuse. The heme portion of the molecule undergoes chemical degradation and is excreted as bile pigments by the liver into the bile. These bile pigments are bilirubin and biliverdin, which contribute to the color of feces. Chemical breakdown of heme is also what causes a bruise on the skin to change color from red/purple to blue to green to yellow.

Abnormal Red Blood Cell Counts

As discussed in the Medical Focus on page 214, anemia is an illness in which the patient has a tired, run-down feeling. The cells are not getting enough oxygen due to a reduction in the amount of hemoglobin or the number of red blood cells. **Hemolysis** (bursting of red blood cells) can also cause anemia.

Blood Substitutes

In the emergency room (ER) setting, it's a problem you and your co-workers will face every day. Your patient may have survived a serious automobile accident, or perhaps he was involved in a shooting. A young woman may have hemorrhaged following the unexpected early delivery of her baby. Or maybe your patient is a young acute lymphoblastic leukemia sufferer (see page 214), whose hematocrit (red blood cell count, see page 209) has dropped dangerously low because of chemotherapy. These patients all share a common need—an immediate blood transfusion to save their lives. Without transfusion, blood loss will cause tissue cells to die from lack of oxygen. For this reason, emergency room caregivers often refer to the "golden hour" for treatment of patients. Patients who receive the best possible care, including blood transfusions, within an hour of admission to the ER have the best chance of surviving and recovering.

If the emergency room is a major trauma center in a large city hospital, donor blood for transfusion is usually available. The correct blood can be matched to the patient's blood type. If there isn't time to match donor and recipient blood, the ready supply of O-negative blood can theoretically be donated to anyone. But what if the transfusion is needed in a remote area, such as a wartime field hospital or the accident scene on an isolated stretch of highway? Military medics and EMT personnel often can't store and transport whole blood. What if the hospital is in a rural area? Small regional hospitals face regular shortages of donor blood for transfusion.

Even when the blood is properly matched, receiving a transfusion always carries a small but significant risk. Because blood is a tissue, transfusion is in effect a "tissue transplant." If the patient's immune system detects that the proteins on the red blood cell membrane are foreign, the transfused cells will be rejected (see Fig. 11.9). This process, called a transfusion reaction, can be fatal. Donor blood may be infected with viruses, including HIV (which causes AIDS) and hepatitis B and C viruses. Currently, the transfusion recipient also faces the risk of infection with prions (protein infectious particles). Prions, which are smaller than viruses, cause Creutzfeldt-Jacob disease, the human form of mad cow disease.

Researchers are currently investigating the use of blood substitutes to solve some of the problems inherent in blood transfusion. The most promising blood substitutes use the hemoglobin molecule as their basic component. Hemoglobin is the oxygen-transporting molecule contained in red blood cells (see page 211 and Fig. 11A). Natural hemoglobin taken out of red blood cells cannot be introduced into the bloodstream. It breaks down immediately into smaller molecules that are toxic, especially to nerve cells, the liver, and the kidneys. However, hemoglobin that is first chemically altered to prevent it from breaking down can be safely transfused. Once in the cardiovascular system, the hemoglobin will transport oxygen in much the same way that it does inside an intact red blood cell. The modified hemoglobin is slowly broken down and eliminated from the body, without harming the patient's liver or kidneys. What's more, adequate supplies of hemoglobin are readily available, and don't rely on human blood donors. One developer uses blood from cattle. Another uses human hemoglobin produced by genetically engineered bacteria (also the source of the human insulin injected by diabetics).

Blood substitutes have additional benefits. Hemoglobin-based blood substitutes are better oxygen transporters than whole blood, although they remain in the patient's body for only a few days. Unlike whole blood, blood substitutes are free of disease-causing contaminants and can be stored for months at room temperature. Moreover, blood substitutes cannot cause a transfusion reaction because they lack the protein membrane of a red blood cell. This makes them the perfect "one-size-fits-all" substance for transfusion, and perhaps the ideal solution for critical-care emergencies. Blood substitutes are currently in widespread clinical trials in South Africa, where the AIDS outbreak has caused a critical shortage of available donors for whole blood. Other clinical trials are under way in the United States and Europe.

iron
heme group
helical shape of the polypeptide molecule

Figure 11A Hemoglobin contains four polypeptide chains (blue). There is an iron-containing heme group in the center of each chain. Oxygen combines loosely with iron when hemoglobin is oxygenated. Oxyhemoglobin is bright red, and deoxyhemoglobin is a dark maroon color.

White Blood Cells

White blood cells (WBCs, or **leukocytes)** differ from red blood cells in that they are usually larger, have a nucleus, lack hemoglobin, and are translucent unless stained. White blood cells are not as numerous as red blood cells; there are only 5,000–11,000 per mm^3 of blood. White blood cells fight infection and in this way are important contributors to homeostasis. This function of white blood cells is discussed at greater length in Chapter 13, which concerns immunity.

White blood cells are derived from stem cells in the red bone marrow, and they, too, undergo several maturation stages (see Fig. 11.2). Each type of white blood cell is apparently capable of producing a specific growth factor that circulates back to the bone marrow to stimulate its own production.

Red blood cells are confined to the blood, but white blood cells are able to squeeze through pores in the capillary wall (Fig. 11.4). Therefore, they are found in tissue fluid and lymph (the fluid within lymphatic vessels) and in lymphatic organs. When an infection is present, white blood cells greatly increase in number. Many white blood cells live only a few days—they probably die while engaging pathogens. Others live months or even years.

Types of White Blood Cells

White blood cells are classified into the **granular leukocytes** and the **agranular leukocytes.** Both types of cells have granules in the cytoplasm surrounding the nucleus, but the granules are more visible upon staining in granular leukocytes. (The white cells in Figure 11.2 have been stained with Wright stain.) The granules contain various enzymes and proteins, which help white blood cells defend the body. There are three types of granular leukocytes and two types of agranular leukocytes. They differ somewhat by the size of the cell and the shape of the nucleus (see Fig. 11.1), and they also differ in their functions.

Granular Leukocytes Neutrophils (see Fig. 13.3*a*) are the most abundant of the white blood cells. They have a multi-lobed nucleus joined by nuclear threads; therefore, they are also called polymorphonuclear. Some of their granules take up acid stain, and some take up basic stain (creating an overall lilac color). Neutrophils are the first type of white blood cell to respond to an infection, and they engulf pathogens during phagocytosis**.**

Eosinophils (see Fig. 13.3*b*) have a bilobed nucleus, and their large, abundant granules take up eosin and become a red color. (This accounts for their name, eosinophil.) Among several functions, they increase in number in the event of a parasitic worm infection. Eosinophils also lessen an allergic reaction by phagocytizing antigen-antibody complexes involved in an allergic attack.

Basophils (see Fig. 13.3*c*) have a U-shaped or lobed nucleus. Their granules take up the basic stain and become dark

blue in color. (This accounts for their name, basophil.) In the connective tissues, basophils, as well as a similar type of cells called mast cells, release histamine and heparin. Histamine, which is associated with allergic reactions, dilates blood vessels and causes contraction of smooth muscle. Heparin prevents clotting and promotes blood flow.

Agranular Leukocytes The agranular leukocytes include lymphocytes, which have a spherical nucleus, and monocytes, which have a kidney-shaped nucleus. **Lymphocytes** are responsible for specific immunity to particular pathogens and their toxins (poisonous substances). Lymphocytes (see Fig. 13.3*d*) are of two types, B lymphocytes and T lymphocytes. Pathogens have **antigens,** surface molecules that the immune system can recognize as foreign. When an antigen is recognized as foreign, B lymphocytes will form antibodies against it. **Antibodies** are proteins that neutralize antigens. T lymphocytes, on the other hand, directly attack and destroy any cell, such as a pathogen that has foreign antigens. B lymphocytes and T lymphocytes are discussed more fully in Chapter 13.

Monocytes (see Fig. 13.3*e*) are the largest of the white blood cells, and after taking up residence in the tissues, they differentiate into even larger macrophages. **Macrophages** phagocytize pathogens, old cells, and cellular debris. They also stimulate other white blood cells, including lymphocytes, to defend the body.

Abnormal White Cell Counts

Abnormal white blood cell counts are discussed in the Medical Focus on page 214. Because specific white blood cells increase with particular infections, a differential white cell count, also discussed in the Medical Focus, can be quite helpful in diagnosing the cause of a particular illness.

Abnormal Red and White Blood Cell Counts

Polycythemia is a disorder in which an excessive number of red blood cells makes the blood so thick that it is unable to flow properly. An increased risk of clot formation is also associated with this condition.

In **anemia,** either the number of red cells is insufficient, or the cells do not have enough hemoglobin. Normally, the blood hemoglobin level is 12 to 17 grams per 100 milliliters. In **iron deficiency anemia,** a common type of anemia, the hemoglobin count is low, and the individual feels tired and run-down. The person's diet may not contain enough iron. Certain foods, such as raisins and liver, are rich in iron, and including these in the diet can help prevent this type of anemia.

In another type of anemia, called **pernicious anemia,** the digestive tract is unable to absorb enough vitamin B_{12}, which is essential to the proper formation of red cells. Without it, large numbers of immature red cells tend to accumulate in the bone marrow. A special diet and injections of vitamin B_{12} are effective treatments for pernicious anemia.

In **aplastic anemia,** the red bone marrow has been damaged due to radiation or chemicals, and not enough red blood cells are produced. *Hemolysis* is the rupturing of red blood cells. In **hemolytic anemia,** the rate of red blood cell destruction increases. **Hemolytic disease of the newborn,** discussed at the end of this chapter (see page 219), is also a type of anemia.

Sickle-cell disease is a hereditary condition in which the individual has sickle-shaped red blood cells (Fig. 11B). Such cells tend to rupture and wear out easily as they pass through the narrow capillaries, leading to the symptoms of anemia. Sickle-cell disease is most common among blacks because the sickle-shaped cells protect against malaria, a disease prevalent in parts of Africa. The parasite that causes malaria cannot infect sickle-shaped red blood cells.

Certain viral illnesses, such as influenza, measles, and mumps, cause the white blood cell count to decrease. **Leukopenia** is a total white blood cell count below 5,000 per cubic millimeter. Other illnesses, including appendicitis and bacterial infections, cause the white blood cell count to increase dramatically. **Leukocytosis** is a white blood cell count above 10,000 per cubic millimeter.

Illness often causes an increase in a particular type of white blood cell. For this reason, a **differential white blood cell count,** involving the microscopic examination of a blood sample and the counting of each type of white blood cell to a total of 100 cells,

Figure 11B Sickle-shaped red blood cells, as seen by a scanning electron microscope.

may be done as part of the diagnostic procedure. For example, the characteristic finding in the viral disease **mononucleosis** is a great number of lymphocytes that are larger than mature lymphocytes and that stain more darkly. This condition takes its name from the fact that lymphocytes are mononuclear.

Leukemia is a form of cancer characterized by uncontrolled production of abnormal white blood cells. These cells accumulate in the bone marrow, lymph nodes, spleen, and liver so that these organs are unable to function properly. **Acute lymphoblastic leukemia (ALL),** which represents over 80% of the acute leukemias in children, also occurs in adults. Chemotherapy is used to destroy abnormal cells and restore normal blood cell production. Intraspinal injection of drugs and craniospinal irradiation are measures that prevent leukemic cells from infiltrating the central nervous system. In general, the prognosis is more favorable for children between the ages of 2 and 10 years than for either older or younger patients. The prognosis is somewhat better in females because leukemia recurs in the testes of 8–16% of males. Remission occurs in 78% of adult patients after chemotherapy, and the median period of remission is 20 months. With chemotherapy, 50–60% of children survive past five years, and of those among this group who do not have a relapse, 85% are considered cured.

11.3 Platelets and Hemostasis

Platelets (thrombocytes) are formed elements necessary to the process of **hemostasis**, the cessation of bleeding.

Platelets

Platelets result from fragmentation of certain large cells, called **megakaryocytes**, that develop in red bone marrow. Platelets are produced at a rate of 200 billion per day, and the blood contains 150,000–300,000 per mm^3. Because platelets have no nucleus, they last at most ten days, assuming they are not used sooner than that in hemostasis.

Hemostasis

Hemostasis is divided into three events: vascular spasm, platelet plug formation, and coagulation (Fig. 11.5).

Vascular spasm, the constriction of a broken blood vessel, is the immediate response to blood vessel injury. Platelets release serotonin, a chemical that prolongs smooth muscle contraction.

Platelet plug formation is the next event in hemostasis. Platelets don't normally adhere to damaged blood vessel walls, but when the lining of a blood vessel breaks, connective

Figure 11.5 Hemostasis requires three events: vascular spasm, platelet plug formation, and coagulation. Coagulation is further broken down into four steps.

tissue, including collagen fibers, is exposed. Platelets adhere to collagen fibers and release a number of substances, including one that promotes platelet aggregation so that a so-called *platelet plug* forms. As a part of normal activities, small blood vessels often break, and a platelet plug is usually sufficient to stop the bleeding.

Coagulation, also called blood clotting, is the last event to bring about hemostasis. As you will see, two plasma proteins, called **fibrinogen** and **prothrombin,** participate in blood clotting. Vitamin K, found in green vegetables and also formed by intestinal bacteria, is necessary for the production of prothrombin. If, by chance, vitamin K is missing from the diet, **hemorrhagic bleeding** disorders develop.

Coagulation

Coagulation requires many clotting factors and enzymatic reactions that are preliminary to the few we will consider. One important preliminary step that occurs in the body is the release of **tissue thromboplastin,** a clotting factor that interacts with platelets, other clotting factors, and calcium ions (Ca^{2+}). Figure 11.5 breaks down the subsequent clotting process into four steps: ① After thromboplastin is released, **prothrombin activator** is formed. ② Prothrombin activator then converts prothrombin to **thrombin.** ③ Thrombin, in turn, severs two short amino acid chains from each fibrinogen molecule, and these activated fragments join end-to-end, forming long threads of **fibrin.** ④ Fibrin threads wind around the platelet plug in the damaged area of the blood vessel and provide the framework for the clot. Red blood cells also are trapped within the fibrin threads; these cells make a clot appear red.

Clot retraction follows, and the clot gets smaller as platelets contract. A fluid called **serum** (plasma minus fibrinogen and prothrombin) is squeezed from the clot. A fibrin clot is present only temporarily. As soon as blood vessel repair is initiated, an enzyme called *plasmin* destroys the fibrin network and restores the fluidity of the plasma.

Disorders of Hemostasis

Among the many possible disorders of hemostasis, we will mention but a few. **Thrombocytopenia,** a low platelet count, can be due to any impairment of the red bone marrow. Despite the presence of anticoagulants in the blood, sometimes a clot forms in an unbroken blood vessel. Such a clot is called a **thrombus** if it remains stationary. Should the clot dislodge and travel in the blood, it is called an **embolus.** If **thromboembolism** is not treated, a heart attack can occur, as discussed in Chapter 12.

Hemophilia is an inherited clotting disorder caused by a deficiency in a clotting factor. (So-called hemophilia A is due to the lack of clotting factor VIII.) The slightest bump can cause bleeding into the joints. Cartilage degeneration in the joints and resorption of underlying bone can follow. Bleeding into muscles can lead to nerve damage and muscular atrophy. The most frequent cause of death is bleeding into the brain with accompanying neurological damage.

11.4 Capillary Exchange

The pumping of the heart sends blood by way of arteries to the capillaries where exchange takes place across thin capillary walls (Fig. 11.6). Blood that has passed through the capillaries returns to the heart via veins. Capillary walls are largely composed of one layer of epithelial cells connected by tight junctions. Capillaries are extremely numerous. The body most likely contains a billion capillaries, and their total surface area is estimated at 6,300 square meters. Therefore, most cells of the body are near a capillary.

In the tissues of the body, metabolically active cells require oxygen and nutrients and give off wastes, including carbon dioxide. During capillary exchange—not including the gas-exchanging surfaces of the lungs—oxygen and nutrients leave a capillary, and cellular wastes, including carbon dioxide, enter a capillary. Certainly, arterial blood contains more oxygen and nutrients than venous blood, and venous blood contains more wastes than arterial blood.

The internal environment of the body consists of blood and tissue fluid. **Tissue fluid** is simply the fluid that surrounds the cells of the body. In other words, substances that leave a capillary pass through tissue fluid before entering the body's cells, and substances that leave the body's cells pass through tissue fluid before entering a capillary. The composition of tissue fluid stays relatively constant because of capillary exchange. Tissue fluid is mainly water. Any excess tissue fluid is collected by lymphatic capillaries, which are always found near blood capillaries.

Blood Capillaries

Water and other small molecules can cross through the cells of a capillary wall or through tiny clefts that occur between the cells. Large molecules in plasma, such as the plasma proteins, are too large to pass through capillary walls.

Three processes influence capillary exchange—blood pressure, diffusion, and osmotic pressure:

Blood pressure, which is created by the pumping of the heart, is the pressure of blood against a vessel's (e.g., capillary) walls.

Diffusion, as you know, is simply the movement of substances from the area of higher concentration to the area of lower concentration.

Osmotic pressure is a force caused by a difference in solute concentration on either side of a membrane.

To understand osmotic pressure, consider that water will cross a membrane toward the side that has the greater concentration of solutes, and the accumulation of this water results in a pressure. The presence of the plasma proteins, and also salts to some degree, means that blood has a greater osmotic pressure than does tissue fluid. Therefore, the osmotic pressure of blood pulls water into and retains water inside a capillary.

Notice in Figure 11.6 that a capillary has an arterial end (contains arterial blood) and a venous end (contains venous blood). In between, a capillary has a midsection. We will now consider the exchange of molecules across capillary walls at each of these locations.

Figure 11.6 Capillary exchange. At the arterial end of a capillary, blood pressure is higher than osmotic pressure; therefore, water tends to leave the bloodstream. In the midsection of a capillary, small molecules follow their concentration gradients: Oxygen and nutrients leave the capillary, while wastes, including carbon dioxide, enter the capillary. At the venous end of a capillary, osmotic pressure is higher than blood pressure; therefore, water tends to enter the bloodstream.

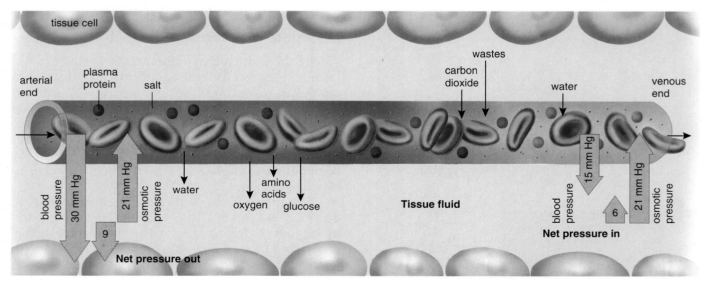

Arterial End of Capillary

When arterial blood enters tissue capillaries, it is bright red because the hemoglobin in red blood cells is carrying oxygen. Blood is also rich in nutrients, which are dissolved in plasma.

At the arterial end of a capillary, blood pressure, an outward force, is higher than osmotic pressure, an inward force. Pressure is measured in terms of mm Hg (mercury); in this case, blood pressure is 30 mm Hg, and osmotic pressure is 21 mm Hg. Because blood pressure is higher than osmotic pressure at the arterial end of a capillary, water and other small molecules (e.g., glucose and amino acids) exit a capillary at its arterial end.

Red blood cells and a large proportion of the plasma proteins generally remain in a capillary because they are too large to pass through its wall. The exit of water and other small molecules from a capillary creates tissue fluid. Therefore, tissue fluid consists of all the components of plasma, except that it contains fewer plasma proteins.

Midsection of Capillary

Diffusion takes place along the length of the capillary, as small molecules follow their concentration gradient by moving from the area of higher to the area of lower concentration. In the tissues, the area of higher concentration of oxygen and nutrients is always blood, because after these molecules have passed into tissue fluid, they are taken up and metabolized by cells. The cells use oxygen and glucose in the process of cellular respiration, and they use amino acids for protein synthesis.

As a result of metabolism, tissue cells give off carbon dioxide and other wastes. Because tissue fluid is always the area of greater concentration for waste materials, they diffuse into a capillary.

Venous End of Capillary

At the venous end of the capillary, blood pressure is much reduced to only about 15 mm Hg, as shown in Figure 11.6. Blood pressure is reduced at the venous end because capillaries have a greater cross-sectional area at their venous end than their arterial end. However, there is no reduction in osmotic pressure, which remains at 21 mm Hg and is now higher than blood pressure. Therefore, water tends to enter a capillary at the venous end. As water enters a capillary, it brings with it additional waste molecules. Blood that leaves the capillaries is deep maroon in color because red blood cells now contain reduced hemoglobin—hemoglobin that has given up its oxygen and taken on hydrogen ions.

In the end, about 85% of the water that left a capillary at the arterial end returns to it at the venous end. Therefore, retrieving fluid by means of osmotic pressure is not completely effective. The body has an auxiliary means of collecting tissue fluid; any excess usually enters lymphatic capillaries.

Figure 11.7 Lymphatic capillaries. Lymphatic capillaries lie near blood capillaries. The black arrows show the flow of blood. The yellow arrows show that lymph is formed when lymphatic capillaries take up excess tissue fluid.

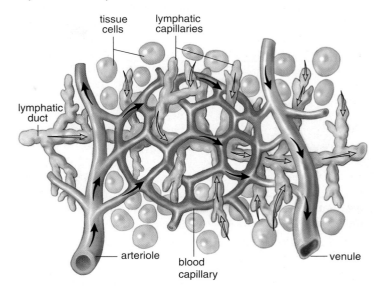

Lymphatic Capillaries

Lymphatic vessels are a one-way system of vessels. Notice that lymphatic capillaries have blind ends that lie near blood capillaries (Fig. 11.7). Lymphatic vessels have a structure similar to that of cardiovascular veins, except that their walls are thinner and they have more valves. The valves prevent the backward flow of lymph as lymph flows toward the thoracic cavity. Lymphatic capillaries join to form larger vessels that merge into the lymphatic ducts (see Fig. 13.1). Lymphatic ducts empty into cardiovascular veins within the thoracic cavity.

Lymph, the fluid carried by lymphatic vessels, has the same composition as tissue fluid. Why? Because lymphatic capillaries absorb excess tissue fluid at the blood capillaries. The lymphatic system contributes to homeostasis in several ways. One way is to maintain normal blood volume and pressure by returning excess tissue fluid to the blood.

Edema

Edema is localized swelling that occurs when tissue fluid accumulates. Edema can be caused by several factors: an increase in capillary permeability; a decrease in the uptake of water at the venous end of blood capillaries due to a decrease in plasma proteins; an increase in venous pressure; or insufficient uptake of tissue fluid by the lymphatic capillaries. Another cause of edema is blocked lymphatic vessels. One dramatic cause of a blockage is the parasitic infection of lymphatic vessels by a small worm. An affected leg can become so large that the disease is called **elephantiasis.**

Figure 11.8 Types of blood. In the ABO system, blood type depends on the presence or absence of antigens A and B on the surface of red blood cells. In these drawings, A and B antigens are represented by different shapes on the red blood cells. The possible anti-A and anti-B antibodies in the plasma are shown for each blood type. Notice that an anti-B antibody cannot bind to an A antigen, and vice versa.

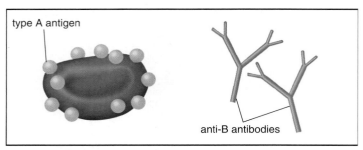

type A antigen

anti-B antibodies

Type A blood. Red blood cells have type A surface antigens. Plasma has anti-B antibodies.

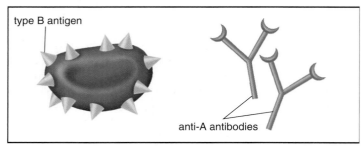

type B antigen

anti-A antibodies

Type B blood. Red blood cells have type B surface antigens. Plasma has anti-A antibodies.

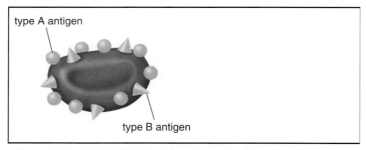

type A antigen

type B antigen

Type AB blood. Red blood cells have type A and type B surface antigens. Plasma has neither anti-A nor anti-B antibodies.

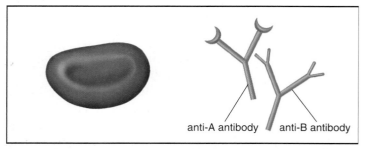

anti-A antibody   anti-B antibody

Type O blood. Red blood cells have neither type A nor type B surface antigens. Plasma has both anti-A and anti-B antibodies.

11.5 Blood Typing and Transfusions

A **blood transfusion** is the transfer of blood from one individual into the blood of another. In order for transfusions to be safely done, it is necessary for blood to be typed so that **agglutination** (clumping of red blood cells) does not occur. Blood typing usually involves determining the ABO blood group and whether the individual is Rh$^-$ (negative) or Rh$^+$ (positive).

ABO Blood Groups

ABO blood typing is based on the presence or absence of two possible antigens, called type A antigen and type B antigen, on the surface of red blood cells. Whether these antigens are present or not depends on the particular inheritance of the individual.

A person with type A antigen on the surface of the red blood cells has type A blood; one with type B blood has type B antigen on the surface of the red blood cells. What antigens would be present on the surface of red blood cells if the person has type AB blood or type O blood? Notice in Figure 11.8 that a person with type AB blood has both antigens, and a person with type O blood has no antigens on the surface of the red blood cells.

It so happens that an individual with type A blood has anti-B antibodies in the plasma; a person with type B blood has anti-A antibodies in the plasma; and a person with type O blood has both antibodies in the plasma (Fig. 11.8). These antibodies are not present at birth, but they appear over the course of several months after birth.

Figure 11.9 Blood transfusions. No agglutination (a) versus agglutination (b) is determined by whether antibodies are present that can combine with antigens.

type A blood of donor   anti-B antibody of type A recipient   no binding

a. No agglutination

type A blood of donor   anti-A antibody of type B recipient   binding

b. Agglutination

Figure 11.10 Hemolytic disease of the newborn. Due to a pregnancy in which the child is Rh positive, an Rh-negative mother can begin to produce antibodies against Rh-positive red blood cells. In another pregnancy, these antibodies can cross the placenta and cause hemolysis of an Rh-positive child's red blood cells.

Child is Rh positive; mother is Rh negative.

Red blood cells leak across placenta.

Mother makes anti-Rh antibodies.

Antibodies attack Rh-positive red blood cells in child.

Blood compatibility is very important when transfusions are done. The antibodies in the plasma must not combine with the antigens on the surface of the red blood cells, or else agglutination occurs. With agglutination, anti-A antibodies have combined with type A antigens, or anti-B antibodies have combined with type B antigens, or both types of binding have occurred. Therefore, agglutination is expected if the donor has type A blood and the recipient has type B blood (Fig. 11. 9). What about other combinations of blood types? Try out all other possible donors and recipients to see if agglutination will occur. Type O blood is sometimes called the *universal donor* because it has no antigens on the red blood cells, and type AB blood is sometimes called the *universal recipient* because this blood type has no antibodies in the plasma. In practice, however, there are other possible blood groups, aside from ABO blood groups, so it is necessary to physically put the donor's blood on a slide with the recipient's blood and observe whether the blood types match (no agglutination occurs) before blood can be safely given from one person to another.

As explained in the What's New reading on page 212, the use of blood substitutes does away with the problems of matching blood types.

Rh Blood Groups

The designation of blood type usually also includes whether the person has or does not have the Rh factor on the red blood cell. Rh⁻ individuals normally do not have antibodies to the Rh factor, but they make them when exposed to the Rh factor.

If a mother is Rh⁻ and the father is Rh⁺, a child can be Rh⁺. The Rh⁺ red blood cells may begin leaking across the placenta into the mother's cardiovascular system (Fig. 11.10), as placental tissues normally break down before and at birth. The presence of these Rh⁺ antigens causes the mother to produce anti-Rh antibodies. In a subsequent pregnancy with another Rh⁺ baby, the anti-Rh antibodies may cross the placenta and destroy the child's red blood cells. This is called *hemolytic disease of the newborn (HDN)* because hemolysis continues after the baby is born. Due to red blood cell destruction, excess bilirubin in the blood can lead to brain damage and mental retardation or even death.

The Rh problem is prevented by giving Rh⁻ women an Rh immunoglobulin injection no later than 72 hours after giving birth to an Rh⁺ child. This injection contains anti-Rh antibodies that attack any of the baby's red blood cells in the mother's blood before these cells can stimulate her immune system to produce her own antibodies. This injection is not beneficial if the woman has already begun to produce antibodies; therefore, the timing of the injection is most important.

11.6 Effects of Aging

Anemias, leukemias, and clotting disorders increase in frequency with age. As with other disorders, good health habits can help prevent these conditions from appearing.

Iron deficiency anemia most frequently results from a poor diet, but pernicious anemia signals that the digestive tract is unable to absorb enough vitamin B₁₂.

Leukemia is a form of cancer that generally increases in frequency with age because of both intrinsic (genetic) and extrinsic (environmental) reasons.

Thromboembolism, a clotting disorder, may be associated with the progressive development of atherosclerosis in an elderly person. When arteries develop plaque (see Fig. 12B, p. 241), thromboembolism often follows. For many people, atherosclerosis can be controlled by diet and exercise, as discussed in the Chapter 12 Medical Focus, "Preventing Cardiovascular Disease."

Selected New Terms

Basic Key Terms

agglutination (uh-glu″tĭ-na′shun), p. 218

agranular leukocyte (a-gran′yū-ler lu′ko-sīt), p. 213

albumin (al-byū′min), p. 209

antibody (an′tĭ-bod″e), p. 213

antigen (an′tĭ-jen), p. 213

basophil (ba′so-fil), p. 213

coagulation (ko-ag″yū-la′shun), p. 215

edema (ĕ-de′muh), p. 217

eosinophil (e″o-sin′o-fil), p. 213

erythropoietin (ĕ-rith″ro-poy′ĕ-tin), p. 211

fibrin (fi′brin), p. 215

fibrinogen (fi-brin′o-jen), p. 215

formed element (formd el′ĕ-ment), p. 209

granular leukocyte (gran′u-ler lu′ko-sīt), p. 213

hematocrit (he-mat′o-krit), p. 209

hematopoiesis (he″muh-to-poy-e′sis), p. 210

hemoglobin (he″mo-glo′bin), p. 211

hemolysis (he-mol′ĭ-sis), p. 211

lymph (limf), p. 217

lymphatic vessel (lim-fat′ik ves′l), p. 217

lymphocyte (lim′fo-sīt), p. 213

megakaryocyte (meg″uh-kār′e-o-sīt), p. 215

monocyte (mon′o-sīt), p. 213

neutrophil (nu′tro-fil), p. 213

osmotic pressure (oz-mot′ik presh′ur), p. 209

pathogen (path′o-jen), p. 209

plasma (plaz′muh), p. 209

platelet (plāt′let), p. 215

prothrombin (pro-throm′bin), p. 215

prothrombin activator (pro-throm′bin ak′tĭ-va″tor), p. 215

red blood cell (red blud sel), p. 211

stem cell (stem sel), p. 210

thrombin (throm′bin), p. 215

tissue fluid (tish′u flu′id), p. 216

white blood cell (whīt blud sel), p. 213

Clinical Key Terms

acute lymphoblastic leukemia (uh-kyūt′ lim-fo-blas′tik lu-ke′me-uh), p. 214

anemia (uh-ne′me-uh), p. 214

aplastic anemia (a-plas′tik uh-ne′me-uh), p. 214

blood transfusion (blud trans-fyū′zhun), p. 218

differential white blood cell count (dif″er-en′shul whīt blud sel kownt), p. 214

elephantiasis (el″ĕ-fan-ti′uh-sis), p. 217

embolus (em′bo-lus), p. 215

hemolytic anemia (he-mo-lĭt′ik uh-ne′me-uh), p. 214

hemolytic disease of the newborn (he-mo-lĭt′ik dĭ-zēz′ ov thah nu′born), p. 214

hemophilia (he-mo-fil′e-uh), p. 215

hemorrhagic (hem′o-raj-ik), p. 215

iron deficiency anemia (i′ern dĭ-fĭ′shun-se uh-ne′me-uh), p. 214

leukemia (lu-ke′me-uh), p. 214

leukocytosis (lu″ko-si-to′-sis), p. 214

leukopenia (lu″ko-pe′ne-uh), p. 214

mononucleosis (mon″o-nu″kle-o′sis), p. 214

pernicious anemia (per-nĭ′shus uh-ne′me-uh), p. 214

polycythemia (pol″e-si-the′me-uh), p. 214

sickle-cell disease (sĭ′kl sel dĭ-zēz′), p. 214

thrombocytopenia (throm″bo-si-to-pe′ne-uh), p. 215

thromboembolism (throm″bo-em′bo-lizm), p. 215

thrombus (throm′bus), p. 215

11.1 The Composition and Functions of Blood

A. Blood, which is composed of formed elements and plasma, has several functions. It transports hormones, oxygen, and nutrients to the cells and carbon dioxide and other wastes away from the cells. It fights infections. It regulates body temperature, and keeps the pH of body fluids within normal limits. All of these functions help maintain homeostasis.

B. Small organic molecules such as glucose and amino acids are dissolved in plasma and serve as nutrients for cells; urea is a waste product. Large organic molecules include the plasma proteins.

C. Plasma is mostly water (92%) and the plasma proteins (8%). The plasma proteins, most of which are produced by the liver, occur in three categories: albumins, globulins, and fibrinogen. The plasma proteins maintain osmotic pressure, help regulate pH, and transport molecules. Some plasma proteins have specific functions: The gamma globulins, which are antibodies produced by B lymphocytes, function in immunity; fibrinogen and prothrombin are necessary to blood clotting.

11.2 The Blood Cells

All blood cells, including red blood cells, are produced within red bone marrow from stem cells, which are ever capable of dividing and producing new cells.

A. Red blood cells are small, biconcave disks that lack a nucleus. They contain hemoglobin, the respiratory pigment, which combines with oxygen and transports it to the tissues. Red blood cells live about 120 days and are destroyed in the liver and spleen when they are old or abnormal. The production of red blood cells is controlled by the oxygen concentration of the blood. When the oxygen concentration decreases, the kidneys increase their production of erythropoietin, and more red blood cells are produced.

B. White blood cells are larger than red blood cells, have a nucleus, and are translucent unless stained. Like red blood cells, they are produced in the red bone marrow. White blood cells are divided into the granular leukocytes and the agranular leukocytes. The granular leukocytes have conspicuous granules; in eosinophils, granules are red when stained with eosin, and in basophils, granules are blue when stained with a basic dye. In neutrophils, some of the granules take up eosin, and others take up the basic dye, giving them a lilac color. Neutrophils are the most plentiful of the white blood cells, and they are able to phagocytize pathogens. Many neutrophils die within a few days when they are fighting an infection. The agranulocytes include the lymphocytes and the monocytes, which function in specific immunity. On occasion, the monocytes become large phagocytic cells of great significance. They engulf worn-out red blood cells and pathogens at a ferocious rate.

11.3 Platelets and Hemostasis

A. The extremely plentiful platelets result from fragmentation of megakaryocytes.

B. The three events of hemostasis are vascular spasm, platelet plug formation, and coagulation. The first several steps of coagulation result in tissue thromboplastin, a clotting factor that brings about the formation of prothrombin activator, which breaks down prothrombin to thrombin. Thrombin changes fibrinogen to fibrin threads, entrapping cells. The fluid that escapes from a clot is called serum and consists of plasma minus fibrinogen and prothrombin.

11.4 Capillary Exchange

A. This discussion pertains to capillary exchange in tissues of body parts— not including the gas-exchanging surfaces of the lungs. At the arterial end of a cardiovascular capillary, blood pressure is greater than osmotic pressure; therefore, water leaves the capillary. In the midsection, oxygen and nutrients diffuse out of the capillary, while carbon dioxide and other wastes diffuse into the capillary. At the venous end, osmotic pressure created by the presence of proteins exceeds blood pressure, causing water to enter the capillary.

B. Retrieving fluid by means of osmotic pressure is not completely effective. There is always some fluid that is not picked up at the venous end of the cardiovascular capillary. This excess tissue fluid enters the lymphatic capillaries. Lymph is tissue fluid contained within lymphatic vessels. The lymphatic system is a one-way system, and lymph is returned to the blood by way of a cardiovascular vein.

11.5 Blood Typing and Transfusions

A. Type A, type B, both type A and B, or no antigens can be on the surface of red blood cells. In the plasma, there are two possible antibodies: anti-A or anti-B. If the corresponding antigen and antibody are put together during a transfusion, agglutination occurs. Therefore, it is necessary to determine an individual's blood type before a transfusion is given.

B. Another important antigen is the Rh antigen. This particular antigen must also be considered in transfusing blood, and it is important during pregnancy because an Rh^- mother may form antibodies to the Rh antigen when giving birth to an Rh^+ child. These antibodies can cross the placenta and destroy the red blood cells of any subsequent Rh^+ child.

11.6 Effects of Aging

As we age, anemias, leukemias, and clotting disorders increase in frequency.

1. Name the two main components of blood, and describe the functions of blood. (pp. 208–9)
2. List and discuss the major components of plasma. Name several plasma proteins, and give a function for each. (p. 209)
3. What is hemoglobin, and how does it function? (p. 211)
4. Describe the life cycle of red blood cells, and tell how the production of red blood cells is regulated. (p. 211)

5. Name the five types of white blood cells; describe the structure and give a function for each type. (p. 213)
6. Name the steps that take place when blood clots. Which substances are present in blood at all times, and which appear during the clotting process? (p. 215)
7. What forces operate to facilitate exchange of molecules across the capillary wall? (pp. 216–17)

8. What are the four ABO blood types? For each, state the antigen(s) on the red blood cells and the antibody(ies) in the plasma. (p. 218)
9. Explain why a person with type O blood cannot receive a transfusion of type A blood. (p. 219)
10. Problems can arise if the mother is which Rh type and the father is which Rh type? Explain why this is so. (p. 219)

I. Fill in the blanks.

1. The liquid part of blood is called _____.
2. Red blood cells carry _____, and white blood cells _____.
3. Hemoglobin that is carrying oxygen is called _____.
4. Human red blood cells lack a _____ and only live about _____ days.
5. The most common granular leukocyte is the _____, a phagocytic white blood cell.
6. B lymphocytes produce _____, and T lymphocytes attack and _____ pathogens.

7. At a capillary, _____, _____, and _____ leave the arterial end, and _____ and _____ enter the venous end.
8. When a blood clot occurs, fibrinogen has been converted to _____ threads.
9. AB blood has the antigens _____ and _____ on the red blood cells and _____ of these antibodies in the plasma.
10. Hemolytic disease of the newborn can occur when the mother is _____ and the father is _____.

II. Match the terms in the key to the descriptions in questions 11–14.

Key:
   a. hematocrit
   b. red blood cell count
   c. white blood cell count
   d. hemoglobin

11. 5,000 to 11,000 per cubic millimeter
12. 4 to 6 million per cubic millimeter in males
13. Just under 45% of blood volume
14. 200 million molecules in one red blood cell
15. Label the following diagram.

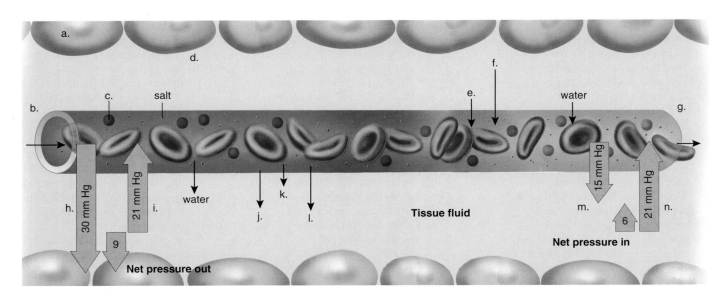

Medical Terminology Reinforcement Exercise

Consult Appendix B for help in pronouncing and analyzing the meaning of the terms that follow.

1. hematemesis (hem″uh-tem′ĕ-sis)
2. erythrocytometry (ĕ-rith″ro-si-tom′ĕ-tre)
3. leukocytogenesis (lu″ko-si″to-jen′ĕ-sis)
4. hemophobia (he″mo-fo′be-uh)
5. afibrinogenemia (uh-fi″brin-o-jĕ-ne′me-uh)
6. lymphosarcoma (lim″fo-sar-ko′muh)
7. phagocytosis (fag″o-si-to′sis)
8. phlebotomy (flĕ-bot′o-me)
9. hemocytoblast (he′mo-si′to-blast)
10. megaloblastic anemia (meg′uh-lo-blas′tik uh-ne′me-uh)
11. microcytic hypochromic anemia (mi′kro-sit′ik hi″po-kro′mik uh-ne′me-uh)
12. hematology (he′muh-tol′o-je)
13. lymphedema (limf′uh-de′muh)
14. antithrombin (an″te-throm′bin)

Website Link

Visit the Student Edition of the Online Learning Center at http://www.mhhe.com/maderap5 for additional quizzes, interactive learning exercises, and other study tools.

The Cardiovascular System

chapter

12

Red blood cells are seen in an arteriole *(top right)* and a venule *(bottom left)*. Capillaries are in the center of the micrograph.

100 μm

chapter outline & learning objectives

After you have studied this chapter, you should be able to:

12.1 Anatomy of the Heart (p. 225)
- Describe the location of the heart and its functions.
- Describe the wall and coverings of the heart.
- Trace the path of blood through the heart, naming its chambers and valves.
- Describe the operation of the heart valves.
- Describe the coronary circulation, and discuss several coronary circulation disorders and possible treatments.

12.2 Physiology of the Heart (p. 230)
- Describe the conduction system of the heart.
- Label and explain a normal electrocardiogram.
- Describe the cardiac cycle and the heart sounds.
- Describe the cardiac output and regulation of the heartbeat.

12.3 Anatomy of Blood Vessels (p. 234)
- Name the three types of blood vessels, and describe their structure and function.

12.4 Physiology of Circulation (p. 236)
- Explain how blood pressure changes throughout the vascular system, and describe the factors that determine blood pressure.
- Describe how blood pressure is regulated.
- Define pulse, and tell where the pulse may be taken.
- Describe shock due to hypotension and various medical consequences of hypertension.

12.5 Circulatory Routes (p. 242)
- Name the two circuits of the cardiovascular system, and trace the path of blood from the heart to any organ in the body and back to the heart.

- Describe the major systemic arteries and the major systemic veins.
- Describe several special circulations: blood supply to the liver, blood supply to the brain, and fetal circulation.

12.6 Effects of Aging (p. 248)
- Describe the anatomical and physiological changes that occur in the cardiovascular system as we age.

12.7 Homeostasis (p. 248)
- Describe how the cardiovascular system works with other systems of the body to maintain homeostasis.

What's New
Infections Causing Atherosclerosis? (p. 229)

Medical Focus
The Electrocardiogram (p. 231)

Preventing Cardiovascular Disease (pp. 240–41)

Chapter 11 described how oxygen and nutrients are exchanged for carbon dioxide and other waste molecules at tissue capillaries (see Fig. 11.6). We emphasized that cells are dependent on the functioning of capillaries for this purpose. In this chapter, we will study how blood is moved to and from tissue (systemic) capillaries and also to and from lung (pulmonary) capillaries where oxygen enters and carbon dioxide exits the blood.

The cardiovascular system consists of two components: (1) the heart, which pumps blood so that it flows to tissue capillaries and lung capillaries, and (2) the blood vessels through which the blood flows. As you can see in Figure 12.1, certain blood vessels are a part of the pulmonary circuit, and others are a part of the systemic circuit.

In this chapter, we will first study the anatomy and physiology of the heart and of the blood vessels. Then, we will take a look at various circulations in the body. A crucial aspect of circulation is that it connects the body's cells with the organs of exchange, such as the lungs where oxygen enters and carbon dioxide exits the blood, the small intestine where nutrient molecules enter the blood, and the kidneys where metabolic wastes exit the blood.

12.1 Anatomy of the Heart

The heart is located in the thoracic cavity between the lungs within the mediastinum. It is a hollow, cone-shaped, muscular organ about the size of a fist. Figure 12.1 shows that the base (the widest part) of the heart is superior to its apex (the pointed tip), which rests on the diaphragm. Also, the heart is on a slant; the base is directed toward the right shoulder, and the apex points to the left hip. The base is deep to the second rib, and the apex is at the level of the fifth intercostal space.

As the heart pumps the blood through the pulmonary and systemic vessels, it performs these functions:

1. keeps O_2-poor blood separate from O_2-rich blood;
2. keeps the blood flowing in one direction—blood flows away from and then back to the heart in each circuit;
3. creates blood pressure, which moves the blood through the circuits;
4. regulates the blood supply based on the current needs of the body.

Figure 12.1 Cardiovascular system. The right side of the heart pumps blood through vessels of the pulmonary circuit. The left side of the heart pumps blood through vessels of the systemic circuit. Gas exchange occurs as blood passes through lung (pulmonary) capillaries. Gas exchange and nutrient-for-waste exchange occur as blood passes through tissue (systemic) capillaries. In this illustration, red vessels carry O_2-rich blood, and blue vessels carry O_2-poor blood.

Figure 12.2 The coverings and wall of the heart. The heart wall has three layers, from deep to superficial: endocardium, myocardium, and epicardium.

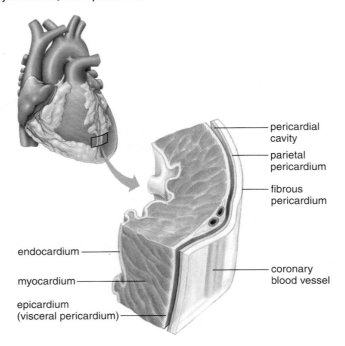

- pericardial cavity
- parietal pericardium
- fibrous pericardium
- endocardium
- myocardium
- coronary blood vessel
- epicardium (visceral pericardium)

The Wall and Coverings of the Heart

In Chapter 4, we mentioned that the heart is enclosed by a two-layered serous membrane called the **pericardium.** One layer, the **visceral** (meaning "organ") **pericardium,** is considered part of the heart wall; it forms the **epicardium,** the outer surface of the heart. The **myocardium** is the thickest part of the heart wall and is made up of cardiac muscle (see Fig. 4.13). When cardiac muscle fibers contract, the heart beats. The inner **endocardium** is composed of simple squamous epithelium. Endothelium not only lines the heart, but it also continues into and lines the blood vessels. Its smooth nature helps prevent blood from clotting unnecessarily.

The pericardial cavity, which contains a few milliliters of **pericardial fluid,** develops when the visceral pericardium doubles back to become the **parietal** (meaning "wall") **pericardium,** the other serous layer. The pericardial fluid reduces friction as the heart beats. The parietal pericardium is fused to a **fibrous pericardium** (Fig. 12.2). The fibrous pericardium is a layer of fibrous connective tissue that adheres to the great blood vessels at the heart's base and anchors the heart to the wall of the mediastinum. The coverings of the heart confine the heart to its location while still allowing it to contract and carry out its function of pumping the blood.

A layer of the heart can become inflamed due to infection, cancer, injury, or a complication of surgery. The suffix "itis" added to the name of a heart condition tells which layer is affected. For example, pericarditis refers to inflammation of the pericardium, and endocarditis refers to inflammation of the endocardium.

Chambers of the Heart

The heart has four hollow chambers: two superior **atria** (sing., atrium) and two inferior **ventricles** (Fig. 12.3). Each atrium has a wrinkled anterior pouch called an auricle. Internally, the atria are separated by the **interatrial septum,** and the ventricles are separated by the **interventricular septum.** Therefore, the heart has a left and a right side.

The thickness of a chamber's myocardium is suited to its function. The atria have thin walls, and they send blood into the adjacent ventricles. The ventricles are thicker, and they pump blood into blood vessels that travel to parts of the body. The left ventricle has a thicker wall than the right ventricle; the right ventricle pumps blood to the lungs, which are nearby. The left ventricle pumps blood to all the other parts of the body.

Right Atrium

At its posterior wall, the **right atrium** receives O_2-poor blood from three veins: the *superior vena cava,* the *coronary sinus,* and the *inferior vena cava.* Venous blood passes from the right atrium into the right ventricle through an **atrioventricular (AV) valve.** This valve, like the other heart valves, directs the flow of blood and prevents any backflow. The AV valve on the right side of the heart is specifically called the **tricuspid valve** because it has three cusps, or flaps.

Right Ventricle

In the **right ventricle,** the cusps of the tricuspid valve are connected to fibrous cords, called the **chordae tendineae** (meaning "heart strings"). The chordae tendineae in turn are connected to the **papillary muscles,** which are conical extensions of the myocardium.

Blood from the right ventricle passes through a **semilunar valve** into the *pulmonary trunk.* Semilunar valves are so called because their cusps are thought to resemble half-moons. This particular semilunar valve, called the **pulmonary semilunar valve,** prevents blood from flowing back into the right ventricle.

Note in Figure 12.3 that the pulmonary trunk divides into the left and right pulmonary arteries. For help in remembering how blood flows through the heart, trace the path of O_2-poor blood from the vena cava to the pulmonary arteries that take blood to the lungs (see Figs. 12.1 and 12.3*b*).

Left Atrium

At its posterior wall, the **left atrium** receives O_2-rich blood from four *pulmonary veins.* Two pulmonary veins come from each lung. Blood passes from the left atrium into the left ventricle through an AV valve. The AV valve on the left side is specifically called the **bicuspid (mitral) valve** because it has two cusps.

Figure 12.3 Internal heart anatomy. **a.** The heart has four valves. The two atrioventricular valves allow blood to pass from the atria to the ventricles, and the two semilunar valves allow blood to pass out of the heart. **b.** A diagrammatic representation of the heart allows you to trace the path of the blood through the heart.

a.

b.

Left Ventricle

The **left ventricle** forms the apex of the heart. The cavity of the left ventricle is oval-shaped, while that of the right ventricle is crescent-shaped. The papillary muscles in the left ventricle are quite large, and the chordae tendineae attached to the AV valve are thicker and stronger than those in the right ventricle. As mentioned, the AV valve on the left side is also called the bicuspid (or mitral) valve.

Blood passes from the left ventricle through a semilunar valve into the aorta. This semilunar valve is appropriately called the **aortic semilunar valve.** The semilunar cusps of this valve are larger and thicker than those of the pulmonary semilunar valve.

Just beyond the aortic semilunar valve, some blood passes into the *coronary arteries*, blood vessels that lie on and nourish the heart itself. The rest of the blood stays in the aorta, which continues as the arch of the aorta and then the descending aorta.

To make sure you understand this discussion, trace the path of O_2-rich blood through the heart, from the pulmonary veins to the aorta (see Figs. 12.1 and 12.3*b*).

Operation of the Heart Valves

Let's take a look at how the valves of the heart operate to direct a one-way flow of blood from the atria to the ventricles to the arteries. The AV valves are normally open. When a ventricle contracts, however, the pressure of the blood forces the cusps of an AV valve to meet and close. The force of the blood is often likened to a strong wind that can cause an umbrella to turn inside out. However, the papillary muscles contract, causing the chordae tendineae to tighten and pull on the valve and thus preventing it from reverting into an atrium.

A semilunar valve is normally closed—the contraction of a ventricle opens it. Then, when the ventricle relaxes, the blood in the artery pushes backward, closing the valve.

Like mechanical valves, the heart valves are sometimes leaky; they don't close properly, and there is a backflow of blood. When a person has rheumatic fever, a bacterial infection that began in the throat has spread throughout the body. The bacteria attack connective tissue in the heart valves as well as other organs. Most often, the bicuspid valve and the aortic semilunar valve become leaky. In that case, the valve can be replaced with a synthetic valve or one taken from a pig's heart.

Figure 12.4 Anterior view of exterior heart anatomy. **a.** The great vessels (venae cavae, pulmonary trunk, pulmonary arteries, and aorta) are attached to the base of the heart. The right ventricle forms most of the anterior surface of the heart, and the left ventricle forms most of the posterior surface. **b.** The coronary arteries and cardiac veins pervade cardiac muscle. The coronary arteries bring oxygen and nutrients to cardiac cells, which derive no benefit from the blood coursing through the heart.

Coronary Circuit

Cardiac muscle fibers and the other types of cells in the wall of the heart are not nourished by the blood in the chambers; diffusion of oxygen and nutrients from this blood to all the cells that make up the heart would be too slow. Instead, these cells receive nutrients and rid themselves of wastes at capillaries embedded in the heart wall.

Two **coronary arteries,** termed the left and right coronary arteries, branch from the aorta just beyond the aortic semilunar valve (Fig. 12.4). Each of these arteries branches and then rebranches, until the heart is encircled by small arterial blood vessels. Some of these join so that there are several routes to reach any particular capillary bed in the heart. Alternate routes are helpful if an obstruction should occur along the path of blood reaching cardiac muscle cells.

After blood has passed through cardiac capillaries, it is taken up by vessels that join to form veins. The coronary veins are specifically called **cardiac veins.** The cardiac veins enter a coronary sinus, which is essentially a thin-walled vein. The coronary sinus enters the right ventricle.

Coronary Circuit Disorders

As discussed in the What's New reading on page 229, heart diseases are especially associated with **atherosclerosis,** a degenerative disorder of arterial walls. First, soft masses of fatty materials, particularly cholesterol, accumulate in the arterial wall. Further changes result in **plaque,** protrusions that interfere with blood flow. If the coronary artery is partially occluded (blocked) by atherosclerosis, the individual may suffer from **ischemic heart disease.** Although enough oxygen may normally reach the heart, the person experiences insufficiency during exercise or stress. This may lead to **angina pectoris,** chest pain that is often accompanied by a radiating pain in the left arm.

The blood may clot in an unbroken blood vessel, particularly if plaque is present. As mentioned in Chapter 11, **thromboembolism** is present when a blood clot breaks away from its place of origin and is carried to a new location. Thromboembolism leads to heart attacks when the embolus blocks a coronary artery and a portion of the heart dies due to lack of oxygen. Dead tissue is called an infarct, and therefore, a heart attack is termed a **myocardial infarction.**

What's New

Infections Causing Atherosclerosis?

What if your potential heart attack or stroke could be prevented by having an inexpensive blood test and taking a round of antibiotics? New research hints that this might be possible in the future.

Scientists agree that atherosclerosis begins with injury to the arterial wall. The injured wall of the artery first develops a fatty streak, which hardens to form plaque. Hypertension and unfavorable levels of cholesterol are seen in individuals with atherosclerosis. However, could a bacterial or viral infection cause the injury that starts atherosclerosis, as some scientists think? If so, antibiotics or antiviral drugs might slow or stop the damaging effects of atherosclerosis.

Recent research shows that when a person develops atherosclerotic plaques, the body's defenses are activated, just as they are when a person suffers a bacterial or viral infection. A protein in the blood called C-reactive protein, or CRP, is an important piece of evidence that atherosclerosis activates body defenses. For example, CRP levels rise in your blood if you suffer from a cold or are recovering from a wound. High blood levels of CRP in a seemingly healthy person could mean that the arteries are inflamed. Indeed, recent studies show that people with the highest blood levels of CRP have double the risk of heart attack. In individuals with angina, the evidence is scarier: High CRP consistently predicted eventual heart attack.

Elevated CRP can be measured with a simple blood test. Currently, the American Heart Association recommends testing for people who have two or more coronary risk factors.

One possible way to prevent clots from forming is to take aspirin. Aspirin reduces the stickiness of platelets and thereby lowers the probability that clots will form. The dosage should remain limited because long-term aspirin use might have harmful effects, including bleeding in the brain.

Surgical Procedures Two surgical procedures are associated with **occluded coronary arteries**. In **balloon angioplasty**, a plastic tube is threaded into an artery of an arm or leg and is guided through a major blood vessel toward the heart. Once the tube reaches a blockage, a balloon attached to the end of the tube can be inflated to break up the clot or to open up a vessel clogged with plaque (Fig. 12.5). In some cases, a small metal-mesh cylinder called a vascular stent is inserted into a blood vessel during balloon angioplasty. The stent holds the vessel open and decreases the risk of future occlusion. In a **coronary bypass operation**, a portion of a blood vessel from another part of the body, such as a large vein in the leg, is sutured from the aorta to the coronary artery, past the point of obstruction. This procedure allows blood to flow normally again from the aorta to the heart. Figure 12.6 shows a triple bypass in which three blood vessels have been used to allow blood to flow freely from the aorta to cardiac muscle by way of the coronary artery.

Figure 12.6 Coronary bypass surgery. During this operation, the surgeon grafts segments of another vessel between the aorta and the coronary vessels, bypassing areas of blockage.

Figure 12.5 Balloon angioplasty. As described in the text, a balloon inserted in an artery can be inflated to open up a clogged coronary blood vessel.

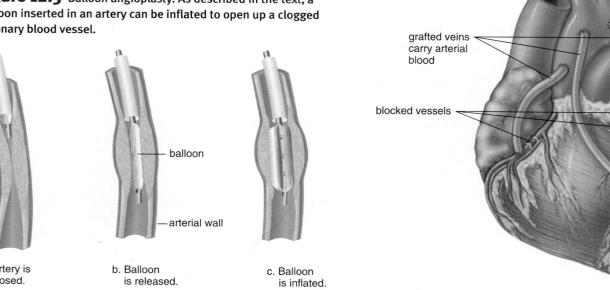

grafted veins carry arterial blood

blocked vessels

balloon

arterial wall

a. Artery is closed.

b. Balloon is released.

c. Balloon is inflated.

12.2 Physiology of the Heart

The physiology of the heart pertains to its pumping action—that is, the heartbeat. It is estimated that the heart beats two-and-a-half billion times in a lifetime, continuously recycling some 5 liters (L) of blood to keep us alive. In this section, we will consider what causes the heartbeat, what it consists of, and its consequences.

Conduction System of the Heart

The **conduction system of the heart** is a route of specialized cardiac muscle fibers that initiate and stimulate contraction of the atria and ventricles. The conduction system is said to be *intrinsic*, meaning that the heart beats automatically without the need for external nervous stimulation. The conduction system coordinates the contraction of the atria and ventricles so that the heart is an effective pump. Without this conduction system, the atria and ventricles would contract at different rates.

Nodal Tissue

The heartbeat is controlled by nodal tissue, which has both muscular and nervous characteristics. This unique type of cardiac muscle is located in two regions of the heart: The **SA (sinoatrial) node** is located in the upper posterior wall of the right atrium; the **AV (atrioventricular) node** is located in the base of the right atrium very near the interatrial septum (Fig. 12.7).

The SA node initiates the heartbeat and automatically sends out an excitation impulse every 0.85 second. The SA node normally functions as the pacemaker because its intrinsic rate is the fastest in the system. From the SA node, impulses spread out over the atria, causing them to contract.

When the impulses reach the AV node, there is a slight delay that allows the atria to finish their contraction before the ventricles begin their contraction. The signal for the ventricles to contract travels from the AV node through the two branches of the **atrioventricular bundle (AV bundle)** before reaching the numerous and smaller **Purkinje fibers.** The AV bundle, its branches, and the Purkinje fibers consist of specialized cardiac muscle fibers that efficiently cause the ventricles to contract.

The SA node is called the **pacemaker** because it usually keeps the heartbeat regular. If the SA node fails to work properly, the ventricles still beat due to impulses generated by the AV node. But the beat is slower (40 to 60 beats per minute). To correct this condition, it is possible to implant an artificial pacemaker, which automatically gives an electrical

Figure 12.7 Conduction system of the heart. **(1)** The SA node sends out a stimulus, which causes the atria to contract. **(2)** When this stimulus reaches the AV node, it signals the ventricles to contract. **(3)** Impulses pass down the two branches of the atrioventricular bundle to the Purkinje fibers, and **(4)** thereafter, the ventricles contract.

① Stimulus originates in the SA node and travels across the walls of the atria, causing them to contract.

② Stimulus arrives at the AV node and travels along the AV bundle.

③ Stimulus descends to the apex of the heart through the bundle branches.

④ After stimulus reaches the Purkinje fibers, the ventricles contract.

SA node

AV node

branches of AV bundle

Purkinje fibers

The Electrocardiogram

A graph that records the electrical activity of the myocardium during a cardiac cycle is called an **electrocardiogram,** or **ECG.** * An ECG is obtained by placing on the patient's skin several electrodes that are wired to a voltmeter (an instrument for measuring voltage). As the heart's chambers contract and then relax, the change in polarity is measured in millivolts.

An ECG consists of a set of waves: the P wave, a QRS complex, and a T wave (Fig. 12A). The P wave represents depolarization of the atria as an impulse started by the SA node travels throughout the atria. The P wave signals that the atria are going to be in systole and that the atrial myocardium is about to contract. The QRS complex represents depolarization of the ventricles following excitation of the Purkinje fibers. It signals that the ventricles are going to be in systole and that the ventricular myocardium is about to contract. The QRS complex shows greater voltage changes than the P wave because the ventricles have more muscle mass than the atria. The T wave represents repolarization of the ventricles. It signals that the ventricles are going to be in diastole and that the ventricular myocardium is about to relax. Atrial diastole does not show up on an ECG as an independent event because the voltage changes are masked by the QRS complex.

An ECG records the duration of electrical activity and therefore can be used to detect arrhythmia, an irregular or abnormal heartbeat. A rate of fewer than 60 heartbeats per minute is called **bradycardia,** and more than 100 heartbeats per minute is called **tachycardia.** Another type of arrhythmia is **fibrillation,** in which the heart beats rapidly but the contractions are uncoordinated. The heart can sometimes be defibrillated by briefly applying a strong electrical current to the chest.

*Also known as EKG (German, ElectroKardioGramm)

It is important to understand that an ECG only supplies information about the heart's electrical activity. To be used in diagnosis, an ECG must be coupled with other information, including X rays, studies of blood flow, and a detailed history from the patient.

b.

Figure 12A Electrocardiogram. **a.** A portion of an electrocardiogram. **b.** An enlarged normal cycle.

stimulus to the heart every 0.85 second. Should the AV node be damaged, the ventricles still beat because all cardiac muscle cells can contract on their own. However, the beat is so slow that the condition is called a **heart block.**

An area other than the SA node can become the pacemaker when it develops a rate of contraction that is faster than the SA node. This site, called an **ectopic pacemaker,** may cause an extra beat, if it operates only occasionally, or it can even pace the heart for a while. Caffeine and nicotine are two substances that can stimulate an ectopic pacemaker.

Electrocardiogram

With the contraction of any muscle, including the myocardium, electrolyte changes occur that can be detected by electrical recording devices. These changes occur as a muscle action potential sweeps over the cardiac muscle fibers. The resulting record, called an electrocardiogram, helps a physician detect and possibly diagnose the cause of an irregular heartbeat. There are many types of irregular heartbeats, called **arrhythmias.** The Medical Focus on this page discusses the electrocardiogram and some types of arrhythmias.

Cardiac Cycle and Heart Sounds

A **cardiac cycle** includes all the events that occur during one heartbeat. On average, the heart beats about 70 times a minute, although a normal adult heart rate can vary from 60 to 100 beats per minute. After tracing the path of blood through the heart, it might seem that the right and left sides of the heart beat independently of one another, but actually, they contract together. First the two atria contract simultaneously; then the two ventricles contract together. The term **systole** refers to contraction of heart muscle, and the term **diastole** refers to relaxation of heart muscle. During the cardiac cycle, *atrial systole* is followed by *ventricular systole*.

As shown in Figure 12.8, the three phases of the cardiac cycle are:

Phase 1: Atrial Systole. Time = 0.15 sec. During this phase, both atria are in systole (contracted), while the ventricles are in diastole (relaxed). Rising blood pressure in the atria forces the blood to enter the two ventricles through the AV valves. At this time, both atrioventricular valves are open, and the semilunar valves are closed.

Phase 2: Ventricular Systole. Time = 0.30 sec. During this phase, both ventricles are in systole (contracted), while

the atria are in diastole (relaxed). Rising blood pressure in the ventricles forces the blood to enter the pulmonary trunk leading to the pulmonary arteries and aorta through the semilunar valves. At this time, both semilunar valves are open, and the atrioventricular valves are closed.

Phase 3: Atrial and Ventricular Diastole. Time = 0.40 sec. During this period, both atria and both ventricles are in diastole (relaxed). At this point, pressure in all the heart chambers is low. Blood returning to the heart from the superior and inferior venae cavae and the pulmonary veins fills the right and left atria and flows passively into the ventricles. At this time, both atrioventricular valves are open, and the semilunar valves are closed.

Heart Sounds

A heartbeat produces the familiar "LUB-DUP" sounds as the chambers contract and the valves close. The first heart sound, "lub," is heard when the ventricles contract and the atrioventricular valves close. This sound lasts longest and has a lower pitch. The second heart sound, "dup," is heard when the relaxation of the ventricles allows the semilunar valves to close.

Heart murmurs, which are clicking or swishing sounds heard after the "lub," are often due to ineffective valves. These leaky valves allow blood to pass back into the atria after the atrioventricular valves have closed, or back into the ventricles after the semilunar valves have closed. A trained physician or health professional can diagnose heart murmurs from their sound and timing. It is possible to replace the defective valve with an artificial valve.

Cardiac Output

Cardiac output (CO) is the volume of blood pumped out of a ventricle in one minute. (The same amount of blood is pumped out of each ventricle in one minute.) Cardiac output is dependent on two factors:

heart rate (HR), which is the beats per minute; *stroke volume (SV),* which is the amount of blood pumped by a ventricle each time it contracts.

The CO of an average human is 5,250 ml (or 5.25 L) per minute, which equates to about the total volume of blood in the human body. Each minute, the right ventricle pumps about 5.25 L through the pulmonary circuit, while the left ventricle pumps about 5.25 L through the systemic circuit. And this is only the resting cardiac output!

Cardiac output can vary because stroke volume and heart rate can vary, as discussed next. In this way, the heart regulates the blood supply, dependent on the body's needs.

Figure 12.8 Stages in the cardiac cycle. Phase 1: atrial systole. Phase 2: ventricular systole. Phase 3: atrial and ventricular diastole.

Time	Atria	Ventricles
0.15 sec	Systole	Diastole
0.30 sec	Diastole	Systole
0.40 sec	Diastole	Diastole

Phase 1: atrial systole

Phase 3: atrial and ventricular diastole

Phase 2: ventricular systole

Heart Rate

A **cardioregulatory center** in the medulla oblongata of the brain can alter the heart rate by way of the autonomic nervous system (Fig. 12.9). Parasympathetic motor impulses conducted by the vagus nerve cause the heart rate to slow, and sympathetic motor impulses conducted by sympathetic motor fibers cause the heart rate to increase.

The cardioregulatory center receives sensory input from receptors within the cardiovascular system. For example, *baroreceptors* are present in the aorta just after it leaves the heart and in the carotid arteries, which take blood from the aorta to the brain. If blood pressure falls, as it sometimes does when we stand up quickly, the baroreceptors signal the cardioregulatory center. Thereafter, sympathetic motor impulses to the heart cause the heart rate to increase. Once blood pressure begins to rise above normal, nerve impulses from the cardioregulatory center cause the heart rate to decrease. Such reflexes help control cardiac output and, therefore, blood pressure, as discussed in section 12.4.

The cardioregulatory center is under the influence of the cerebrum and the hypothalamus. Therefore, when we feel anxious, the sympathetic motor nerves are activated, and the adrenal medulla releases the hormones norepinephrine and epinephrine. The result is an increase in heartbeat rate. On the other hand, activities such as yoga and meditation lead to activation of the vagus nerve, which slows the heartbeat rate.

Other factors affect the heartbeat rate as well. For example, a low body temperature slows the rate. Also, the proper electrolyte concentrations are needed to keep the heart rate regular.

Stroke Volume

Stroke volume, which is the amount of blood that leaves a ventricle, depends on the strength of contraction. The degree of contraction depends on the blood electrolyte concentration and the activity of the autonomic system. Otherwise two factors influence the strength of contraction.

Venous Return Venous return is the amount of blood entering the heart by way of the venae cavae (right side of heart) or pulmonary veins (left side of heart). Any event that decreases or increases the volume or speed of blood entering the heart will affect the strength of contraction—called Starling's Law. A slow heart rate allows more time for the ventricles to fill and therefore increases the strength of contraction. A low venous return, as might happen if there is blood loss, decreases the strength of contraction. Exercise increases the strength of contraction because skeletal muscle contraction puts pressure on the veins and speeds venous return.

Difference in Blood Pressure The strength of ventricular contraction has to be strong enough to oppose the blood pressure within the attached arteries. If a person has hypertension or atherosclerosis, the opposing arterial pressure may reduce the effectiveness of contraction and the stroke volume.

Figure 12.9 The cardioregulatory center regulates the heart rate and the vasomotor center regulates constriction of blood vessels, according to input received from baroreceptors in the carotid artery and aortic arch.

Regulation of heart rate:

1. Baroreceptors in the aortic arch and carotid arteries monitor blood pressure.

2. Nerve impulses from the baroreceptors signal the cardioregulatory center.

3. Increased parasympathetic impulses decrease heart rate.

4. Increased sympathetic impulses increase heart rate.

Regulation of blood pressure:

5. Increased sympathetic impulses cause blood vessels to constrict.

12.3 Anatomy of Blood Vessels

Blood vessels are of three types: arteries, capillaries, and veins (Fig. 12.10). These vessels function to:

1. transport blood and its contents (see page 209);
2. carry out exchange of gases in the pulmonary capillaries and exchange of gases plus nutrients for waste at the systemic capillaries (see page 216);
3. regulate blood pressure;
4. direct blood flow to those systemic tissues that most require it at the moment.

Arteries and Arterioles

Arteries (Fig. 12.10*a*) transport blood away from the heart. They have thick, strong walls composed of three layers: (1) The **tunica interna** is an endothelium layer with a basement membrane. (2) The **tunica media** is a thick middle layer of smooth muscle and elastic fibers. (3) The **tunica externa** is an outer connective tissue layer composed principally of elastic and collagen fibers. Arterial walls are sometimes so thick that they are supplied with blood vessels. The radius of an artery allows the blood to flow rapidly and the elasticity of an artery allows it to expand when the heart contracts and recoil when the heart rests. This means that blood continues to flow in an artery even when the heart is in diastole.

Arterioles are small arteries just visible to the naked eye. The middle layer of these vessels has some elastic tissue but is composed mostly of smooth muscle whose fibers encircle the arteriole. If the muscle fibers contract, the lumen (cavity) of the arteriole decreases; if the fibers relax, the lumen of the arteriole enlarges. Whether arterioles are constricted or dilated affects blood distribution and blood pressure. When a muscle is actively contracting, for example, the arterioles in the vicinity dilate so that the needs of the muscle for oxygen and glucose are met. As we shall see, the autonomic nervous system helps control blood pressure by regulating the number of arterioles that are contracted. The greater the number of vessels contracted, the higher the resistance to blood flow, and hence, the higher the blood pressure. The greater the number of vessels dilated, the lower the resistance to blood flow, and hence, the lower the blood pressure.

Arteriosclerosis

The plaques associated with atherosclerosis (see page 228) lead to the deposition of calcium salts and the formation of nonelastic scar tissue, resulting in increased rigidity of the vessel wall. This process of hardening of the arteries, or **arteriosclerosis,** not only contributes to hypertension but also increases the risk of a heart attack or stroke.

Figure 12.10 Blood vessels. The walls of arteries and veins have three layers. The tunica interna is an endothelium with a basement membrane; the tunica media is smooth muscle tissue and elastic fibers; the tunica externa is composed of connective tissue. **a.** Arteries have a thicker wall than veins because they have a thicker middle layer than veins. **b.** Capillary walls are one-cell-thick endothelium. **c.** Veins are larger in diameter than arteries, so collectively, veins have a larger holding capacity than arteries.

arteriole

venule

b. Capillary

valve

endothelium
(tunica interna)

smooth muscles
and elastic fibers
(tunica media)

connective tissue
(tunica externa)

a. Artery

c. Vein

Capillaries

Arterioles branch into **capillaries** (Fig. 12.10b), which are extremely narrow, microscopic blood vessels with a wall composed of only one layer of endothelial cells. *Capillary beds* (networks of many capillaries) are present in all regions of the body; consequently, a cut in any body tissue draws blood. Capillaries are an important part of the cardiovascular system because nutrient and waste molecules are exchanged only across their thin walls. Oxygen and glucose diffuse out of capillaries into the tissue fluid that surrounds cells, and carbon dioxide and other wastes diffuse into the capillaries (see Fig. 11.6). Because capillaries serve the needs of the cells, the heart and other vessels of the cardiovascular system can be considered a means by which blood is conducted to and from capillaries.

Not all capillary beds are open or in use at the same time. For instance, after a meal, the capillary beds of the digestive tract are usually open, and during muscular exercise, the capillary beds of the skeletal muscles are open.

Most capillary beds have a shunt that allows blood to move directly from an arteriole to a venule (a small vessel leading to a vein) when the capillary bed is closed. Sphincter muscles, called *precapillary sphincters*, encircle the entrance to each capillary (Fig. 12.11). When the capillary bed is closed, the capillary sphincters are constricted, preventing blood from entering the capillaries; when the capillary bed is open, the capillary sphincters are relaxed. As would be expected, the larger the number of capillary beds open, the lower the blood pressure.

Veins and Venules

Veins and smaller vessels called **venules** carry blood from the capillary beds to the heart. The venules first drain the blood from the capillaries and then join together to form a vein. The wall of a vein is much thinner than that of an artery because the middle layer of muscle and elastic fibers is thinner (see Fig. 12.10c). Within some veins, especially the major veins of the arms and legs, **valves** allow blood to flow only toward the heart when they are open and prevent the backward flow of blood when they are closed.

At any given time, more than half of the total blood volume is found in the veins and venules. If blood is lost due to, for example, hemorrhaging, sympathetic nervous stimulation causes the veins to constrict, providing more blood to the rest of the body. In this way, the veins act as a blood reservoir.

Varicose Veins and Phlebitis

Varicose veins are abnormal and irregular dilations in superficial (near the surface) veins, particularly those in the lower legs. Varicose veins in the rectum, however, are commonly called piles, or more properly, **hemorrhoids.** Varicose veins develop when the valves of the veins become weak and ineffective due to backward pressure of the blood.

Phlebitis, or inflammation of a vein, is a more serious condition because thromboembolism can occur. In this instance, the embolus may eventually come to rest in a pulmonary arteriole, blocking circulation through the lungs. This condition, termed **pulmonary embolism,** can result in death.

Figure 12.11 Anatomy of a capillary bed. A capillary bed forms a maze of capillary vessels that lies between an arteriole and a venule. When sphincter muscles are relaxed, the capillary bed is open, and blood flows through the capillaries. When sphincter muscles are contracted, blood flows through a shunt that carries blood directly from an arteriole to a venule. As blood passes through a capillary in the tissues, it gives up its oxygen (O_2). Therefore, blood goes from being O_2-rich in the arteriole (red color) to being O_2-poor in the vein (blue color).

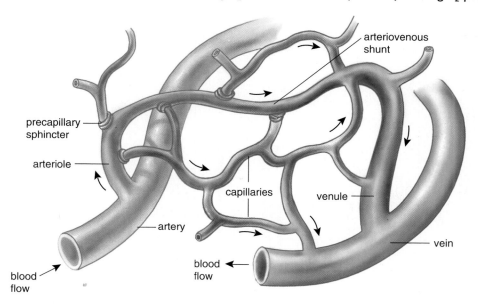

12.4 Physiology of Circulation

Circulation is the movement of blood through blood vessels, from the heart and then back to the heart. In this section, we discuss various factors affecting circulation.

Velocity of Blood Flow

The velocity of blood flow is slowest in the capillaries. What might account for this? Consider that the aorta branches into the other arteries, and these in turn branch into the arterioles, and so forth until blood finally flows into the capillaries. Each time an artery branches, the total cross-sectional area of the blood vessels increases, reaching the maximum cross-sectional area in the capillaries (Fig. 12.12). The slow rate of blood flow in the capillaries is beneficial because it allows time for the exchange of gases in pulmonary capillaries and for the exchange of gases and nutrients for wastes in systemic capillaries (see Fig. 11.6).

Conversely, blood flow increases as venules combine to form veins, and velocity is faster in the venae cavae than in the smaller veins. The cross-sectional area of the two venae cavae is more than twice that of the aorta, and the velocity of the blood returning to the heart remains low compared to the blood leaving the heart. In a resting individual, it takes only a minute for a drop of blood to go from the heart to the foot and back again to the heart! Blood pressure causes blood flow because blood always flows from a higher to a lower pressure difference.

Blood Pressure

Blood pressure is the force of blood against a blood vessel wall. You would expect blood pressure to be highest in the aorta. Why? Because the pumping action of the heart forces blood into the aorta. Further, Figure 12.13 shows that systemic blood pressure decreases progressively with distance from the left ventricle. Blood pressure is lowest in the venae cavae because they are farthest from the left ventricle.

Note also in Figure 12.13 that blood pressure fluctuates in the arterial system between systolic blood pressure and diastolic blood pressure. Certainly, we can correlate this with the action of the heart. During systole, the left ventricle is pumping blood out of the heart, and during diastole the left ventricle is resting.

More important than the systolic and diastolic pressure is the *mean arterial blood pressure (MABP)*. What might determine MABP? One factor is *cardiac output (CO)* (see page 232). In other words, the greater the amount of blood leaving the left ventricle, the greater the pressure of blood against the wall of an artery. Another factor that determines blood pressure is *peripheral resistance*, which is the friction between blood and the walls of a blood vessel. All things being equal, the smaller the blood vessel, the greater the resistance and the higher the blood pressure. Similarly, total blood vessel length increases blood pressure because a longer vessel offers greater resistance. An obese person is apt to have high blood pressure because about 200 miles of additional blood vessels develop for each extra pound of fat.

Figure 12.12 Velocity of blood flow changes throughout the systemic circuit. Velocity changes according to the total cross-sectional area of vessels.

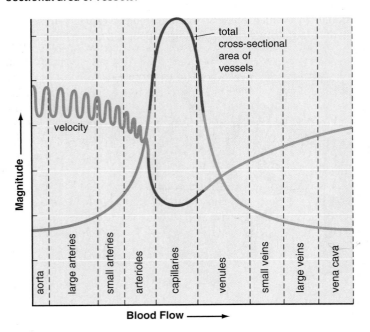

Figure 12.13 Blood pressure changes throughout the systemic circuit. Blood pressure decreases with distance from the left ventricle.

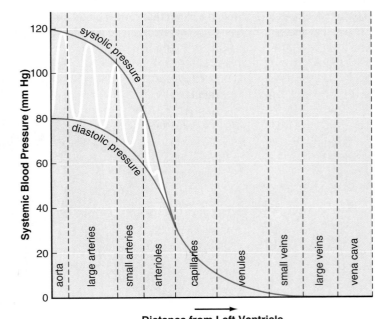

Let's summarize our discussion so far. The two factors that affect blood pressure are:

↑**Cardiac output**   ↑**Peripheral resistance**
  Heart rate   Arterial diameter and length
  Stroke volume

Cardiac Output Again

Our previous discussion on page 232 emphasized that the heart rate and the stroke volume determine CO. We learned that the heartbeat is intrinsic but is under extrinsic (nervous) control. Therefore, it can speed up. The faster the heart rate, the greater the blood pressure (assuming constant peripheral resistance). Similarly, the larger the stroke volume, the greater the blood pressure. However, stroke volume and heart rate increase blood pressure only if the venous return is adequate.

Venous Return Venous return depends on three factors:

1. a blood pressure difference—blood pressure is about 16 mm Hg in venules versus 0 mm Hg in the right atrium;
2. the skeletal muscle pump and the respiratory pump, both of which are effective because of the presence of valves in veins;
3. total blood volume in the cardiovascular system.

The **skeletal muscle pump** works like this: When skeletal muscles contract, they compress the weak walls of the veins. This causes the blood to move past a valve (Fig. 12.14). Once past the valve, backward pressure of blood closes the valve and prevents its return.

The **respiratory pump** works like this: When inhalation occurs, thoracic pressure falls and abdominal pressure rises as the chest expands. This aids the flow of venous blood back to the heart because blood flows in the direction of reduced pressure. During exhalation, the pressure reverses, but the valves in the veins prevent backward flow.

As you might suspect, gravity can assist the return of venous blood from the head to the heart but not the return of blood from the extremities and trunk to the heart. The importance of the skeletal muscle pump in maintaining CO and blood pressure can be demonstrated by forcing a person to stand rigidly still for a number of hours. Frequently, the person faints because blood collects in the limbs, robbing the brain of oxygen. In this case, fainting is beneficial because the resulting horizontal position aids in getting blood to the head.

As stated, the amount of venous return also depends on the total blood volume in the cardiovascular system. As you know, this volume in the pulmonary circuit and the systemic circuit is 5 L. If this amount of blood decreases, say due to hemorrhaging, blood pressure falls. On the other hand, if blood volume increases (due to water retention, for example), blood pressure rises.

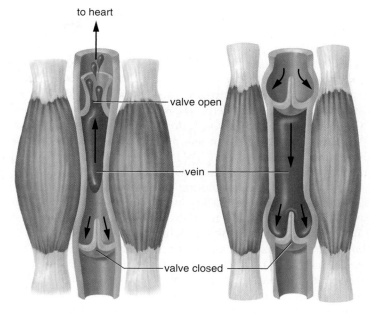

Figure 12.14 Skeletal muscle pump. **a.** When skeletal muscles contract and compress a vein, blood is squeezed past a valve. **b.** When muscles relax, the backward flow of blood closes the valve.

to heart

valve open

vein

valve closed

a. Contracted skeletal muscles   b. Relaxed skeletal muscles

Peripheral Resistance

The nervous system and the endocrine system both affect peripheral resistance.

Neural Regulation of Peripheral Resistance A **vasomotor center** in the medulla oblongata controls vasoconstriction. This center is under the control of the cardioregulatory center. As mentioned on page 233, if blood pressure falls, baroreceptors in the blood vessels signal the cardioregulatory center. Thereafter, impulses conducted along sympathetic nerve fibers cause the heart rate to increase *and* the arterioles to constrict via the vasomotor center. The result is a rise in blood pressure. What factors lead to a reduction in blood pressure? If blood pressure rises above normal, the baroreceptors signal the cardioregulatory center in the medulla oblongata. Subsequently, the heart rate decreases *and* the arterioles dilate.

Nervous control of blood vessels also causes blood to be shunted from one area of the body to another. During exercise, arteries in the viscera and skin are more constricted than those in the muscles. Therefore, blood flow to the muscles increases. Also, dilation of the precapillary sphincters in muscles means that blood will flow to the muscles and not to the viscera.

Hormonal Regulation of Peripheral Resistance Certain hormones cause blood pressure to rise. Epinephrine and norepinephrine increase the heart rate, as previously mentioned.

When the blood volume and blood sodium level are low, the kidneys secrete the enzyme **renin**. Renin converts the plasma protein angiotensinogen to angiotensin I, which is changed to angiotensin II by a converting enzyme found in the lungs. Angiotensin II stimulates the adrenal cortex to release aldosterone. The effect of this system, called the renin-angiotensin-aldosterone system, is to raise the blood volume and pressure in two ways. First, angiotensin II constricts the arterioles directly, and second, aldosterone causes the kidneys to reabsorb sodium. When the blood sodium level rises, water is reabsorbed, and blood volume and pressure are maintained.

Two other hormones play a role in the homeostatic maintenance of blood volume. As discussed in Chapter 10, antidiuretic hormone (ADH) helps increase blood volume by causing the kidneys to reabsorb water. Also, when the atria of the heart are stretched due to increased blood volume, cardiac cells release a hormone called **atrial natriuretic hormone (ANH),** which inhibits renin secretion by the kidneys and aldosterone secretion by the adrenal cortex. The effect of ANH, therefore, is to cause sodium excretion—that is, *natriuresis*. When sodium is excreted, so is water, and therefore blood volume and blood pressure decrease (Fig. 12.15).

Figure 12.15 Blood volume maintenance. Normal blood volume is maintained by ADH (antidiuretic hormone) and aldosterone, whose actions raise blood volume, and by ANH (atrial natriuretic hormone), whose actions lower blood volume.

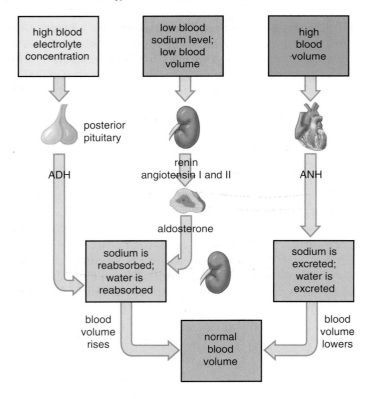

Evaluating Circulation

Taking a patient's pulse and blood pressure are two ways to evaluate circulation.

Pulse

The surge of blood entering the arteries causes their elastic walls to stretch, but then they almost immediately recoil. This alternating expansion and recoil of an arterial wall can be felt as a **pulse** in any artery that runs close to the body's surface, termed **pulse points** (Fig. 12.16). It is customary to feel the pulse by placing several fingers on the radial artery, which lies near the outer border of the palm side of a wrist. The common carotid artery, on either side of the trachea in the neck, is another accessible location for feeling the pulse. Normally, the pulse rate indicates the rate of the heartbeat because the arterial walls pulse whenever the left ventricle contracts. The pulse is usually 70 times per minute, but can vary between 60 and 80 times per minute.

Blood Pressure

Blood pressure is usually measured in the brachial artery with a sphygmomanometer, an instrument that records changes in terms of millimeters (mm) of mercury (Fig. 12.17). A blood pressure cuff connected to the sphygmomanometer is wrapped around the patient's arm, and a stethoscope is placed over the brachial artery. The blood pressure cuff is in-

Figure 12.16 The pulse rate. Pulse points are the locations where the pulse can be taken. Each pulse point is named after the appropriate artery.

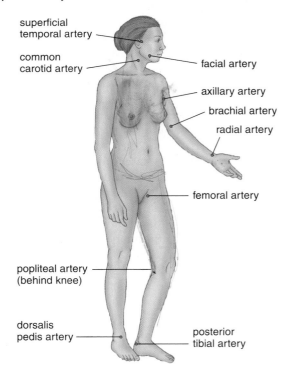

flated until no blood flows through it; therefore, no sounds can be heard through the stethoscope. The cuff pressure is then gradually lowered. As soon as the cuff pressure declines below systolic pressure, blood flows through the brachial artery each time the left ventricle contracts. The blood flow is turbulent below the cuff. This turbulence produces vibrations in the blood and surrounding tissues that can be heard through the stethoscope. These sounds are called *Korotkoff sounds,* and the cuff pressure at which the Korotkoff sounds are heard the first time is the systolic pressure. As the pressure in the cuff is lowered still more, the Korotkoff sounds change tone and loudness. When the cuff pressure no longer constricts the brachial artery, no sound is heard. The cuff pressure at which the Korotkoff sounds disappear is the diastolic pressure.

Normal resting blood pressure for a young adult is 120/80. The higher number is the *systolic pressure,* the pressure recorded in an artery when the left ventricle contracts. The lower number is the *diastolic pressure,* the pressure recorded in an artery when the left ventricle relaxes.

It is estimated that about 20% of all Americans suffer from **hypertension,** which is high blood pressure. Hypertension is present when the systolic blood pressure is 140 or greater, or the diastolic blood pressure is 90 or greater. While both systolic and diastolic pressures are considered important, the diastolic pressure is emphasized when medical treatment is being considered.

Hypertension is sometimes called a silent killer because it may not be detected until a stroke or heart attack occurs. It has long been thought that a certain genetic makeup might account for the development of hypertension. Now researchers have discovered two genes that may be involved in some individuals. One gene codes for angiotensinogen, the plasma protein mentioned previously (see page 238). Angiotensinogen is converted to a powerful vasoconstrictor in part by the product of the second gene. Persons with hypertension due to overactivity of these genes might one day be cured by gene therapy.

At present, however, the best safeguard against developing hypertension is to have regular blood pressure checks and to adopt a lifestyle that lowers the risk of hypertension as described in the Medical Focus on pages 240–41.

Stroke and Aneurysm Various cardiovascular diseases—myocardial infarction (see page 228), stroke, and aneurysm—are associated with hypertension and atherosclerosis. A **cerebrovascular accident (CVA),** also called a **stroke,** often results when a small cranial arteriole bursts or is blocked by an embolus. Lack of oxygen causes a portion of the brain to die, and paralysis or death can result. A person is sometimes forewarned of a stroke by a feeling of numbness in the hands or the face, difficulty in speaking, or temporary blindness in one eye.

Aneurysm (expansion of the blood vessel wall into a "sac") weakens blood vessels, possibly causing them to burst. Aneurysms are most often seen in the abdominal artery or in the arteries leading to the brain. Atherosclerosis and hypertension can weaken the wall of an artery to the point that an aneurysm develops. If a major vessel such as the aorta should burst, death is likely. It is possible to replace a damaged or diseased portion of a vessel with a plastic tube. Cardiovascular function is preserved, because exchange with tissue cells can still take place at the capillaries.

Figure 12.17 Use of a sphygmomanometer. The technician inflates the cuff with air, gradually reduces the pressure, and listens with a stethoscope for the sounds that indicate blood is moving past the cuff in an artery. This is systolic blood pressure. The pressure in the cuff is further reduced until no sound is heard, indicating that blood is flowing freely through the artery. This is diastolic pressure.

Congestive Heart Failure

In **congestive heart failure,** a damaged left side of the heart fails to pump adequate blood, and blood backs up in the pulmonary circuit. Therefore, pulmonary blood vessels have become *congested.* The congested vessels leak fluid into tissue spaces, causing pulmonary edema. The result is shortness of breath, fatigue, and a constant cough with pink, frothy sputum. Treatment consists of the three Ds: diuretics (to increase urinary output), digoxin (to increase the heart's contractile force), and dilators (to relax the blood vessels). If necessary, a heart transplant is done.

Preventing Cardiovascular Disease

All of us can take steps to prevent cardiovascular disease, the most frequent cause of death in the United States. Genetic factors that predispose an individual to cardiovascular disease include family history of heart attack under age 55, male gender, and ethnicity (African Americans are at greater risk). However, people with one or more of these risk factors need not despair. It only means that they need to pay particular attention to the following guidelines for a heart-healthy lifestyle.

The Don'ts

Smoking

Hypertension is recognized as a major contributor to cardiovascular disease. When a person smokes, the drug nicotine, present in cigarette smoke, enters the bloodstream. Nicotine causes the arterioles to constrict and the blood pressure to rise. Restricted blood flow and cold hands are associated with smoking in most people. Cigarette smoke also contains carbon monoxide, and hemoglobin combines preferentially and nonreversibly with carbon monoxide. Therefore, the presence of carbon monoxide lowers the oxygen-carrying capacity of the blood, and the heart must pump harder to propel the blood through the lungs. Smoking also damages the arterial wall and accelerates the formation of atherosclerosis and plaque (Fig. 12B).

Drug Abuse

Stimulants, such as cocaine and amphetamines, can cause an irregular heartbeat and lead to heart attacks in people who are using drugs even for the first time. Intravenous drug use may also result in a cerebral blood clot and stroke.

Too much alcohol can destroy just about every organ in the body, the heart included. But investigators have discovered that people who take an occasional drink have a 20% lower risk of heart disease than do teetotalers. Two to four drinks a week is the recommended limit for men; one to three drinks is the recommendation for women.

Weight Gain

Hypertension also occurs more often in persons who are more than 20% above the recommended weight for their height. Because more tissue requires servicing, the heart must send extra blood out under greater pressure in those who are overweight. It may be very difficult to lose weight once it is gained, and therefore weight control should be a lifelong endeavor. Even a slight decrease in weight can bring a reduction in hypertension. A 4.5-kilogram weight loss doubles the chance that blood pressure can be normalized without drugs.

The Do's

Healthy Diet

It was once thought that a low-salt diet could protect against cardiovascular disease, and that still may be true in certain persons. Theoretically, hypertension occurs because the more salty the blood, the greater the osmotic pressure and the higher the water content. However, in recent years, the emphasis has switched to a diet low in saturated fats and cholesterol as protective against cardiovascular disease. Cholesterol is ferried in the blood by two types of plasma lipoproteins, called LDL (low-density lipoprotein) and HDL (high-density lipoprotein). LDL (called "bad" lipoprotein) takes cholesterol from the liver to the tissues, and HDL (called "good" lipoprotein) transports cholesterol out of the tissues to the liver. When the LDL level in the blood is abnormally high or the HDL level is abnormally low, cholesterol accumulates in arterial walls. At first, this accumulation is a "fatty streak" beneath the endothelium. Then smooth muscle cells migrate from the muscular layer of the vessel and cover the fatty streak. When the muscle cells continue to divide, benign smooth muscle tumors, called *atheromas*, are present (i.e., atherosclerosis). The presence of plaque (Fig. 12B) can interfere with circulation. Finally, fibroblast growth and scar tissue, called *sclerosis*, covers the plaque, which is also invaded by Ca^{2+}. Now, a rigid artery of smaller diameter contributes to hypertension and cardiovascular disease.

It is recommended that everyone know his or her blood cholesterol level. Individuals with a high blood cholesterol level (240 mg/100 ml) should be further tested to determine their LDL cholesterol level. The LDL cholesterol level, together with other risk factors such as age, family history, general health, and whether the patient smokes, determine who needs dietary therapy to lower their LDL. Cholesterol-lowering drugs are reserved for high-risk patients.

Evidence is mounting to suggest a role for antioxidant vitamins (A, E, and C) in the prevention of cardiovascular disease. Antioxidants protect the body from free radicals that may damage HDL cholesterol through oxidation or damage the lining of an artery, leading to a blood clot that can block the vessel. Nutritionists believe that consuming at least five servings of fruit and vegetables a day may protect against cardiovascular disease.

Exercise

People who exercise are less apt to have cardiovascular disease. One study found that moderately active men who spent an average of 48 minutes a day on a leisure-time activity such as gardening, bowling, or dancing had one-third fewer heart attacks than their peers who spent an average of only 16 minutes each day on such activities. Exercise helps keep weight under control, may help minimize stress, and reduces hypertension. The heart beats faster when exercising, but exercise slowly increases the heart's capacity. This means that the heart can beat more slowly when we are at rest and still do the same amount of work. One physician recommends that his cardiovascular patients walk for one hour, three times a week. In addition, they are to practice meditation and yoga-like stretching and breathing exercises to reduce stress.

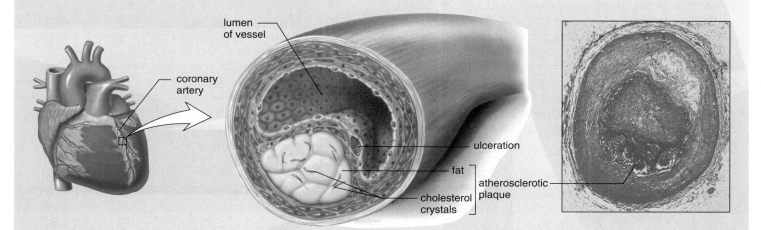

Figure 12B Coronary arteries and plaque. Plaque (in yellow) is an irregular accumulation of cholesterol and other substances. When plaque is present in a coronary artery, a heart attack is more apt to occur because of restricted blood flow.

12.5 Circulatory Routes

Blood vessels belong to either the pulmonary circuit or the systemic circuit. The path of blood through the **pulmonary circuit** can be traced as follows: Blood from all regions of the body first collects in the right atrium and then passes into the right ventricle, which pumps it into the pulmonary trunk. The pulmonary trunk divides into the **pulmonary arteries,** which in turn divide into the arterioles of the lungs. The arterioles then take blood to the pulmonary capillaries, where carbon dioxide and oxygen are exchanged. The blood then enters the pulmonary venules and flows through the **pulmonary veins** back to the left atrium. Because the blood in the pulmonary arteries is O_2-poor but the blood in the pulmonary veins is O_2-rich, it is not correct to say that all arteries carry blood that is high in oxygen and that all veins carry blood that is low in oxygen. In fact, just the reverse is true in the pulmonary circuit.

The **systemic circuit** includes all of the other arteries and veins of the body. The largest artery in the systemic circuit is the aorta, and the largest veins are the **superior vena cava** and **inferior vena cava.** The superior vena cava collects blood from the head, chest, and arms, and the inferior vena cava collects blood from the lower body regions. Both venae cavae enter the right atrium. The aorta and venae cavae are the major pathways for blood in the systemic system.

The path of systemic blood to any organ in the body begins in the left ventricle, which pumps blood into the **aorta.** Branches from the aorta go to the major body regions and organs. Tracing the path of blood to any organ in the body requires mentioning only the aorta, the proper branch of the aorta, the organ, and the returning vein to the vena cava. In many instances, the artery and vein that serve the same organ have the same name. For example, the path of blood to and from the kidneys is: left ventricle; aorta; renal artery; arterioles, capillaries, venules; renal vein; inferior vena cava; right atrium. In the systemic circuit, unlike the pulmonary circuit, arteries contain O_2-rich blood and appear bright red, while veins contain O_2-poor blood and appear dark maroon.

The Major Systemic Arteries

After the aorta leaves the heart, it divides into the *ascending aorta,* the *aortic arch,* and the *descending aorta* (Fig. 12.18). The left and right coronary arteries, which supply blood to the heart, branch off the ascending aorta (Table. 12.1).

Three major arteries branch off the aortic arch: the **brachiocephalic artery,** the **left common carotid artery,** and the **left subclavian artery.** The brachiocephalic artery divides into the **right common carotid** and the **right subclavian arteries.** These blood vessels serve the head (right and left common carotids) and arms (right and left subclavians).

The descending aorta is divided into the *thoracic aorta,* which branches off to the organs within the thoracic cavity, and the *abdominal aorta,* which branches off to the organs in the abdominal cavity.

The descending aorta ends when it divides into the **common iliac arteries** that branch into the **internal iliac artery** and the **external iliac artery.** The internal iliac artery serves the pelvic organs, and the external iliac artery serves the legs. These and other arteries are shown in Figure 12.18.

Table 12.1 The Aorta and Its Principal Branches		
Portion of Aorta	**Major Branch**	**Regions Supplied**
Ascending aorta	Left and right coronary arteries	Heart
Aortic arch	Brachiocephalic artery	
	Right common carotid	Right side of head
	Right subclavian	Right arm
	Left common carotid artery	Left side of head
	Left subclavian artery	Left arm
Descending aorta		
Thoracic aorta	Intercostal artery	Thoracic wall
Abdominal aorta	Celiac artery	Stomach, spleen, and liver
	Superior mesenteric artery	Small and large intestines (ascending and transverse colons)
	Renal artery	Kidney
	Gonadal artery	Ovary or testis
	Inferior mesenteric artery	Lower digestive system (transverse and descending colons, and rectum)
	Common iliac artery	Pelvic organs and legs

Figure 12.18 Major arteries (a.) of the body.

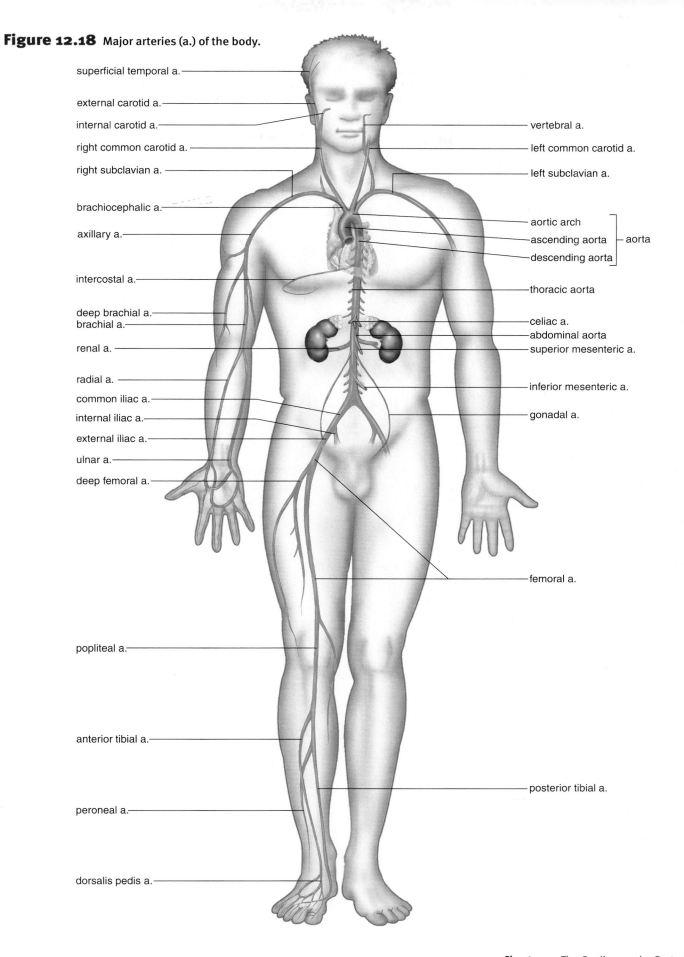

superficial temporal a.

external carotid a.

internal carotid a.

right common carotid a.

right subclavian a.

brachiocephalic a.

axillary a.

intercostal a.

deep brachial a.

brachial a.

renal a.

radial a.

common iliac a.

internal iliac a.

external iliac a.

ulnar a.

deep femoral a.

popliteal a.

anterior tibial a.

peroneal a.

dorsalis pedis a.

vertebral a.

left common carotid a.

left subclavian a.

aortic arch

ascending aorta

descending aorta

aorta

thoracic aorta

celiac a.

abdominal aorta

superior mesenteric a.

inferior mesenteric a.

gonadal a.

femoral a.

posterior tibial a.

Figure 12.19 Major veins (v.) of the body.

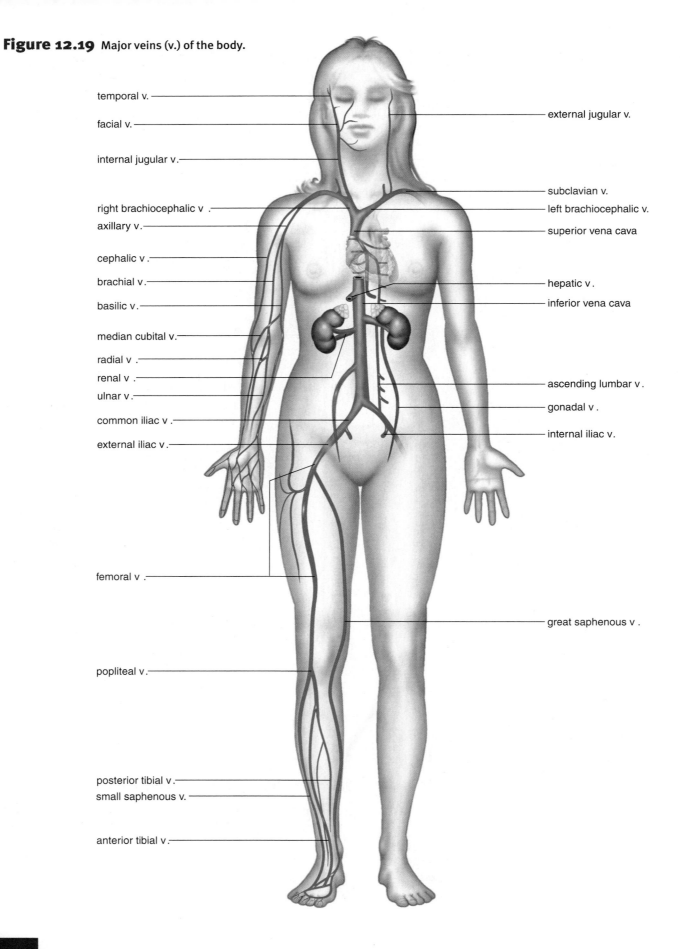

temporal v.

facial v.

internal jugular v.

right brachiocephalic v.

axillary v.

cephalic v.

brachial v.

basilic v.

median cubital v.

radial v.

renal v.

ulnar v.

common iliac v.

external iliac v.

femoral v.

popliteal v.

posterior tibial v.

small saphenous v.

anterior tibial v.

external jugular v.

subclavian v.

left brachiocephalic v.

superior vena cava

hepatic v.

inferior vena cava

ascending lumbar v.

gonadal v.

internal iliac v.

great saphenous v.

Table 12.2	Principal Veins That Join the Venae Cavae	
Vein	**Region Drained**	**Vena Cava**
Right and left brachiocephalic veins	Head, neck, and upper extremities	Form superior vena cava
Right and left common iliac veins	Lower extremities	Form inferior vena cava
Right and left renal veins	Kidneys	Enters inferior vena cava
Right and left hepatic veins	Liver, digestive tract, and spleen	Enters inferior vena cava

The Major Systemic Veins

Figure 12.19 shows the major veins of the body. The **external** and **internal jugular veins** drain blood from the brain, head, and neck. An external jugular vein enters a **subclavian vein** that, along with an internal jugular vein, enters a **brachiocephalic vein.** Right and left brachiocephalic veins merge, giving rise to the superior vena cava.

In the abdominal cavity, as discussed in more detail later, the **hepatic portal vein** receives blood from the abdominal viscera and enters the liver. Emerging from the liver, the **hepatic veins** enter the inferior vena cava.

In the pelvic region, veins from the various organs enter the **internal iliac** veins, while the veins from the legs enter the **external iliac veins.** The internal and external iliac veins become the **common iliac veins** that merge, forming the inferior vena cava. Table 12.2 lists the principal veins that enter the venae cavae.

Special Systemic Circulations

Hepatic Portal System

The **hepatic portal system** (Fig. 12.20) carries blood from the stomach, intestines, and other organs to the liver. The term portal system is used to describe the following unique pattern of circulation:

capillaries → vein → capillaries → vein

Capillaries of the digestive tract drain into the superior mesenteric vein and the splenic vein, which join to form the hepatic portal vein. The gastric veins empty directly into the hepatic portal vein. The hepatic portal vein carries blood to capillaries in the liver. The hepatic capillaries allow nutrients and wastes to diffuse into liver cells for further processing. Then, hepatic capillaries join to form venules that enter a hepatic vein. The hepatic veins enter the inferior vena cava.

In addition to receiving venous blood from the intestine, the liver also receives arterial blood via the hepatic artery. The hepatic artery is not a part of the hepatic portal system.

Figure 12.20 Hepatic portal system. This system provides venous drainage of the digestive organs and takes venous blood to the liver. (v. = vein.)

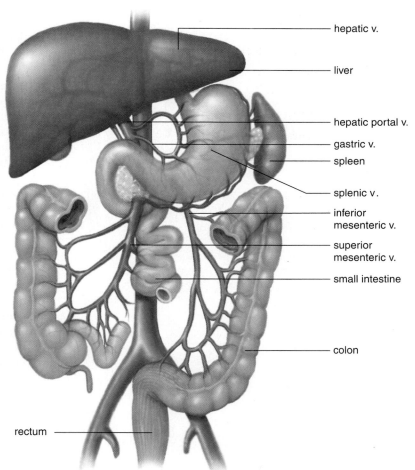

Hypothalamus-Hypophyseal Portal System

The body has other portal systems. For example, the vascular link between the hypothalamus and the anterior pituitary through which the hypothalamus sends hypothalamic-releasing hormones to the anterior pituitary is a portal system.

Blood Supply to the Brain

The brain is supplied with O_2-rich blood by the anterior and posterior cerebral arteries and the carotid arteries. These arteries give off branches. that join to form the **cerebral arterial circle** (circle of Willis), a vascular route in the region of the pituitary gland (Fig. 12.21). Because the blood vessels form a circle, alternate routes are available for bringing arterial blood to the brain and thus supplying the brain with oxygen. The presence of the cerebral arterial circle also equalizes blood pressure in the brain's blood supply.

Figure 12.21 Cerebral arterial circle. The arteries that supply blood to the brain form the cerebral arterial circle (circle of Willis). (a. = artery.)

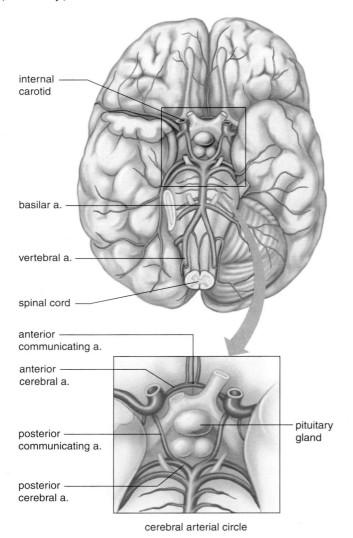

internal carotid

basilar a.

vertebral a.

spinal cord

anterior communicating a.

anterior cerebral a.

posterior communicating a.

posterior cerebral a.

pituitary gland

cerebral arterial circle

Fetal Circulation

As Figure 12.22 shows, the fetus has four circulatory features that are not present in adult circulation:

1. The **foramen ovale,** or *oval window,* is an opening between the two atria. This window is covered by a flap of tissue that acts as a valve.
2. The **ductus arteriosus,** or *arterial duct,* is a connection between the pulmonary artery and the aorta.
3. The **umbilical arteries** and **vein** are vessels that travel to and from the placenta, leaving waste and receiving nutrients.
4. The **ductus venosus,** or *venous duct,* is a connection between the umbilical vein and the inferior vena cava.

All of these features can be related to the fact that the fetus does not use its lungs for gas exchange, since it receives oxygen and nutrients from the mother's blood at the placenta. During development, the lungs receive only enough blood to supply their developmental need for oxygen and nutrients.

The path of blood in the fetus can be traced, beginning from the right atrium (Fig. 12.22). Most of the blood that enters the right atrium passes directly into the left atrium by way of the foramen ovale because the blood pressure in the right atrium is somewhat greater than that in the left atrium. The rest of the fetal blood entering the right atrium passes into the right ventricle and out through the pulmonary trunk. However, because of the ductus arteriosus, most pulmonary trunk blood passes directly into the aortic arch. Notice that, whatever route blood takes, most of it reaches the aortic arch instead of the pulmonary circuit vessels.

Blood within the aorta travels to the various branches, including the iliac arteries, which connect to the umbilical arteries leading to the placenta. Exchange between maternal and fetal blood takes place at the placenta. Blood in the umbilical arteries is O_2-poor, but blood in the umbilical vein, which travels from the placenta, is O_2-rich. The umbilical vein enters the ductus venosus, which passes directly through the liver. The ductus venosus then joins with the inferior vena cava, a vessel that contains O_2-poor blood. The vena cava returns this mixture to the right atrium.

Changes at Birth Sectioning and tying the umbilical cord permanently separates the newborn from the placenta. The first breath inflates the lungs and oxygen enters the blood at the lungs instead of the placenta. O_2-rich blood returning from the lungs to the left side of the heart usually causes a flap on the left side of the interatrial septum to close the foramen ovale. What remains is a depression called the *fossa ovalis.* Incomplete closure occurs in nearly one out of four

Figure 12.22 Fetal circulation. Arrows indicate the direction of blood flow. The lungs are not functional in the fetus. The blood passes directly from the right atrium to the left atrium via the foramen ovale or from the right ventricle to the aorta via the pulmonary trunk and ductus venosus. The umbilical arteries take fetal blood to the placenta where exchange of molecules between fetal and maternal blood takes place. Oxygen and nutrient molecules diffuse into the fetal blood, and carbon dioxide and urea diffuse from the fetal blood. The umbilical vein returns blood from the placenta to the fetus.

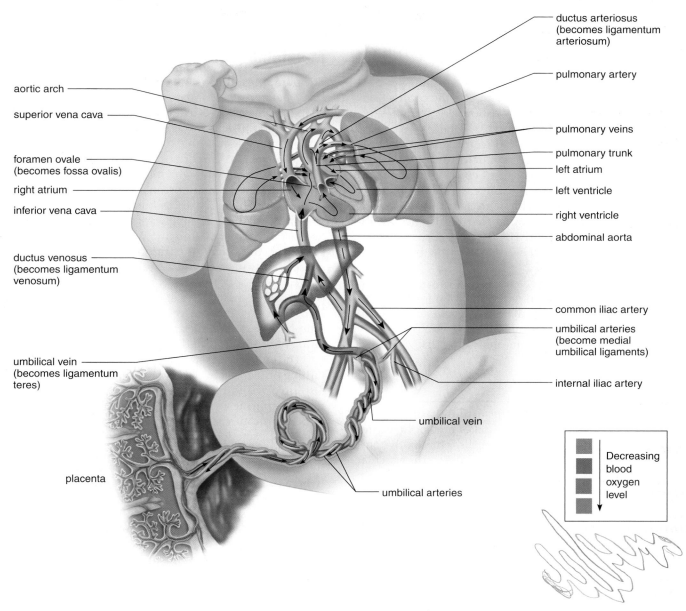

individuals, but even so, blood rarely passes from the right atrium to the left atrium because either the opening is small or it closes when the atria contract. In a small number of cases, the passage of O$_2$-poor blood from the right side to the left side of the heart is sufficient to cause **cyanosis,** a bluish cast to the skin. This condition can now be corrected by open-heart surgery.

The fetal blood vessels and shunts constrict and become fibrous connective tissue called ligamentums in all cases except the distal portions of the umbilical arteries, which become the medial umbilical ligaments. Regardless, these structures run between internal organs. For example, the ligamentum teres attaches the umbilicus to the liver.

12.6 Effects of Aging

The heart generally grows larger with age, primarily because of fat deposition in the epicardium and myocardium. In many middle-aged people, the heart is covered by a layer of fat, and the number of collagenous fibers in the endocardium increases. With age, the valves, particularly the aortic semilunar valve, become thicker and more rigid.

As a person ages, the myocardium loses some of its contractile power and some of its ability to relax. The resting heart rate decreases throughout life, and the maximum possible rate during exercise also decreases. With age, the contractions become less forceful; the heart loses about 1% of its reserve pumping capacity each year after age 30.

In the elderly, arterial walls tend to thicken with plaque and become inelastic, signaling that atherosclerosis and arteriosclerosis are present. The chances of coronary thrombosis and heart attack increase with age. Increased blood pressure was once believed to be inevitable with age, but now hypertension is known to result from other conditions, such as kidney disease and atherosclerosis. The Medical Focus on pages 240–41 describes how diet and exercise in particular can help prevent atherosclerosis.

The occurrence of varicose veins increases with age, particularly in people who are required to stand for long periods. Thromboembolism as a result of varicose veins can lead to death if a blood clot settles in a major branch of a pulmonary artery. (This disorder is called pulmonary embolism.)

12.7 Homeostasis

Homeostasis is possible only if the cardiovascular system delivers oxygen and nutrients to and takes metabolic wastes from the tissue fluid surrounding the cells. Human Systems Work Together on page 249 tells how the cardiovascular system works with other systems of the body to maintain homeostasis.

Maintaining Blood Composition, pH, and Temperature

The composition of the blood is maintained by the other systems of the body. Growth factors regulate the manufacture of formed elements in the red bone marrow, which is a lymphatic organ. In this way, the skeletal system contributes to the cardiovascular system. Red blood cells assist the respiratory system by carrying oxygen, and the immune system could not function without the ability of white blood cells to fight infection.

The digestive system absorbs nutrients into the blood, and the lungs and kidneys remove metabolic wastes from blood. One of the most important functions of the kidneys is to maintain the pH of the blood within normal limits. The liver, of course, is a key regulator of blood components by producing plasma proteins, storing glucose until it is needed, transforming ammonia into urea, and changing other poisons into molecules that are also excreted.

The blood distributes heat created by muscle contraction to the rest of the body. Blood vessels in the skin dilate when body temperature rises and constrict when heat needs to be conserved. In this way, the integumentary system plays a key role in regulating body temperature.

Maintaining Blood Pressure

The pumping of the heart is critical to creating the blood pressure that moves blood to the lungs, where oxygen is exchanged for carbon dioxide, and to the tissues, where gas exchange and nutrient-for-waste exchange take place. Only then is the brain able to think, the lungs to breathe, and the muscles to move. The importance of the heart to survival can be seen in the speed with which it develops during prenatal life. Long before other major organs, the heart and its vessels have taken shape and are ready to function.

The body has multiple ways to maintain blood pressure. Sensory receptors within the aortic arch signal regulatory centers in the brain when blood pressure falls. This center subsequently increases heartbeat and constricts blood vessels. Thereafter, blood pressure is restored. The lymphatic system collects excess tissue fluid at blood capillaries and returns it to cardiovascular veins in the thoracic cavity. In this way, the lymphatic system makes an important contribution to regulating blood volume and pressure.

The endocrine system assists the nervous system in maintaining homeostasis, so it is not surprising that hormones are also involved in regulating blood pressure. Epinephrine and norepinephrine bring about the constriction of arterioles. Other hormones, such as aldosterone, ADH, and ANH, regulate urine excretion. After all, if water is retained, blood volume and pressure will rise, and if water is excreted, blood volume and pressure will drop. In fact, some drugs prescribed for hypertension increase the amount of urine excreted.

Venous return from the capillaries to the heart is assisted by two other systems of the body: the muscular and respiratory systems. Skeletal muscle contraction pushes blood past the valves in the veins, and breathing movements encourage the flow of blood toward the heart in the thoracic cavity. Without smooth muscle, the walls of arterioles would not be able to constrict and in this way help raise blood pressure.

Platelets are necessary to blood clotting, which prevents the loss of blood and the loss of pressure. Clots, however, are not enough to stop massive blood loss. An individual who loses more than 10% of his or her blood will suffer a sudden drop in blood pressure and usually go into shock. The decreased pressure triggers the body's last defense: A powerful wave of sympathetic impulses constricts the veins and arterioles throughout the body to slow the drop in blood pressure. Heart rate soars as high as 200 beats a minute to maintain blood flow, especially to the brain and heart itself. Because of this reflex, you can lose as much as 40% of your total blood volume and still live.

Human Systems Work Together

Integumentary System

Blood vessels deliver nutrients and oxygen to skin, carry away wastes; blood clots if skin is broken.

Skin prevents water loss; helps regulate body temperature; protects blood vessels.

Skeletal System

Blood vessels deliver nutrients and oxygen to bones; carry away wastes.

Rib cage protects heart; red bone marrow produces blood cells; bones store Ca^{2+} for blood clotting.

Muscular System

Blood vessels deliver nutrients and oxygen to muscles; carry away wastes.

Muscle contraction keeps blood moving in heart and blood vessels.

Nervous System

Blood vessels deliver nutrients and oxygen to neurons; carry away wastes.

Brain controls nerves that regulate the heart and dilation of blood vessels.

Endocrine System

Blood vessels transport hormones from glands; blood services glands; heart produces atrial natriuretic hormone.

Epinephrine increases blood pressure; ADH, aldosterone, and atrial natriuretic hormone factors help regulate blood volume; growth factors control blood cell formation.

How the Cardiovascular System works with other body systems

Lymphatic System/Immunity

Blood vessels transport leukocytes and antibodies; blood services lymphatic organs and is source of tissue fluid that becomes lymph.

Lymphatic vessels collect excess tissue fluid and return it to blood vessels; lymphatic organs store lymphocytes; lymph nodes filter lymph, and the spleen filters blood.

Respiratory System

Blood vessels transport gases to and from lungs; blood services respiratory organs.

Gas exchange in lungs rids body of carbon dioxide, helping to regulate the pH of blood; breathing aids venous return.

Digestive System

Blood vessels transport nutrients from digestive tract to body; blood services digestive organs.

Digestive tract provides nutrients for plasma protein formation and blood cell formation; liver detoxifies blood, makes plasma proteins, destroys old red blood cells.

Urinary System

Blood vessels deliver wastes to be excreted; blood pressure aids kidney function; blood services urinary organs.

Kidneys filter blood and excrete wastes; maintain blood volume, pressure, and pH; produce renin and erythropoietin.

Reproductive System

Blood vessels transport sex hormones; vasodilation causes genitals to become erect; blood services reproductive organs.

Sex hormones influence cardiovascular health; sexual activities stimulate cardiovascular system.

Selected New Terms

Basic Key Terms

aorta (a-or'tuh), p. 242

arteriole (ar-te're-ōl), p. 234

artery (ar'ter-e), p. 234

atrioventricular node (a″tre-o-ven-trik'yū-ler nōd), p. 230

atrioventricular valve (a″tre-o-ven-trik'yū-ler valv), p. 226

atrium (a'tre-um), p. 226

bicuspid valve (bi-kus'pid valv), pp. 226

capillary (kap'ĭ-lār″e), p. 235

cardioregulatory center (kar″de-o-reg'yū-luh-tor-e sen'ter), p. 233

cerebral arterial circle (sĕr'ĕ-bral ar-te're'al ser'kl), p. 246

coronary artery (kor'ŏ-na-re ar'ter-e), p. 228

diastole (di-as'to-le), p. 232

ductus arteriosus (duk'tus ar-tēr-e-o'sus), p. 246

ductus venosus (duk'tus vĕ-no'sus), p. 246

endocardium (en″do-kar'de-um), p. 226

foramen ovale (fo-ra'men o-vah'le), p. 246

hepatic portal system (hĕ-pat'ik por'tal sis'tem), p. 245

inferior vena cava (in-fēr'e-or ve'nuh ka'vuh), p. 242

interatrial septum (in″ter-a'tre-al sep'tum), p. 226

interventricular septum (in″ter-ven-trik'yū-ler sep'tum), p. 226

myocardium (mi″o-kar'de-um), p. 226

pericardium (pĕr-ĭ-kar'de-um), p. 226

pulmonary artery (pul'mo-nĕr″e ar'ter-e), p. 242

pulmonary circuit (pul'mo-nĕr″e ser″kyū-la'shun), p. 242

pulmonary vein (pul'mo-nĕr″e vān), p. 242

pulse (puls), p. 238

Purkinje fiber (per-kin'je fi'ber), p. 230

semilunar valve (sem″e-lu'ner valv), p. 226

sinoatrial (SA) node (si″no-a'tre-ul nōd), p. 230

superior vena cava (su-pĕr'e-or ve'nuh ka'vuh), p. 242

systemic circuit (sis-tem'ik ser″kut), p. 242

systole (sis'to-le), p. 232

tricuspid valve (tri-kus'pid valv), p. 226

umbilical artery and vein (um-bil'ĭ-kl ar'ter-e and vān), p. 246

vein (vān), p. 235

ventricle (ven'trĭ-kl), p. 226

venule (ven'ūl), p. 235

Clinical Key Terms

aneurysm (an'yer'ĭzm), p. 239

angina pectoris (an-ji'nuh pek'to-ris), p. 228

arrhythmia (uh-rith'me-uh), p. 231

arteriosclerosis (ar-te″re-o-sklĕ-ro'sis), p. 234

atherosclerosis (ath″er-o″sklĕ-ro'sis), p. 228

bradycardia (brad″e-kar'de-uh), p. 231

cerebrovascular accident (sĕr″e-bro-vas'kyū-ler ak'si-dent), p. 239

congestive heart failure (kon-jes'tiv hart fāl'yer), p. 239

coronary bypass operation (kor'ŏ-na-re bi'pas op-er-a'shun), p. 229

cyanosis (si″uh-no'sis), p. 247

ectopic pacemaker (ek-top'ik pās'ma-ker), p. 231

electrocardiogram (e-lek″tro-kar'de-o-gram″), p. 231

fibrillation (fĭ″brĭ-la'shun), p. 231

heart block (hart blok), p. 231

heart murmur (hart mer'mer), p. 232

hemorrhoid (hem'royd), p. 235

hypertension (hi″per-ten'shun), p. 239

ischemic heart disease (is-kem'ik hart dĭ-zēz'), p. 228

myocardial infarction (mi″o-kar'de-ul in-fark'shun), p. 228

occluded coronary arteries (ŏ-klūd'ed kor'ŏ-na-re ar'ter-ēz), p. 229

phlebitis (flĭ-bi'tus), p. 235

plaque (plak), p. 228

pulmonary embolism (pul'mo-nĕr″e em'bo-lizm), p. 235

tachycardia (tak'ĭ kar'de-uh), p. 231

thromboembolism (throm″bo-em'bol-izm), p. 228

varicose vein (vār'ĭ-kōs vān), p. 235

Summary

12.1 Anatomy of the Heart

A. The heart keeps O_2-poor blood separate from O_2-rich blood and blood flowing in one direction. It creates blood pressure and regulates the supply of blood to meet current needs.

B. The heart is covered by the pericardium. The visceral pericardium is equal to the epicardium of the heart wall. Myocardium is cardiac muscle, and endocardium is its lining.

C. The heart has a right and left side and four chambers, consisting of two atria and two ventricles. The heart valves are the tricuspid valve, the pulmonary semilunar valve, the bicuspid valve, and the aortic semilunar valve.

D. The right side of the heart pumps blood to the lungs (pulmonary circuit), and the left side pumps blood to the tissues (systemic circuit). The myocardium is serviced by blood in the coronary circuit. Myocardial infarction is often preceded by atherosclerosis, angina pectoris, or thromboembolism.

12.2 Physiology of the Heart

A. The conduction system of the heart includes the SA node, the AV node, the AV bundle, the bundle branches, and the Purkinje fibers. The SA node causes the atria to contract. The AV node and the rest of the conduction system cause the ventricles to contract.

B. The heartbeat (cardiac cycle) is divided into three phases: (1) In atrial systole, the atria contract; (2) in ventricular systole, the ventricles contract; and (3) in atrial and ventricular diastole, both the atria and the ventricles rest. The heart sounds are due to the closing of the heart valves.

C. The cardiac output (amount of blood discharged by the heart in one minute) depends on stroke volume and heart rate. The heart rate is regulated largely by the cardioregulatory center and the autonomic nervous system.

12.3 Anatomy of Blood Vessels

A. Blood vessels transport blood; carry out exchange in pulmonary capillaries and systemic capillaries; regulate blood pressure; and direct blood flow.

B. Arteries and arterioles carry blood away from the heart; veins and venules carry blood to the heart; and capillaries join arterioles to venules.

12.4 Physiology of Circulation

A. Velocity of blood flow varies according to total cross-sectional area; therefore, blood flow is slowest in the capillaries.

B. Blood pressure decreases with distance from the left ventricle. Cardiac output (CO) and resistance to flow determine blood pressure. Venous return affects CO. The skeletal muscle pump and the respiratory pump assist venous return. A vasomotor center regulates peripheral resistance. Neural regulation of peripheral resistance is via a vasomotor center in the medulla that is under the control of the cardioregulatory center. Several different hormones regulate blood pressure through their influence over kidney reabsorption of water.

C. To evaluate a person's circulation, it is customary to take the pulse and blood pressure. Stroke, heart attack, and aneurysm are associated with hypertension and atherosclerosis. Congestive heart failure is due to low cardiac output.

12.5 Circulatory Routes

A. The pulmonary arteries transport O_2-poor blood to the pulmonary capillaries, and the pulmonary veins return O_2-rich blood to the heart. In the systemic circuit, blood travels from the left ventricle to the aorta, systemic arteries, arterioles, and capillaries, and then from the capillaries to the venules and veins to the right atrium of the heart. The systemic circuit serves the body proper.

B. The hepatic portal system carries blood from the stomach and intestines to the liver.

C. Circulation to the brain includes the cerebral arterial circle, which protects all regions of the brain from reduced blood supply.

D. Fetal circulation includes four unique features: (1) the foramen ovale, (2) the ductus arteriosus, (3) the umbilical arteries and vein, and (4) the ductus venosus. These features are necessary because the fetus does not use its lungs for gas exchange.

12.6 Effects of Aging

As we age, the cardiovascular system is more apt to suffer from all the disorders discussed in this chapter.

12.7 Homeostasis

The cardiovascular system is essential to homeostasis because it functions to assure exchange at the pulmonary capillaries and the systemic capillaries. There are many examples of the interaction of the cardiovascular system with other systems. For example, the endocrine system is dependent on the cardiovascular system to transport its hormones; and hormones help maintain blood pressure. Blood vessels deliver wastes to the kidneys and the kidneys help maintain blood pressure. The respiratory system is dependent on the cardiovascular system to transport gases to and from cells, and the respiratory system assists venous return.

Study Questions

1. State the location and functions of the heart. (p. 225)
2. Describe the wall and coverings of the heart. (p. 226)
3. Name the chambers and valves of the heart. Trace the path of blood through the heart. (pp. 226–27)
4. Describe the coronary circuit, and discuss several coronary circuit disorders. (p. 228)
5. Describe the conduction system of the heart and an electrocardiogram. (pp. 230–31)
6. Describe the cardiac cycle (using the terms systole and diastole), and explain the heart sounds. (p. 232)
7. What is cardiac output (CO)? What two factors determine CO? How are these factors regulated? (pp. 232–33)
8. What types of blood vessels are in the body? Discuss their structure and function. (pp. 234–35)
9. What factors determine velocity of blood flow? Blood pressure? In what vessel is blood pressure highest? Lowest? (p. 236)
10. What mechanisms assist venous return to the heart? Discuss nervous and hormonal control of blood pressure. (pp. 237–38)
11. What is pulse? How do you take a person's pulse? How do you take a person's blood pressure? What does a blood pressure of 120/80 mean? (pp. 238–39)
12. What are hypertension, stroke, aneurysm, and congestive heart failure? (p. 239)
13. Trace the path of blood from the superior mesenteric artery to the aorta, indicating which of the vessels are in the systemic circuit and which are in the pulmonary circuit. (pp. 242–44)
14. Give examples to show that the cardiovascular system functions to maintain homeostasis and that interactions with other systems help it and the other systems maintain homeostasis. (p. 248)

Objective Questions

Fill in the blanks.

1. When the left ventricle contracts, blood enters the _____ .
2. The right side of the heart pumps blood to the _____ .
3. The _____ node is known as the pacemaker.
4. Arteries are blood vessels that take blood _____ the heart.
5. The blood vessels that serve the heart are the _____ arteries and veins.
6. The major blood vessels taking blood to and from the arms are the _____ arteries and veins. Those taking blood to and from the legs are the _____ arteries and veins.
7. Blood vessels to the brain end in a circular path known as the _____ .
8. The human body contains a hepatic portal system that takes blood from the _____ to the _____ .
9. The force of blood against the walls of a vessel is termed _____ .
10. Blood moves in arteries due to _____ and in veins movement is assisted by _____ .
11. The blood pressure recorded when the left ventricle contracts is called the _____ pressure, and the pressure recorded when the left ventricle relaxes is called the _____ pressure.
12. The two factors that affect blood pressure are _____ and _____ .
13. In the fetus, the opening between the two atria is called the _____ , and the connection between the pulmonary artery and the aorta is called the _____ .
14. The valve between the left atrium and left ventricle is the _____ , or mitral, valve.

Medical Terminology Reinforcement Exercise

Consult Appendix B for help in pronouncing and analyzing the meaning of the terms that follow.

1. cryocardioplegia (kri-o-kar″de-o-ple′je-uh)
2. echocardiography (ek″o-kar″de-og′ruh-fe)
3. percutaneous transluminal coronary angioplasty (per″kyū-ta′ne-us trans″lu″mĭ-nal kor′ŏ-nā-re an′je-o-plas″te)
4. vasoconstriction (vas″o-kon-strik′shun)
5. valvuloplasty (val′vu-lo-plas″te)
6. antihypertensive (an″tĭ-hi″per-ten′siv)
7. arrhythmia (uh-rith′me-uh)
8. thromboendarterectomy (throm″bo-end″ar-ter-ek′to-me)
9. cardiovalvulitis (kar′de-o-val-yū-li′tis)
10. vasospasm (va′-so-spazm)
11. pericardiocentesis (pĕr-ĭ-kar′de-o-sen-te′sis)
12. ventriculotomy (ven-trik-yū-lot′o-me)
13. phlebectasia (fleb-ek-ta′ze-uh)
14. myocardiorrhaphy (mi′o-kar-de-or′uh-fe)

Website Link

Visit the Student Edition of the Online Learning Center at http://www.mhhe.com/maderap5 for additional quizzes, interactive learning exercises, and other study tools.

The Lymphatic System and Body Defenses

In this falsely colored TEM, a cancer cell (blue nucleus) is being attacked by T lymphocytes (green).

chapter outline & learning objectives

After you have studied this chapter, you should be able to:

13.1 Lymphatic System

The **lymphatic system** consists of lymphatic vessels and the lymphatic organs. This system, which is closely associated with the cardiovascular system, has three main functions that contribute to homeostasis:

1. **Fluid balance.** The lymphatic system takes up excess tissue fluid and returns it to the bloodstream. Recall that lymphatic capillaries lie very near blood capillaries, and they serve as an auxiliary way to take up fluid that has exited the blood capillaries (see Fig. 11.7).
2. **Fat absorption.** The lymphatic system absorbs fats from the digestive tract and transports them to the bloodstream. Special lymphatic capillaries called lacteals are located in the intestinal villi (see Fig. 15.7). This function ensures the absorption of dietary lipids as well as lipid-soluble vitamins.
3. **Defense.** The lymphatic system helps defend the body against disease. This function is carried out by the white blood cells present in lymphatic vessels and lymphatic organs.

Lymphatic Vessels

Lymphatic vessels form a one-way system that begins with lymphatic capillaries. Most regions of the body are richly supplied with lymphatic capillaries, tiny, closed-ended vessels whose walls consist of simple squamous epithelium (Fig. 13.1). Lymphatic capillaries take up excess tissue fluid. Tissue fluid is mostly water, but it also contains solutes (e.g., nutrients, electrolytes, and oxygen) derived from plasma and cellular products (i.e., hormones, enzymes, and wastes) secreted by cells. These all become **lymph,** the fluid inside lymphatic vessels.

The lymphatic capillaries join to form lymphatic vessels that merge before entering one of two ducts: the thoracic duct or the right lymphatic duct. The larger, thoracic duct returns lymph collected from the body below the thorax and the left arm and left side of the head and neck into the left subclavian vein. The right lymphatic duct returns lymph from the right arm and right side of the head and neck into the right subclavian vein.

The construction of the larger lymphatic vessels is similar to that of cardiovascular veins, including the presence of valves. The movement of lymph within lymphatic capillaries is largely dependent upon skeletal muscle contraction. Lymph forced through lymphatic vessels as a result of muscular compression is prevented from flowing backward by one-way valves.

Edema is localized swelling caused by the accumulation of tissue fluid that has not been collected by the lymphatic system. This can happen if too much tissue fluid is made and/or if not enough of it is drained away. Edema can lead to tissue damage and eventual death, illustrating the importance of the function of the lymphatic system. The fat absorption and defense functions of the lymphatic system are equally im-

Figure 13.1 The lymphatic system. Lymphatic vessels drain excess fluid from the tissues and return it to the cardiovascular system. The enlargement shows that lymphatic vessels, like cardiovascular veins, have valves to prevent backward flow. The tonsils, spleen, thymus gland, and red bone marrow are among those lymphatic organs that assist immunity.

portant. Unfortunately, cancer cells sometimes enter lymphatic vessels and move undetected to other regions of the body where they produce secondary tumors. In this way, the lymphatic system sometimes assists metastasis, the spread of cancer far from its place of origin.

13.2 Organs, Tissues, and Cells of the Immune System

The **immune system,** which plays an important role in keeping us healthy, consists of a network of lymphatic organs, tissues, and cells as well as products of these cells, including antibodies and regulatory agents. **Immunity** is the ability to react to antigens so that the body remains free of disease. **Disease,** a state of homeostatic imbalance, can be due to infection and/or to the failure of the immune system to function properly.

Primary Lymphatic Organs

Lymphatic (lymphoid) organs contain large numbers of lymphocytes, the type of white blood cell that plays a pivotal role in immunity. The *primary lymphatic organs* are the red bone marrow and the thymus gland (Fig. 13.2, *left*). Lymphocytes originate and/or mature in these organs.

Red Bone Marrow

Red bone marrow is the site of stem cells that are ever capable of dividing and producing blood cells. Some of these cells become the various types of white blood cells: neutrophils, eosinophils, basophils, lymphocytes, and monocytes (Fig. 13.3).

In a child, most bones have red bone marrow, but in an adult it is limited to the sternum, vertebrae, ribs, part of the pelvic girdle, and the proximal heads of the humerus and femur.

The red bone marrow consists of a network of reticular tissue fibers, which support the stem cells and their progeny. They are packed around thin-walled sinuses filled with venous blood. Differentiated blood cells enter the bloodstream at these sinuses.

Lymphocytes differentiate into the B lymphocytes and the T lymphocytes. Bone marrow is not only the source of B lymphocytes, but also the place where B lymphocytes mature. T lymphocytes mature in the thymus.

Figure 13.2 The lymphatic organs. *Left:* The red bone marrow and thymus gland are the primary lymphatic organs. *Right:* Lymph nodes and the spleen, as well as other lymphatic organs such as the tonsils, are secondary lymphatic organs.

Figure 13.3 The five types of white blood cells. These cell types differ according to structure and function. The frequency of each type of cell is given as a percentage of the total.

a. Neutrophil
40–70%
Phagocytizes primarily bacteria

b. Eosinophil
1–4%
Phagocytizes and destroys antigen-antibody complexes

c. Basophil
0–1%
Releases histamine when stimulated

d. Lymphocyte
20–45%
B type produces antibodies in blood and lymph; T type kills virus-containing cells.

e. Monocyte
4–8%
Becomes macrophage—phagocytizes bacteria and viruses

Medical Focus

Bone Marrow Transplants

Cancer patients require a bone marrow transplant when high doses of chemotherapy and radiation have killed off cancerous cells but have also destroyed the patient's bone marrow. A bone marrow transplant allows the patient to receive much higher doses of chemotherapy to improve the chances of curing the disease. However, without healthy bone marrow, the patient will die.

In autologous marrow transplants, the marrow is removed from the patient before cancer therapy begins; the marrow is stored alive, and then it is returned to the patient. In allogenic marrow transplants, the marrow is donated by someone else. As with any other allogenic transplant, bone marrow transplants require careful matching of donor and recipient tissue and administration of drugs to suppress the immune system and avoid transplant rejection.

Bone marrow for a transplant can be obtained in a doctor's office. With the donor lying on his or her stomach or side, a large needle is positioned perpendicular to the pelvis and pushed into the bone, using a screwing motion. When the needle is deep enough in the bone to be anchored, a syringe is attached in order to remove a sample of bone marrow. Then, to perform the transplant, the marrow, which has been treated as necessary, is then injected into the recipient's bloodstream. The bone marrow stem cells are expected to migrate to the recipient's marrow and produce new formed elements.

If available, umbilical cord blood can also be used for transplantation. The immature cells found in cord blood are easier to match between nonrelated people [than are bone marrow cells.] When cord blood is used, there is also a far less chance of the recipient rejecting the transplant.

Thymus Gland

The soft, bilobed **thymus gland** is located in the thoracic cavity between the trachea and the sternum superior to the heart. The thymus varies in size, but it is largest in children and shrinks as we get older. Connective tissue divides the thymus into lobules, which are filled with lymphocytes. The thymus gland produces thymic hormones, such as thymosin, that are thought to aid in the maturation of T lymphocytes. Thymosin may also have other functions in immunity.

Immature T lymphocytes migrate from the bone marrow through the bloodstream to the thymus, where they mature. Only about 5% of these cells ever leave the thymus. These T lymphocytes have survived a critical test: If any show the ability to react with "self" cells, they die. If they have potential to attack a foreign cell, they leave the thymus.

The thymus is absolutely critical to immunity; without a thymus, the body does not reject foreign tissues, blood lymphocyte levels are drastically reduced, and the body's response to most antigens is poor or absent.

Lymph Nodes and Illnesses

The internal structure of a lymph node is designed to filter out any foreign material from the lymph. An infection that causes swelling and tenderness of nearby lymph nodes is called **lymphadenitis.** If the infection is not contained, **lymphangitis,** an infection of the lymphatic vessels, may result. Red streaks can be seen through the skin, indicating that the infection may spread to the bloodstream.

Failure of the lymphatic vessels to remove tissue fluid results in an accumulation of tissue fluid, a condition called edema. A dramatic example of edema occurs when a parasitic roundworm clogs the lymphatic vessels, resulting in tremendous swelling of the arm, leg, or external genitals, a condition called **elephantiasis.** Edema can also be due to a low osmotic pressure of the blood, as when plasma proteins are excreted by the kidneys instead of being retained in the blood. Then extra tissue fluid forms, and lymphatic vessels may not be able to absorb it all.

Pulmonary edema is a life-threatening condition associated with congestive heart failure. Due to a weak heart, blood backs up in the pulmonary circulation, causing an increase in blood pressure, which leads to excess tissue fluid. The walls of the air sacs in the lungs may rupture, and the patient may suffocate.

When surgery is used to diagnose or treat cancer, regional lymph nodes are usually removed for examination. The presence or absence of tumor cells in the nodes can be used to determine how far the disease has spread and to aid in the decision concerning additional treatment, such as radiation or chemotherapy. Cancer of lymphatic tissue is called **lymphoma.** In **Hodgkin disease,** billions of lymphoma cells create swollen lymph nodes in the neck. The lymphoma cells can migrate and grow in the spleen, liver, and bone marrow. The prognosis is good, however, if Hodgkin disease is diagnosed early.

Secondary Lymphatic Organs

The secondary lymphatic organs are the spleen, the lymph nodes, and other organs, such as the tonsils, Peyer patches, and the appendix. All the secondary organs are places where lymphocytes encounter and bind with antigens, after which they proliferate and become actively engaged cells.

Spleen

The **spleen,** the largest lymphatic organ, is located in the upper left region of the abdominal cavity posterior to the stomach. Connective tissue divides the spleen into partial compartments, each of which contains tissue known as white pulp and red pulp (see Fig. 13.2). The white pulp contains a concentration of lymphocytes; the red pulp, which surrounds venous sinuses, is involved in filtering the blood. Blood entering the spleen must pass through the sinuses before exiting. Lymphocytes and macrophages react to pathogens, and macrophages engulf debris and also remove any old, worn-out red blood cells.

The spleen's outer capsule is relatively thin, and an infection or a blow can cause the spleen to burst. Although the spleen's functions are replaced by other organs, a person without a spleen is often slightly more susceptible to infections and may have to receive antibiotic therapy indefinitely.

Lymph Nodes

Lymph nodes, which are small, ovoid structures, occur along lymphatic vessels. Connective tissue forms the capsule of a lymph node and also divides the organ into compartments (see Fig. 13.2). Each compartment contains a nodule packed with B lymphocytes and a sinus that increases in size toward the center of the node. As lymph courses through the sinuses, it is filtered by macrophages, which engulf pathogens and debris. T lymphocytes, also present in sinuses, fight infections and attack cancer cells.

Each portion of the anterior cavity (see Fig 1.5) contains superficial and deep lymph nodes, named for their location. For example, inguinal nodes are in the groin, and axillary nodes are in the armpits. Physicians often feel for the presence of swollen, tender lymph nodes in the neck as evidence that the body is fighting an infection. This is a noninvasive, preliminary way to help make such a diagnosis.

Lymphatic Nodules

Lymphatic nodules are concentrations of lymphatic tissue not surrounded by a capsule. The **tonsils** are patches of lymphatic tissue located in a ring about the pharynx (see Fig. 14.2). The tonsils perform the same functions as lymph nodes, but because of their location, they are the first to encounter pathogens and antigens that enter the body by way of the nose and mouth.

Peyer patches are located in the intestinal wall, and the **appendix.** These structures encounter pathogens that enter the body by way of the intestinal tract.

visual focus

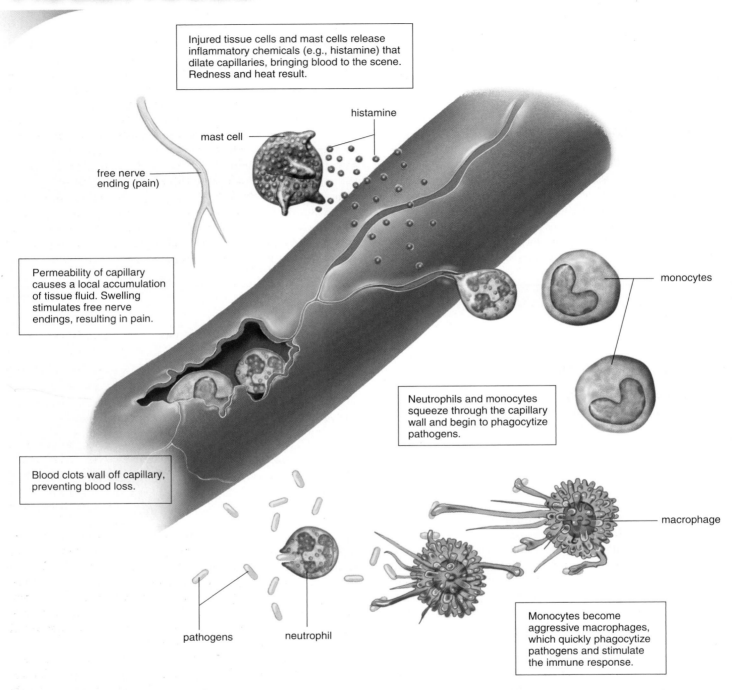

Injured tissue cells and mast cells release inflammatory chemicals (e.g., histamine) that dilate capillaries, bringing blood to the scene. Redness and heat result.

histamine

mast cell

free nerve ending (pain)

Permeability of capillary causes a local accumulation of tissue fluid. Swelling stimulates free nerve endings, resulting in pain.

monocytes

Neutrophils and monocytes squeeze through the capillary wall and begin to phagocytize pathogens.

Blood clots wall off capillary, preventing blood loss.

macrophage

pathogens   neutrophil

Monocytes become aggressive macrophages, which quickly phagocytize pathogens and stimulate the immune response.

Figure 13.4 Inflammatory reaction. Mast cells, which are related to basophils, a type of white blood cell, are involved in the inflammatory reaction. When a blood vessel is injured, mast cells release substances such as histamine. Histamine dilates blood vessels and increases their permeability so that tissue fluid leaks from the vessel. Swelling in the area stimulates pain receptors (free nerve endings). Neutrophils and monocytes (which become macrophages) squeeze through the capillary wall. These white blood cells begin to phagocytize pathogens (e.g., disease-causing viruses and bacteria), especially those combined with antibodies. Blood clotting seals off the capillary, preventing blood loss.

13.3 Nonspecific and Specific Defenses

Immunity includes nonspecific defenses and specific defenses. The four types of nonspecific defenses—barriers to entry, the inflammatory reaction, natural killer cells, and protective proteins—are effective against many types of infectious agents. Specific defenses are effective against a particular infectious agent.

Nonspecific Defenses

Barriers to Entry

The *skin and mucous membranes* lining the respiratory, digestive, and urinary tracts serve as mechanical barriers to entry by pathogens. The *secretions of oil glands* contain chemicals that weaken or kill certain bacteria on the skin. The *ciliated cells* that line the upper respiratory tract sweep mucus and trapped particles up into the throat, where they can be swallowed or expectorated (coughed out). The *acid pH of the stomach* inhibits the growth of or kills many types of bacteria. The *microbes that normally reside* in the intestine and other areas, such as the vagina, prevent pathogens from taking up residence.

Inflammatory Reaction

Whenever tissue is damaged by physical or chemical agents or by pathogens, a series of events occurs that is known as the **inflammatory reaction.** Figure 13.4 illustrates the participants in the inflammatory reaction. **Mast cells,** which occur in tissues, resemble basophils, one of the types of white cells found in the blood.

The inflamed area has four outward signs: redness, heat, swelling, and pain. All of these signs are due to capillary changes in the damaged area. Chemical mediators, such as **histamine,** released by damaged tissue cells and mast cells, cause the capillaries to dilate and become more permeable. Excess blood flow due to enlarged capillaries causes the skin to redden and become warm. Increased permeability of capillaries allows proteins and fluids to escape into the tissues, resulting in swelling. The swollen area stimulates free nerve endings, causing the sensation of pain.

Migration of phagocytes, namely neutrophils and monocytes, also occurs during the inflammatory reaction. Neutrophils and monocytes are amoeboid and can change shape to squeeze through capillary walls and enter tissue fluid. After monocytes appear on the scene, they differentiate into **macrophages,** large phagocytic cells that are able to devour as many as a hundred pathogens and still survive. Some tissues, particularly connective tissue, have resident macrophages, which routinely act as scavengers, devouring old blood cells, bits of dead tissue, and other debris. Macrophages also release colony-stimulating factors, which

pass by way of blood to the red bone marrow, where the factors stimulate the production and the release of white blood cells, primarily neutrophils. Endocytic vesicles form when neutrophils and macrophages engulf pathogens. When the vesicle combines with a lysosome, a cellular organelle, the pathogen is destroyed by hydrolytic enzymes. As the infection is being overcome, some phagocytes die. These—along with dead tissue cells, dead bacteria, and living white blood cells—form **pus,** a whitish material. The presence of pus indicates that the body is trying to overcome an infection.

Sometimes an inflammation persists, and the result is chronic inflammation that is often treated by administering anti-inflammatory agents such as aspirin, ibuprofen, or cortisone. These medications act against the chemical mediators released by the white blood cells in the damaged area.

The inflammatory reaction can be accompanied by other responses to the injury. A blood clot can form to seal a break in a blood vessel. The antigens along with the released chemical mediators can move through the tissue fluid and lymph to the lymph nodes. Now lymphocytes mount a specific defense to the infection as described on page 260.

Natural Killer Cells

Natural killer (NK) cells kill virus-infected cells and tumor cells by cell-to-cell contact. They are large, granular lymphocytes with no specificity and no memory. Their number is not increased by prior exposure to any kind of cell.

Protective Proteins

The **complement system,** often simply called complement, is composed of a number of blood plasma proteins designated by the letter C and a subscript. A limited amount of activated complement protein is needed because a cascade effect occurs: Each activated protein in a series is capable of activating many other proteins.

The complement proteins are activated when pathogens enter the body. The proteins "complement" certain immune responses, which accounts for their name. For example, they are involved in and amplify the inflammatory response because complement proteins attract phagocytes to the scene. Some complement proteins bind to the surface of pathogens already coated with antibodies, which ensures that the pathogens will be phagocytized by a neutrophil or macrophage.

Certain other complement proteins join to form a membrane attack complex that produces holes in the walls and plasma membranes of bacteria. Fluids and salts then enter the bacterial cell to the point that it bursts.

Interferon is a protein produced by virus-infected cells. Interferon binds to receptors of noninfected cells, causing them to prepare for possible attack by producing substances that interfere with viral replication. Interferon is specific to the species; therefore, only human interferon can be used in humans.

Specific Defenses

Specific defenses respond to **antigens,** which are surface molecules the immune system can recognize as foreign. Because we do not ordinarily become immune to our own cells, it is said that the immune system is able to distinguish "self" from "nonself." Lymphocytes are capable of recognizing an antigen because they have **antigen receptors**—plasma membrane receptor proteins that combine with a specific antigen.

Immunity usually lasts for some time. For example, once we recover from the measles, we usually do not get the illness a second time. Immunity is primarily the result of the action of the **B lymphocytes** and the **T lymphocytes.** B lymphocytes mature in the *b*one marrow,[1] and T lymphocytes mature in the *t*hymus gland. B lymphocytes, also called B cells, give rise to plasma cells, which produce antibodies. **Antibodies** are proteins shaped like the antigen receptor and capable of combining with and neutralizing a specific antigen. These antibodies are secreted into the blood, lymph, and other body fluids. In contrast, T lymphocytes, also called T cells, do not produce antibodies. Instead, certain T cells directly attack cells that bear nonself proteins. Other T cells regulate the immune response.

B Cells and Antibody-Mediated Immunity

When a B cell encounters a specific antigen, it is activated to divide many times. Most of the resulting cells are plasma cells. A **plasma cell** is a mature B cell that mass-produces antibodies against a specific antigen. The **clonal selection theory** states that the antigen selects which lymphocyte will undergo clonal expansion and produce plasma cells bearing the same type of antigen receptor. Notice in Figure 13.5 that different types of antigen receptors are represented by color. The B cell with blue receptors undergoes clonal expansion because a specific antigen (red dots) is present and binds to its receptors. B cells are stimulated to divide and become plasma cells by helper T-cell secretions called cytokines, as discussed later in this section. Some members of the clone become memory cells, which are the means by which long-term immunity is possible. If the same antigen enters the system again, **memory B cells** quickly divide and give rise to more lymphocytes capable of quickly producing antibodies.

Once the threat of an infection has passed, the development of new plasma cells ceases, and those present undergo apoptosis. **Apoptosis** is a process of programmed cell death

---

[1] Historically, the B stands for bursa of Fabricius, an organ in the chicken where these cells were first identified.

Figure 13.5 Clonal selection theory as it applies to B cells.

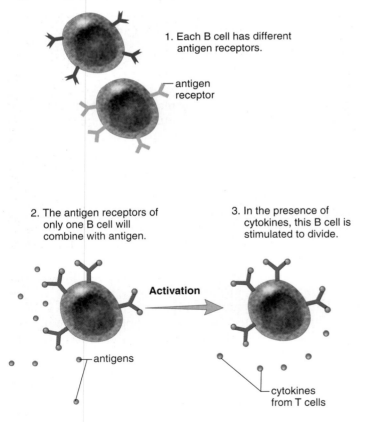

1. Each B cell has different antigen receptors.

antigen receptor

2. The antigen receptors of only one B cell will combine with antigen.

Activation

antigens

3. In the presence of cytokines, this B cell is stimulated to divide.

cytokines from T cells

memory B cell

Clonal expansion

plasma cell

4. Chosen B cell gives rise to memory cells and antibody-producing plasma cells.

Apoptosis

5. After infection passes, plasma cells undergo apoptosis.

antibody

involving a cascade of specific cellular events leading to the death and destruction of the cell.

Defense by B cells is called **antibody-mediated immunity** because the various types of B cells produce antibodies. It is also called humoral immunity because these antibodies are present in blood and lymph. A humor is any fluid normally occurring in the body.

Structure of IgG

The most common type of antibody is IgG, a Y-shaped protein molecule with two arms. Each arm has a "heavy" (long) polypeptide chain and a "light" (short) polypeptide chain. These chains have constant regions, where the sequence of amino acids is set, and variable regions, where the sequence of amino acids varies between antibodies (Fig. 13.6). The constant regions are not identical among all the antibodies. Instead, they are almost the same within different classes of antibodies. The variable regions form an antigen-binding site, and their shape is specific to a particular antigen. The antigen combines with the antibody at the antigen-binding site in a lock-and-key manner.

The antigen-antibody reaction can take several forms, but quite often the reaction produces complexes of antigens combined with antibodies. Such antigen-antibody complexes, sometimes called immune complexes, mark the antigens for destruction. For example, an antigen-antibody complex may be engulfed by neutrophils or macrophages, or it may activate complement. Complement makes pathogens more susceptible to phagocytosis, as discussed previously.

Other Types of Antibodies

There are five different classes of circulating antibody proteins, or **immunoglobulins (Igs)** (Table 13.1). IgG antibodies are the major type in blood, and lesser amounts are also found in lymph and tissue fluid. IgG antibodies bind to pathogens and their toxins. IgM antibodies are pentamers, meaning that they contain five of the Y-shaped structures shown in Figure 13.6a. These antibodies appear in blood soon after an infection begins and disappear before it is over. They are good activators of the complement system. IgA anti-

bodies are monomers or dimers containing two Y-shaped structures. They are the main type of antibody found in body secretions. They bind to pathogens before they reach the bloodstream. The main function of IgD molecules seems to be to serve as antigen receptors on immature B cells. IgE antibodies are responsible for immediate allergic responses.

Figure 13.6 Structure of the most common antibody (IgG). **a.** An IgG antibody contains two heavy (long) polypeptide chains and two light (short) chains arranged so that there are two variable regions, where a particular antigen is capable of binding with an antibody (V = variable region, C = constant region). **b.** Computer model of an antibody molecule. The antigen combines with the two side branches.

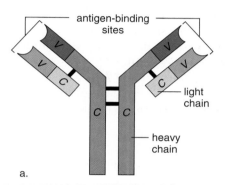

antigen-binding sites

light chain

heavy chain

a.

b.

Table 13.1	Antibodies	
Classes	**Presence**	**Function**
IgG	Main antibody type in circulation	Binds to pathogens, activates complement proteins, and enhances phagocytosis
IgM	Antibody type found in circulation; largest antibody	Activates complement proteins; clumps cells
IgA	Main antibody type in secretions such as saliva and milk	Prevents pathogens from attaching to epithelial cells in digestive and respiratory tract
IgD	Antibody type found on surface of virgin B cells	Presence signifies readiness of B cell
IgE	Antibody type found as antigen receptors on basophils in blood and on mast cells in tissues	Responsible for immediate allergic response and protection against certain parasitic infections

T Cells and Cell-Mediated Immunity

When T cells leave the thymus, they have unique antigen receptors just as B cells do. Unlike B cells, however, T cells are unable to recognize an antigen present in lymph, blood, or the tissues without help. The antigen must be presented to them by an **antigen-presenting cell (APC).** When an APC presents a viral or cancer cell antigen, the antigen is first linked to a major histocompatibility complex (MHC) protein in the plasma membrane.

Human MHC proteins are called **HLA (human leukocyte-associated) antigens.** Because they mark the cell as belonging to a particular individual, HLA antigens are self proteins. The importance of self proteins in plasma membranes was first recognized when it was discovered that they contribute to the specificity of tissues and make it difficult to transplant tissue from one human to another. In other words, when the donor and the recipient are histo (tissue)-compatible, a transplant is more likely to be successful.

Figure 13.7 shows a macrophage presenting an antigen, represented by a red circle, to a particular T cell. This T cell has the type of antigen receptor that will combine with this specific antigen. In the figure, the different types of antigen receptors are represented by color. Presentation of the antigen leads to activation of the T cell. An activated T cell produces cytokines and undergoes clonal expansion. **Cytokines** are signaling chemicals that stimulate various immune cells (e.g., macrophages, B cells, and other T cells) to perform their functions. Many copies of the activated T cell are produced during clonal expansion. They destroy any cell, such as a virus-infected cell or a cancer cell, that displays the antigen presented earlier.

As the illness disappears, the immune reaction wanes, and fewer cytokines are produced. Now, the activated T cells become susceptible to apoptosis. As mentioned previously, apoptosis is programmed cell death that contributes to homeostasis by regulating the number of cells present in an organ, or in this

Figure 13.7 Clonal selection theory as it applies to cytotoxic T cells.

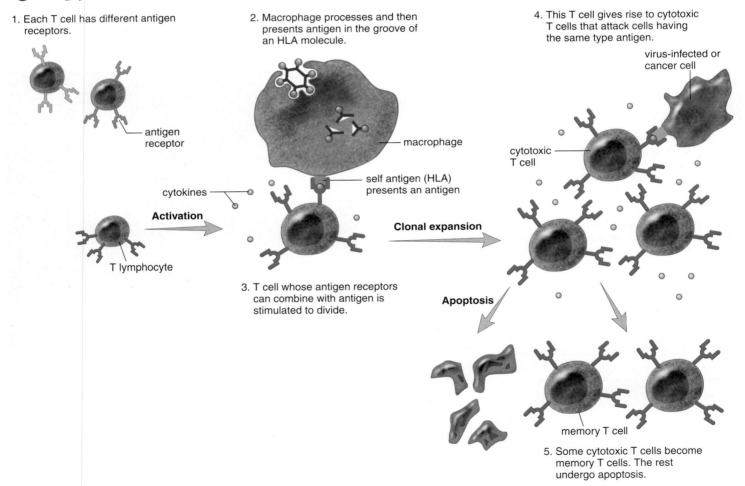

1. Each T cell has different antigen receptors.

antigen receptor

cytokines

Activation

T lymphocyte

2. Macrophage processes and then presents antigen in the groove of an HLA molecule.

macrophage

self antigen (HLA) presents an antigen

3. T cell whose antigen receptors can combine with antigen is stimulated to divide.

Clonal expansion

4. This T cell gives rise to cytotoxic T cells that attack cells having the same type antigen.

virus-infected or cancer cell

cytotoxic T cell

Apoptosis

memory T cell

5. Some cytotoxic T cells become memory T cells. The rest undergo apoptosis.

case, in the immune system. When apoptosis does not occur as it should, T-cell cancers (i.e., lymphomas and leukemias) can result.

Apoptosis also occurs in the thymus as T cells are maturing. Any T cell that has the potential to destroy the body's own cells undergoes suicide.

Types of T Cells

The two main types of T cells are cytotoxic T cells and helper T cells. **Cytotoxic T (T_c) cells** can bring about the destruction of antigen-bearing cells, such as virus-infected or cancer cells. Cancer cells also have nonself proteins.

Cytotoxic T cells have storage vacuoles containing perforin molecules. **Perforin** molecules perforate a plasma membrane, forming a pore that allows water and salts to enter. The cell then swells and eventually bursts. Cytotoxic T cells are responsible for so-called **cell-mediated immunity** (Fig. 13.8).

Helper T (T_h) cells regulate immunity by secreting cytokines, the chemicals that enhance the response of other immune cells. Because HIV, the virus that causes AIDS, infects helper T cells and certain other cells of the immune system, it inactivates the immune response.

Notice in Figure 13.7 that a few of the clonally expanded T cells are memory T cells. They remain in the body and can jump-start an immune reaction to an antigen previously present in the body.

Cytokines and Immunity

Whenever cancer develops, it is possible that cytotoxic T cells have not been activated. With this possibility in mind, cytokines have been used as immunotherapeutic drugs to enhance the ability of T cells to fight cancer. Interferon, discussed on page 259, and also **interleukins,** which are cytokines produced by various white blood cells, are also being administered for this purpose.

Figure 13.8 Cell-mediated immunity. **a.** How a cytotoxic T (T_c) cell destroys a virus-infected or cancer cell. **b.** The scanning electron micrograph shows T_c cells attacking and destroying a cancer cell (target cell).

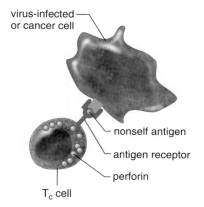

virus-infected or cancer cell
nonself antigen
antigen receptor
perforin
T_c cell

1. Activated T_c cell binds with nonself antigen presented by virus-infected or cancer cell.

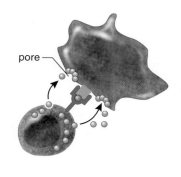

pore

2. T_c cell discharges perforin molecules, which combine to form pores in target cell's plasma membrane.

water and salts

3. Water and salts enter virus-infected or cancer cell.

4. The target cell bursts.

a. Cytotoxic (T_c) cell attacks a target cell.

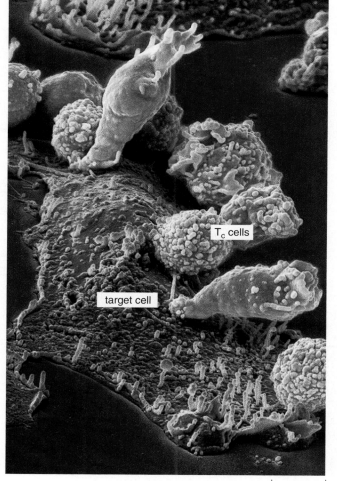

T_c cells

target cell

b. Scanning electron micrograph

1 μm

AIDS Epidemic

Acquired immunodeficiency syndrome (AIDS) is caused by a group of related retroviruses known as HIV (human immunodeficiency viruses). In the United States, AIDS is usually caused by HIV-1, which enters a host by attaching itself to a plasma protein called a CD4 receptor. HIV-1 infects helper T cells, the type of lymphocyte that stimulates B cells to produce antibodies and cytotoxic T cells to destroy virus-infected cells. Macrophages, which present antigens to helper T cells and thereby stimulate them, are also under attack.

HIV is a retrovirus, meaning that its genetic material consists of RNA instead of DNA. Once inside the host cell, HIV uses a special enzyme called reverse transcriptase to make a DNA copy (called cDNA) of its genetic material. Now cDNA integrates into a host chromosome, where it directs the production of more viral RNA. Each strand of viral RNA brings about synthesis of an outer protein coat called a capsid. The viral enzyme protease is necessary to the formation of capsids. Capsids assemble with RNA strands to form viruses, which bud from the host cell.

Transmission of AIDS

HIV infection spreads when infected cells in body secretions, such as semen, and in blood are passed to another individual. To date, as many as 64 million people worldwide may have contracted HIV, and almost 22 million have died. A new infection is believed

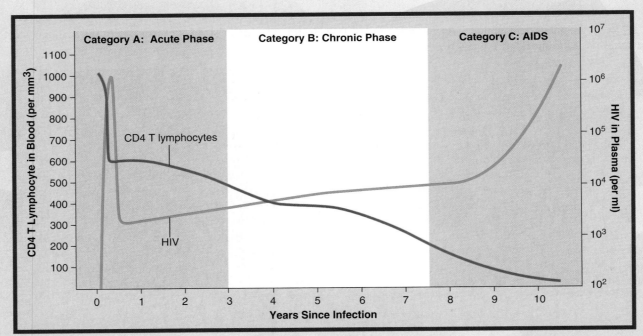

Figure 13A Stages of an HIV infection. In category A individuals, the number of HIV in plasma rises upon infection and then falls. The number of CD4 T lymphocytes falls, but stays above 400 per mm³. In category B individuals, the number of HIV in plasma is slowly rising, and the number of T lymphocytes is decreasing. In category C individuals, the number of HIV in plasma rises dramatically as the number of T lymphocytes falls below 200 per mm³.

to occur every 15 seconds, the majority in heterosexuals. HIV infections are not distributed equally throughout the world. Most infected people live in Africa (66%) where the infection first began, but new infections are now occurring at the fastest rate in Southeast Asia and the Indian subcontinent.

HIV is transmitted by sexual contact with an infected person, including vaginal or rectal intercourse and oral/genital contact. Also, needle-sharing among intravenous drug users is high-risk behavior. Babies born to HIV-infected women may become infected before or during birth, or through breast-feeding after birth.

HIV first spread through the homosexual community, and male-to-male sexual contact still accounts for the largest percentage of new AIDS cases in the United States. But the largest increases in HIV infections are occurring through heterosexual contact or by intravenous drug use. Now, women account for 20% of all newly diagnosed cases of AIDS. The rise in the incidence of AIDS among women of reproductive age is paralleled by a rise in the incidence of AIDS in children younger than 13.

Phases of an HIV Infection

The Centers for Disease Control and Prevention recognize three stages of an HIV-1 infection, called categories A, B, and C. During the category A stage, the helper T-lymphocyte count is 500 per mm^3 or greater (Fig. 13A). For a period of time after the initial infection with HIV, people don't usually have any symptoms at all. A few (1–2%) do have mononucleosis-like symptoms that may include fever, chills, aches, swollen lymph nodes, and an itchy rash. These symptoms disappear, however, and no other symptoms appear for quite some time. Although there are no symptoms, the person is highly infectious. Despite the presence of a large number of viruses in the plasma, the HIV blood test is not yet positive because it tests for the presence of antibodies and not for the presence of HIV itself. This means that HIV can still be transmitted before the HIV blood test is positive.

Several months to several years after a nontreated infection, the individual will probably progress to category B, in which the helper T-lymphocyte count is 200 to 499 per mm^3. During this stage, the patient may experience swollen lymph nodes in the neck, armpits, or groin that persist for three months or more. Other symptoms that indicate category B are severe fatigue not related to exercise or drug use; unexplained persistent or recurrent fevers, often with night sweats; persistent cough not associated with smoking, a cold, or the flu; and persistent diarrhea.

The development of non-life-threatening but recurrent infections is a signal that the disease is progressing. One possible infection is thrush, a fungal infection that is identified by the presence of white spots and ulcers on the tongue and inside the mouth. The fungus may also spread to the vagina, resulting in a chronic infection there. Another frequent infection is herpes simplex, with painful and persistent sores on the skin surrounding the anus, the genital area, and/or the mouth.

Previously, the majority of infected persons proceeded to category C, in which the helper T-lymphocyte count is below 200 per mm^3 and the lymph nodes degenerate. The patient is now suffering from AIDS, characterized by severe weight loss and weakness due to persistent diarrhea and coughing, and will most likely contract an opportunistic infection. An **opportunistic infection** is one that only has the opportunity to occur because the immune system is severely weakened. Persons with AIDS die from one or more opportunistic diseases, such as *Pneumocystis carinii* pneumonia, *Mycobacterium tuberculosis*, toxoplasmic encephalitis, Kaposi's sarcoma, or invasive cervical cancer. This last condition has been added to the list because the incidence of AIDS has now increased in women.

Treatment for AIDS

Therapy usually consists of combining two drugs that inhibit reverse transcriptase with another that inhibits protease, an enzyme needed for formation of a viral capsid. This multidrug therapy, when taken according to the manner prescribed, usually seems to prevent mutation of the virus to a resistant strain. The sooner drug therapy begins after infection, the better the chances that the immune system will not be destroyed by HIV. Also, medication must be continued indefinitely. Unfortunately, an HIV strain resistant to all known drugs has been reported, and persons who become infected with this strain have no drug therapy available to them.

The likelihood of transmission from mother to child at birth can be lessened if the mother takes an inhibitor of reverse transcriptase called AZT and if the child is delivered by cesarean section.

Many investigators are working on a vaccine for AIDS. Some are trying to develop a vaccine in the traditional way. Others are working on subunit vaccines that utilize just a single HIV protein as the vaccine. So far, no method has resulted in sufficient antibodies to keep an infection at bay. After many clinical trials, none too successful, most investigators now agree that a combination of various vaccines may be the best strategy to bring about a response in both B lymphocytes and cytotoxic T cells.

13.4 Induced Immunity

Immunity occurs naturally through infection or is brought about artificially (induced) by medical intervention. The two types of induced immunity are active and passive. In **active immunity,** the individual alone produces antibodies against an antigen; in **passive immunity,** the individual is given prepared antibodies via an injection.

Active Immunity

Active immunity sometimes develops naturally after a person is infected with a pathogen. However, active immunity is often induced when a person is well so that future infection will not take place. To prevent infections, people are immunized artificially against them. The United States is committed to immunizing all children against the common types of childhood disease, as discussed in the Medical Focus on page 267.

Immunization involves the use of **vaccines,** substances that contain an antigen to which the immune system responds. Traditionally, vaccines are the pathogens themselves, or their products, that have been treated so they are no longer virulent (able to cause disease). Today, it is possible to genetically engineer bacteria to mass-produce a protein from pathogens, and this protein can be used as a vaccine. This method has now produced a vaccine against hepatitis B, a viral-induced disease, and is being used to prepare a vaccine against malaria, a protozoan-induced disease.

After a vaccine is given, it is possible to follow an immune response by determining the amount of antibody present in a sample of plasma—this is called the **antibody titer.** After the first exposure to a vaccine, a primary response occurs. For a period of several days, no antibodies are present; then the titer rises slowly, levels off, and gradually declines as the antibodies bind to the antigen or simply break down (Fig. 13.9). After a second exposure to the vaccine, a secondary response is expected. The titer rises rapidly to a level much greater than before; then it

Figure 13.9 During immunization, the primary response, after the first exposure to a vaccine, is minimal, but the secondary response, which may occur after the second exposure, shows a dramatic rise in the amount of antibody present in plasma.

Figure 13.10 Passive immunity. Breast-feeding is believed to prolong the passive immunity an infant receives from the mother because antibodies are present in the mother's milk.

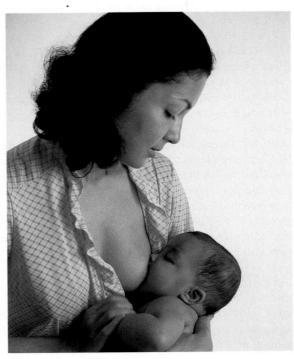

slowly declines. The second exposure is called a "booster" because it boosts the antibody titer to a high level. The high antibody titer now is expected to help prevent disease symptoms even if the individual is exposed to the disease-causing antigen.

Active immunity is dependent upon the presence of memory B cells and memory T cells that are capable of responding to lower doses of antigen. Active immunity is usually long-lasting, although a booster may be required every so many years.

Passive Immunity

Passive immunity occurs when an individual is given prepared antibodies (immunoglobulins) to combat a disease. Since these antibodies are not produced by the individual's plasma cells, passive immunity is temporary. For example, newborn infants are passively immune to some diseases because antibodies have crossed the placenta from the mother's blood. These antibodies soon disappear, however, so that within a few months, infants become more susceptible to infections. Breast-feeding prolongs the natural passive immunity an infant receives from the mother because antibodies are present in the mother's milk (Fig. 13.10).

Even though passive immunity does not last, it is sometimes used to prevent illness in a patient who has been unexpectedly exposed to an infectious disease. Usually, the patient receives a gamma globulin injection (serum that contains antibodies), perhaps taken from individuals who have recovered from the illness. In the past, horses were immunized, and serum

Medical Focus

Immunization: The Great Protector

Immunization protects children and adults from diseases. The success of immunization is witnessed by the fact that the smallpox vaccination is no longer required because the disease has been eradicated. However, parents today often fail to get their children immunized because they do not realize the importance of immunizations or cannot bear the expense. Newspaper accounts of an outbreak of measles at a U.S. college or hospital, therefore, are not uncommon because many adults were not immunized as children.

Figure 13B shows a recommended immunization schedule for children. The United States is now committed to the goal of immunizing all children against the common types of childhood diseases listed. Diphtheria, whooping cough, and *Haemophilus influenzae* infection are all life-threatening respiratory diseases. Tetanus is characterized by muscular rigidity, including a locked jaw. These extremely serious infections are all caused by bacteria; the rest of the diseases listed are caused by viruses. Polio is a type of paralysis; measles and rubella, sometimes called German measles, are characterized by skin rashes; and mumps is characterized by enlarged parotid and other salivary glands.

Adults, rather than children, are more likely to contract a disease through sexual contact. Hepatitis B virus (HBV) is a blood-borne pathogen that is spread in the United States mainly by sexual contact and intravenous drug use. Health-care workers who are exposed to blood or blood products are also at risk, and maternal-neonatal transmission is a possibility as well. Recovery from an initial bout of hepatitis (inflammation of the liver) can lead to chronic hepatitis and then cancer of the liver. Fortunately, a hepatitis B vaccine is now available . Cervical cancer has recently been linked to the occurrence of genital warts, a sexually transmitted disease caused by human papillomavirus. Therefore, a new vaccine for papillomavirus, type 16, the most frequent cause of genital warts, should be administered, especially to girls before they become sexually active. Perhaps more vaccines for sexually transmitted diseases will one day become available.

Even though bacterial infections (e.g., tetanus) can be cured by antibiotic therapy, it is better to be immunized. Some patients are allergic to antibiotics, and the reaction can be fatal. In addition, antibiotics not only kill off disease-causing bacteria, but they also reduce the number of beneficial bacteria in the intestinal tract and elsewhere. These beneficial bacteria may have checked the spread of pathogens that now are free to multiply and to invade the body. This is why antibiotic therapy is often followed by a secondary infection, such as a vaginal yeast infection in women. Antibiotic therapy also leads to resistant bacterial strains that are difficult to cure, even with antibiotics.

Resistant strains of bacteria now cause gonorrhea, a disease that has no vaccine.

Therefore, everyone should avail themselves of appropriate vaccinations. Preventing a disease by becoming actively immune to it is preferable to becoming ill and needing antibiotic therapy to be cured.

Suggested Immunization Schedule

Vaccine	Age (months)	Age (years)
Hepatitis B	Birth–18	11–12
Diphtheria, tetanus, pertussis (DTP)	2, 4, 6, 15–18	4–6
Tetanus only		11–12, 14–16
Haemophilus influenzae, type b	2, 4, 6, 12–15	
Polio	2, 4, 6–18	4–6
Pneumococcal	2, 4, 6, 12–15	
Measles, mumps, rubella (MMR)	12–15	4–6, 11–12
Varicella (chickenpox)	12–18	11–12
Hepatitis A (in selected areas)	24	4–12
Human papillomavirus, type 16	—	12–14

Figure 13B Suggested immunization schedule for infants and young children.

Emerging Diseases

Emerging diseases are caused by microbes that have only recently become pathogens in humans. HIV infection is an emerging disease that was unknown until the early 1980s. A hemorrhagic fever caused by the Ebola virus was first seen in 1976. West Nile encephalitis has been known in the United States only since 1999. Severe acute respiratory syndrome (SARS) and monkey pox both arose in 2003.

Viruses tend to exhibit host specificity. Some viruses infect plants, others choose animals, and some only infect bacteria. But even greater specificity is sometimes seen: Some animal viruses infect only particular species and possibly just a particular tissue in that species. The HIV virus, for example, infects primarily human lymphocytes, and SARS attacks the human respiratory system. To understand the host specificity of a virus, it is necessary to examine viral structure. Viruses are composed of two basic parts (Fig. 13C). The core of the virus is its genetic material, which can be either DNA or RNA. The genetic material is covered by a protective protein coat called a capsid. Animal viruses have an additional outer covering called the envelope. Often the envelope contains protein spikes that allow the virus to attach to one type of host cell and not another. Following attachment, the virus enters the cell, takes over its metabolic machinery, and reproduces. Viruses only reproduce inside living cells.

The genetic material of a virus is well known for its high mutation rate. Some of these mutations affect the structure of the protein spikes so that a virus that previously could only infect a particular animal species can now also infect the human species. For example, AIDS and Ebola are caused by viruses that at one time infected only monkeys and apes. Birds are the host reservoir for West Nile virus, which is transmitted by a mosquito bite. In the United States, monkey pox is passed to humans from pet prairie dogs that have been exposed to infected animals imported from Africa. The virus that causes SARS is also an example of a mutant virus that most likely jumped species. A coronavirus resembling the SARS virus was isolated from six palm civets, a cat-like carnivore sold for food in China.

SARS originated in China, as have other viral diseases, including new strains of the flu virus. What is there about China and Africa that makes them breeding grounds for new viruses? In China, new strains of the flu apparently come from domesticated animals that wander freely through people's homes. SARS, on the other hand, is believed to have crossed over to people from a wild animal rather than from livestock. Also, the Chinese and Africans often use wild animals for food and traditional medicines, practices that health officials are now trying to discourage.

Figure 13C A coronavirus is believed to cause SARS.

---

was taken from them to provide the needed antibodies against such diseases as diphtheria, botulism, and tetanus. Unfortunately, a patient who received these antibodies became ill about 50% of the time, because the serum contained proteins that the individual's immune system recognized as foreign. This was called serum sickness. But problems can also occur with products made in other ways. An immunoglobulin intravenous product called Gammagard was withdrawn from the market because of its possible implication in the transmission of hepatitis.

Monoclonal Antibodies

Every plasma cell derived from the same B cell secretes antibodies against a specific antigen. These are **monoclonal antibodies** because all of them are the same type and because they are produced by plasma cells derived from the same B cell. One method of producing monoclonal antibodies in vitro (outside the body in glassware) is depicted in Figure 13.11. B lymphocytes are removed from an animal (today, usually mice are used) and are exposed to a particular antigen. The resulting plasma cells are fused with myeloma cells (malignant plasma cells that live and divide indefinitely). The fused cells are called hybridomas—*hybrid*- because they result from the fusion of two different cells, and -*oma* because one of the cells is a cancer cell.

At present, monoclonal antibodies are being used for quick and certain diagnosis of various conditions. For example, a particular hormone is present in the urine of a pregnant woman. A monoclonal antibody can be used to detect this hormone; if it is present, the woman knows she is pregnant. Monoclonal antibodies are also used to identify infections. And because they can distinguish between cancerous and normal tissue cells, they are used to carry radioactive isotopes or toxic drugs to tumors, which can then be selectively destroyed.

Figure 13.11 Production of monoclonal antibodies. Plasma cells of the same type (derived from immunized mice) are fused with myeloma (cancerous) cells, producing hybridoma cells that are "immortal." Hybridoma cells divide and continue to produce the same type of antibody, called monoclonal antibodies.

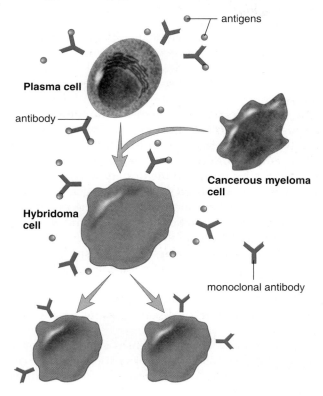

antigens

Plasma cell

antibody

Cancerous myeloma cell

Hybridoma cell

monoclonal antibody

Immunity Side Effects

The immune system usually protects us from disease because it can distinguish self from nonself. Sometimes, however, it responds in a manner that harms the body, as when individuals develop allergies, suffer tissue rejection, or have an autoimmune disease.

Allergies

Allergies are hypersensitivities to substances such as pollen or animal hair that ordinarily would do no harm to the body. The response to these antigens, called **allergens,** usually includes some degree of tissue damage. There are four types of allergic responses, but we will consider only two of them: immediate allergic response and delayed allergic response.

Immediate Allergic Response An **immediate allergic response** can occur within seconds of contact with the antigen. The response is caused by antibodies known as IgE (see Table 13.1). IgE antibodies are attached to the plasma membrane of mast cells in the tissues and also to basophils in the blood. When an allergen attaches to the IgE antibodies on these cells, mast cells release histamine and other substances that bring

about the allergic symptoms. When pollen is an allergen, histamine stimulates the mucosal membranes of the nose and eyes to release fluid, causing the runny nose and watery eyes typical of **hay fever.** If a person has **asthma,** the airways leading to the lungs constrict, resulting in difficult breathing accompanied by wheezing. When food contains an allergen, nausea, vomiting, and diarrhea result.

Anaphylactic shock is an immediate allergic response that occurs because the allergen has entered the bloodstream. Bee stings and penicillin shots are known to cause this reaction because both inject the allergen into the blood. Anaphylactic shock is characterized by a sudden and life-threatening drop in blood pressure due to increased permeability of the capillaries by histamine. Taking epinephrine can delay this reaction until medical help is available.

Allergy shots sometimes prevent the onset of immediate allergic responses. It has been suggested that injections of the allergen may cause the body to build up high quantities of IgG antibodies, and these combine with allergens received from the environment before they have a chance to reach the IgE antibodies located in the membrane of mast cells and basophils.

Delayed Allergic Response A **delayed allergic response** is initiated by memory T cells at the site of allergen contact in the body. The allergic response is regulated by the cytokines secreted by both T cells and macrophages.

A classic example of a delayed allergic response is the skin test for tuberculosis (TB). When the test result is positive, the tissue where the antigen was injected becomes red and hardened. This shows that there was prior exposure to tubercle bacilli, the cause of TB. Contact dermatitis, which occurs when a person is allergic to poison ivy, jewelry, cosmetics, and many other substances that touch the skin, is also an example of a delayed allergic response.

Tissue Rejection

Certain organs, such as skin, the heart, and the kidneys, could be transplanted easily from one person to another if the body did not attempt to reject them. Rejection of transplanted tissue results because the recipient's immune system recognizes that the transplanted tissue is not "self." Cytotoxic T cells respond by causing disintegration of the transplanted tissue.

Organ rejection can be controlled by carefully selecting the organ to be transplanted and administering **immunosuppressive** drugs. It is best if the transplanted organ has the same type of HLA antigens as those of the recipient, because T_c cells recognize foreign HLA antigens. Two well-known immunosuppressive drugs, cyclosporine and tacrolimus, both act by inhibiting the response of T cells to cytokines.

Researchers hope that tissue engineering, including the production of organs that lack antigens or that can be protected in some way from the immune system, will one day do away with the problem of rejection (see the What's New reading on page 9).

Diseases of the Immune System

When a person has an **autoimmune disease,** cytotoxic T cells or antibodies mistakenly attack the body's own cells as if they bear foreign antigens. Exactly what causes autoimmune diseases is not known. However, sometimes they occur after an individual has recovered from an infection.

In the autoimmune disease **myasthenia gravis,** neuromuscular junctions do not work properly, and muscular weakness results. In **multiple sclerosis (MS),** the myelin sheath of nerve fibers breaks down, and this causes various neuromuscular disorders. A person with **systemic lupus erythematosus (SLE)** has various symptoms prior to death due to kidney damage. In **rheumatoid arthritis,** the joints are affected. Researchers suggest that heart damage following rheumatic fever and type I diabetes are also autoimmune illnesses. As yet, there are no cures for autoimmune diseases, but they can be controlled with drugs.

When a person has an immune deficiency, the immune system is unable to protect the body against disease. AIDS (see the Medical Focus on page 264) is an example of an acquired immune deficiency. As a result of a weakened immune system, AIDS patients show a greater susceptibility to a variety of diseases, and also have a higher risk of cancer. Immune deficiency may also be congenital (that is, inherited). Infrequently, a child may be born with an impaired B- or T-cell system caused by a defect in lymphocyte development. In **severe combined immunodeficiency disease (SCID),** both antibody- and cell-mediated immunity are lacking or inadequate. Without treatment, even common infections can be fatal. Gene therapy has been successful in SCID patients (see page 399).

13.5 Effects of Aging

With advancing age, people become more susceptible to all types of infections and disorders because the immune system exhibits lower levels of function. One reason is that the thymus gland degenerates. Having reached its maximum size in early childhood, it begins to shrink after puberty and has virtually disappeared by old age. As the gland decreases in size, so does the number of T cells. The T cells remaining do not respond to foreign antigens; therefore, the chance of having cancer increases with age.

Among the elderly, the B cells sometimes fail to form clones. Or, when they do form clones, the antibodies released may not function well. Therefore, infections are more common among the elderly. Also, the antibodies are more likely to attack the body's own tissues, increasing the incidence of autoimmune diseases.

The response of elderly individuals to vaccines is decreased. However, considering that their overall level of immune response is low, it is better that these people be vaccinated than not. For this reason, elderly individuals are encouraged to get an influenza (flu) vaccination each year.

13.6 Homeostasis

The three functions of the lymphatic system listed on page 254 assist homeostasis. The lymphatic system helps the digestive system by absorbing fats. In the process of absorbing dietary fats, lacteals also absorb fat-soluble vitamins. The lymphatic system assists the cardiovascular system by absorbing excess tissue fluid. The lymphatic vessels return excess tissue fluid as lymph to cardiovascular veins in the thorax. Without this assistance, it would be more difficult for the body to maintain the blood volume and pressure needed for capillary exchange.

The lymphatic organs, along with the immune system, protect us from infectious diseases. Nonspecific ways of protecting the body from disease precede specific immunity. The skin and the mucous membranes of the respiratory tract, the digestive tract, and the urinary system all resist invasion by viruses and bacteria. If a pathogen should enter the body, the infection is localized as much as possible. During the inflammatory reaction, the phagocytic white blood cells immediately rush to the scene and engulf as many pathogens as possible. Macrophages are especially good at devouring viruses and bacteria by phagocytosis. If the infection cannot be confined and pathogens do enter the blood, complement is a series of proteins that work in diverse ways to keep the blood free of disease-causing organisms and their toxins.

Not surprisingly, specific defenses are dependent upon blood cells; the lymphocytes and macrophages play central roles. B and T cells have antigen receptors and can distinguish self from nonself. The binding of the antigen selects which specific B or T cells will undergo clonal expansion. B cells are capable of recognizing an antigen directly, but T cells must have the antigen displayed by an APC in the groove of an HLA antigen. Plasma cells (mature B cells) produce antibodies, but T cells kill virus-infected and cancer cells outright.

The lymphatic organs play a central role in immunity. White blood cells are made in the red bone marrow where B cells also mature. T cells mature in the thymus. The spleen filters the blood directly. Clonal expansion of lymphocytes occurs in the lymph nodes, which also filter the lymph.

A strong connection exists between the immune, nervous, and endocrine systems. Lymphocytes have receptor proteins for a wide variety of hormones, and the thymus gland produces hormones that influence the immune response. Cytokines help the body recover from disease by affecting the brain's temperature control center. The high body temperature of a fever is thought to create an unfavorable environment for the foreign invaders. Also, cytokines bring about a feeling of sluggishness, sleepiness, and loss of appetite. These behaviors tend to make us take care of ourselves until we feel better. A close connection between the immune and endocrine systems is illustrated by the ability of cortisone to mollify the inflammatory reaction in the joints.

Human Systems Work Together

Integumentary System

Lymphatic vessels pick up excess tissue fluid; immune system protects against skin infections.

Skin serves as a barrier to pathogen invasion; Langerhans cells phagocytize pathogens; protects lymphatic vessels.

Skeletal System

Lymphatic vessels pick up excess tissue fluid; immune system protects against infections.

Red bone marrow produces leukocytes involved in immunity.

Muscular System

Lymphatic vessels pick up excess tissue fluid; immune system protects against infections.

Skeletal muscle contraction moves lymph; physical exercise enhances immunity.

Nervous System

Lymphatic vessels pick up excess tissue fluid; immune system protects against infections of nerves.

Microglia engulf and destroy pathogens.

Endocrine System

Lymphatic vessels pick up excess tissue fluid; immune system protects against infections.

Thymus is necessary to maturity of T lymphocytes.

How the Lymphatic System works with other body systems

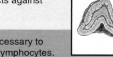

Cardiovascular System

Lymphatic organs produce and store formed elements; lymphatic vessels transport leukocytes and return tissue fluid to blood vessels; spleen serves as blood resevoir, filters blood. Blood vessels transport leukocytes and antibodies; blood services lymphatic organs and is source of tissue fluid that becomes lymph.

Respiratory System

Lymphatic vessels pick up excess tissue fluid; immune system protects against respiratory tract and lung infections.

Tonsils and adenoids occur along respiratory tract; breathing aids lymph flow.

Digestive System

Lacteals absorb fats; Peyer patches prevent invasion of pathogens; appendix contains lymphatic tissue.

Digestive tract provides nutrients for lymphatic organs; stomach acidity prevents pathogen invasion of body.

Urinary System

Lymphatic system picks up excess tissue fluid, helping to maintain blood pressure for kidneys to function; immune system protects against infections.

Kidneys control volume of body fluids, including lymph.

Reproductive System

Female immune system does not attack sperm or fetus, even though they are foreign to the body.

Sex hormones influence immune functioning; acidity of vagina helps prevent pathogen invasion of body; milk passes antibodies to newborn.

Selected New Terms

Basic Key Terms

active immunity (ak′tiv ĭ-myū′nĭ-te), p. 266

antibodies (an′tĭ-bod″ēz), p. 260

antibody-mediated immunity (an″tĭ-bod″e-me′de-āt-ed ĭ-myū′nĭ-te), p. 261

antigen (an′tĭ-jen), p. 260

apoptosis (ap″o-to′-sis), p. 260

B lymphocytes (B lim′fo-sītz), p. 260

cell-mediated immunity (sel me″de-āt′ed ĭ-myū′nĭ-te), p. 263

complement system (kom′plĕ-ment sis′tem), p. 259

cytokines (si′to-kīnz), p. 262

cytotoxic T cells (si′to-tok′sik T selz), p.263

helper T cells (help′er T selz), p. 263

histamine (his′tuh-min), p. 259

HLA (human leukocyte-associated) antigens (hyū′mun lu′ko-sīt-uh-so′se-a-ted an′tĭ-jenz), p. 262

immunity (ĭ-myū-nĭ-te), p. 255

inflammatory reaction (in-flam′uh-to″re re-ak′shun), p. 259

lymph (limf), p. 254

lymphatic organ (lim-fat′ik or′gan), p. 255

lymphatic system (lim-fat′ik sis′tem), p. 254

lymphatic vessel (lim-fat′ik ves′el), p. 254

lymph node (limf nōd), p. 257

macrophage (mak′ro-fāj″), p. 259

memory B cells (mem′o-re B selz), p. 260

monoclonal antibodies (mon″o-klōn′al an″tĭ-bod′ēz), p. 268

natural killer cells (nat′u-ral kil′er selz), p. 259

passive immunity (păs′-iv ĭ-myū′nĭ-te), p. 266

Peyer patches (pi′er pach′ĕz), p. 257

plasma cells (plaz′muh selz), p. 260

pus (pus), p. 259

red bone marrow (red bōn mar′o), p. 255

spleen (splēn), p. 257

thymus gland (thi′mus gland), p. 256

T lymphocytes (T lim′fo-sītz), p. 260

tonsils (ton′silz), p. 257

Clinical Key Terms

AIDS (acquired immunodeficiency syndrome) (uh-kwīr′d ĭ-myū″no-dĭ-fī′shun-se sin′drōm), p. 264

allergies (al′er-jēz), p. 269

anaphylactic shock (an″uh-fĭ-lak′tik shok), p. 269

antibody titer (an″tĭ-bod″e ti′ter), p. 266

asthma (az′muh), p. 269

autoimmune disease (aw″to-ĭ-myūn′ dĭ-zez′), p. 270

delayed allergic response (de-lād′ uh-ler′jik re-spons′), p. 269

edema (ĕ-de′muh), p. 254

elephantiasis (ĕ″luh-fun-ti′uh-sis), p. 257

hay fever (hā fē′vĕr), p. 269

Hodgkin disease (hoj″kin dĭ-zēz′), p. 257

immediate allergic response (ĭ-mē′de-ut uh-ler′jik re-spons′), p. 269

immunization (ĭ-myū-nĭ-za′shun), p. 266

immunosuppressive drugs (ĭ-myū″no-sŭ-pres′iv drugz), p. 269

interferon (in″ter-fēr′on), p. 259

lymphadenitis (lim-fad″ĕ-ni′tis), p. 257

lymphangitis (lim″fan-jī′tis), p. 257

lymphoma (lim-fo′muh), p. 257

multiple sclerosis (mul′tĭ-pl skler-o′sis), p. 270

myasthenia gravis (mi″as-the′ne-uh grah′vis), p. 270

opportunistic infection (op″er-tu-nis′tik in-fek′shun), p. 265

pulmonary edema (pul′mo-nĕr″e ĕ-de′muh), p. 257

rheumatoid arthritis (ru′muh-toid ar-thri′tis), p. 270

severe combined immunodeficiency disease (sĕ-vēr′ kum-bīnd′ ĭ-myū″no-dĭ-fī′shun-se di-zēz′), p. 270

systemic lupus erythematosus (sis-tem′ik lu′pus er-ĭ-the-muh-to′sus), p. 270

vaccines (vak-sēnz′), p. 266

Summary

13.1 Lymphatic System

A. The lymphatic system consists of lymphatic vessels and lymphatic organs. The lymphatic vessels return excess tissue fluid to the bloodstream, absorb fats at intestinal villi, and help the immune system defend the body against disease.

B. Lymphatic capillaries have thin walls, and larger vessels are structured the same as cardiovascular veins, with valves that prevent backward flow.

13.2 Organs, Tissues, and Cells of the Immune System

Lymphocytes are produced and accumulate in the lymphatic organs (primary organs: red bone marrow, thymus gland; secondary organs: lymph nodes, spleen, and other lymphatic tissues). Lymph is cleansed of pathogens and/or their toxins in lymph nodes, and blood is cleansed of pathogens in the spleen. T lymphocytes mature in the thymus, while B lymphocytes mature in the red bone marrow where all blood cells are produced. White blood cells are necessary for nonspecific and specific defenses.

13.3 Nonspecific and Specific Defenses
A. Immunity involves nonspecific and specific defenses. Nonspecific defenses include barriers to entry, the inflammatory reaction, natural killer cells, and protective proteins.
B. Specific defenses require B lymphocytes and T lymphocytes, also called B cells and T cells. B cells undergo clonal selection with production of plasma cells and memory B cells after their antigen receptors combine with a specific antigen. Plasma cells secrete antibodies and eventually undergo apoptosis. Plasma cells are responsible for antibody-mediated immunity. IgG antibody is a Y-shaped molecule that has two binding sites for a specific antigen. Memory B cells remain in the body and produce antibodies if the same antigen enters the body at a later date.
C. T cells are responsible for cell-mediated immunity. The two main types of T cells are cytotoxic T cells and helper T cells. Cytotoxic T cells kill virus-infected or cancer cells on contact because they bear a nonself antigen. Helper T cells produce cytokines and stimulate other immune cells. Like B cells, each T cell bears antigen receptors. However, for a T cell to recognize an antigen, the antigen must be presented by an antigen-presenting cell (APC), usually a macrophage, in the groove of an HLA (human leukocyte-associated antigen). Thereafter, the activated T cell undergoes clonal expansion until the illness has been stemmed. Then most of the activated T cells undergo apoptosis. A few cells remain, however, as memory T cells. Cytokines, including interferon and interleukins, are used in an attempt to promote the body's ability to recover from cancer and to treat AIDS.

13.4 Induced Immunity
A. Immunity can be induced in various ways. Vaccines are available to induce long-lasting, active immunity, and antibodies sometimes are available to provide an individual with temporary, passive immunity. Monoclonal antibodies are produced in the laboratory and used for diagnosis and treatment purposes.
B. Allergic responses occur when the immune system reacts vigorously to substances not normally recognized as foreign. Immediate allergic responses, usually consisting of coldlike symptoms, are due to the activity of antibodies. Delayed allergic responses, such as contact dermatitis, are due to the activity of T cells.

13.5 Effects of Aging
The thymus gets smaller as we age, and fewer antibodies are produced. The elderly are at great risk of infections, cancer, and autoimmune diseases.

13.6 Homeostasis
The lymphatic system assists the cardiovascular system by returning excess tissue fluid to the bloodstream. It assists the digestive system by absorbing fats from the intestinal tract, and it assists the immune system through the functioning of its lymphatic organs.

Study Questions

1. What is the lymphatic system, and what are its three functions? (p. 254)
2. Describe the structure and the function of red bone marrow, the thymus, the spleen, lymph nodes, and the tonsils. (pp. 255–57)
3. What are the body's nonspecific defense mechanisms? (p. 259)
4. Describe the inflammatory reaction, and give a role for each type of cell and molecule that participates in the reaction. (pp. 258–59)
5. What is the clonal selection theory as it applies to B cells? B cells are responsible for which type of immunity? (pp. 260–61)
6. Describe the structure of an antibody, and define the terms variable regions and constant regions. (pp. 260–61)
7. Describe the clonal selection theory as it applies to T cells. (pp. 262–63)
8. Name the two main types of T cells, and state their functions. (p. 263)
9. What are cytokines, and how are they used in immunotherapy? (p. 263)
10. How is active immunity artificially achieved? How is passive immunity achieved? (pp. 266–67)
11. How are monoclonal antibodies produced, and what are their applications? (p. 268)
12. Discuss allergies, tissue rejection, and autoimmune diseases as they relate to the immune system. (pp. 269–70)
13. How do the lymphatic and immune systems help maintain homeostasis? (pp. 270–71)
14. How does the skeletal system assist the immune system in maintaining homeostasis? (pp. 270–71)

Objective Questions

Fill in the blanks.

1. Lymphatic vessels contain _____, which close, preventing lymph from flowing backward.
2. _____ and _____ are two types of white blood cells produced and stored in the lymphatic organs.
3. Lymph nodes cleanse the _____, while the spleen cleanses the _____.
4. _____ and _____ are phagocytic white blood cells.
5. T lymphocytes have matured in the _____.
6. A stimulated B cell divides and differentiates into antibody-secreting _____ cells and also into _____ cells that are ready to produce the same type of antibody at a later time.
7. B cells are responsible for _____-mediated immunity.
8. Cytotoxic T cells are responsible for _____-mediated immunity.
9. Immunization with _____ brings about active immunity.
10. Allergic reactions are associated with the release of _____ from mast cells.
11. Whereas _____ immunity occurs when an individual is given antibodies to combat a disease, _____ immunity occurs when an individual develops the ability to produce antibodies against a specific antigen.
12. Barriers to entry, protective proteins, and the inflammatory reaction are all examples of _____ defenses.
13. Proteins that function to form holes in bacterial cell walls comprise the _____ system.

Medical Terminology Reinforcement Exercise

Consult Appendix B for help in pronouncing and analyzing the meaning of the terms that follow.

1. metastasis (mě-tas'tuh-sis)
2. allergist (al'er-jist)
3. immunosuppressant (i-myū"no-sŭ-pres'ant)
4. immunotherapy (i-myū"no-thěr'uh-pe)
5. splenorrhagia (sple"no-ra'je-uh)
6. lymphadenopathy (lim-fad"ě-nop'uh-the)
7. lymphangiography (lim-fan"je-og'ruh-fe)
8. eosinophilia (e'oh-sin'o-fil'e-uh)
9. thymectomy (thi-mek'to-me)
10. lymphopenia (limf'o-pe'ne-uh)
11. agammaglobulinemia (ā-gam'uh-glob'yū-lǐ-ne'me-uh)
12. pyemia (pi-ē'me-uh)
13. tonsillotomy (ton'sǐ-lot'o-me)
14. hypersensitivity (hi'per-sen-sǐ-tiv'ǐ-te)

Website Link

Visit the Student Edition of the Online Learning Center at http://www.mhhe.com/maderap5 for additional quizzes, interactive learning exercises, and other study tools.

The Respiratory System

chapter 14

The cilia of cells lining the bronchial wall help keep the lungs clean by moving trapped particles.

chapter outline & learning objectives

After you have studied this chapter, you should be able to:

14.1 The Respiratory System (p. 276)

- Describe the events that comprise respiration.
- Describe the structure and function of the respiratory system organs.
- Describe the structure and importance of the respiratory membrane.

14.2 Mechanism of Breathing (p. 281)

- Describe vital capacity and its relationship to other measurements of breathing capacity.
- Describe ventilation, including inspiration and expiration.
- Tell where the respiratory center is located, and explain how it controls the normal breathing rate.

14.3 Gas Exchange and Transport (p. 284)

- Describe the process of gas exchange in the lungs and the tissues.
- Explain how oxygen and carbon dioxide are transported in the blood.

14.4 Respiration and Health (p. 286)

- Name and describe the various infections of the respiratory tract.
- Describe the effects of smoking on the respiratory tract and on overall health.

14.5 Effects of Aging (p. 290)

- Describe the anatomical and physiological changes that occur in the respiratory system as we age.

14.6 Homeostasis (p. 290)

- Describe how the respiratory system works with other systems of the body to maintain homeostasis.

Medical Focus

Respiratory and Nonrespiratory Patterns (p. 284)

The Most Often Asked Questions About Tobacco and Health (p. 289)

What's New

Lung Volume Reduction for Emphysema (p. 280)

14.1 The Respiratory System

The primary function of the respiratory system is to allow oxygen from the air to enter the blood and carbon dioxide from the blood to exit into the air. During **inspiration**, or inhalation (breathing in), and **expiration**, or exhalation (breathing out), air is conducted toward or away from the lungs by a series of cavities, tubes, and openings, illustrated in Figure 14.1.

The respiratory system also works with the cardiovascular system to accomplish these four respiratory events:

1. breathing, the entrance and exit of air into and out of lungs;
2. external respiration, the exchange of gases (oxygen and carbon dioxide) between air and blood;
3. internal respiration, the exchange of gases between blood and tissue fluid;
4. transport of gases to and from the lungs and the tissues.

Cellular respiration, which produces ATP, uses the oxygen and produces the carbon dioxide that makes gas exchange with the environment necessary. Without a continuous supply of ATP, the cells cease to function. The four events listed here allow cellular respiration to continue.

The Respiratory Tract

Table 14.1 traces the path of air from the nose to the lungs. As air moves in along the airways, it is cleansed, warmed, and moistened. Cleansing is accomplished by coarse hairs just inside the nostrils and by cilia and mucus in the nasal cavities and the other airways of the respiratory tract. In the nose, the hairs and the cilia act as screening devices. In the trachea and other airways, the cilia beat upward, carrying mucus, dust, and occasional bits of food that "went down the wrong way" into the pharynx, where the accumulation can be swallowed or expectorated. The air is warmed by heat given off by the blood vessels lying close to the surface of the lining of the airways, and it is moistened by the wet surface of these passages.

Conversely, as air moves out during expiration, it cools and loses its moisture. As the air cools, it deposits its moisture on the lining of the trachea and the nose, and the nose may even drip as a result of this condensation. The air still retains so much moisture, however, that upon expiration on a cold day, it condenses and forms a small cloud.

Figure 14.1 The respiratory tract extends from the nasal cavities to the lungs, which are composed of air sacs called alveoli. Gas exchange occurs between the air in the alveoli and the blood within a capillary network that surrounds the alveoli. Notice in the blow-up that the pulmonary arteriole is colored blue—it carries O_2-poor blood away from the heart to the alveoli. Then carbon dioxide leaves the blood, and oxygen enters the blood. The pulmonary venule is colored red—it carries O_2-rich blood from the alveoli toward the heart.

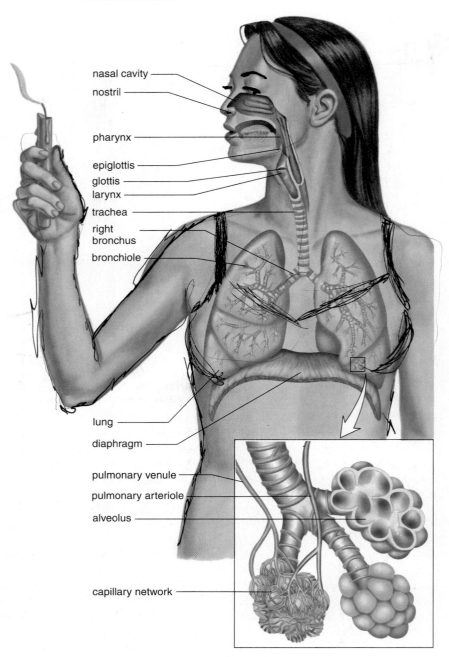

nasal cavity
nostril
pharynx
epiglottis
glottis
larynx
trachea
right bronchus
bronchiole
lung
diaphragm
pulmonary venule
pulmonary arteriole
alveolus
capillary network

Table 14.1 Path of Air

Structure	Description	Function
Upper Respiratory Tract		
Nasal cavitities	Hollow spaces in nose	Filter, warm, and moisten air
Pharynx	Chamber posterior to oral cavity; lies between nasal cavity and larynx	Connection to surrounding regions
Glottis	Opening into larynx	Passage of air into larynx
Larnyx	Cartilaginous organ that houses the vocal cords; voice box	Sound production
Lower Respiratory Tract		
Trachea	Flexible tube that connects larynx with bronchi	Passage of air to bronchi
Bronchi	Paired tubes inferior to the trachea that enter the lungs	Passage of air to lungs
Bronchioles	Branched tubes that lead from bronchi to alveoli	Passage of air to each alveolus
Lungs	Soft, cone-shaped organs that occupy lateral portions of thoracic cavity	Gas exchange

Figure 14.2 The path of air. This drawing shows the path of air from the nasal cavities to the trachea, which is a part of the lower respiratory tract. The other organs are in the upper respiratory tract.

frontal sinus
nostril
hard palate
uvula
tongue
hyoid bone
larynx
trachea

superior / middle / inferior — nasal conchae
sphenoidal sinus
pharyngeal tonsil
nasopharynx
opening of auditory tube
palatine tonsil
oropharynx
lingual tonsil
epiglottis
laryngopharynx
esophagus

The Nose

The **nose,** a prominent feature of the face, is the only external portion of the respiratory system. Air enters the nose through external openings called **nostrils.** The nose contains two **nasal cavities,** which are narrow canals separated from one another by a septum composed of bone and cartilage (Fig. 14.2). Mucous membrane lines the nasal cavities. The nasal **conchae** are bony ridges that project laterally into the nasal cavity. They increase the surface area for moistening and warming air during inhalation and for trapping water droplets during exhalation. Odor receptors are on the cilia of cells located high in the recesses of the nasal cavities.

The tear (lacrimal) glands drain into the nasal cavities by way of tear ducts. For this reason, crying produces a runny nose. The nasal cavities also communicate with the **paranasal sinuses,** air-filled spaces that reduce the weight of the skull and act as resonating chambers for the voice. If the ducts leading from the sinuses become inflamed, fluid may accumulate, causing a sinus headache. The nasal cavities are separated from the oral cavity by a partition called the palate, which has two portions. Anteriorly, the hard palate is supported by bone, and posteriorly the soft palate is not so supported.

The Pharynx

The **pharynx** is a funnel-shaped passageway that connects the nasal and oral cavities to the larynx. Consequently, the pharynx, commonly referred to as the "throat," has three parts: the nasopharynx, where the nasal cavities open posterior to the soft palate; the oropharynx, where the oral cavity joins the pharynx; and the laryngopharynx, which opens into the larynx. The soft palate has a soft extension called the uvula that can be seen projecting into the oropharynx.

The tonsils form a protective ring at the junction of the oral cavity and the pharynx. Being lymphatic tissue, the tonsils contain lymphocytes that protect against invasion of inhaled pathogens. Here, both B cells and T cells are prepared to respond to antigens that may subsequently invade internal tissues and fluids. In this way, the respiratory tract assists the immune system in maintaining homeostasis.

In the pharynx, the air passage and the food passage cross because the larynx, which receives air, is anterior to the esophagus, which receives food. The larynx lies at the top of the trachea. The larynx and trachea are normally open, allowing air to pass, but the esophagus is normally closed and opens only when a person swallows.

Figure 14.3 Placement of the vocal cords. **a.** This frontal section of the larynx shows the location of the vocal cords. **b.** Viewed from above, the vocal cords can be seen to stretch from anterior to posterior across the larynx. When air is forced past the vocal cords, they vibrate, producing sound. The vocal cords are taut when we produce a high-pitched sound (*top*), and they relax as the pitch deepens (*bottom*).

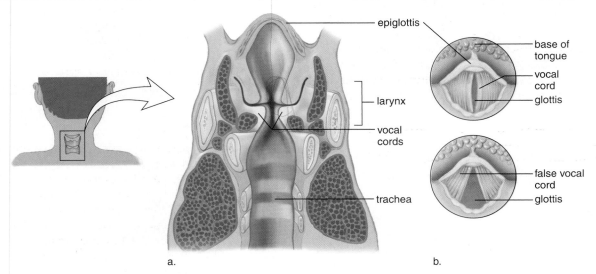

a.

b.

The Larynx

The **larynx** is a cartilaginous structure that serves as a passageway for air between the pharynx and the trachea. The larynx can be pictured as a triangular box whose apex, the Adam's apple, is located at the anterior of the neck. The larynx is called the voice box because it houses the vocal cords. The **vocal cords** are mucosal folds supported by elastic ligaments, and the slit between the vocal cords is an opening called the **glottis** (Fig. 14.3). When air is expelled past the vocal cords through the glottis, the vocal cords vibrate, producing sound. At the time of puberty, the growth of the larynx and the vocal cords is much more rapid and accentuated in the male than in the female, causing the male to have a more prominent Adam's apple and a deeper voice. The voice "breaks" in the young male due to his inability to control the longer vocal cords. These changes cause the lower pitch of the voice in males.

The high or low pitch of the voice is regulated when speaking and singing by changing the tension on the vocal cords. The greater the tension, as when the glottis becomes more narrow, the higher the pitch. When the vocal cords relax, the glottis is wider, and the pitch is lower (Fig. 14.3*b*). The loudness, or intensity, of the voice depends upon the amplitude of the vibrations—that is, the degree to which the vocal cords vibrate.

When food is swallowed, the larynx moves upward against the **epiglottis**, a flap of tissue that prevents food from passing through the glottis into the larynx. You can detect this movement by placing your hand gently on your larynx and swallowing.

The Trachea

The **trachea**, commonly called the windpipe, is a tube connecting the larynx to the primary bronchi. The trachea lies ventral to the esophagus and is held open by C-shaped cartilaginous rings. The open part of the C-shaped rings faces the esophagus, and this allows the esophagus to expand when swallowing. The mucosa that lines the trachea has a layer of pseudostratified ciliated columnar epithelium. (Pseudostratified means that while the epithelium appears to be layered, actually each cell touches the basement membrane.) The cilia that project from the epithelium keep the lungs clean by sweeping mucus, produced by goblet cells, and debris toward the pharynx:

Smoking is known to destroy these cilia, and consequently the soot in cigarette smoke collects in the lungs. Smoking is discussed more fully in the Medical Focus on page 289.

If the trachea is blocked because of illness or the accidental swallowing of a foreign object, it is possible to insert a breathing tube by way of an incision made in the trachea. This tube acts as an artificial air intake and exhaust duct. The operation is called a **tracheostomy.**

The Bronchial Tree

The trachea divides into right and left primary bronchi (sing., **bronchus**), which lead into the right and left lungs (see Fig. 14.1). The bronchi branch into a great number of secondary bronchi that eventually lead to **bronchioles**. The bronchi resemble the trachea in structure, but as the bronchial tubes divide and subdivide, their walls become thinner, and the small rings of cartilage are no longer present. During an asthma attack, the smooth muscle of the bronchioles contracts, causing bronchiolar constriction and characteristic wheezing. Each bronchiole leads to an elongated space enclosed by a multitude of air pockets, or sacs, called alveoli (sing., **alveolus**). The components of the bronchial tree beyond the primary bronchi, including the alveoli, compose the lungs.

The Lungs

The **lungs** are paired, cone-shaped organs that occupy the thoracic cavity except for the mediastinum, a central area that contains the primary bronchi, the heart, and other organs. The right lung has three lobes, and the left lung has two lobes, allowing room for the heart whose apex points left. A lobe is further divided into lobules, and each lobule has a bronchiole serving many alveoli. The apex is the superior narrow portion of a lung, and the base is the inferior broad portion that curves to fit the dome-shaped diaphragm, the muscle that separates the thoracic cavity from the abdominal cavity. The lateral surfaces of the lungs follow the contours of the ribs in the thoracic cavity.

Each lung is enclosed by a double layer of serous membrane called the **pleura.** The visceral pleura adheres to the surface of the lung, while the parietal pleura lines the thoracic cavity. The pleura produces a lubricating serous fluid that allows its two layers to slide against one another. **Surface tension** is the tendency for water molecules to cling to each other (due to hydrogen bonding between the molecules) and to form a droplet. Surface tension holds the two pleural layers together when the lungs recoil during expiration.

The Alveoli

With each inhalation, air passes by way of the bronchial tree to the alveoli. An alveolar sac is made up of simple squamous epithelium surrounded by blood capillaries. Gas exchange occurs between the air in the alveoli and the blood in the capillaries (Fig. 14.4). Oxygen diffuses across the alveolar and capillary walls to enter the bloodstream, while carbon dioxide diffuses from the blood across these walls to enter the alveoli.

The alveoli must stay open to receive the inhaled air if gas exchange is to occur. Gas exchange takes place across moist cellular membranes, and yet the surface tension of water lining the alveoli is capable of causing them to close up. The alveoli are lined with a **surfactant**, a film of lipoprotein that lowers the surface tension and prevents them from closing. The lungs collapse in some newborn babies, especially premature infants, who lack this film. The condition, called **infant respiratory distress syndrome,** is now treatable by surfactant replacement therapy.

Figure 14.4 Gas exchange in the lungs. The lungs consist of portions of the bronchial tree leading to the alveoli, each of which is surrounded by an extensive capillary network. Notice that the pulmonary artery and arteriole carry O_2-poor blood (colored blue), and the pulmonary vein and venule carry O_2-rich blood (colored red).

blood flow

bronchiole

lobule

blood flow

pulmonary arteriole

pulmonary artery

pulmonary vein

alveoli

blood flow

pulmonary venule

Blood supply of alveoli

Capillary network of one alveolus

Respiratory Membrane Gas exchange occurs very rapidly because of the characteristics of the so-called respiratory membrane (Fig. 14.5). The **respiratory membrane** consists of the juxtaposed alveolar epithelium and the capillary endothelium. At times, their basement membranes are fused, meaning that very little tissue fluid separates the two portions[1] of the respiratory membrane and they are indeed one membrane. This membrane is extremely thin—only 0.2–0.6 µm thick.

The total surface area of the respiratory membrane is the same as the area of the alveoli, namely 50–70 m². The blood that enters the many pulmonary capillaries spreads thin. The red blood cells within the capillaries are pressed up against the narrow capillary walls, and little plasma is present. This too facilitates the speed of gas exchange during external respiration. As discussed in the What's New reading on this page, a person with emphysema has a reduced amount of respiratory membrane.

---

[1] The respiratory membrane has two portions but four layers: alveolar epithelium plus its basement membrane, and a basement membrane of endothelium plus the capillary endothelium.

Figure 14.5 The respiratory membrane consists of the alveolar wall and the capillary wall.

surfactant-secreting cell

macrophage

alveolus

respiratory membrane

capillary lumen

What's New

Lung Volume Reduction for Emphysema

"By the time I was diagnosed," the patient complains, "I couldn't walk across this room without stopping to catch my breath. I lost 40 pounds because I didn't have the energy to eat. I had to quit a job I loved, because I just couldn't do the work anymore. Now I'm hooked to this oxygen tank. I know there are risks involved, but I'm willing to take a chance on surgery. I just can't live my life like this."

This patient has emphysema, a degenerative disease most often caused by prolonged cigarette smoking. The respiratory membrane breaks down, and there are fewer (but enlarged) alveoli. Gas exchange is reduced because there is less surface area for the diffusion of respiratory gases into the blood. Air is trapped in the alveoli, and exhaling becomes very difficult. The lungs themselves become larger and less elastic, and the patient develops a barrel-chested appearance. On X ray, the diaphragm (which is normally curved when at rest; see page 282) appears flattened as the lungs increase in size. Exercise—and even normal daily activities—become impossible for the person.

Patients suffering the end-stage of emphysema may be candidates for lung volume reduction surgery, or LVRS. In LVRS, the diseased upper lobes of the lungs are surgically removed. The remaining healthy lung tissue is sealed, usually with a flap of peri-cardium. Removal of the diseased portion of the lung allows the remaining healthy tissue to expand and fill the thoracic cavity. This improves gas exchange because the thorax is filled with the healthiest possible tissue. The diaphragm can return to its normal curved position at rest, allowing the patient to once again take a deep breath.

Before being approved for this surgery, the patient must undergo preoperative rehabilitation. The first step in the rehabilitation process is to quit smoking—forever. The next step includes drug treatment to widen the bronchial tubes and improve blood circulation. Physical and respiratory therapy enables the patient to tolerate exercise. Similar treatments are continued after the surgery has been completed. Studies have shown that patients who complete the rehabilitation before and after surgery have the best recovery.

LVRS is a complicated and potentially dangerous procedure, and it certainly is not a cure for emphysema. However, the benefits of the surgery can be dramatic for some patients. Improvements in oxygenation of the blood, tolerance for exercise, and overall lung function enable some patients to resume near-normal lives.

Figure 14.6 Vital capacity. A spirometer measures the amount of air inhaled and exhaled with each breath. During inspiration, the pen moves up, and during expiration, the pen moves down. The volume of one normal breath (tidal volume) multiplied by the number of breaths per minute is called the minute ventilation. A lower-than-normal minute ventilation can be a sign of pulmonary malfunction. Vital capacity (red) is the maximum amount of air a person can exhale after taking the deepest inhalation possible.

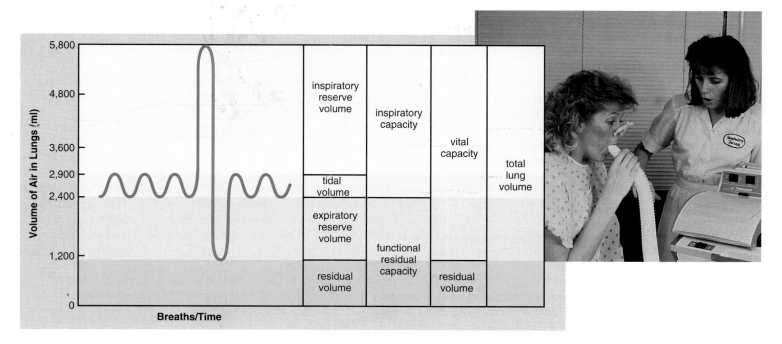

14.2 Mechanism of Breathing

During breathing, air moves into the lungs from the nose or mouth (called inspiration, or inhalation), and then moves out of the lungs during expiration, or exhalation. A free flow of air from the nose or mouth to the lungs and from the lungs to the nose or mouth is vitally important. Therefore, a technique has been developed that allows physicians to determine if there is a medical problem that prevents the lungs from filling with air upon inspiration and releasing air from the body upon expiration. An instrument called a spirometer records the volume of air exchanged during normal breathing and during deep breathing. A spirogram shows the measurements recorded by a spirometer when a person breathes as directed by a technician (Fig. 14.6).

Respiratory Volumes

Normally when we are relaxed, only a small amount of air moves in and out with each breath. This amount of air, called the **tidal volume,** is only about 500 ml.

It is possible to increase the amount of air inhaled, and therefore the amount exhaled, by deep breathing. The maximum volume of air that can be moved in plus the maximum volume that can be moved out during a single breath is the **vital capacity.** It is called vital capacity because your life depends on breathing, and the more air you can move, the better off you are. A number of different illnesses, discussed in section 14.4, can decrease vital capacity.

Vital capacity varies by how much we can increase inspiration and expiration over the tidal volume amount. We can increase inspiration by not only expanding the chest but also by lowering the diaphragm. Forced inspiration usually increases the volume of air beyond the tidal volume by 2,900 ml, and that amount is called the **inspiratory reserve volume.** We can increase the amount of air expired by contracting the abdominal and internal intercostal muscles. This so-called **expiratory reserve volume** is usually about 1,400 ml of air. You can see from Figure 14.6 that vital capacity is the sum of the tidal, inspiratory reserve, and expiratory reserve volumes.

It's a curious fact that some of the inhaled air never reaches the alveoli; instead, it fills the nasal cavities, trachea, bronchi, and bronchioles (see Fig. 14.1). In an average adult, some 70% of the tidal volume does reach the alveoli; but 30% remains in the airways. These passages are not used for gas exchange, and therefore they are said to contain dead-space air. To ensure that a large portion of inhaled air reaches the lungs, it is better to breathe slowly and deeply. Also, note in Figure 14.6 that even after a very deep exhalation, some air (about 1,000 ml) remains in the alveoli; this is called the **residual volume.** This air is not as useful for gas exchange because it has been depleted of oxygen. In some lung diseases, such as emphysema (see What's New on page 280), the residual volume builds up because the individual has difficulty emptying the lungs. This means that the vital capacity is reduced because the lungs have more residual volume.

Ventilation

To understand **ventilation,** the manner in which air enters and exits the lungs, it is helpful to be aware of the following conditions:

1. *The lungs lie within the sealed-off thoracic cavity.* The rib cage, consisting of the ribs joined to the vertebral column posteriorly and to the sternum anteriorly, forms the top and sides of the thoracic cavity. The intercostal muscles lie between the ribs. The diaphragm and connective tissue form the floor of the thoracic cavity.
2. *The lungs adhere to the thoracic wall by way of the pleura.* (Any space between the two layers of the pleura is minimal due to the surface tension of the fluid between them.)
3. *A continuous column of air extends from the pharynx to the alveoli of the lungs.*

Inspiration

Inspiration is the active phase of ventilation because this is the phase in which the diaphragm and the external inter-costal muscles contract (Fig. 14.7a). In its relaxed state, the diaphragm is dome-shaped; during deep inspiration, it contracts and lowers. Also, the external intercostal muscles contract, and the rib cage moves upward and outward.

Following contraction of the diaphragm and the external intercostal muscles, the volume of the thoracic cavity will be larger than it was before. As the thoracic volume increases, the lungs expand due to conditions 1 and 2. Now the air pressure within the alveoli (called intrapulmonary pressure) decreases, creating a partial vacuum. In other words, alveolar pressure is now less than atmospheric pressure (air pressure outside the lungs), and air will naturally flow from outside the body into the respiratory passages and into the alveoli due to condition 3.

It is important to realize that air comes into the lungs because they have already opened up; air does not force the lungs open. This is why it is sometimes said that *humans breathe by negative pressure.* The creation of a partial vacuum in the alveoli causes air to enter the lungs. While inspiration is the active phase of breathing, the actual flow of air into the alveoli is passive.

Figure 14.7 Inspiration versus expiration. **a.** During inspiration, the thoracic cavity and lungs expand so that intrapleural pressure decreases. Now air flows into the lungs. **b.** During expiration, the thoracic wall and lungs recoil, assuming their original positions and pressures. Now air is forced out. The internal intercostal muscles only contract during forceful expiration.

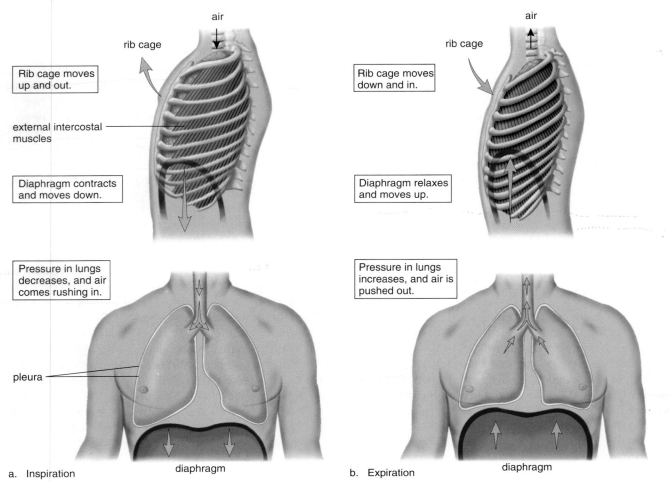

Rib cage moves up and out.

external intercostal muscles

Diaphragm contracts and moves down.

Pressure in lungs decreases, and air comes rushing in.

pleura

a. Inspiration

diaphragm

Rib cage moves down and in.

Diaphragm relaxes and moves up.

Pressure in lungs increases, and air is pushed out.

b. Expiration

diaphragm

Expiration

Usually, expiration is the passive phase of ventilation, and no effort is required to bring it about. During expiration, the diaphragm and the intercostal muscles relax. Therefore, the diaphragm resumes its dome shape and the rib cage moves down and in (Fig. 14.7b). As the volume of the thoracic cavity decreases, the lungs are free to recoil due to conditions 1 and 2 listed on page 282. Now the air pressure within the alveoli (called intrapulmonary pressure) increases above atmospheric pressure and air will naturally flow to outside the body due to condition 3.

What keeps the alveoli from collapsing as a part of expiration? The presence of surfactant lowers the surface tension within the alveoli. Also, as the lungs recoil, pressure between the two layers of pleura decreases, and this tends to make the alveoli stay open. The importance of a reduced intrapleural pressure is demonstrated when, by design or accident, air enters the intrapleural space. Now the lung collapses.

While inspiration is the active phase of breathing, expiration is usually passive—that is, the diaphragm and external intercostal muscles are relaxed when expiration occurs. However, when breathing is deeper and/or more rapid, expiration can also be active. Contraction of the internal intercostal muscles can force the rib cage to move downward and inward. Also, when the abdominal wall muscles contract, they push on the viscera, which push against the diaphragm, and the increased pressure in the thoracic cavity helps expel air.

Control of Ventilation

Normally, adults have a breathing rate of 12 to 20 ventilations per minute. The rhythm of ventilation is controlled by a **respiratory center** located in the medulla oblongata of the brain.

The respiratory center automatically sends out impulses by way of nerves to the diaphragm and the external intercostal muscles of the rib cage (Fig. 14.8). When the respiratory center stops sending neuronal signals to the diaphragm and the rib cage, the diaphragm relaxes resuming its dome shape and the rib cage moves down and in. The respiratory center acts rhythmically to bring about breathing at a normal rate and volume.

Although the respiratory center controls the rate and depth of breathing, its activity can be influenced by nervous input and chemical input.

Nervous Input An example of nervous control of the respiratory center is the so-called *Hering-Breuer reflex*. During exercise, the depth of inspiration can increase due to recruitment of muscle fibers in the diaphragm and intercostal muscles. Then, stretch receptors in the alveolar walls are stimulated, and they initiate inhibitory nerve impulses that travel from the inflated lungs to the respiratory center. This causes the respiratory center to stop sending out nerve impulses. This reflex helps support rhythmic respiratory movements by limiting the extent of inspiration.

Figure 14.8 Nervous control of breathing. During inspiration, the respiratory center stimulates the external intercostal muscles to contract via the intercostal nerves and stimulates the diaphragm to contract via the phrenic nerve. Should the tidal volume increase above 1.5 liters, stretch receptors send inhibitory nerve impulses to the respiratory center via the vagus nerve. In any case, expiration occurs due to lack of stimulation from the respiratory center to the diaphragm and intercostal muscles.

Chemical Input The respiratory center is directly sensitive to the levels of carbon dioxide (CO_2) and hydrogen ions (H^+). When they rise, due to cellular respiration, the respiratory center increases the rate and depth of breathing. The center is not affected directly by low oxygen (O_2) levels. However, chemoreceptors in the **carotid bodies,** located in the carotid arteries, and in the **aortic bodies,** located in the aorta, are sensitive to the level of oxygen in the blood. (Do not confuse the carotid and aortic bodies with the carotid and aortic sinuses, which monitor blood pressure.) When the concentration of oxygen decreases, these bodies communicate with the respiratory center, and the rate and depth of breathing increase. The Medical Focus on page 284 describes some modified ventilation rates that occur due to various circumstances.

Medical Focus

Respiratory and Nonrespiratory Patterns

The normal pattern of quiet breathing is termed **eupnea**. A condition called **Cheyne-Stokes respiration** is characterized by alternate periods of **hyperpnea** (deep and labored breathing) and **apnea** (no breathing or shallow breathing). In this condition, the respiratory center is apparently being controlled largely by chemical input so that the breathing rate first increases when CO_2 and H^+ are high and O_2 is low and then decreases when CO_2 and H^+ are low and O_2 is high. Cheyne-Stokes respiration is associated with abnormal environmental conditions (e.g., high altitude) or physiological disorders (e.g., congestive heart failure).

Other factors can also affect respiration. A sudden cold stimulus, such as a plunge into cold water, causes temporary apnea. A sudden, severe pain has the same effect, but prolonged pain triggers the stress syndrome, which causes an increased breathing rate. A rather interesting stimulus is stretching of the anal sphincter muscle, which causes inspiration. Various other patterns of nonrespiratory air movements are of interest.

Prior to a *cough*, the glottis closes. Then the glottis suddenly opens as a blast of air is forced upward from the lower respiratory tract. A *sneeze* is like a cough except that the blast of air is directed into the nasal passages by a depression of the uvula that closes off the pharynx and mouth. When a person *laughs* or cries, air is released in a series of short expirations; therefore, it is necessary to study the facial expression to know if a person is crying or laughing. A *hiccup* occurs when the diaphragm contracts spasmodically while the glottis is closed. Air striking the vocal cords causes the hiccup.

Sighing and *yawning* require a long inspiration followed by a shorter expiration. The sound that accompanies expiration serves as a means of communication. Yawning has the benefit of making a person more alert when drowsiness occurs. The neurophysiology of yawning is complex, and knowledge of its mechanisms is incomplete because it is apparently under the control of various neurotransmitters.

Figure 14.9 External and internal respiration. During external respiration in the lungs, CO_2 leaves the blood and O_2 enters the blood passively by diffusion. During internal respiration in the tissues, O_2 leaves the blood and CO_2 enters the blood passively by diffusion.

14.3 Gas Exchange and Transport

Gas exchange and transport are critical to homeostasis. As mentioned previously, respiration includes not only the exchange of gases in the lungs, but also the exchange of gases in the tissues. Recall that diffusion is the movement of molecules from the area of higher concentration to the area of lower concentration. The principles of diffusion alone govern whether oxygen (O_2) or carbon dioxide (CO_2) enters or leaves the blood in the lungs and in the tissues.

External Respiration

External respiration is the exchange of gases in the lungs. Specifically, during external respiration, gases are exchanged between the air in the alveoli and the blood in the pulmonary capillaries. Blood that enters the pulmonary capillaries is dark maroon because it is relatively O_2-poor.

Once inspiration has occurred, the alveoli have a higher concentration of O_2 than does blood entering the lungs. Therefore, O_2 diffuses from the alveoli into the blood. The reverse is true of CO_2. The alveoli have a lower concentration of CO_2 than does blood entering the lungs. Therefore, CO_2 diffuses out of the blood into the alveoli. This CO_2 exits the body during expiration.

Another way to explain gas exchange in the lungs is to consider the partial pressure of the gases involved. Gases exert pressure, and the amount of pressure each gas exerts is its partial pressure, symbolized as P_{O_2} and P_{CO_2}. Alveolar air has a much higher P_{O_2} than does blood. Therefore, O_2 diffuses into the blood from the alveoli. The pressure pattern is the reverse for CO_2. Blood entering the pulmonary capillaries has a higher P_{CO_2} than the air in the alveoli. Therefore, CO_2 diffuses out of the blood into the alveoli.

Internal Respiration

Internal respiration refers to the exchange of gases in the tissues. Specifically, during internal respiration, gases are exchanged between the blood in systemic capillaries and the tissue fluid. Blood that enters the systemic capillaries is a bright red color because the blood is O_2-rich. Tissue fluid, on the other hand, has a low concentration of O_2. Why? Because the cells are continually consuming O_2 during cellular respiration. Therefore, O_2 diffuses from the blood into the tissue fluid. Tissue fluid has a higher concentration of CO_2 than does the blood entering the tissues. Why? Because CO_2 is an end product of cellular respiration. Therefore, CO_2 diffuses from the tissue fluid into the blood. Figure 14.9 summarizes our discussion of gas exchange in the lungs and tissues and shows the differences in O_2 and CO_2 that lead to diffusion of these gases.

Again, we can explain exchange in the tissues by considering the partial pressure of the gases involved. In this case, oxygen diffuses out of the blood into the tissues because the P_{O_2} in tissue fluid is lower than that of the blood. And the carbon dioxide diffuses into the blood from the tissues because the P_{CO_2} in tissue fluid is higher than that of the blood.

Gas Transport

The mode of transport of oxygen and carbon dioxide in the blood differs, although red blood cells are involved in transporting both of these gases.

Oxygen Transport

After O_2 enters the blood in the lungs, it enters red blood cells and combines with the iron portion of **hemoglobin,** the pigment in red blood cells. Hemoglobin is remarkably suited to the task of transporting oxygen because it both combines with and releases oxygen. The higher concentration of oxygen in the alveoli, plus the slightly higher pH and slightly cooler temperature, causes hemoglobin to take up oxygen and become **oxyhemoglobin** (HbO_2). The lower concentration of oxygen in the tissues, plus the slightly lower pH and slightly warmer temperature in the tissues, causes hemoglobin to release oxygen and become deoxyhemoglobin (Hb). This equation summarizes our discussion of oxygen transport:

$$Hb \quad + \quad O_2 \underset{}{\overset{lungs}{\rightleftharpoons}} \quad HbO_2$$

Carbon Dioxide Transport

Transport of CO_2 to the lungs involves a number of steps. After CO_2 diffuses into the blood at the tissues, it enters the red blood cells, where:

1. A small amount is taken up by hemoglobin, forming **carbaminohemoglobin.**
2. Most of the CO_2 combines with water, forming carbonic acid (H_2CO_3). The carbonic acid dissociates to hydrogen ions (H^+) and bicarbonate ions (HCO_3^-). The release of these hydrogen ions explains why the blood in systemic capillaries has a lower pH than the blood in pulmonary capillaries.
3. The difference in pH is slight because the globin portion of hemoglobin combines with excess hydrogen ions and becomes **reduced hemoglobin (HHb).**

Bicarbonate ions are carried in the plasma because they diffuse out of red blood cells and go into the plasma. Most of the carbon dioxide in blood is carried as HCO_3^-, the **bicarbonate ion.** As bicarbonate ions diffuse out of red blood cells, chloride ions (Cl^-) diffuse into them. This so-called **chloride shift** maintains the electrical balance between the plasma and the red blood cells.

In pulmonary capillaries, a reverse reaction occurs. Bicarbonate combines with hydrogen ions to form carbonic acid, which this time splits into CO_2 and H_2O, and the CO_2 diffuses out of the blood into the alveoli. The following equation summarizes our discussion of carbon dioxide transport:

$$CO_2 \ + \ H_2O \underset{lungs}{\overset{tissues}{\rightleftharpoons}} H_2CO_3 \underset{lungs}{\overset{tissues}{\rightleftharpoons}} H^+ \ + \ HCO_3^-$$

14.4 Respiration and Health

The respiratory tract is constantly exposed to environmental air. The quality of this air can affect our health. The presence of a disease means that homeostasis is threatened, and if the condition is not brought under control, death is possible.

Upper Respiratory Tract Infections

The upper respiratory tract consists of the nasal cavities, the pharynx, and the larynx. Upper respiratory infections (URI) can spread from the nasal cavities to the sinuses, middle ears, and larynx. Viral infections sometimes lead to secondary bacterial infections. What we call "strep throat" is a primary bacterial infection caused by *Streptococcus pyogenes* that can lead to a generalized upper respiratory infection and even a systemic (affecting the body as a whole) infection. Although antibiotics have no effect on viral infections, they are successfully used to treat most bacterial infections, including strep throat. The symptoms of strep throat are severe sore throat, high fever, and white patches on a dark red throat.

Sinusitis

Sinusitis is an infection of the cranial sinuses, the cavities within the facial skeleton that drain into the nasal cavities. Only about 1–3% of upper respiratory infections are accompanied by sinusitis. Sinusitis develops when nasal congestion blocks the tiny openings leading to the sinuses. Symptoms include postnasal discharge as well as facial pain that worsens when the patient bends forward. Pain and tenderness usually occur over the lower forehead or over the cheeks. If the latter, toothache is also a complaint. Successful treatment depends on restoring proper drainage of the sinuses. Even a hot shower and sleeping upright can be helpful. Otherwise, spray decongestants are preferred over oral antihistamines, which thicken rather than liquefy the material trapped in the sinuses.

Otitis Media

Otitis media is a bacterial infection of the middle ear. The middle ear is not a part of the respiratory tract, but this infection is considered here because it is a complication often seen in children who have a nasal infection. Infection can spread by way of the **auditory (eustachian) tube** that leads from the nasopharynx to the middle ear. Pain is the primary symptom of a middle ear infection. A sense of fullness, hearing loss, vertigo (dizziness), and fever may also be present. Antibiotics almost always bring about a full recovery, and recurrence is probably due to a new infection. Tubes (called tympanostomy tubes) are sometimes placed in the eardrums of children with multiple recurrences to help prevent the buildup of pressure in the middle ear and the possibility of hearing loss. Normally, the tubes fall out with time.

Tonsillitis

Tonsillitis occurs when the **tonsils,** masses of lymphatic tissue in the pharynx, become inflamed and enlarged. The tonsils in the posterior wall of the nasopharynx are often called adenoids. If tonsillitis occurs frequently and enlargement makes breathing difficult, the tonsils can be removed surgically in a **tonsillectomy.** Fewer tonsillectomies are performed today than in the past because we now know that the tonsils remove many of the pathogens that enter the pharynx; therefore, they are a first line of defense against invasion of the body.

Laryngitis

Laryngitis is an infection of the larynx with accompanying hoarseness leading to the inability to talk in an audible voice. Usually, laryngitis disappears with treatment of the upper respiratory infection. Persistent hoarseness without the presence of an upper respiratory infection is one of the warning signs of cancer, and therefore should be looked into by a physician.

Lower Respiratory Tract Disorders

Lower respiratory tract disorders include infections, restrictive pulmonary disorders, obstructive pulmonary disorders, and lung cancer.

Lower Respiratory Infections

Acute bronchitis, pneumonia, and tuberculosis are infections of the lower respiratory tract. **Acute bronchitis** is an infection of the primary and secondary bronchi. Usually, it is preceded by a viral URI that has led to a secondary bacterial infection. Most likely, a nonproductive cough has become a deep cough that expectorates mucus and perhaps pus.

Pneumonia is a viral or bacterial infection of the lungs in which the bronchi and alveoli fill with thick fluid (Fig. 14.10). Most often, it is preceded by influenza. High fever and chills, with headache and chest pain, are symptoms of pneumonia. Rather than being a generalized lung infection, pneumonia may be localized in specific lobules of the lungs; obviously, the more lobules involved, the more serious is the infection. Pneumonia can be caused by a bacterium that is usually held in check but has gained the upper hand due to stress and/or reduced immunity. AIDS patients are subject to a particularly rare form of pneumonia caused by the protozoan *Pneumocystis carinii.* Pneumonia of this type is almost never seen in individuals with a healthy immune system.

Pulmonary tuberculosis is caused by the tubercle bacillus, a type of bacterium. When tubercle bacilli invade the lung tissue, the cells build a protective capsule about the foreigners, isolating them from the rest of the body. This tiny capsule is called a tubercle. If the resistance of the body is high, the imprisoned organisms die, but if the resistance is low, the organisms eventually can be liberated. If a chest X ray detects active tubercles, the individual is put on appropriate drug therapy to ensure the localization of the disease and the eventual destruction of any live bacteria. It is possible to tell if a person has ever been exposed to tuberculosis with a test in which a highly diluted extract of the bacillus is injected into the skin of the patient. A person who has never been in contact with the tubercle bacillus shows no reaction, but one who has had or is fighting an infection shows an area of inflammation that peaks in about 48 hours.

Restrictive Pulmonary Disorders

In restrictive pulmonary disorders, vital capacity is reduced because the lungs have lost their elasticity. Inhaling particles such as silica (sand), coal dust, asbestos, and, now it seems, fiberglass can lead to **pulmonary fibrosis,** a condition in which fibrous connective tissue builds up in the lungs. The lungs cannot inflate properly and are always tending toward deflation. Breathing asbestos is also associated with the development of cancer. Because asbestos was formerly used widely as a fireproofing and insulating agent, unwarranted exposure has occurred. It has been projected that two million deaths caused by asbestos exposure—mostly in the workplace—will occur in the United States between 1990 and 2020.

Obstructive Pulmonary Disorders

In obstructive pulmonary disorders, air does not flow freely in the airways, and the time it takes to inhale or exhale maximally is greatly increased. Several disorders, including chronic bronchitis, emphysema, and asthma, are referred to as chronic obstructive pulmonary disorders (COPD) because they tend to recur.

In **chronic bronchitis,** the airways are inflamed and filled with mucus. A cough that brings up mucus is common. The bronchi have undergone degenerative changes, including the loss of cilia and their normal cleansing action. Under these conditions, an infection is more likely to occur. Smoking cig-

Figure 14.10 Common bronchial and pulmonary diseases. Exposure to infectious pathogens and/or polluted air, including tobacco smoke, causes the diseases and disorders shown here.

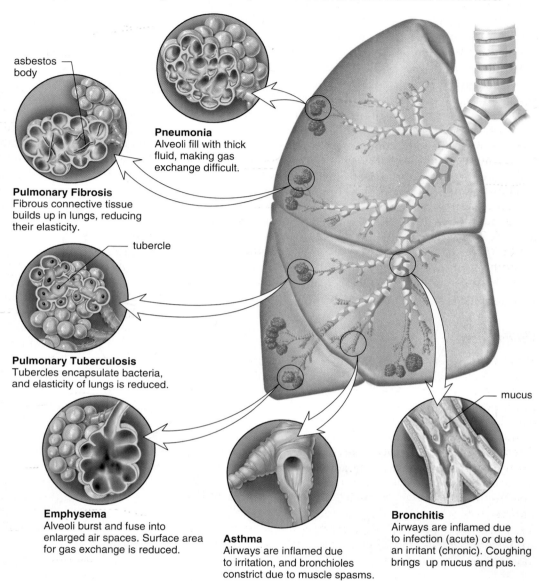

asbestos body

Pneumonia
Alveoli fill with thick fluid, making gas exchange difficult.

Pulmonary Fibrosis
Fibrous connective tissue builds up in lungs, reducing their elasticity.

tubercle

Pulmonary Tuberculosis
Tubercles encapsulate bacteria, and elasticity of lungs is reduced.

Emphysema
Alveoli burst and fuse into enlarged air spaces. Surface area for gas exchange is reduced.

Asthma
Airways are inflamed due to irritation, and bronchioles constrict due to muscle spasms.

mucus

Bronchitis
Airways are inflamed due to infection (acute) or due to an irritant (chronic). Coughing brings up mucus and pus.

arettes and cigars is the most frequent cause of chronic bronchitis. Exposure to other pollutants can also cause chronic bronchitis.

Emphysema is a chronic and incurable disorder in which the alveoli are distended and their walls damaged so that the surface area available for gas exchange is reduced. Emphysema is often preceded by chronic bronchitis. Air trapped in the lungs leads to alveolar damage and a noticeable ballooning of the chest. The elastic recoil of the lungs is reduced, so not only are the airways narrowed, but the driving force behind expiration is also reduced. The victim is breathless and may have a cough. Because the surface area for gas exchange is reduced, less oxygen reaches the heart and the brain. Even so, the heart works furiously to force more blood through the lungs, and an increased workload on the heart can result. Lack of oxygen to the brain can make the person feel depressed, sluggish, and irritable. Before therapy can begin, the patient must stop smoking. Then, exercise, drug therapy, supplemental oxygen, and surgery (see the What's New reading on page 280) may relieve the symptoms and possibly slow the progression of emphysema.

Asthma is a disease of the bronchi and bronchioles that is marked by wheezing, breathlessness, and sometimes a cough and expectoration of mucus. The airways are unusually sensitive to specific irritants, which can include a wide range of allergens such as pollen, animal dander, dust, cigarette smoke, and industrial fumes. Even cold air can be an irritant. When exposed to the irritant, the smooth muscle in the bronchioles undergoes spasms. It now appears that chemical mediators given off by immune cells in the bronchioles cause the spasms. Most asthma patients have some degree of bronchial inflammation that reduces the diameter of the airways and contributes to the seriousness of an attack. Asthma is not curable, but it is treatable. Special inhalers can control the inflammation and hopefully prevent an attack, while other types of inhalers can stop the muscle spasms should an attack occur.

Lung Cancer

Lung cancer used to be more prevalent in men than in women, but recently it has surpassed breast cancer as a cause of death in women. The recent increase in the incidence of lung cancer in women is directly correlated to increased numbers of women who smoke. Autopsies on smokers have revealed the progressive steps by which the most common form of lung cancer develops. The first event appears to be thickening and callusing of the cells lining the primary bronchi. (Callusing occurs whenever cells are exposed to irritants.) Then cilia are lost, making it impossible to prevent dust and dirt from settling in the lungs. Following this, cells with atypical nuclei appear in the callused lining. A tumor consisting of disordered cells with atypical nuclei is considered cancer in situ (at one location) (Fig. 14.11). A final step occurs when some of these cells break loose and penetrate other tissues, a process called metastasis. Now the cancer has spread. The original tumor may grow until a bronchus is blocked, cutting off the supply of air to that lung. The entire lung then collapses, the secretions trapped in the lung spaces become infected, and pneumonia or a lung abscess (localized area of pus) results. The only treatment that offers a possibility of cure is to remove a lobe or the whole lung before metastasis has had time to occur. This operation is called **pneumonectomy**. If the cancer has spread, chemotherapy and radiation are also required.

The Medical Focus on page 289 lists the various illnesses, including cancer, that are apt to occur when a person smokes. Current research indicates that passive smoking—exposure to smoke created by others who are smoking—can also cause lung cancer and other illnesses associated with smoking. If a person stops voluntary smoking and avoids passive smoking, and if the body tissues are not already cancerous, they may return to normal over time.

Figure 14.11 Normal lung versus cancerous lung. **a.** Normal lung with heart in place. Note the healthy red color. **b.** Lungs of a heavy smoker. Notice how black the lungs are except where cancerous tumors have formed.

a.

b.

Human Systems Work Together

Integumentary System

Gas exchange in lungs provides oxygen to skin and rids body of carbon dioxide from skin.

Skin helps protect respiratory organs and helps regulate body temperature.

How the Respiratory System works with other body systems

Cardiovascular System

Gas exchange in lungs rids body of carbon dioxide, helping to regulate the pH of blood; breathing aids venous return.

Blood vessels transport gases to and from lungs; blood services respiratory organs.

Skeletal System

Gas exchange in lungs provides oxygen and rids body of carbon dioxide.

Rib cage protects lungs and assists breathing; bones provide attachment sites for muscles involved in breathing.

Lymphatic System/Immunity

Tonsils and adenoids occur along respiratory tract; breathing aids lymph flow; lungs carry out gas exchange.

Lymphatic vessels pick up excess tissue fluid; immune system protects against respiratory tract and lung infections.

Muscular System

Lungs provide oxygen for contracting muscles and rid the body of carbon dioxide from contracting muscles.

Muscle contraction assists breathing; physical exercise increases respiratory capacity.

Digestive System

Gas exchange in lungs provides oxygen to the digestive tract and excretes carbon dioxide from the digestive tract.

Breathing is possible through the mouth because digestive tract and respiratory tract share the pharynx.

Nervous System

Lungs provide oxygen for neurons and rid the body of carbon dioxide produced by neurons.

Respiratory centers in brain regulate breathing rate.

Urinary System

Lungs excrete carbon dioxide, provide oxygen, and convert angiotensin I to angiotensin II, leading to kidney regulation.

Kidneys compensate for water lost through respiratory tract; work with lungs to maintain blood pH.

Endocrine System

Gas exchange in lungs provides oxygen and rids body of carbon dioxide.

Epinephrine promotes ventilation by dilating bronchioles; growth factors control production of red blood cells that carry oxygen.

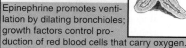

Reproductive System

Gas exchange increases during sexual activity.

Sexual activity increases breathing; pregnancy causes breathing rate and vital capacity to increase.

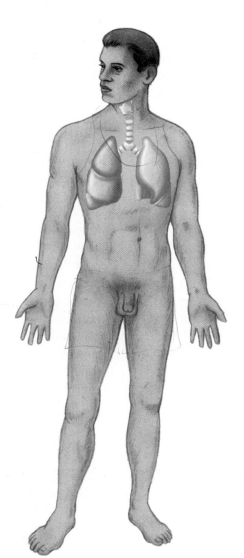

Basic Key Terms

alveolus (al-ve'o-lus), p. 279

aortic body (a-or'tik bod'e), p. 283

auditory tube (aw'dĭ-tor-e tūb), p. 286

bicarbonate ion (bi-kar'bo-nāt i'on), p. 285

bronchiole (brong'ke-ōl), p. 279

bronchus (brong'kus), p. 279

carbaminohemoglobin (kar-buh-me"no-he"mo-glo'bin), p. 285

carotid body (kar-ah'tid bod'e), p. 283

concha (kong'kuh), p. 277

epiglottis (ĕ"pĭ-glot'is), p. 278

expiration (eks"pĭ-ra'shun), p. 276

expiratory reserve volume (ek-spi'ruh-to-re re-zerv' vol'yūm), p. 281

external respiration (eks-ter'nal res"pĭ-ra'shun), p. 285

glottis (glot'is), p. 278

hemoglobin (he'mo-glo-bin), p. 285

inspiration (in"spĭ-ra'shun), p. 276

inspiratory reserve volume (in-spi'ruh-to-re re-zerv' vol'yūm), p. 281

internal respiration (in-ter'nal res"pĭ-ra'shun), p. 285

larynx (lār'inks), p. 278

lungs (lungz), p. 279

nasal cavities (na'zal kav'ĭ-tēz), p. 277

nose (nōz), p. 277

oxyhemoglobin (ok"se-he"mo-glo'bin), p. 285

paranasal sinus (pār-uh-na'zul si'nus), p. 277

pharynx (fār'inks), p. 277

pleura (pler'uh), p. 279

reduced hemoglobin (re-dūs'd he'mo-glo-bin), p. 285

residual volume (re-zid'yū-ul vol'yūm), p. 281

respiratory center (res'pĭ-ruh-tor-e sen'ter), p. 283

surface tension (ser'fus ten'shun), p. 279

surfactant (sur-fak'tant), p. 279

tidal volume (ti'dul vol'yūm), p. 281

tonsil (tahn'sil), p. 286

trachea (tra'ke-uh), p. 278

ventilation (ven"tĭ-la'shun), p. 282

vital capacity (vi'tal kuh-pas'ĭ-te), p. 281

vocal cord (vo'kul kord), p. 278

Clinical Key Terms

acute bronchitis (uh-kyūt brong-ki'tis) , p. 286

apnea (ap'ne-uh), p. 284

asthma (az'muh), p. 288

Cheyne-Stokes respiration (shān-stōks res"pĭ-ra'shun), p. 284

chronic bronchitis (kron'ik brong-ki'tis), p. 287

emphysema (em"fĭ-se'muh), p. 287

hyperpnea (hi"per-ne'uh), p. 284

infant respiratory distress syndrome (in'funt res'pĭ-ruh-tor-e dis-tres' sin'drōm), p. 279

laryngitis (lār-in-ji'tis), p. 286

lung cancer (lung kan'ser), p. 288

otitis media (o-ti'tis me'-de-uh), p. 286

pneumonectomy (nu-mah-nek'tuh-me), p. 288

pneumonia (nu-mo'ne-uh), p. 286

pulmonary fibrosis (pul'mo-nēr"e fi-bro'sis), p. 287

pulmonary tuberculosis (pul'mo-nēr"e tū-ber"kyū-lo'sis), p. 286

sinusitis (si-nŭ-si'tis), p. 286

tonsillectomy (ton'sĭ-lek'to-me), p. 286

tonsillitis (ton-sil-ī'tis), p. 286

tracheostomy (tra"ke-ahs'to-me), p. 278

Summary

14.1 **The Respiratory System**
   A. The nasal cavities, which filter, warm, and humidify incoming air, open into the pharynx.
   B. The food and air passages cross in the pharynx, which conducts air to the larynx and food to the esophagus.
   C. The larynx is the voice box. It houses the vocal cords. The glottis, a slit between the vocal cords, is covered by the epiglottis when food is being swallowed.
   D. The trachea and the primary bronchi are held open by cartilaginous rings. The rings gradually disappear as the primary bronchi branch into bronchioles, which enter the alveoli. The lungs are composed of the air tubes and alveoli beyond the primary bronchi and the alveoli.
   E. The respiratory membrane is the juxtaposed alveolar wall and the capillary wall. The large expanse and thinness of the respiratory membrane allows rapid gas exchange.

14.2 Mechanism of Breathing

A. Tidal volume is the amount of air inhaled and exhaled with each breath. Vital capacity is the total volume of air that can be moved in and out of the lungs during a single breath. Some air remains in the lungs after expiration. This is called the residual volume. Passages within the airways are called dead space because no gas exchange takes place in the airways.

B. Ventilation is the movement of gases into and out of the lungs. The pleural membranes, which enclose the lungs, attach them to the thoracic wall. During inspiration, the thoracic cavity increases in size as the diaphragm lowers, and the rib cage moves upward and outward. Therefore, the lungs expand, creating a partial vacuum, which causes air to rush in. During expiration, the diaphragm relaxes and resumes its dome shape. As the rib cage and lungs recoil, air is pushed out of the lungs. Expiration can be forceful when the internal intercostal muscles contract, causing the rib cage to move farther downward and inward. Also, contraction of the abdominal wall pushes the viscera against the diaphragm, and the increased pressure expels air.

C. The respiratory center in the medulla oblongata rhythmically controls the ventilation rate. The respiratory center increases the rate when CO_2 and H^+ levels increase, as detected by the center or the carotid and aortic bodies. The latter also detects a low O_2 level and stimulates the respiratory center, which then increases the ventilation rate.

14.3 Gas Exchange and Transport

A. Diffusion accounts for the movement of gases during external respiration and internal respiration. External respiration occurs when CO_2 moves from the area of higher concentration in the blood to lower concentration in the alveoli. O_2 moves from a higher concentration in the alveoli to a lower concentration in the blood. Internal respiration occurs when O_2 moves from a higher concentration in the blood to a lower concentration in the tissue fluid, and CO_2 moves from a higher concentration in the tissue fluid to a lower concentration in the blood. The occurrence of cellular respiration always causes gas transport.

B. Oxygen is transported to the tissues in combination with hemoglobin as oxyhemoglobin (HbO_2). Carbon dioxide is mainly carried to the lungs within the plasma as the bicarbonate ion (HCO_3^-). Hemoglobin combines with hydrogen ions and becomes reduced (HHb), and this helps maintain the pH level of the blood within normal limits.

14.4 Respiration and Health

A. A number of illnesses are associated with the respiratory tract. These disorders can be divided into those that affect the upper respiratory tract and those that affect the lower respiratory tract. Infections of the nasal cavities, sinuses, throat, tonsils, and larynx are all well known. In addition, infections can spread from the nasopharynx to the ears.

B. The lower respiratory tract is subject to infections such as acute bronchitis, pneumonia, and pulmonary tuberculosis. In restrictive pulmonary disorders, exemplified by pulmonary fibrosis, the lungs lose their elasticity. In obstructive pulmonary disorders, exemplified by chronic bronchitis, emphysema, and asthma, the bronchi (and bronchioles) do not effectively conduct air to and from the lungs. Smoking, which is associated with chronic bronchitis and emphysema, can eventually lead to lung cancer.

14.5 Effects of Aging

All aspects of respiration decline with age. The elderly often die from pulmonary infections.

14.6 Homeostasis

A. The respiratory system carries on two main functions: (1) gas exchange, which is essential to the process of cellular respiration, and (2) maintenance of blood pH.

B. The respiratory system works with other systems of the body. The cardiovascular system transports gases, and breathing helps systemic venous blood return to the heart. The respiratory tract assists defense against pathogens by keeping the tract clean of debris. Also, the tonsils are lymphatic tissue where antigens are presented to T cells. The nervous system maintains rhythmic ventilation, and the sensory organs for olfaction are located in the nasal cavities. The respiratory center responds to the increased gas exchange needs of the muscular system when we exercise.

Study Questions

1. Name and explain the four events that comprise respiration. (p. 276)

2. What is the path of air from the nose to the lungs? Describe the structure and state the function of all the organs mentioned. (pp. 276–80)

3. What is the respiratory membrane, and how does its structure promote rapid gas exchange? (p. 280)

4. What is the difference between tidal volume and vital capacity? Of the air we inhale, some is not used for gas exchange. Why not? (p. 281)

5. What three conditions should be borne in mind in order to understand ventilation? (p. 282)

6. Explain the volume and pressure changes necessary to inspiration and expiration. How is ventilation controlled? (pp. 282–83)

7. Contrast external respiration with internal respiration, and explain why there is a flow of gases during each of these. (p. 285)

8. How are oxygen and carbon dioxide transported in the blood? What role does hemoglobin play in the transport of CO_2? (p. 285)

9. Name and describe several upper and several lower respiratory tract disorders (other than cancer). If appropriate, explain why breathing is difficult with these conditions. (pp. 286–88)

10. List the steps by which lung cancer develops. (p. 288)

Objective Questions

Fill in the blanks.

1. In tracing the path of air, the _____ immediately follows the pharynx.
2. The lungs contain air sacs called _____.
3. The breathing rate is primarily regulated by the amount of _____ in the blood.
4. Air enters the lungs after they have _____.
5. Gas exchange is dependent on the physical process of _____.
6. During external respiration, oxygen _____ the blood.

7. During internal respiration, carbon dioxide _____ the blood.
8. Carbon dioxide is carried in the blood as _____ ions.
9. The most likely cause of emphysema and chronic bronchitis is _____.
10. Most cases of lung cancer actually begin in the _____.
11. The amount of air moved in and out of the respiratory system with each normal breath is called the _____.

12. The total amount of air that can be moved in and out of the lungs during a single breath is called the _____.
13. The _____ closes the opening into the larynx during swallowing.
14. The respiratory membrane consists of the walls of the _____ and _____.
15. Label the following diagram of the respiratory tract.

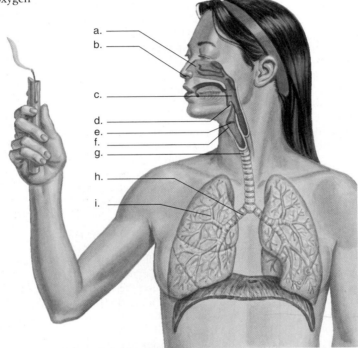

a.
b.
c.
d.
e.
f.
g.
h.
i.

Medical Terminology Reinforcement Exercise

Consult Appendix B for help in pronouncing and analyzing the meaning of the terms that follow.

1. eupnea (yūp-ne′uh)
2. nasopharyngitis (na″zo-făr″in-ji′tis)
3. tracheostomy (tra″ke-ahs′to-me)
4. pneumonomelanosis (nu-mo″no-mel″uh-no′sis)
5. pleuropericarditis (pler″o-pĕr″ĭ-kar″di′tis)
6. bronchoscopy (brong-kos′kuh-pe)
7. dyspnea (disp′ne-uh)
8. laryngospasm (luh-ring′go-spazm)
9. hemothorax (he″mo-tho′raks)
10. otorhinolaryngology (o″to-ri″no-lăr″in-gol′o-je)
11. hypoxemia (hi″pok-se′me-uh)
12. pulmonectomy (pul-mo-nek′to-me)
13. hypercapnea (hi-per-kap′ne-uh)
14. spirometry (spy-rom′uh-tre)
15. thoracentesis (thor′uh-sen-te′sis)

Website Link

Visit the Student Edition of the Online Learning Center at http://www.mhhe.com/maderap5 for additional quizzes, interactive learning exercises, and other study tools.

The Digestive System

The surface of the human tongue, showing papillae (purple) that contain taste buds (SEM).

Chapter Outline & Learning Objectives

After you have studied this chapter, you should be able to:

15.1 Anatomy of the Digestive System (p. 296)

- Trace the path of food through the alimentary canal, and describe the general structure and function of each organ mentioned.
- Describe peristalsis, and state its function.
- Describe the wall of the small intestine, and relate its anatomy to nutrient absorption.
- Name the hormones produced by the alimentary canal that help control digestive secretions.

15.2 Accessory Organs of Digestion (p. 308)

- Name five accessory organs of digestion.
- Describe the location, anatomy, and functions of the pancreas, the liver, and the gallbladder.

- Name and describe three disorders of the liver.

15.3 Chemical Digestion (p. 311)

- Name and state the functions of the digestive enzymes for carbohydrates, proteins, and fats.

15.4 Effects of Aging (p. 312)

- Describe the anatomical and physiological changes that occur in the digestive system as we age.

15.5 Homeostasis (p. 312)

- Describe how the digestive system works with other systems of the body to maintain homeostasis.

15.6 Nutrition (p. 314)

- State the functions of glucose, fats, and amino acids in the body.
- Define the terms essential fatty acid, essential amino acid, and vitamin.
- Describe the functions of the major vitamins and minerals in the body.

Medical Focus

Human Teeth (p. 297)

Constipation (p. 306)

Antioxidants (p. 315)

15.1 Anatomy of the Digestive System

The organs of the digestive system are located within a tube called the **alimentary canal,** or **gastrointestinal tract.** The tube begins with the mouth and ends with the anus (Fig. 15.1). Although the term digestion, strictly speaking, means the breakdown of food by enzymatic action, we will expand the term to include both the physical and chemical processes that reduce food to small, soluble molecules.

Figure 15.1 Digestive system. Trace the path of food from the mouth to the anus. The large intestine consists of the cecum, the colon (composed of the ascending, transverse, descending, and sigmoid colon), the rectum, and the anal canal. Note also the location of the accessory organs of digestion: the pancreas, the liver, and the gallbladder.

The functions of the digestive system are to:

1. ingest the food;
2. break food down into small molecules that can cross plasma membranes;
3. absorb these nutrient molecules;
4. eliminate nondigestible wastes.

The Mouth

The **mouth,** which receives food, is bounded externally by the lips and cheeks. The space between the lips and cheeks and the teeth is the **vestibule.**

The tongue is composed of skeletal muscle whose contraction changes the shape of the tongue. Muscles exterior to the tongue cause it to move about. Rough projections on the tongue, called papillae, help it handle food and also contain the sensory receptors called taste buds. A fold of mucous membrane, called a frenulum, on the underside of the tongue attaches it to the floor of the mouth. If the frenulum is too short, the individual cannot speak clearly and is said to be tongue-tied. Posteriorly, the tongue is anchored to the hyoid bone.

The mouth has a roof that separates it from the nasal cavities. The roof has two parts: an anterior (toward the front) **hard palate** and a posterior (toward the back) **soft palate** (see Fig. 15.2). The hard palate contains several bones, while the soft palate is muscular only. The soft palate ends in a finger-shaped projection called the **uvula.**

Three pairs of **salivary glands** send juices (saliva) by way of ducts to the mouth. The parotid glands lie anterior and somewhat inferior to the ears between the cheek and the masseter muscle. They have ducts that open on the inner surface of the cheek at the location of the second upper molar. The parotid glands swell when a person has the mumps, a disease caused by a viral infection. The sublingual glands are located beneath the tongue, and the submandibular glands are in the floor of the mouth on the inside surface of the lower jaw. The ducts from the sublingual and submandibular glands open under the tongue. You can locate the openings for the salivary glands if you use your tongue to feel for small flaps on the inside of your cheek and under your tongue. Saliva contains bicarbonate and an enzyme called **salivary amylase** that begins the process of digesting starch.

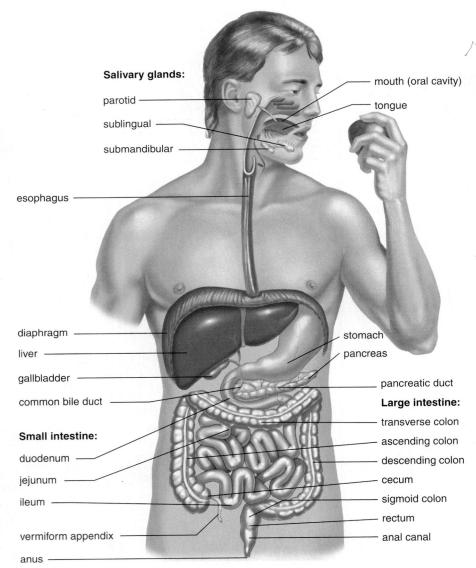

Salivary glands:

parotid

sublingual

submandibular

esophagus

diaphragm

liver

gallbladder

common bile duct

Small intestine:

duodenum

jejunum

ileum

vermiform appendix

anus

mouth (oral cavity)

tongue

stomach

pancreas

pancreatic duct

Large intestine:

transverse colon

ascending colon

descending colon

cecum

sigmoid colon

rectum

anal canal

Medical Focus

Human Teeth

During the first two years of life, the 20 deciduous, or baby, teeth appear. Eventually, the deciduous teeth are replaced by the adult teeth. Normally, adults have 32 teeth (Fig. 15A*a*). One-half of each jaw has teeth of four different types: (1) two chisel-shaped incisors for biting, (2) one pointed canine (cuspid) for tearing, (3) two fairly flat premolars (bicuspids) for grinding, and (4) three more flattened molars for crushing. The last molars, called the wisdom teeth, may fail to come in, or if they do, they may grow in crooked and be useless. Frequently, wisdom teeth are extracted.

Each tooth (Fig. 15A*b*) has a crown and a root. The crown has a layer of enamel, an extremely hard outer covering of calcium compounds; dentin, a thick layer of bonelike material; and an inner pulp, which contains the nerves and blood vessels.

Dentin and pulp are also in the root. **Caries,** tooth decay commonly called cavities, occur when bacteria within the mouth break down sugar and give off acids that corrode the teeth. Once these acids dissolve the enamel and dentin, the pulp is compromised, triggering a toothache. Fluoride treatments, particularly in children, can make the enamel stronger and more resistant to decay.

Gum disease is more likely as we age. One example is inflammation of the gums, called **gingivitis,** that may spread to the periodontal membrane lining the tooth socket (Fig. 15A*b*). When this occurs, the individual develops **periodontitis,** characterized by loss of bone and loosening of the teeth. Brushing and flossing the teeth after every meal cleans the teeth and stimulates the gums, preventing these conditions. Care should be taken to brush away from the gums to prevent gum recession.

Figure 15A **a.** The chisel-shaped incisors bite; the pointed canines tear; the fairly flat premolars grind; and the flattened molars crush food. The last molar, called a wisdom tooth, may fail to erupt, or if it does, it is sometimes crooked and useless. Often dentists recommend the extraction of the wisdom teeth. **b.** Longitudinal section of a tooth. The crown is the portion that projects above the gum line and can be replaced by a dentist if damaged. When a "root canal" is done, the nerves are removed. When the periodontal membrane is inflamed, the teeth can loosen.

Table 15.1 Path of Food

Organ	Function of Organ	Special Feature(s)	Function of Special Feature(s)
Oral cavity	Receives food, starts digestion of starch	Teeth Tongue	Chew food Forms bolus
Pharynx	Passageway	—	—
Esophagus	Passageway	—	—
Stomach	Storage of food, acidity kills bacteria; starts digestion of protein	Gastric glands	Release gastric juices
Small intestine	Digestion of all foods, absorption of nutrients	Intestinal glands Villi	Release fluids Absorb nutrients
Large intestine	Absorption of water, storage of indigestible remains	—	—

The Pharynx

Table 15.1 traces the path of food. From the mouth, food passes through the pharynx and esophagus to the stomach, small intestine, and large intestine. The food passage and the air passage cross in the **pharynx** because the trachea is ante-rior to the esophagus, a long muscular tube that takes food to the stomach (Fig. 15.2).

The tonsils are embedded in the mucous membrane of the pharynx. The **palatine tonsils** are on either side of the tongue close to the soft palate, and the **pharyngeal tonsils,** or adenoids, are in the nasopharynx. The tonsils help protect the body against infection. When the tonsils become inflamed, the person has tonsillitis. If the tonsillitis keeps recurring, the tonsils may be surgically removed (called a tonsillectomy).

The pharynx has three parts: (1) The **nasopharynx,** posterior to the nasal cavity, serves as a passageway for air; (2) the **oropharynx,** posterior to the soft palate, is a passageway for both air and food; and (3) the **laryngopharynx,** just inferior to the esophagus, is a passageway for food entering the esophagus.

Figure 15.2 Swallowing. When food is swallowed, the soft palate closes off the nasopharynx, and the epiglottis covers the glottis, forcing the bolus to pass down the esophagus. Therefore, a person does not breathe while swallowing.

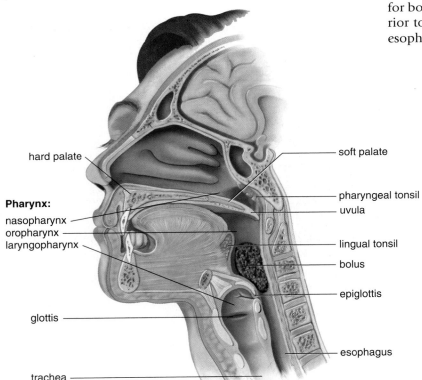

hard palate
soft palate

Pharynx:
nasopharynx
oropharynx
laryngopharynx

pharyngeal tonsil
uvula

lingual tonsil
bolus

epiglottis

glottis

esophagus

trachea

Swallowing

During swallowing, food normally enters the esophagus because other possible avenues are blocked. Swallowing is a **reflex action** performed automatically (without our willing it). When we swallow, the soft palate moves back to close off the **nasopharynx,** and the trachea moves up under the **epiglottis** so that food is less likely to enter it. (We do not breathe when we swallow.) The tongue presses against the soft palate, sealing off the oral cavity, and the esophagus opens to receive a food **bolus** (Fig. 15.2).

Unfortunately, we have all had the unpleasant experience of having food "go the wrong way." The wrong way may be either into the nasal cavities or into the trachea. If it is the latter, coughing will most likely force the food up out of the trachea and into the pharynx again.

The Esophagus

The **esophagus** is a muscular tube that passes from the pharynx through the thoracic cavity and diaphragm into the abdominal cavity, where it joins the stomach. The esophagus is ordinarily collapsed, but it opens and receives the bolus when swallowing occurs.

A rhythmic contraction called **peristalsis** pushes the food along the alimentary canal. Peristalsis begins in the esophagus and continues in all the organs of the alimentary canal. Occasionally, peristalsis begins even though there is no food in the esophagus. This produces the sensation of a lump in the throat.

The esophagus plays no role in the chemical digestion of food. Its sole purpose is to conduct the food bolus from the mouth to the stomach. **Sphincters** are muscles that encircle tubes and act as valves; tubes close when sphincters contract, and they open when sphincters relax. The entrance of the esophagus to the stomach is marked by a constriction, often called the esophageal sphincter, although the muscle is not as developed as in a true sphincter. Relaxation of the sphincter allows the bolus to pass into the stomach, while contraction prevents the acidic contents of the stomach from backing up into the esophagus.

Heartburn, which feels like a burning pain rising up into the throat, occurs during reflux when some of the stomach contents escape into the esophagus. When vomiting occurs, a contraction of the abdominal muscles and diaphragm propels the contents of the stomach upward through the esophagus.

The Wall of the Digestive Tract

The wall of the esophagus in the abdominal cavity is comparable to that of the alimentary canal, which has these layers (Fig. 15.3):

Mucosa (mucous membrane layer) A layer of epithelium supported by connective tissue and smooth muscle lines the **lumen** (central cavity). This layer contains glandular epithelial cells that secrete digestive enzymes and goblet cells that secrete mucus.

Submucosa (submucosal layer) A broad band of loose connective tissue that contains blood vessels lies beneath the mucosa. Lymph nodules, called Peyer patches, are in the submucosa. Like the tonsils, they help protect us from disease.

Muscularis (smooth muscle layer) Two layers of smooth muscle make up this section. The inner, circular layer encircles the gut; the outer, longitudinal layer lies in the same direction as the gut. (The stomach also has oblique muscles.)

Serosa (serous membrane layer) Most of the alimentary canal has a serosa, a very thin, outermost layer of squamous epithelium supported by connective tissue. The serosa secretes a serous fluid that keeps the outer surface of the intestines moist so that the organs of the abdominal cavity slide against one another. The esophagus has an outer layer composed only of loose connective tissue called the *adventitia*.

Figure 15.3 Wall of the alimentary canal. **a.** Several different types of tissues are found in the wall of the alimentary canal. Note the placement of circular muscle inside longitudinal muscle. **b.** Micrograph of the wall of the esophagus.

Figure 15.4 Anatomy and histology of the stomach. **a.** The stomach has a thick wall with deep folds that allow it to expand and fill with food. **b.** The lining of the stomach has gastric glands, which secrete mucus and a gastric juice active in protein digestion.

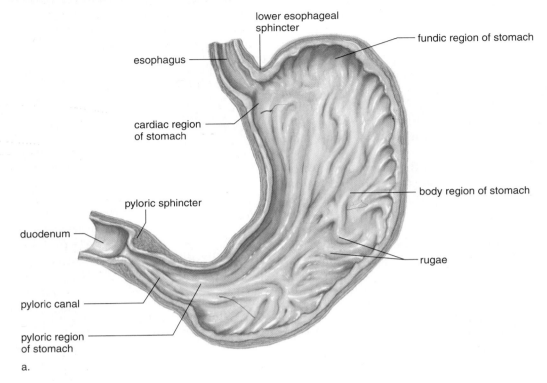

lower esophageal sphincter

fundic region of stomach

esophagus

cardiac region of stomach

body region of stomach

pyloric sphincter

duodenum

rugae

pyloric canal

pyloric region of stomach

a.

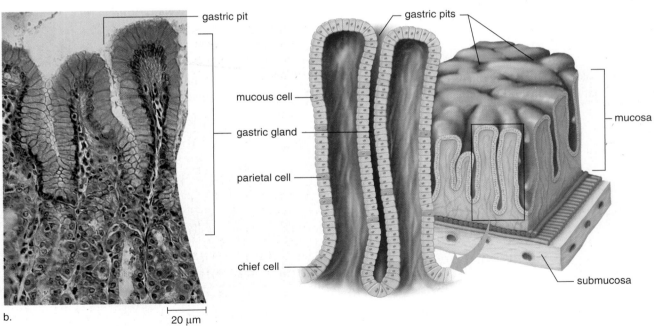

gastric pit

gastric pits

mucous cell

gastric gland

mucosa

parietal cell

chief cell

submucosa

b.

20 μm

The Stomach

The **stomach** (Fig. 15.4) is a thick-walled, J-shaped organ that lies on the left side of the abdominal cavity deep to the liver and diaphragm. The stomach is continuous with the esophagus above and the duodenum of the small intestine below.

The length of the stomach remains at about 25 cm (10 in.) regardless of the amount of food it holds, but the diameter varies, depending on how full it is. As the stomach expands, deep folds in its wall, called **rugae,** gradually disappear. When full, it can hold about 4 liters (1 gallon). The stomach receives food from the esophagus, stores food, mixes food with its juices (thereby starting the digestion of proteins), and moves food into the small intestine.

Regions of the Stomach

The stomach has four regions. The cardiac region, which is near the heart, surrounds the lower esophageal sphincter where food enters the stomach. The fundic region, which holds food temporarily, is an expanded portion superior to the cardiac region. The body region, which comes next, is the main part. The pyloric region narrows to become the pyloric canal leading to the pyloric sphincter through which food enters the duodenum, the first part of the small intestine.

Digestive Functions of the Stomach

The stomach both physically and chemically acts on food. Its wall contains three muscle layers: One layer is longitudinal, another is circular, and the third is obliquely arranged. This muscular wall not only moves the food along, but it also churns, mixing the food with gastric juice and breaking it down to small pieces.

The term *gastric* always refers to the stomach. The columnar epithelial lining of the stomach has millions of *gastric pits*, which lead into **gastric glands** (Fig. 15.4b,c). The gastric glands produce gastric juice, which contains pepsinogen, HCl, and mucus. *Chief cells* secrete pepsinogen, which becomes the enzyme **pepsin** when exposed to hydrochloric acid (HCl) released by *parietal cells*. The HCl causes the stomach to have a high acidity with a pH of about 2, and this is beneficial because it kills most of the bacteria present in food. Although HCl does not digest food, it does break down the connective tissue of meat and activate pepsin.

The wall of the stomach is protected by the thick layer of mucus secreted by the *mucous cells*. If, by chance, HCl penetrates this mucus, the wall can begin to break down, and an ulcer results. An **ulcer** is an open sore in the wall caused by the gradual disintegration of tissue. It now appears that most ulcers are due to a bacterial infection *(Helicobacter pylori)* that impairs the ability of mucous cells to produce protective mucus.

Alcohol is absorbed in the stomach, but food substances are not. Normally, the stomach empties in about 2–6 hours. When food leaves the stomach, it is a thick, soupy liquid called **chyme.** Chyme enters the small intestine in squirts by way of the pyloric sphincter, which acts like a valve, repeatedly opening and closing.

Peritoneum

The abdominal wall and the organs of the abdomen are covered by peritoneum, a serous membrane (Fig. 15.5). The portion of the peritoneum that lines the wall is called the parietal peritoneum. The portion that covers the organs is called the visceral peritoneum. In between the organs, the visceral peritoneum is a double-layered mesentery that supports the visceral organs, including the blood vessels, nerves, and lymphatic vessels

Some portions of the mesentery have specific names. The **lesser omentum** is mesentery that runs between the stomach and the liver. The **greater omentum** is indeed "greater." It hangs down in front of the intestines like a large, double-layered apron. The greater omentum has several functions: It contains fat that cushions and insulates the abdominal cavity; it contains macrophages that can take up and rid the body of pathogens; and it can wall off portions of the alimentary wall that may be infected, keeping the infection from spreading to other parts of the so-called peritoneal cavity.

Figure 15.5 Mesentery formed by two layers of the peritoneal membrane supports the abdominal viscera. Deep folds of the peritoneal membrane, called the greater omentum, cover these organs anteriorly.

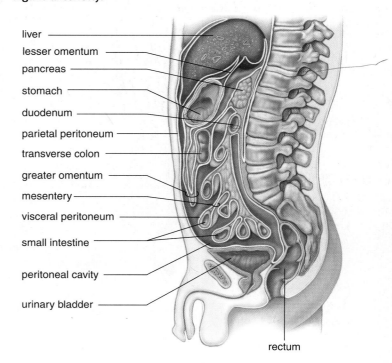

liver
lesser omentum
pancreas
stomach
duodenum
parietal peritoneum
transverse colon
greater omentum
mesentery
visceral peritoneum
small intestine
peritoneal cavity
urinary bladder

rectum

The Small Intestine

The **small intestine** extends from the pyloric valve of the stomach to the ileocecal valve, where it joins the large intestine. It is named for its small diameter (compared to that of the large intestine), but perhaps it should be called the long intestine. The small intestine takes up a large portion of the abdominal cavity, averaging about 6 m (18 ft) in length.

All the contents of food—fats, proteins, and carbohydrates—are digested in the small intestine to soluble molecules that can be absorbed. To this end, the small intestine receives secretions from the pancreas and liver and produces intestinal juices. Absorption of nutrients for the body's cells, such as amino acids and sugars, occurs in the small intestine. It also transports nondigestible remains to the large intestine.

Regions of the Small Intestine

The small intestine has the following regions (Fig. 15.6):

Duodenum The first 25 cm (10 in.) contain distinctive glands that secrete mucus and also receive the pancreatic secretions and the bile from the liver through a common duct. Folds and villi (Fig. 15.6) are more numerous at the end than at the beginning.

Jejunum The next 1 m (3 ft) contains folds and villi, more at the beginning than at the end.

Ileum The last 2 m (6–7 ft) contain fewer folds and villi than the jejunum. The ileum wall contains Peyer patches, aggregates of lymph nodules mentioned in Chapter 13.

Figure 15.6 Regions of the small intestine. The duodenum is attached to the stomach. The jejunum leads to the ileum, which is attached to the large intestine.

stomach

duodenum (25 cm)

ascending colon

jejunum (1m)

cecum

mesentery

appendix

ileum (2 m)

Wall of the Small Intestine

It has been suggested that the surface area of the small intestine is approximately that of a tennis court. Three features contribute to increasing its surface area: circular folds, villi, and microvilli (Fig. 15.7). The **circular folds** are permanent transverse folds involving the mucosa and submucosa of the small intestine. The **villi** (sing., villus) are fingerlike projections of the mucosa into the lumen of the small intestine. The villi are so numerous and closely packed that they give the wall a velvet-like appearance. A villus has an outer layer of columnar epithelial cells, and each of these cells has thousands of microscopic extensions called **microvilli.** Collectively, in electron micrographs, microvilli give the villi a fuzzy border known as a "brush border" (Fig. 15.7d). Because the microvilli bear the intestinal enzymes, these enzymes are called brush-border enzymes.

Functions of the Small Intestine The digestive process is brought to completion in the small intestine. Ducts from the gallbladder and pancreas join to form one duct that enters the duodenum (see Fig. 15.8). The small intestine receives bile from the gallbladder and pancreatic juice from the pancreas via this duct. **Bile** emulsifies fat—emulsification causes fat droplets to disperse in water. The intestine has a slightly basic pH because pancreatic juice contains sodium bicarbonate ($NaHCO_3$), which neutralizes chyme. The enzymes in pancreatic juice and the enzymes produced by the intestinal wall complete the process of food digestion.

The other primary function of the small intestine is *absorption of nutrients*. The tremendous increase in surface area created by the circular folds, villi, and microvilli makes this an efficient process—the greater the surface area, the greater is the volume of intake in a given unit of time. Also, a villus contains a generous supply of blood capillaries and a small lymphatic capillary, called a **lacteal** (Fig. 15.7c,d). The lymphatic system, as you know, is an adjunct to the cardiovascular system; its vessels carry a fluid called lymph to the cardiovascular veins. Sugars (digested in part from carbohydrates) and amino acids (digested from protein) enter the blood capillaries of a villus. Glycerol and fatty acids (digested from fats) enter the epithelial cells of the villi, and within these cells are joined and packaged as lipoprotein droplets, which enter a lacteal. After nutrients are absorbed, they are eventually carried to all the cells of the body by the bloodstream.

As we noted previously, a third function of the small intestine is movement of nondigested remains to the large intestine. The wall of the small intestine has two types of movements: segmentation and peristalsis. Segmentation refers to localized contractions and constrictions that serve to bring chyme into contact with digestive juices and to encourage absorption. Peristalsis in particular then moves nondigested remains toward the large intestine.

Figure 15.7 Anatomy of the small intestine. The wall of the small intestine has folds that bear fingerlike projections called villi. Villi in turn have projections called microvilli. The products of digestion are absorbed by microvilli and they enter the blood capillaries and the lacteals of the villi.

lumen

circular folds

a. **Small intestine**

mucosa

submucosa

circular muscle

longitudinal muscle

serosa

villi

b. **Section of intestinal wall**

100 μm

villus

lacteal

blood capillaries

goblet cell

Peyer patch

arteriole

venule

lymphatic vessel

c. **Villi**

d. **Electron micrograph of microvilli**

Regulation of Digestive Secretions

The secretion of digestive juices is promoted by the nervous system and by hormones. A **hormone** is a substance produced by one set of cells that affects a different set of cells, the so-called target cells. Hormones are usually transported by the bloodstream. For example, when a person has eaten a meal particularly rich in protein, the stomach produces the hormone gastrin. Gastrin enters the bloodstream, and soon the stomach is churning, and the secretory activity of gastric glands is increasing. A hormone produced by the duodenal wall, GIP (gastric inhibitory peptide), works opposite to gastrin: It inhibits gastric gland secretion.

Cells of the duodenal wall produce two other hormones that are of particular interest—secretin and CCK (cholecystokinin). Acid, especially hydrochloric acid (HCl) present in chyme, stimulates the release of secretin, while partially digested protein and fat stimulate the release of CCK. Soon after these hormones enter the bloodstream, the pancreas increases its output of pancreatic juice, which helps digest food, and the gallbladder increases its output of bile. The gallbladder contracts to release stored bile. Figure 15.8 summarizes the actions of gastrin, secretin, and CCK.

Figure 15.8 Hormonal control of digestive gland secretions. Gastrin (blue), produced by the lower part of the stomach, enters the bloodstream and thereafter stimulates the upper part of the stomach to produce more gastric juice. Secretin (green) and CCK (purple), produced by the duodenal wall, stimulate the pancreas to secrete its juice and the gallbladder to release bile.

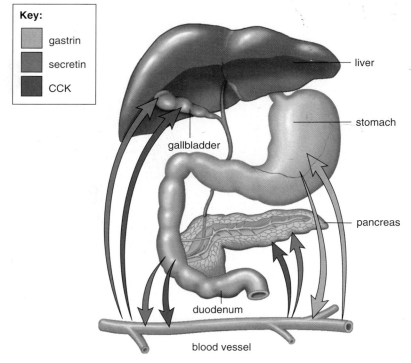

Key:
- gastrin
- secretin
- CCK

liver

stomach

gallbladder

pancreas

duodenum

blood vessel

The Large Intestine

The **large intestine,** which includes the cecum, the colon, the rectum, and the anal canal (Fig. 15.9), is larger in diameter than the small intestine (6.5 cm compared to 2.5 cm), but it is shorter in length (see Fig. 15.1). The large intestine absorbs water, salts, and some vitamins. It also stores indigestible material until it is eliminated at the anus.

The **cecum,** which lies below the junction with the small intestine, is the blind end of the large intestine. The cecum has a small projection called the **vermiform appendix** (*vermiform* means wormlike). In humans, the appendix also may play a role in fighting infections. This organ is subject to inflammation, a condition called appendicitis. If inflamed, the appendix should be removed before the fluid content rises to the point that the appendix bursts, a situation that may cause **peritonitis,** a generalized infection of the lining of the abdominal cavity. Peritonitis can lead to death.

The **colon** has four portions: the **ascending colon,** which goes up the right side of the body to the level of the liver; the **transverse colon,** which crosses the abdominal cavity just below the liver and the stomach; the **descending colon,** which passes down the left side of the body; and the **sigmoid colon,** which enters the **rectum,** the last 20 cm of the large intestine. The rectum opens at the **anus,** where **defecation,** the expulsion of feces, occurs. When feces are forced into the rectum by peristalsis, a defecation reflex occurs. The stretching of the rectal wall initiates nerve impulses to the spinal cord, and shortly thereafter the rectal muscles contract and the anal sphincters relax (see Fig. 15B). Ridding the body of indigestible remains is another way the digestive system helps maintain homeostasis.

Feces are three-quarters water and one-quarter solids. Bacteria, **fiber** (indigestible remains), and other indigestible materials are in the solid portion. Bacterial action on indigestible materials causes the odor of feces and also accounts for the presence of gas. A breakdown product of bilirubin (see page 310) and the presence of oxidized iron cause the brown color of feces.

For many years, it was believed that facultative bacteria (bacteria that can live with or without oxygen), such as *Escherichia coli,* were the major inhabitants of the colon, but new culture methods show that over 99% of the colon bacteria are obligate anaerobes (bacteria that die in the presence of oxygen). Not only do the bacteria break down indigestible material, but they also produce B-complex vitamins and most of the vitamin K needed by our bodies. In this way, they perform a service for us.

Water is considered unsafe for swimming when the coliform (nonpathogenic intestinal) bacterial count reaches a certain number. A high count indicates that a significant amount of feces has entered the water. The more feces present, the greater is the possibility that disease-causing bacteria are also present.

Figure 15.9 The large intestine. **a.** The colon has four regions: the ascending colon, the transverse colon, the descending colon, and the sigmoid colon. **b.** The rectum and anal canal are at the distal end of the alimentary canal. **c.** The intestinal mucosa has many goblet cells.

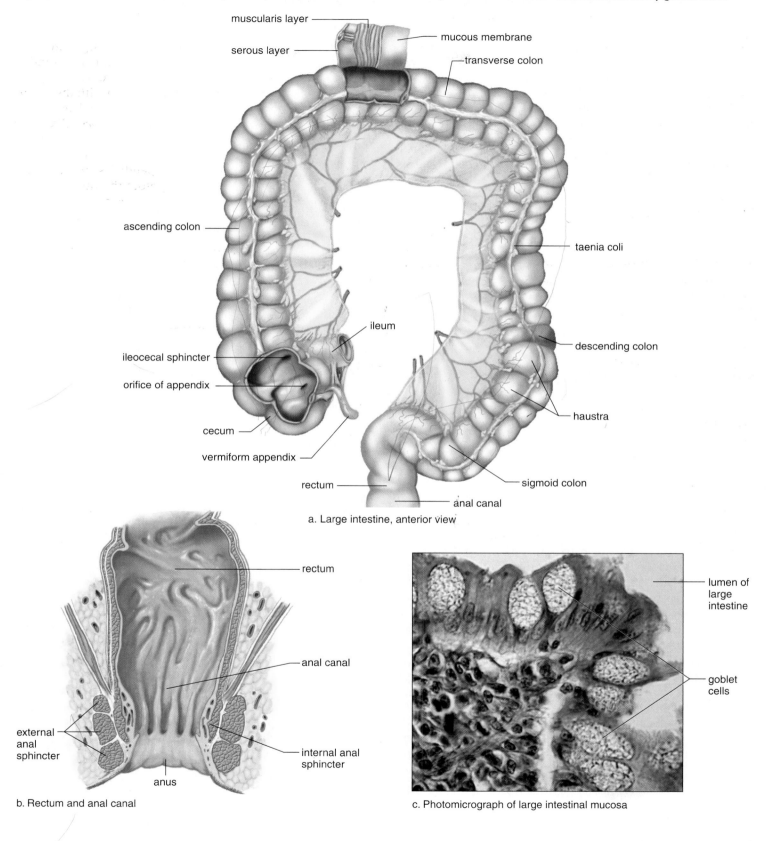

a. Large intestine, anterior view

b. Rectum and anal canal

c. Photomicrograph of large intestinal mucosa

Constipation

The colon of the large intestine has four regions: the ascending colon, the transverse colon, the descending colon, and the sigmoid colon (see Fig. 15.9a). Water is removed from the nondigestible intestinal contents entering the ascending colon from the small intestine. At this point, bacteria begin their action; they use cellulose as an energy source as they produce fatty acids and vitamins that can also be used by their host. They also release hydrogen gas and sulfur-containing compounds that contribute to human flatulence (gas). Feces, which consist of nondigested intestinal contents, bacteria, and sloughed-off intestinal cells, begin to form in the transverse colon. From there, they are propelled down the descending colon toward the rectum by periodic, firm contractions called peristalsis. When sufficient feces are in the rectum (130–200 grams), a defecatory urge is felt. The involuntary defecation reflex contracts the rectal muscles and relaxes the internal anal sphincter, a ring of muscle that closes off the rectum (Fig. 15B). Then, feces move toward the anus. A pushing motion, along with relaxation of the external anal sphincter, propels feces from the body. Since these activities are under voluntary control, it is possible to control defecation.

Defecation normally occurs from three times a week to three times a day; therefore, some variation in occurrence is nothing to worry about. However, if the frequency of defecation declines and if defecation becomes difficult, constipation is present. If constipation is a continuing problem, a physician can help record the movement of materials through the large intestine via several tests. The patient swallows about 20 small markers that will show up on an X ray. At intervals during the following week, X rays are taken, and the number and locations of the markers are noted. If muscle contraction of the intestinal wall is insufficient, the markers move slowly along their course. Injured nerves, certain drugs, dehydration, and prolonged overuse of stimulatory laxatives can bring about this difficulty. Some or all of these problems frequently occur in the elderly. On the other hand, markers may move normally at first and then slow down considerably in the descending colon and rectum. Habitual disregard of the defecatory urge may have caused this problem, or a cancerous polyp might be obstructing normal movement. If the former is the case, it is possible to retrain the rectum to work properly. Sitting on the toilet for about 20 minutes each morning

Diarrhea and Constipation

Two common everyday complaints associated with the large intestine are **diarrhea** and **constipation.** The major causes of diarrhea are infection of the lower intestinal tract and nervous stimulation. In the case of infection, such as food poisoning caused by eating contaminated food, the intestinal wall becomes irritated, and peristalsis increases. Water is not absorbed, and the diarrhea that results rids the body of the infectious organisms. In nervous diarrhea, the nervous system stimulates the intestinal wall, and diarrhea results. Prolonged diarrhea can lead to dehydration because of water loss and to disturbances in the heart's contraction due to an imbalance of salts in the blood.

When a person is constipated, the feces are dry and hard. The Medical Focus on this page discusses the causes of constipation and how it can be prevented. Chronic constipation

is associated with the development of hemorrhoids, enlarged and inflamed blood vessels at the anus.

Polyps

The colon is subject to the development of **polyps,** small growths arising from the epithelial lining. Polyps, whether benign or cancerous, can be removed surgically along with a portion of the colon if necessary. If colon cancer is detected while still confined to a polyp, the expected outcome is a complete cure. If the last portion of the rectum and the anal canal must be removed, then the intestine is sometimes attached to the abdominal wall through a procedure known as a **colostomy,** and the digestive remains are collected in a plastic bag fastened around the opening. Recently, the use of metal staples has permitted surgeons to join the colon to a piece of rectum that formerly was considered too short.

can encourage a return of the reflexes that have disappeared, but straining is not recommended.

Temporary constipation due to traveling, pregnancy, or medication can sometimes be relieved by increasing dietary fiber, drinking plenty of water, and getting moderate amounts of exercise. The use of oral laxatives (agents that aid emptying of the intestine) is a last resort. Bulk-forming laxatives, such as those that contain bran, psyllium, and methyl cellulose, are considered best because they promote the defecation reflex. Laxatives that contain osmotic agents, such as carbohydrates or salts (lactulose, milk of magnesia, or Epsom salts), cause water to move into rather than out of the colon. Stool softeners (mineral oil or those that contain docusate) should be used sparingly. Mineral oil reduces the absorption of fat-soluble vitamins, and docusate can cause liver damage. Laxatives that contain chemical stimulants (such as phenolphthalein in Ex-Lax and Feen-A-Mint) can damage the defecation reflex and lead to a dependence on their use. Aside from laxatives, rectal suppositories are sometimes helpful in providing lubrication and stimulating the defecation reflex. Enemas introduce water into the colon and, therefore, also help stimulate defecation.

Figure 15B Defecation reflex. The accumulation of feces in the rectum causes it to stretch, which initiates a reflex action resulting in rectal contraction.

Some investigators believe that dietary fat increases the likelihood of colon cancer because dietary fat causes an increase in bile secretion. It could be that intestinal bacteria convert bile salts to substances that promote the development of cancer. On the other hand, fiber in the diet seems to inhibit the development of colon cancer. Dietary fiber absorbs water and adds bulk, thereby diluting the concentration of bile salts and facilitating the movement of substances through the intestine. Regular elimination reduces the time that the colon wall is exposed to any cancer-promoting agents in feces.

Other Disorders of the Large Intestine

The appendix is a fingerlike projection from the cecum of the large intestine. Unfortunately, the appendix can become infected, resulting in **appendicitis,** a very painful condition in which the fluid content of the appendix can increase to the point that it bursts. The appendix should be removed before it bursts to avoid a generalized infection of the peritoneal membrane of the abdominal cavity.

Diverticulosis is characterized by the presence of diverticula, or saclike pouches, in the colon. Ordinarily, these pouches cause no problems. But about 15% of people with diverticulosis develop an inflammation known as diverticulitis. The symptoms of diverticulitis are similar to those of appendicitis—cramps or steady pain with local tenderness. Fever, loss of appetite, nausea, and vomiting may also occur. Today, high-fiber diets are recommended to prevent the development of these conditions and of cancer of the colon.

15.2 Accessory Organs of Digestion

The salivary glands and even the teeth are accessory organs of digestion that were discussed earlier (see pages 296–97). The pancreas, liver, and gallbladder are also accessory digestive organs. Figure 15.10 shows how the pancreatic duct from the pancreas and the common bile duct from the liver and gallbladder join before entering the duodenum.

The Pancreas

The **pancreas** lies deep in the abdominal cavity, behind the peritoneum, resting on the posterior abdominal wall. Its broad end, called the head, more than fills the loop formed by the duodenum, and its tail extends in the opposite direction (Fig. 15.10). The pancreas has both an endocrine and an exocrine function. Pancreatic islets (islets of Langerhans) secrete insulin and glucagon, hormones that help keep the blood glucose level within normal limits.

In this chapter, however, we are interested in the exocrine function of the pancreas. Most pancreatic cells, called pancreatic acinar cells, produce pancreatic juice, which is

Figure 15.10 The pancreas is an exocrine gland when it secretes digestive enzymes into tubes that join to become the pancreatic duct. The pancreatic duct and the common bile duct empty into the duodenum of the small intestine. Pancreatic juice contains enzymes that digest all types of food: carbohydrates, fats, proteins, and nucleic acids.

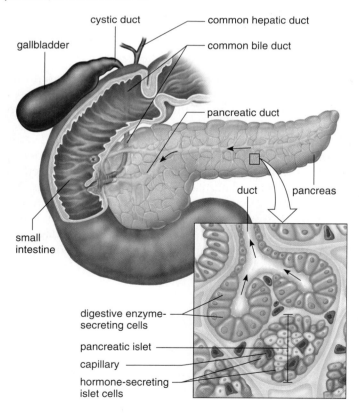

secreted into tiny tubes that unite, forming ever-larger ones. Finally, a single pancreatic duct extends the length of the pancreas to the duodenum.

Pancreatic Juice

Pancreatic juice contains sodium bicarbonate ($NaHCO_3$) and digestive enzymes for all types of food. Sodium bicarbonate neutralizes chyme; whereas pepsin acts best in an acid pH of the stomach, pancreatic enzymes require a slightly basic pH. **Pancreatic amylase** digests starch, **trypsin** digests protein, and **lipase** digests fat. Pancreatic juice also contains two nucleases, which are enzymes that break down nucleic acid molecules into nucleotides.

In cystic fibrosis, a thick mucus blocks the pancreatic duct, and the patient must take supplemental pancreatic enzymes by mouth for proper digestion to occur.

The Liver

The **liver,** which is the largest organ in the body, lies mainly in the upper right section of the abdominal cavity, just inferior to the diaphragm (see Fig. 15.1).

Liver Structure

The liver has two main lobes, the right lobe and the smaller left lobe, separated by a ligament. Each lobe is divided into many hepatic lobules that serve as its structural and functional units (Fig. 15.11). A lobule consists of many hepatic cells arranged in longitudinal groups that radiate out from a central vein. Hepatic sinusoids separate the groups of cells from each other. Large fixed phagocytic cells called *Kupffer cells* are attached to the lining of the hepatic sinusoids. They remove pathogens and debris that may have entered the hepatic portal vein at the small intestine.

Portal triads consisting of the following three structures are located between the lobules: a bile duct that takes bile away from the liver; a branch of the hepatic artery that brings O_2-rich blood to the liver; and a branch of the hepatic portal vein that transports nutrients from the intestines. The bile ducts merge to form the common hepatic duct.

The central veins of the lobules enter a hepatic vein. With the help of Figure 12.20, trace the path of blood from the intestines to the liver via the hepatic portal vein and from the liver to the inferior vena cava via the hepatic veins.

Liver Functions

As the blood from the hepatic portal vein passes through the liver, hepatic cells remove poisonous substances and detoxify them. The liver also removes nutrients and works to keep the contents of the blood constant. It removes and stores iron and the fat-soluble vitamins A, D, E, and K; makes the plasma proteins from amino acids; and helps regulate the quantity of cholesterol in the blood.

Figure 15.11 Macroscopic and microscopic anatomy of the liver. **a.** The liver has two lobes viewed anteriorly (*left*) and posteriorly (*right*). **b.** Cross section of a hepatic lobule, illustrating microscopic structure.

liver

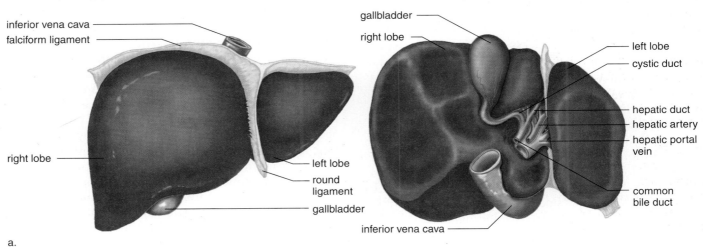

inferior vena cava
falciform ligament

gallbladder
right lobe

left lobe
cystic duct

hepatic duct
hepatic artery
hepatic portal vein

right lobe

left lobe
round ligament

gallbladder

common bile duct

inferior vena cava

a.

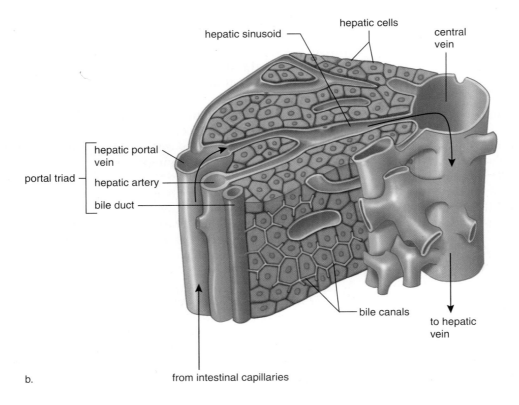

hepatic sinusoid

hepatic cells

central vein

portal triad
hepatic portal vein
hepatic artery
bile duct

bile canals

to hepatic vein

b.

from intestinal capillaries

The liver maintains the blood glucose level at about 100 mg/100 ml (0.1%), even though a person eats intermittently. When insulin is present, any excess glucose in the blood is removed and stored by the liver as glycogen. Between meals, glycogen is broken down to glucose, which enters the hepatic veins, and in this way, the blood glucose level remains constant.

If the supply of glycogen is depleted, the liver converts glycerol (from fats) and amino acids to glucose molecules. The conversion of amino acids to glucose necessitates deamination, the removal of amino groups and the production of ammonia. By a complex metabolic pathway, the liver then combines ammonia with carbon dioxide to form urea:

$$2\ NH_3 \ + \ CO_2 \ \longrightarrow \ H_2N - \overset{\displaystyle O}{\overset{\|}{C}} - NH_2$$

ammonia   carbon dioxide   urea

Urea is the usual nitrogenous waste product from amino acid breakdown in humans. After its formation in the liver, urea is excreted by the kidneys.

The liver produces bile, which is stored in the gallbladder. Bile has a yellowish-green color because it contains the bile pigment bilirubin, which is derived from the breakdown of hemoglobin, the red pigment of red blood cells. Bile also contains bile salts. Bile salts are derived from cholesterol, and they emulsify fat in the small intestine. When fat is emulsified, it breaks up into droplets, providing a much larger surface area, which can be acted upon by a digestive enzyme from the pancreas.

Altogether, the following are significant ways in which the liver helps maintain homeostasis:

1. Detoxifies blood by removing and metabolizing poisonous substances.
2. Stores iron (Fe^{2+}) and the fat-soluble vitamins A, D, E, and K.
3. Makes plasma proteins, such as albumins and fibrinogen, from amino acids.
4. Stores glucose as glycogen after a meal, and breaks down glycogen to glucose to maintain the glucose concentration of blood between eating periods.
5. Produces urea after breaking down amino acids.
6. Destroys old red blood cells; excretes bilirubin, a breakdown product of hemoglobin in bile, a liver product.
7. Helps regulate the blood cholesterol level, converting some to bile salts.

Liver Disorders

When a person has a liver ailment, jaundice may occur. **Jaundice** is a yellowish tint to the whites of the eyes and also to the skin of light-pigmented persons. Bilirubin is deposited in the skin due to an abnormally large amount in the blood. In hemolytic jaundice, red blood cells have been broken down in abnormally large amounts; in obstructive jaundice, bile ducts are blocked, or liver cells are damaged.

Jaundice can also result from **hepatitis,** inflammation of the liver. Viral hepatitis occurs in several forms. Hepatitis A is usually acquired from sewage-contaminated drinking water. Hepatitis B, which is usually spread by sexual contact, can also be spread by blood transfusions or contaminated needles. The hepatitis B virus is more contagious than the AIDS virus, which is spread in the same way. Thankfully, however, a vaccine is now available for hepatitis B. Hepatitis C, which is usually acquired by contact with infected blood and for which there is no vaccine, can lead to chronic hepatitis, liver cancer, and death.

Cirrhosis is another chronic disease of the liver. First the organ becomes fatty, and then liver tissue is replaced by inactive fibrous scar tissue. Cirrhosis of the liver is often seen in alcoholics due to malnutrition and the excessive amounts alcohol (a toxin) the liver is forced to break down.

Hepatitis and cirrhosis affect the entire liver and hinder its ability to repair itself. Therefore, they are life-threatening diseases. The liver has amazing regenerative powers and can recover if the rate of regeneration exceeds the rate of damage. During liver failure, however, there may not be enough time to let the liver heal itself. Liver transplantation is usually the preferred treatment for liver failure, but artificial livers have been developed and tried in a few cases. One type is a cartridge that contains liver cells. The patient's blood passes through the cellulose acetate tubing of the cartridge and is serviced in the same manner as with a normal liver. In the meantime, the patient's liver has a chance to recover.

The Gallbladder

The **gallbladder** is a pear-shaped, muscular sac located in a depression on the inferior surface of the liver (see Fig. 15.11a). About 1,000 ml of bile are produced by the liver each day, and any excess is stored in the gallbladder. Water is reabsorbed by the gallbladder so that bile becomes a thick, mucuslike material. When needed, bile leaves the gallbladder by way of the cystic duct. The cystic duct and the common hepatic duct join to form the common bile duct, which enters the duodenum.

The cholesterol content of bile can come out of solution and form crystals. If the crystals grow in size, they form gallstones. The passage of the stones from the gallbladder may block the common bile duct and cause obstructive jaundice. Then the gallbladder may have to be removed.

Function of Bile Salts

Bile salts carry out emulsification; they break up masses of fat into droplets that can be acted on by enzymes that digest fat. Through their ability to make fats interact with water, they also enhance absorption of fatty acids, cholesterol, and the fat-soluble vitamins A, D, E, and K.

15.3 Chemical Digestion

The digestive enzymes are **hydrolytic enzymes,** which break down substances by the introduction of water at specific bonds. Digestive enzymes have an optimum pH at which they work best.

In the mouth, saliva from the salivary glands has a neutral pH and contains **salivary amylase,** the first enzyme to act on starch:

$$\text{starch} + \text{H}_2\text{O} \xrightarrow{\text{salivary amylase}} \text{maltose}$$

Notice that the name of the enzyme is written above the arrow to indicate that it is not used up. In this case, the enzyme speeds the breakdown of starch to maltose, a disaccharide. Maltose molecules are too large to be absorbed by the alimentary canal; therefore, more digestion is required.

In the stomach, gastric juice secreted by gastric glands has a very low pH—about 2—because it contains hydrochloric acid (HCl). The precursor, pepsinogen, is converted to the enzyme **pepsin** when exposed to HCl. Pepsin acts on protein to produce peptides:

$$\text{protein} + \text{H}_2\text{O} \xrightarrow{\text{pepsin}} \text{peptides}$$

Peptides vary in length, but they are usually too large to be absorbed and must be broken down further.

In the small intestine, starch, proteins, nucleic acids, and fats are all enzymatically broken down. Pancreatic juice, which enters the duodenum, has a basic pH because it contains sodium bicarbonate (NaHCO$_3$). One pancreatic enzyme, **pancreatic amylase,** digests starch:

$$\text{starch} + \text{H}_2\text{O} \xrightarrow{\text{pancreatic amylase}} \text{maltose}$$

Another pancreatic enzyme, **trypsin,** digests protein:

$$\text{protein} + \text{H}_2\text{O} \xrightarrow{\text{trypsin}} \text{peptides}$$

Trypsin is secreted as trypsinogen, which is converted to trypsin in the duodenum.

Lipase, a third pancreatic enzyme, digests fat molecules in the fat droplets after they have been emulsified by bile salts:

$$\text{fat} \xrightarrow{\text{bile salts}} \text{fat droplets}$$
$$\text{fat droplets} + \text{H}_2\text{O} \xrightarrow{\text{lipase}} \text{glycerol} + \text{fatty acids}$$

As mentioned previously, glycerol and fatty acids enter the cells of the villi, and within these cells, they are rejoined and packaged as lipoprotein droplets before entering the lacteals.

Peptidases and **maltase,** enzymes produced by the small intestine, complete the digestion of protein to amino acids and starch to glucose, respectively. Amino acids and glucose are small molecules that cross into the cells of the villi. Peptides, which result from the first step in protein digestion, are digested to amino acids by peptidases:

$$\text{peptides} + \text{H}_2\text{O} \xrightarrow{\text{peptidases}} \text{amino acids}$$

Maltose, a disaccharide that results from the first step in starch digestion, is digested to glucose by maltase:

$$\text{maltose} + \text{H}_2\text{O} \xrightarrow{\text{maltase}} \text{glucose} + \text{glucose}$$

Other disaccharides, each of which has its own enzyme, are digested in the small intestine.

Table 15.2 lists some of the major digestive enzymes produced by the alimentary canal, salivary glands, or the pancreas. Each type of food is broken down by specific enzymes.

Table 15.2 Major Digestive Enzymes

Enzyme	Produced By	Site of Action	Optimum pH	Digestion
Salivary amylase	Salivary glands	Mouth	Neutral	Starch + H$_2$O → maltose
Pancreatic amylase	Pancreas	Small intestine	Basic	
Maltose	Small intestine	Small intestine	Basic	Maltose + H$_2$O → glucose + glucose
Pepsin	Gastric glands	Stomach	Acidic	Protein + H$_2$O → peptides
Trypsin	Pancreas	Small intestine	Basic	
Peptidases	Small intestine	Small intestine	Basic	Peptide + H$_2$O → amino acids
Nuclease	Pancreas	Small intestine	Basic	RNA and DNA + H$_2$O → nucleotides
Nucleotidases	Small intestine	Small intestine	Basic	Nucleotide + H$_2$O → base + sugar + phosphate
Lipase	Pancreas	Small intestine	Basic	Fat droplet + H$_2$O → glycerol + fatty acids

15.4 Effects of Aging

The incidence of gastrointestinal disorders increases with age. Periodontitis, which is common in elderly people, leads to the loss of teeth and the need for false teeth.

The esophagus, which rarely causes any difficulties in younger people, is more prone to disorders in the elderly. The portion of the esophagus normally found inferior to the diaphragm can protrude into the thoracic cavity, causing an esophageal hiatal hernia. In some cases, the lower esophageal sphincter opens inappropriately and allows chyme to regurgitate into the esophagus, causing heartburn. Or in some older persons, chest pain may occur when this sphincter fails to open and a bolus cannot enter the stomach. Eventually, the esophagus may develop a diverticulum that allows food to collect abnormally.

Peristalsis generally slows within the alimentary canal as the muscular wall loses tone. Peptic ulcers increase in frequency with age. The failure of older people to consume sufficient dietary fiber can result in diverticulosis and constipation. Constipation and hemorrhoids are frequent complaints among the elderly, as is fecal incontinence.

The liver shrinks with age and receives a smaller blood supply than in younger years. Notably, it needs more time to metabolize drugs and alcohol. With age, gallbladder difficulties occur; there is an increased incidence of gallstones and cancer of the gallbladder. In fact, cancer of the various organs of the gastrointestinal tract is seen more often among the elderly. For example, most cases of pancreatic cancer occur in people over the age of 60.

15.5 Homeostasis

Human Systems Work Together on page 313 tells how the digestive system works with other systems in the body to maintain homeostasis.

Within the alimentary canal, the food we eat is broken down to nutrients small enough to be absorbed by the villi of the small intestine. Digestive enzymes are produced by the salivary glands, gastric glands, and intestinal glands. Three accessory organs of digestion (the pancreas, the liver, and the gallbladder) also contribute secretions that help break down food. The liver produces bile (stored by the gallbladder), which emulsifies fat. The pancreas produces enzymes for the digestion of carbohydrates, proteins, and fat. Secretions from these glands, which are sent by ducts into the small intestine, are regulated by hormones such as secretin produced by the alimentary canal. Therefore, the alimentary canal is also a part of the endocrine system. Other accessory organs, such as the salivary glands and teeth, are also essential to digestion. The skeletal system assists the digestive system in that the teeth sockets are in the mandible and maxillae.

The liver is the most important of the metabolic organs. The liver has a wide variety of functions and is chemically extremely active, which gives it an influence over all other organs.

Some actions involve the breakdown of complex chemicals; other important ones involve synthesis, particularly the manufacture of protein molecules. The liver assists the urinary system, producing urea, the main nitrogenous end product of human beings. The liver acts as a cleansing station, inactivating hormones and drugs. The Kupffer cells that line the liver's sinusoids mop up unwanted substances and infectious pathogens reaching it from the small intestine. Because the liver is such an important organ, diseases affecting the liver, such as hepatitis and cirrhosis, are extremely dangerous.

The liver and the cardiovascular system work together. A large amount of the body's blood reaches the liver constantly. Between meals, more than three-quarters of this supply comes to the liver by way of the hepatic portal vein, which drains the intestine. The remainder is from the body's main arterial system via the hepatic artery. When food is eaten, more blood is diverted to the intestine to cope with the tasks of digestion and absorption, and blood flow in the hepatic portal vein increases. The liver assists the cardiovascular system by aiding in the breakdown of red blood cells. It assists the urinary system by excreting bilirubin, a hemoglobin breakdown product.

The nutrients absorbed by the alimentary canal are converted by the body into energy and used for physical activities and for the growth and repair of body tissue. As we shall see in section 15.6, carbohydrates and fats are used to fuel all the body's processes and functions, while protein is mainly used as a building material. Besides these three basic components, the body must also have vitamins and minerals. Vitamins are essential for normal growth and development, and because they cannot be manufactured in the body, they must be supplied ready-made in the diet or as supplements. Minerals assist in many body processes, such as normal nerve and muscle function, but are needed only in small quantities.

The muscular system and digestive system work together. The muscular system benefits from the nutrients absorbed by the alimentary canal, but mechanical digestion is in part dependent upon the muscular walls of the alimentary canal. Also, peristalsis pushes food along from organ to organ.

Peyer patches and Kupffer cells are examples that the digestive system and the lymphatic system work together. Peyer patches in the wall of the small intestine are lymphatic tissue. They are an important way for the small intestine to protect itself from invasion by bacteria. The patches contain large numbers of antibody-secreting lymphocytes.

The endocrine system and the digestive system also work together. The secretion of digestive juices is dependent on hormones produced not by the endocrine glands but by the digestive organs themselves. Thus, these organs become a part of the endocrine system. Certainly the pancreas is counted as an endocrine gland when it produces insulin, which causes cells, including the hepatic cells, to take up glucose. Thereafter, glucose is stored in the liver and muscles for future use.

Human Systems Work Together

Integumentary System

Digestive tract provides nutrients needed by skin.

Skin helps to protect digestive organs; helps to provide vitamin D for Ca^{2+} absorption.

Skeletal System

Digestive tract provides Ca^{2+} and other nutrients for bone growth and repair.

Bones provide support and protection; hyoid bone assists swallowing.

Muscular System

Digestive tract provides glucose for muscle activity; liver metabolizes lactic acid following anaerobic muscle activity.

Smooth muscle contraction accounts for peristalsis; skeletal muscles support and help protect abdominal organs.

Nervous System

Digestive tract provides nutrients for growth, maintenance, and repair of neurons and neuroglia.

Brain controls nerves, which innervate smooth muscle and permit tract movements.

Endocrine System

Stomach and small intestine produce hormones.

Hormones help control secretion of digestive glands and accessory organs; insulin and glucagon regulate glucose storage in liver.

How the Digestive System works with other body systems

Cardiovascular System

Digestive tract provides nutrients for plasma protein formation and blood cell formation; liver detoxifies blood, makes plasma proteins, destroys old red blood cells.

Blood vessels transport nutrients from digestive tract to body; blood services digestive organs.

Lymphatic System/Immunity

Digestive tract provides nutrients for lymphatic organs; stomach acidity prevents pathogen invasion of body.

Lacteals absorb fats; Peyer patches prevent invasion by pathogens; appendix contains lymphatic tissue.

Respiratory System

Breathing is possible through the mouth because digestive tract and respiratory tract share the pharynx.

Gas exchange in lungs provides oxygen to digestive tract and excretes carbon dioxide from digestive tract.

Urinary System

Liver synthesizes urea; digestive tract excretes bile pigments from liver and provides nutrients.

Kidneys convert vitamin D to active form needed for Ca^{2+} absorption; compensate for any water loss by digestive tract.

Reproductive System

Digestive tract provides nutrients for growth and repair of organs and for development of fetus.

Pregnancy crowds digestive organs and promotes heartburn and constipation.

15.6 Nutrition

Nutrition involves an interaction between food and the living organism. A nutrient is a substance that the body uses to maintain health. A balanced diet contains all the essential nutrients and includes a variety of foods, proportioned as shown in Figure 15.12.

Following digestion, nutrients enter the blood in the cardiovascular system, which distributes them to the tissues, where they are utilized by the body's cells. Mitochondria use glucose to produce a constant supply of ATP for the cell. In other words, glucose is the body's immediate energy source. Because the brain's only source of energy is glucose, it needs a constant supply.

The liver is able to chemically alter ingested fats to suit the body's needs, with the exception of linoleic acid, a fatty acid the liver is unable to produce. Since linoleic acid is required for construction of plasma membranes, it is considered an **essential fatty acid.** Essential molecules must be present in food because the body is unable to manufacture them. Still, saturated fats should be restricted, as discussed in the Medical Focus on page 240.

If glucose is not available, fats can be metabolized into their components, which are then used as an energy source. Therefore, fats are said to be a long-term energy source. When adipose tissue cells store fats, the body increases in weight. Cells have the capability of converting excess sugar molecules into fats for storage, which accounts for the fact that carbohydrates can also contribute to weight gain.

Amino acids from protein digestion are used by the cells to construct their own proteins, including the enzymes that carry out metabolism. Protein formation requires 20 different types of amino acids. Of these, nine are required in the diet because the body is unable to produce them. These are termed the **essential amino acids.** The body produces the other amino acids by simply transforming one type into another type. Some protein sources, such as meat, are complete in the sense that they provide all the different types of amino acids. Vegetables supply the body with amino acids, but they are incomplete sources because at least one of the essential amino acids is absent. A combination of certain vegetables, however, can provide all of the essential amino acids.

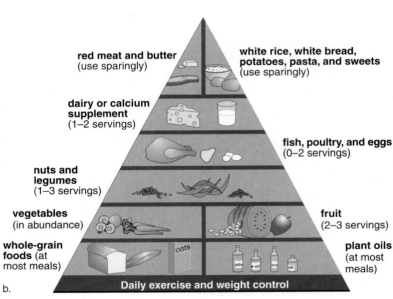

Figure 15.12 Food guide pyramids. **a.** The U.S. Department of Agriculture uses this pyramid, which emphasizes the importance of including grains, fruits, and vegetables in the diet. According to this diet, meats and dairy products are needed in limited amounts; fats, oils, and sweets should be used sparingly. **b.** A new pyramid suggested by nutritionists at Harvard Medical School differs from the pyramid shown in (a) by recommending the inclusion of certain oils in the diet and the restriction of certain carbohydrates.

Source: (a) Data from the U.S. Department of Agriculture

Medical Focus

Antioxidants

Over the past 20 years, numerous statistical studies have been done to determine whether a diet rich in fruits and vegetables protects against cancer. The vitamins C and E and beta-carotene, which is converted to vitamin A in the body, are especially abundant in fruits and vegetables and seem to have a special function in cells.

Cellular metabolism generates free radicals, unstable molecules that can attack and damage other molecules, such as DNA, proteins (e.g., an enzyme), carbohydrates, and lipids, that are found in plasma membranes. The damage to these cellular molecules may lead to disorders, perhaps even cancer. In addition, plaque formation in arteries may begin when arterial linings are injured by damaged cholesterol molecules.

The most common free radical in cells is oxygen in the unstable form O_{32}. Vitamins C and E (and possibly beta-carotene) are believed to defend the body against free radicals, and therefore are termed antioxidants. To receive adequate amounts of these vitamins, you should eat at least five servings of fruits and vegetables daily. Any one of the following is considered "one serving":

- 1 cup of raw leafy greens, such as lettuce or spinach
- $\frac{1}{2}$ cup of raw or cooked vegetables, such as broccoli, cauliflower, peas, green beans, and so on
- one average carrot or one medium potato
- one medium apple, orange, banana, or similar-sized fruit
- $\frac{1}{2}$ cup of grapes or cut fruit, such as diced pineapple
- $\frac{1}{4}$ cup of dried fruit, such as raisins
- $\frac{3}{4}$ cup of pure fruit or vegetable juice

Certain minerals form the structure of metalloenzymes, which serve as antioxidants. Glutathione peroxidase, a major intracellular antioxidant, contains the mineral selenium in its structure. Superoxide dismutase, another antioxidant enzyme, contains either magnesium or copper and iron.

Dietary supplements may provide a potential safeguard against cancer and cardiovascular disease, but taking supplements instead of improving your intake of fruits and vegetables is not the solution. Fruits and vegetables provide hundreds of beneficial compounds that cannot be obtained from a vitamin pill. These beneficial compounds include flavonoids and plant phenolics such as those found in red wine. These substances enhance each other's absorption or action and perform independent biological functions.

Vitamins

Vitamins are *vital* to life because they play essential roles in cellular metabolism. Because the body is unable to produce them, vitamins must be present in the diet. Vitamins are organic molecules, but they differ radically from carbohydrates, fats, and proteins. They are much smaller in size and are not broken down to be used as building blocks or as a source of energy. Instead, the body protects them and provides many of them with protein carriers that transport them in the blood to the cells. In the cells, vitamins become helpers in metabolic processes that break down or synthesize other organic molecules. Because vitamins can be used over and over again, they are required in very small amounts only.

Vitamins fall into two groups: fat-soluble vitamins (vitamins A, D, E, and K) and water-soluble vitamins (the B-complex vitamins and vitamin C) (Table 15.3). Most of the water-soluble vitamins are coenzymes, or enzyme helpers, that help speed up specific reactions. The functions of the fat-soluble vitamins, some of which have been previously discussed, are more specialized. Vitamin A, as noted in Chapter 9, is used to synthesize the visual pigments. Vitamin D is needed to produce a hormone that regulates calcium and phosphorus metabolism (see Chapter 5). Vitamin E, as discussed in the Medical Focus on this page, is an antioxidant. Vitamin K is required to form *prothrombin*, a substance necessary for normal blood clotting (see Chapter 11).

Minerals

In contrast to vitamins, **minerals** are inorganic elements (Table 15.4). An element, you will recall, is one of the basic substances of matter that cannot be broken down further into simpler substances. Minerals sometimes occur as a single atom, in contrast to vitamins, which contain many atoms, and carbohydrates, such as starch, which contain thousands of atoms. Minerals cannot lose their identity, no matter how they are handled. Because they are indestructible, no special precautions are needed to preserve them when cooking.

Minerals are divided into macronutrients, which are needed in gram amounts per day, and micronutrients (trace elements), which are needed in only microgram amounts per day. The macronutrients sodium, magnesium, phosphorus, chlorine, potassium, and calcium serve as constituents of cells and body fluids, and as structural components of tissues. The micronutrients have very specific functions, as noted in Table 15.4. As research continues, more elements will be added to the list of those considered essential.

Table 15.3   Vitamins: Their Role in the Body and Food Sources

Vitamins	Role in Body	Good Food Sources
Fat-Soluble Vitamins		
Vitamin A	Assists in the formation and maintenance of healthy skin, hair, and mucous membranes; aids in the ability to see in dim light (night vision); is essential for proper bone growth, tooth development, and reproduction	Deep yellow/orange and dark green vegetables and fruits (carrots, broccoli, spinach, cantaloupe, sweet potatoes); cheese, milk, and fortified margarine
Vitamin D	Aids in the formation and maintenance of bones and teeth; assists in the absorption and use of calcium and phosphorus	Milk fortified with vitamin D; tuna, salmon, or cod liver oil; also made in the skin when exposed to sunlight
Vitamin E	Protects vitamin A and essential fatty acids from oxidation; prevents plasma membrane damage	Vegetable oils and margarine; nuts; wheat germ and whole-grain breads and cereals; green, leafy vegetables
Vitamin K	Aids in synthesis of substances needed for clotting of blood; helps maintain normal bone metabolism	Green, leafy vegetables, cabbage, and cauliflower; also made by bacteria in intestines of humans, except for newborns
Water-Soluble Vitamins		
Vitamin C	Is important in forming collagen, a protein that gives structure to bones, cartilage, muscle, and vascular tissue; helps maintain capillaries, bones, and teeth; aids in absorption of iron; helps protect other vitamins from oxidation	Citrus fruits, berries, melons, dark green vegetables, tomatoes, green peppers, cabbage, potatoes
B-Complex Vitamins		
Thiamin	Helps in release of energy from carbohydrates; promotes normal functioning of nervous system	Whole-grain products, dried beans and peas, sunflower seeds, nuts
Riboflavin	Helps body transform carbohydrates, proteins, and fats into energy	Nuts, yogurt, milk, whole-grain products, cheese, poultry, leafy green vegetables
Niacin	Helps body transform carbohydrates, proteins, and fats into energy	Nuts, poultry, fish, whole-grain products, dried fruit, leafy greens, beans; can be formed in the body from tryptophan, an essential amino acid found in protein
Vitamin B_6	Aids in the use of fats and amino acids; aids in the formation of protein	Sunflower seeds, beans, poultry, nuts, bananas, dried fruit, leafy green vegetables
Folic acid	Aids in the formation of hemoglobin in red blood cells; aids in the formation of genetic material	Nuts, beans, whole-grain products, fruit juices, dark green leafy vegetables
Pantothenic acid	Aids in the formation of hormones and certain nerve-regulating substances; helps in the metabolism of carbohydrates, proteins, and fats	Nuts, beans, seeds, poultry, dried fruit, milk, dark green leafy vegetables
Biotin	Aids in the formation of fatty acids; helps in the release of energy from carbohydrates	Occurs widely in foods, especially eggs; made by bacteria in the human intestine
Vitamin B_{12}	Aids in the formation of red blood cells and genetic material; helps in the functioning of the nervous system	Milk, yogurt, cheese, fish, poultry, eggs; not found in plant foods unless fortified (as in some breakfast cereals)

Source: From David C. Nieman, et al., *Nutrition*, Revised 1st ed. Copyright © 1992 Wm. C. Brown Communications, Inc., Dubuque, Iowa. Reprinted by permission of C. V. Mosby, St. Louis, MO.

Table 15.4 Minerals: Their Role in the Body and Food Sources

Minerals	Role in Body	Good Food Sources
Macronutrients		
Calcium	Is used for building bones and teeth and for maintaining bone strength; also involved in muscle contraction, blood clotting, and maintenance of plasma membranes	All dairy products; dark green, leafy vegetables; beans, nuts, sunflower seeds, dried fruit, molasses, canned fish
Phosphorus	Is used to build bones and teeth; to release energy from carbohydrates, proteins, and fats; and to form genetic material, plasma membranes, and many enzymes	Beans, sunflower seeds, milk, cheese, nuts, poultry, fish, lean meats
Magnesium	Is used to build bones, to produce proteins, to release energy from muscle carbohydrate stores (glycogen), and to regulate body temperature	Sunflower and pumpkin seeds, nuts, whole-grain products, beans, dark green vegetables, dried fruit, lean meats
Sodium	Regulates body-fluid volume and blood acidity; aids in transmission of nerve impulses	Most of the sodium in the U.S. diet is added to food as salt (sodium chloride) in cooking, at the table, or in commercial processing; animal products contain some natural sodium
Chloride	Is a component of gastric juice and aids in acid-base balance	Table salt, seafood, milk, eggs, meats
Potassium	Assists in muscle contraction, the maintenance of fluid and electrolyte balance in the cells, and the transmission of nerve impulses; also aids in the release of energy from carbohydrates, proteins, and fats	Widely distributed in foods, especially fruits and vegetables, beans, nuts, seeds, and lean meats
Micronutrients (Trace Elements)		
Iron	Is involved in the formation of hemoglobin in the red blood cells of the blood and myoglobin in muscles; also is a part of several enzymes and proteins	Molasses, seeds, whole-grain products, fortified breakfast cereals, nuts, dried fruits, beans, poultry, fish, lean meats
Zinc	Is involved in the formation of protein (growth of all tissues), in wound healing, and in prevention of anemia; is a component of many enzymes	Whole-grain products, seeds, nuts, poultry, fish, beans, lean meats
Iodine	Is an integral component of thyroid hormones	Table salt (fortified), dairy products, shellfish, and fish
Fluoride	Is involved in maintenance of bone and tooth structure	Fluoridated drinking water is the best source; also found in tea, fish, wheat germ, kale, cottage cheese, soybeans, almonds, onions, milk
Copper	Is vital to enzyme systems and in manufacturing red blood cells; is needed for utilization of iron	Nuts, oysters, seeds, crab, wheat germ, dried fruit, whole grains, legumes
Selenium	Functions in association with vitamin E; may assist in protecting tissues and plasma membranes from oxidative damage; may also aid in preventing cancer	Nuts, whole grains, lean pork, cottage cheese, milk, molasses, squash
Chromium	Is required for maintaining normal glucose metabolism; may assist insulin function	Nuts, prunes, vegetable oils, green peas, corn, whole grains, orange juice, dark green vegetables, legumes
Manganese	Is needed for normal bone structure, reproduction, and the normal functioning of the central nervous system; is a component of many enzyme systems	Whole grains, nuts, seeds, pineapple, berries, legumes, dark green vegetables, tea
Molybdenum	Is a component of enzymes; may help prevent dental caries	Tomatoes, wheat germ, lean pork, legumes, whole grains, strawberries, winter squash, milk, dark green vegetables, carrots

Source: From David C. Nieman, et al., *Nutrition*, Revised 1st ed. Copyright © 1992 Wm. C. Brown Communications, Inc., Dubuque, Iowa. Reprinted by permission of C. V. Mosby, St. Louis, MO.

Figure 15.13 Recognizing bulimia nervosa.

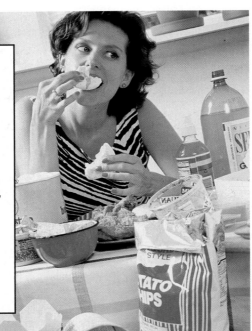

Persons with bulimia nervosa have

- recurrent episodes of binge eating characterized by consuming an amount of food much higher than normal for one sitting and a sense of lack of control over eating during the episode.
- an obsession about their body shape and weight.
- increase in fine body hair, halitosis, and gingivitis.

Body weight is regulated by

- a restrictive diet, excessive exercise.
- purging (self-induced vomiting or misuse of laxatives).

Eating Disorders

Authorities recognize three primary eating disorders: obesity, bulimia nervosa, and anorexia nervosa. Although they exist in a continuum as far as body weight is concerned, all represent an inability to maintain normal body weight because of eating habits.

Obesity

Obesity is most often defined as a body weight 20% or more above the ideal weight for a person's height. By this standard, 28% of women and 10% of men in the United States are obese. Moderate obesity is 41–100% above ideal weight, and severe obesity is 100% or more above ideal weight.

Obesity is most likely caused by a combination of hormonal, metabolic, and social factors. It is known that obese individuals have more fat cells than normal, and when they lose weight, the fat cells simply get smaller; they don't disappear. The social factors that cause obesity include the eating habits of other family members. Consistently eating fatty foods, for example, will make you gain weight. Sedentary activities, such as watching television instead of exercising, also determine how much body fat you have. The risk of heart disease is higher in obese individuals, and this alone tells us that excess body fat is not consistent with optimal health.

Treatment depends on the degree of obesity. Surgery to remove body fat may be required for those who are moderately or greatly overweight. But for most people, a knowledge of good eating habits along with behavior modification may suffice, particularly if a balanced diet is accompanied by a sensible exercise program. A lifelong commitment to a properly planned program is the best way to prevent a cycle of weight gain followed by weight loss. Such a cycle is not conducive to good health.

Bulimia Nervosa

Bulimia nervosa can coexist with either obesity or anorexia nervosa, which is discussed next. People with this condition have the habit of eating to excess (called binge eating) and then purging themselves by some artificial means, such as self-induced vomiting or the use of a laxative. Bulimic individuals are overconcerned about their body shape and weight, and therefore they may be on a very restrictive diet. A restrictive diet may bring on the desire to binge, and typically the person chooses to consume sweets, such as cakes, cookies, and ice cream (Fig. 15.13). The amount of food consumed is far beyond the normal number of calories for one meal, and the person keeps on eating until every bit is gone. Then, a feeling of guilt most likely brings on the next phase, which is a purging of all the calories that have been taken in.

Figure 15.14 Recognizing anorexia nervosa.

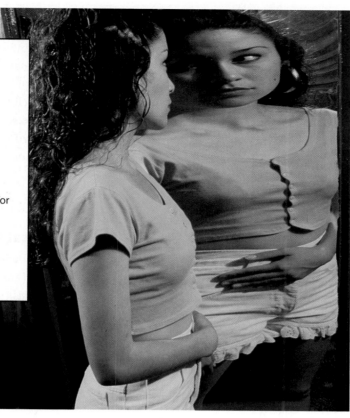

Persons with anorexia nervosa have

- a morbid fear of gaining weight; body weight no more than 85% normal.
- a distorted body image so that person feels fat even when emaciated.
- in females, an absence of a menstrual cycle for at least three months.

Body weight is kept too low by either/or

- a restrictive diet, often with excessive exercise.
- binge eating/purging (person engages in binge eating and then self-induces vomiting or misuses laxatives).

Bulimia can be dangerous to your health. Blood composition is altered, leading to an abnormal heart rhythm, and damage to the kidneys can even result in death. At the very least, vomiting can lead to inflammation of the pharynx and esophagus, and stomach acids can cause the teeth to erode. The esophagus and stomach may even rupture and tear due to strong contractions during vomiting.

The most important aspect of treatment is to get the patient on a sensible and consistent diet. Again, behavioral modification is helpful, and so perhaps is psychotherapy to help the patient understand the emotional causes of the behavior. Medications, including antidepressants, have sometimes helped to reduce the bulimic cycle and restore normal appetite.

Anorexia Nervosa

In **anorexia nervosa**, a morbid fear of gaining weight causes the person to be on a very restrictive diet. Athletes such as distance runners, wrestlers, and dancers are at risk of anorexia nervosa because they believe that being thin gives them a competitive edge. In addition to eating only low-calorie foods, the person may induce vomiting and use laxatives to bring about further weight loss. No matter how thin they have become, people with anorexia nervosa think they are overweight (Fig. 15.14). Such a distorted self-image may prevent recognition of the need for medical help.

Actually, the person is starving and has all the symptoms of starvation, including low blood pressure, irregular heartbeat, constipation, and constant chilliness. Bone density decreases, and stress fractures occur. The body begins to shut down; menstruation ceases in females; the internal organs, including the brain, don't function well; and the skin dries up. Impairment of the pancreas and alimentary canal means that any food consumed does not provide nourishment. Death may be imminent. If so, the only recourse may be hospitalization and force-feeding. Eventually, it is necessary to use behavior therapy and psychotherapy to enlist the cooperation of the person to eat properly. Family therapy may be necessary, because anorexia nervosa in children and teens is believed to be a way for them to gain some control over their lives.

Basic Key Terms

ascending colon (uh-send'ing ko'lon), p. 304

bile (bīl), p. 302

bolus (bo'lus), p. 298

cecum (se'kum), p. 304

chyme (kīm), p. 301

descending colon (de-send'ing ko'lon), p. 304

duodenum (du"o-de'num), p. 302

esophagus (ĕ-sof'uh-gus), p. 299

essential amino acid (ĕ-sen'shul uh-me'no as'id), p. 314

essential fatty acid (ĕ-sen'shul fat'e as'id), p. 314

gallbladder (gawl'blad-er), p. 310

gastric gland (gas'trik gland), p. 301

hard palate (hard pal'ut), p. 296

ileum (il'e-um), p. 302

jejunum (jĕ-ju'num), p. 302

large intestine (larj in-tes'tin), p. 304

liver (liv'er), p. 308

mineral (min'er-al), p. 315

mouth (mowth), p. 296

pancreas (pan'kre-us), p. 308

peristalsis (per"ĭ-stal'sis), p. 299

pharynx (far'inks), p. 298

rectum (rek'tum), p. 304

rugae (roo'je), p. 301

salivary gland (sal'ĭ-vĕr-e gland), p. 296

sigmoid colon (sig'moid ko'lon), p. 304

small intestine (smawl in-tes'tin), p. 302

soft palate (sawft pal'ut), p. 296

sphincter (sfingk'ter), p. 299

stomach (stum'ak), p. 301

transverse colon (trans-vers' ko'lon), p. 304

urea (yū-re'uh), p. 310

vermiform appendix (ver'mĭ-form uh-pen'diks), p. 304

villi (vil'i), p. 302

vitamin (vi'tuh-min), p. 315

Clinical Key Terms

appendicitis (uh"pen-dĭ-si'tis), p. 307

caries (kār'ēz), p. 297

cirrhosis (suh-ro'sis), p. 310

colostomy (kuh-los'tuh-me), p. 306

constipation (kon-stĭ-pa'shun), p. 306

diarrhea (di-uh-re'uh), p. 306

diverticulosis (di"ver-tĭ-kyū-lo'sis), p. 307

gingivitis (jin-juh-vi'tis), p. 297

heartburn (hart'bern), p. 299

hepatitis (hĕ-puh-ti'tis), p. 310

jaundice (jon'dis), p. 310

periodontitis (pĕr"e-o-don-ti'tis), p. 297

polyp (pah'lip), p. 306

ulcer (ul'ser), p. 301

Summary

15.1 Anatomy of the Digestive System
The alimentary canal consists of the mouth, pharynx, esophagus, stomach, small intestine, and large intestine. Only these structures actually contain food, while the salivary glands, liver, and pancreas supply substances that aid in the digestion of food.
A. The salivary glands send saliva into the mouth, where the teeth chew the food and the tongue forms a bolus for swallowing. Saliva contains salivary amylase, an enzyme that begins the digestion of starch.
B. The air passage and the food passage cross in the pharynx. When a person swallows, the air passage is usually blocked off, and food must enter the esophagus, where peristalsis begins.
C. The stomach expands and stores food. While food is in the stomach, the stomach churns, mixing food with the acidic gastric juices. Gastric juices contain pepsin, an enzyme that digests protein.
D. The duodenum of the small intestine receives bile from the liver and pancreatic juice from the pancreas. Bile, which is produced in the liver and stored in the gallbladder, emulsifies fat and readies it for digestion by lipase, an enzyme produced by the pancreas. The pancreas also produces enzymes that digest starch (pancreatic amylase) and protein (trypsin). The intestinal enzymes finish the process of chemical digestion.
E. The walls of the small intestine have fingerlike projections called villi. The villi have microvilli where small nutrient molecules are absorbed. Amino acids and glucose enter the blood vessels of a villus. Glycerol and fatty acids are joined and packaged as lipoproteins before entering lymphatic vessels called lacteals in a villus.

F. The large intestine consists of the cecum, the colon (including the ascending, transverse, descending, and sigmoid colon), and the rectum, which ends at the anus. The large intestine does not produce digestive enzymes; it does absorb water, salts, and some vitamins. Reduced water absorption results in diarrhea. The intake of water and fiber helps prevent constipation.

15.2 Accessory Organs of Digestion
A. Three accessory organs of digestion—the pancreas, liver, and gallbladder—send secretions to the duodenum via ducts. The pancreas produces pancreatic juice, which contains digestive enzymes for carbohydrate, protein, and fat.
B. The liver produces bile, which is stored in the gallbladder. The liver receives blood from the small intestine by way of the hepatic portal vein. It has numerous important functions, and any malfunction of the liver is a matter of considerable concern.

15.3 Chemical Digestion
A. Digestive enzymes are present in digestive juices and break down food into the nutrient molecules glucose, amino acids, fatty acids, and glycerol (see Table 15.2). Salivary amylase and pancreatic amylase begin the digestion of starch. Pepsin and trypsin digest protein to peptides. Lipase digests fat to glycerol and fatty acids. Intestinal enzymes finish the digestion of starch and protein.
B. Digestive enzymes have the usual enzymatic properties. They are specific to their substrate and speed up specific reactions at optimum body temperature and pH.

15.4 Effects of Aging
The structure and function of the digestive system generally decline with age. The various illnesses associated with the digestive system are more likely to be seen among the elderly.

15.5 Homeostasis
The digestive system works with the other systems of the body in the ways described in Human Systems Work Together on page 313.

15.6 Nutrition
A. The nutrients released by the digestive process should provide us with an adequate amount of energy, essential amino acids and fatty acids, and all necessary vitamins and minerals.
B. The diet should be balanced and low in saturated fatty acids and cholesterol molecules, whose intake is linked to cardiovascular disease. Aside from carbohydrates, proteins, and fats, the body requires vitamins and minerals. The vitamins C, E, and A are antioxidants that protect cell contents from damage due to free radicals. The mineral calcium is needed for strong bones.
C. The reasons for eating disorders, including obesity, bulimia nervosa, and anorexia, are being explored in order to help people maintain a normal weight for their height.

Study Questions

1. List the organs of the alimentary canal, and state the contribution of each to the digestive process. (pp. 296–305)
2. Discuss the absorption of the products of digestion into the lymphatic and cardiovascular systems. (p. 302)
3. Name and state the functions of the hormones that assist the nervous system in regulating digestive secretions. (p. 304)
4. Name the accessory digestive organs, and describe the part they play in the digestion of food. (pp. 308–10)
5. Name and discuss any three functions and two serious illnesses of the liver. (pp. 308–10)
6. Discuss the digestion of starch, protein, and fat, listing all the steps that occur with each. (p. 311)
7. How does the digestive system help maintain homeostasis? (pp. 312–13)
8. How does the cardiovascular system assist the digestive system in maintaining homeostasis? (pp. 312–13)
9. What is the chief contribution of each of these constituents of the diet: (a) carbohydrates; (b) proteins; (c) fats; (d) fruits and vegetables? (pp. 314–15)
10. What role do water-soluble vitamins usually play in the body?
11. Name and discuss three eating disorders. (pp. 318–19)

Objective Questions

Fill in the blanks.
1. In the mouth, salivary _____ digests starch.
2. When we swallow, the _____ covers the opening to the larynx.
3. The _____ takes food to the stomach, where _____ is primarily digested.
4. The gastric juices are _____, and therefore, they usually destroy any bacteria in the food.
5. The large intestine has a colon with four _____ and a(n) _____, which leads to the _____.
6. The pancreas transports digestive juices to the _____, the first part of the small intestine.
7. After a meal, the liver stores glucose as _____.
8. The gallbladder stores _____, a substance that _____ fat.
9. Pancreatic juice contains _____ and _____ for digesting protein, _____ for digesting fat, and _____ for digesting starch.
10. The products of digestion are absorbed into the cells of the _____, fingerlike projections of the intestinal wall.

Medical Terminology Reinforcement Exercise

Consult Appendix B for help in pronouncing and analyzing the meaning of the terms that follow.

1. stomatoglossitis (sto"muh-to-glos-si'tis)
2. glossopharyngeal (glos"o-fah-rin' je-al)
3. esophagectasia (ĕ-sof"ah-jek-ta'se-uh)
4. gastroenteritis (gas"tro-en-ter-i' tis)
5. sublingual (sub-ling'gwal)
6. gingivoperiodontitis (jin"jĭ-vo-pĕr"e-o-don-ti'tis)
7. dentalgia (den-tal'je-uh)
8. pyloromyotomy (pi-lo"ro-mi-ot'o-me)
9. cholangiogram (ko-lan'je-o-gram)
10. cholecystolithotripsy (ko"le-sis"to-lith'o-trip"se)
11. proctosigmoidoscopy (prok"to-sig"moy-dos'kuh-pe)
12. colocentesis (ko-lo'sen-te'sis)
13. trichophagia (tri-ko-făj'e-uh)
14. duodenorrhaphy (du-o-dĕ-nor'uh-fe)
15. ileocecal (il'e-o-se'kul)

Website Link

Visit the Student Edition of the Online Learning Center at http://www.mhhe.com/maderap5 for additional quizzes, interactive learning exercises, and other study tools.

The Urinary System and Excretion

This artificially colored radiograph of the urinary system shows the kidneys (green). Urine passes from the renal pelvis (red) of each kidney into a ureter (also red).

Chapter Outline & Learning Objectives

After you have studied this chapter, you should be able to:

16.1 Urinary System (p. 324)
- List and discuss the functions of the urinary system.
- Name and describe the structure and function of each organ in the urinary system.
- Describe how urination is controlled.

16.2 Anatomy of the Kidney and Excretion (p. 326)
- Describe the macroscopic and microscopic anatomy of the kidney.
- State the parts of a kidney nephron, and relate them to the gross anatomy of the kidney.
- Describe the three steps in urine formation, and relate them to the parts of a nephron.

16.3 Regulatory Functions of the Kidneys (p. 330)
- Describe how the kidneys help maintain the fluid and electrolyte balance of blood.

- Name and explain how three hormones— aldosterone, antidiuretic hormone, and atrial natriuretic hormone—work together to maintain blood volume and pressure.
- Describe three mechanisms, including how the kidneys function, to maintain the acid-base balance of blood.

16.4 Problems with Kidney Function (p. 334)
- State, in general, the normal composition of urine and the benefits of doing a urinalysis.
- Discuss the need for hemodialysis and how hemodialysis functions to bring about the normal composition of urine.

16.5 Effects of Aging (p. 336)
- Describe the anatomical and physiological changes that occur in the urinary system as we age.

16.6 Homeostasis (p. 336)
- Describe how the urinary system works with other systems of the body to maintain homeostasis.

Visual Focus
Steps in Urine Formation (p. 328)

Medical Focus
Illnesses Detected by Urinalysis (p. 334)
Prostate Enlargement and Cancer (p. 338)

16.1 Urinary System

The kidneys are the primary organs of excretion. **Excretion** is the removal of metabolic wastes from the body. People sometimes confuse the terms excretion and defecation, but they do not refer to the same process. Defecation, the elimination of feces from the body, is a function of the digestive system. Excretion, on the other hand, is the elimination of metabolic wastes, which are the products of metabolism. For example, the undigested food and bacteria that make up feces have never been a part of the functioning of the body, while the substances excreted in urine were once metabolites in the body.

Functions of the Urinary System

The urinary system produces urine and conducts it to outside the body. As the kidneys produce urine, they carry out four functions: excretion of metabolic wastes, maintenance of water-salt balance, maintenance of acid-base balance, and secretion of hormones.

Excretion of Metabolic Wastes

The kidneys excrete metabolic wastes, notably nitrogenous wastes. Urea is the primary nitrogenous end product of metabolism in human beings, but humans also excrete some ammonium, creatinine, and uric acid.

Urea is a by-product of amino acid metabolism. The breakdown of amino acids in the liver releases ammonia, which the liver combines with carbon dioxide to produce urea. Ammonia is very toxic to cells, but urea is much less toxic. Because it is less toxic, less water is required to excrete urea.

Creatine phosphate is a high-energy phosphate reserve molecule in muscles. The metabolic breakdown of creatine phosphate results in **creatinine.**

The breakdown of nucleotides, such as those containing adenine and thymine, produces **uric acid.** Uric acid is rather insoluble. If too much uric acid is present in blood, crystals form and precipitate out. Crystals of uric acid sometimes collect in the joints, producing a painful ailment called **gout.**

Maintenance of Water-Salt Balance

A principal function of the kidneys is to maintain the appropriate water-salt balance of the blood. As we shall see, blood volume is intimately associated with the salt balance of the body. As you know, salts, such as NaCl, have the ability to cause osmosis, the diffusion of water—in this case, into the blood. The more salts there are in the blood, the greater the blood volume and the greater the blood pressure. In this way, the kidneys are involved in regulating blood pressure.

The kidneys also maintain the appropriate level of other ions (electrolytes), such as potassium ions (K^+), bicarbonate ions (HCO_3^-), and calcium ions (Ca^{2+}), in the blood.

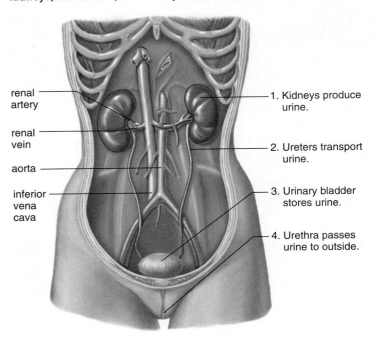

Figure 16.1 The urinary system. Urine is found only within the kidneys, the ureters, the urinary bladder, and the urethra.

renal artery

renal vein

aorta

inferior vena cava

1. Kidneys produce urine.
2. Ureters transport urine.
3. Urinary bladder stores urine.
4. Urethra passes urine to outside.

Maintenance of Acid-Base Balance

The kidneys regulate the acid-base balance of the blood. In order for a person to remain healthy, the blood pH should be just about 7.4. The kidneys monitor and control blood pH, mainly by excreting hydrogen ions (H^+) and reabsorbing the bicarbonate ions (HCO_3^-) as needed to keep blood pH at about 7.4. Urine usually has a pH of 6 or lower because our diet often contains acidic foods.

Secretion of Hormones

The kidneys assist the endocrine system in hormone secretion. The kidneys release renin, a substance that leads to the secretion of the hormone aldosterone from the adrenal cortex, the outer portion of the adrenal glands, which lie atop the kidneys. As described in section 16.3, aldosterone promotes the reabsorption of sodium ions (Na^+) by the kidneys.

Whenever the oxygen-carrying capacity of the blood is reduced, the kidneys secrete the hormone **erythropoietin,** which stimulates red blood cell production.

The kidneys also help activate vitamin D from the skin. Vitamin D is the precursor of the hormone calcitriol, which promotes calcium (Ca^{2+}) absorption from the digestive tract.

Organs of the Urinary System

The urinary system consists of the kidneys, ureters, urinary bladder, and urethra. Figure 16.1 shows these organs and also traces the path of urine.

Kidneys

The **kidneys** are paired organs located near the small of the back in the lumbar region on either side of the vertebral column. They lie in depressions against the deep muscles of the back beneath the peritoneum, where they receive some protection from the lower rib cage. Each kidney is usually held in place by connective tissue, called renal fascia. Masses of adipose tissue adhere to each kidney. A sharp blow to the back can dislodge a kidney, which is then called a **floating kidney.**

The kidneys are bean-shaped and reddish-brown in color. The fist-sized organs are covered by a tough capsule of fibrous connective tissue, called a renal capsule. The concave side of a kidney has a depression called the hilum where a **renal artery** enters and a **renal vein** and a ureter exit the kidney.

Ureters

The **ureters,** which extend from the kidneys to the bladder, are small, muscular tubes about 25 cm long and 5 mm in diameter. Each descends behind the parietal peritoneum, from the hilum of a kidney, to enter the bladder posteriorly at its inferior surface.

The wall of a ureter has three layers. The inner layer is a mucosa (mucous membrane), the middle layer consists of smooth muscle, and the outer layer is a fibrous coat of connective tissue. Peristaltic contractions cause urine to enter the bladder even if a person is lying down. Urine enters the bladder in spurts that occur at the rate of one to five per minute.

Urinary Bladder

The **urinary bladder** is located in the pelvic cavity, below the parietal peritoneum and just posterior to the pubic symphysis. In males, it is directly anterior to the rectum; in females, it is anterior to the vagina and inferior to the uterus. Its function is to store urine until it is expelled from the body. The bladder has three openings—two for the ureters and one for the urethra, which drains the bladder. The *trigone* is a smooth triangular area at the base of the bladder outlined by these three openings (Fig. 16.2).

Collectively, the muscle layers of the bladder wall are called the *detrusor muscle.* The wall contains a middle layer of circular fiber and two layers of longitudinal muscle, and it can expand. The transitional epithelium of the mucosa becomes thinner, and folds in the mucosa called *rugae* disappear as the bladder enlarges.

The bladder has other features that allow it to retain urine. After urine enters the bladder from a ureter, small folds of bladder mucosa act like a valve to prevent backward flow. Two sphincters in close proximity are found where the urethra exits the bladder. The internal sphincter occurs around the opening to the urethra. Inferior to the internal sphincter, the external sphincter is composed of skeletal muscle that can be voluntarily controlled.

Urethra

The **urethra** is a small tube that extends from the urinary bladder to an external opening. The urethra is a different length in females than in males. In females, the urethra is only about 4 cm long. The short length of the female urethra makes bacterial invasion easier and helps explain why females are more prone to urinary tract infections than males. In males, the urethra averages 20 cm when the penis is flaccid (limp, nonerect). As the urethra leaves the male urinary bladder, it is encircled by the prostate gland. In older men, enlargement of the prostate gland can restrict urination. A surgical procedure can usually correct the condition and restore a normal flow of urine.

In females, the reproductive and urinary systems are not connected. In males, the urethra carries urine during urination and sperm during ejaculation. This double function of the urethra in males does not alter the path of urine.

Urination

When the urinary bladder fills to about 250 ml with urine, stretch receptors send sensory nerve impulses to the spinal cord. Subsequently, motor nerve impulses from the spinal cord cause the urinary bladder to contract and the sphincters to relax so that urination, also called **micturition,** is possible (Fig. 16.2). In older children and adults, the brain controls this reflex, delaying urination until a suitable time.

Figure 16.2 Urination. As the bladder fills with urine, sensory impulses go to the spinal cord and then to the brain. The brain can override the urge to urinate. When urination occurs, motor nerve impulses cause the bladder to contract and an internal sphincter to open. Nerve impulses also cause an external sphincter to open.

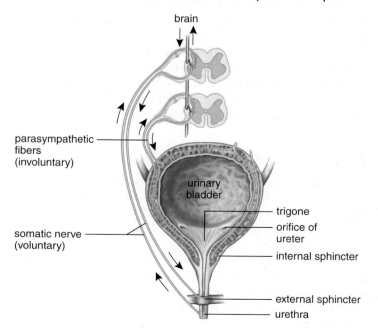

16.2 Anatomy of the Kidney and Excretion

A sagittal section of a kidney shows that many branches of the renal artery and renal vein reach inside a kidney (Fig. 16.3a). Removing the blood vessels shows that a kidney has three regions (Fig. 16.3b). The **renal cortex** is an outer, granulated layer that dips down in between a radially striated inner layer called the renal medulla. The **renal medulla** consists of cone-shaped tissue masses called renal pyramids. The **renal pelvis** is a central space, or cavity, that is continuous with the ureter.

Anatomy of a Nephron

Under higher magnification, the kidney is composed of over one million **nephrons**, sometimes called renal or kidney tubules (Fig. 16.3c). Each nephron has its own blood supply, including two capillary regions (Fig. 16.4). From the renal artery, an afferent arteriole leads to the **glomerulus**, a knot of capillaries inside the glomerular capsule. Blood leaving the glomerulus enters the efferent arteriole. The efferent arteriole takes blood to the **peritubular capillary network**, which surrounds the rest of the nephron. From there, the blood goes into a venule that joins the renal vein.

Parts of a Nephron

Each nephron is made up of several parts. First, the closed end of the nephron is pushed in on itself to form a cuplike structure called the **glomerular capsule** (Bowman's capsule). The inner layer of the glomerular capsule is composed of *podocytes* that have long, cytoplasmic extensions. The podocytes cling to the capillary walls of the glomerulus and leave pores that allow easy passage of small molecules from the glomerulus to the inside of the glomerular capsule.

Next, there is a **proximal convoluted tubule (PCT)**, called "proximal" because it is near the glomerular capsule. The cuboidal epithelial cells lining this part of the nephron have numerous microvilli about 1 μm in length. These microvilli are tightly packed and form a brush border, increasing the surface area for reabsorption.

Figure 16.3 Gross anatomy of the kidney. **a.** A sagittal section of the kidney showing the blood supply. Note that the renal artery divides into smaller arteries, and these divide into arterioles. Venules join to form small veins, which join to form the renal vein. **b.** The same section without the blood supply. Now it is easier to distinguish the renal cortex, the renal medulla, and the renal pelvis, which connects with the ureter. The renal medulla consists of the renal pyramids. **c.** An enlargement showing the placement of nephrons.

Simple squamous epithelium appears as the tube narrows and makes a U-turn called the **loop of the nephron** (loop of Henle). Each loop consists of a descending limb and an ascending limb.

The cuboidal epithelial cells of the **distal convoluted tubule (DCT)** have numerous mitochondria, but they lack microvilli. This is consistent with the active role they play in moving molecules from the blood into the tubule, a process called tubular secretion. The distal convoluted tubules of sev- eral nephrons enter one collecting duct. Many **collecting ducts** carry urine to the renal pelvis.

As shown in Figure 16.4, the glomerular capsule and the convoluted tubules always lie within the renal cortex. The loop of the nephron dips down into the renal medulla; a few nephrons have a very long loop of the nephron, which penetrates deep into the renal medulla. Collecting ducts are also located in the renal medulla, and they give the renal pyramids their lined appearance.

Figure 16.4 Nephron anatomy. A nephron is made up of a glomerular capsule, the proximal convoluted tubule, the loop of the nephron, the distal convoluted tubule, and the collecting duct. The photomicrographs show these structures in cross section; MV = microvilli. You can trace the path of blood about the nephron by following the arrows. (top left: © R. G. Kessel and R. H. Kardon, *Tissues and Organs: A Text Atlas of Scanning Electron Microscopy, 1979*)

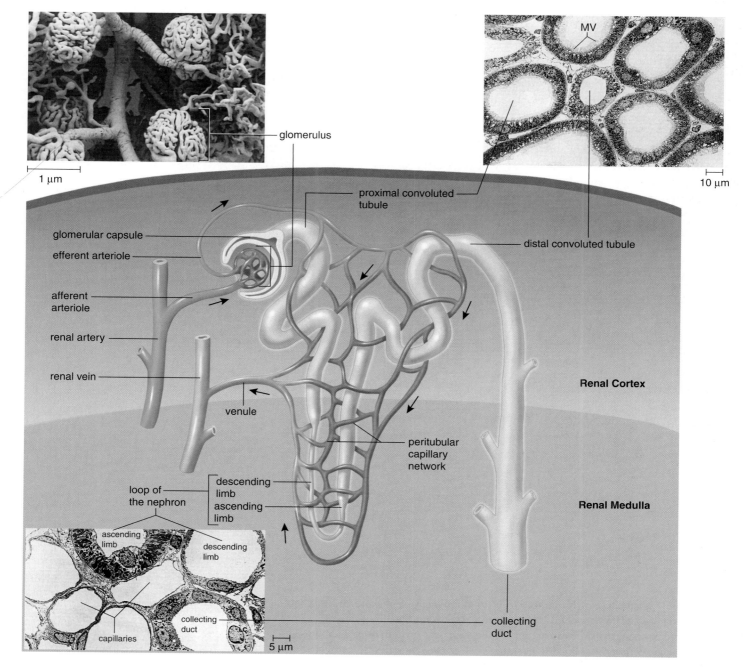

visual focus

Glomerular Filtration

Water, salts, nutrient molecules, and waste molecules move from the glomerulus to the inside of the glomerular capsule. These small molecules are called the glomerular filtrate.

Tubular Reabsorption

Nutrient and salt molecules are actively reabsorbed from the proximal convoluted tubule into the peritubular capillary network, and water flows passively.

Tubular Secretion

Certain molecules are actively secreted from the peritubular capillary network into the distal convoluted tubule.

proximal convoluted tubule (PCT)

glomerular capsule

efferent arteriole

glomerulus

afferent arteriole

renal artery

venule

renal vein

loop of the nephron

H_2O glucose

amino acids

salts

uric acid

urea

H_2O

glucose

amino acids

salts

drugs

ammonia

H^+

distal convoluted tubule (DCT)

Reabsorption of sodium from the DCT and water from the collecting duct are under hormonal control.

collecting duct

peritubular capillary network

H_2O
salts
urea
uric acid
ammonia

Figure 16.5 Steps in urine formation. *Top:* The three main steps in urine formation are described in boxes that are color-coded to arrows showing the movement of molecules into or out of the nephron at specific locations. In the end, urine is composed of the substances within the collecting duct (see gray arrow, lower right).

Excretion

Figure 16.5 gives an overview of urine formation, which is divided into these steps: glomerular filtration, tubular reabsorption, and tubular secretion.

Glomerular Filtration

Glomerular filtration occurs when whole blood enters the afferent arteriole and the glomerulus. Due to glomerular blood pressure, water and small molecules move from the glomerulus to the inside of the glomerular capsule. This is a filtration process because large molecules and formed elements are unable to pass through the capillary wall. In effect, then, blood in the glomerulus has two portions: the filterable components and the nonfilterable components:

Filterable Blood Components	Nonfilterable Blood Components
Water	Formed elements (blood cells and platelets)
Nitrogenous wastes	Plasma proteins
Nutrients	
Salts (ions)	

The **glomerular filtrate** contains small dissolved molecules in approximately the same concentration as plasma. Small molecules that escape being filtered and the nonfilterable components leave the glomerulus by way of the efferent arteriole.

As indicated in Table 16.1, nephrons in the kidneys filter 180 liters of water per day, along with a considerable amount of small molecules (such as glucose) and ions (such as sodium). If the composition of urine were the same as that of the glomerular filtrate, the body would continually lose water, salts, and nutrients. Therefore, we can conclude that the composition of the filtrate must be altered as this fluid passes through the remainder of the tubule.

Tubular Reabsorption

Tubular reabsorption occurs as molecules and ions are both passively and actively reabsorbed from the nephron into the blood of the peritubular capillary network. The osmolarity of the blood is maintained by the presence of both plasma proteins and salt. When sodium ions (Na^+) are actively reabsorbed, chloride ions (Cl^-) follow passively. The reabsorption of salt (NaCl) increases the osmolarity of the blood compared to the filtrate, and therefore water moves passively from the tubule into the blood. About 67% of Na^+ is reabsorbed at the proximal convoluted tubule.

Nutrients such as glucose and amino acids also return to the blood at the proximal convoluted tubule. This is a selective process because only molecules recognized by carrier molecules are actively reabsorbed. Glucose is an example of a

Table 16.1	Reabsorption from Nephrons		
Substance	Amount Filtered (per day)	Amount Excreted (per day)	Reabsorption (%)
Water, L	180	1.8	99.0
Sodium, g	630	3.2	99.5
Glucose, g	180	0.0	100.0
Urea, g	54	30.0	44.0

L = Liter; g = grams

molecule that ordinarily is completely reabsorbed because there is a plentiful supply of carrier molecules for it. However, every substance has a maximum rate of transport, and after all its carriers are in use, any excess in the filtrate will appear in the urine. For example, as reabsorbed levels of glucose approach 1.8–2 mg/ml plasma, the rest appears in the urine. In diabetes mellitus, excess glucose occurs in the blood, and then in the filtrate, and then in the urine, because the liver and muscles have failed to store glucose as glycogen, and the kidneys cannot reabsorb all of it. The presence of glucose in the filtrate increases its osmolarity compared to that of the blood, and therefore less water is reabsorbed into the peritubular capillary network. The frequent urination and increased thirst experienced by untreated diabetics are due to the fact that water is not being reabsorbed.

We have seen that the filtrate that enters the proximal convoluted tubule is divided into two portions: components that are reabsorbed from the tubule into the blood, and components that are not reabsorbed and continue to pass through the nephron to be further processed into urine:

Reabsorbed Filtrate Components	Nonreabsorbed Filtrate Components
Most water	Some water
Nutrients	Much nitrogenous waste
Required salts (ions)	Excess salts (ions)

The substances that are not reabsorbed become the tubular fluid, which enters the loop of the nephron.

Tubular Secretion

Tubular secretion is a second way by which substances are removed from blood and added to the tubular fluid. Hydrogen ions, potassium ions, creatinine, and drugs such as penicillin are some of the substances that are moved by active transport from the blood into the distal convoluted tubule. In the end, urine contains (1) substances that have undergone glomerular filtration but have not been reabsorbed, and (2) substances that have undergone tubular secretion.

16.3 Regulatory Functions of the Kidneys

The kidneys are involved in maintaining the fluid and electrolyte balance, and also the acid-base balance, of the blood. If the kidneys fail to carry out these vital functions, either hemodialysis or a kidney transplant is needed.

Fluid and Electrolyte Balance

The average adult male body is about 60% water by weight. The average adult female body is only about 50% water by weight because females generally have more subcutaneous adipose tissue, which contains less water. About two-thirds of this water is inside the cells (called intracellular fluid), and the rest is largely distributed in the plasma, tissue fluid, and lymph (called extracellular fluid). Water is also present in such fluids as cerebrospinal fluid and synovial fluid; in Figure 16.6, these fluids are referred to as "other" fluids.

Figure 16.6 Location of fluids in the body. Most of the body's water is inside cells (intracellular fluid), and only about one-third is located outside cells (extracellular fluid).

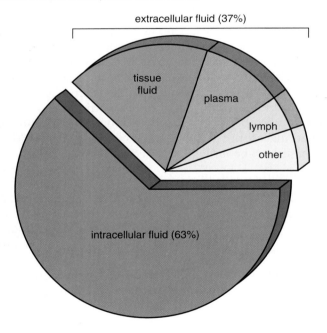

extracellular fluid (37%)

tissue fluid

plasma

lymph

other

intracellular fluid (63%)

For body fluids to be normal, it is necessary for the body to be in fluid balance. The total water intake should equal the total water loss. Table 16.2 shows how water enters the body—namely, in liquids we drink, in foods we eat, and as a by-product of metabolism. We drink water when the osmolarity of the blood rises as determined by the hypothalamus. Table 16.2 also shows how water exits the body—namely, in urine, sweat, exhaled air, and feces. Similar to the gain and loss of water, the body also gains and loses electrolytes. Despite these changes, the kidneys keep the fluid and electrolyte balance of the blood within normal limits. In this way, they also maintain the blood volume and blood pressure.

Reabsorption of Water

Because of the process of osmosis (see Chapter 3, page 43), the reabsorption of salt (NaCl) automatically leads to the reabsorption of water until the osmolarity is the same on both sides of a plasma membrane. Most of the salt, and therefore water, present in the filtrate are reabsorbed across the plasma membranes of the cells lining the proximal convoluted tubule. But the amount of salt and water reabsorbed is not sufficient to result in a hypertonic urine—one in which the osmolarity is higher than that of blood. How is it, then, that humans produce a hypertonic urine? We now know that the excretion of a hypertonic urine is dependent upon the reabsorption of water from the loop of the nephron and the collecting duct.

Loop of the Nephron and Collecting Duct A loop of the nephron has a descending limb and an ascending limb. A long loop of the nephron penetrates deep into the renal medulla. In the ascending limb, salt (NaCl) passively diffuses out of the lower portion and is actively transported out of the upper portion into the tissue of the outer renal medulla (Fig. 16.7). Less and less salt is available for active transport as fluid moves up the thick portion of the ascending limb. Therefore, the concentration of salt is greater in the inner medulla than in the outer medulla. (It is important to realize that water cannot leave the ascending limb because the ascending limb is impermeable to water.)

The large arrow to the side in Figure 16.7 indicates that the *lowest* portion of the inner medulla has the highest concentration of solutes. You can see that this is due not to the presence of salt, but to the presence of urea. Urea is believed to leak from the lower portion of the collecting duct, and it is

Table 16.2	Fluid Balance		
Water Input	**Average ml/day and % of Total**	**Water Output**	**Average ml/day and % of Total**
In liquids	1,000; 40%	In urine	1,300; 52%
In food	1,000; 40%	In sweat	650; 26%
From metabolism	500; 20%	In exhaled air	450; 18%
		In feces	100; 4%
	Total 2,500; 100%		Total 2,500; 100%

Figure 16.7 Reabsorption of water at the loop of the nephron and the collecting duct. A hypertonic environment in the tissues of the medulla of a kidney draws water out of the descending limb and the collecting duct. This water is returned to the cardiovascular system. (The thick black line means the ascending limb is impermeable to water.)

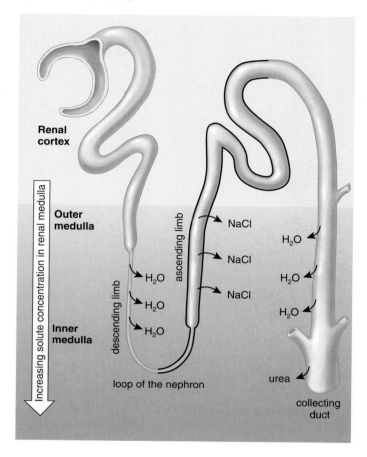

Renal cortex

Increasing solute concentration in renal medulla

Outer medulla

Inner medulla

descending limb

ascending limb

H_2O

H_2O

H_2O

H_2O

NaCl

NaCl

NaCl

H_2O

H_2O

H_2O

urea

loop of the nephron

collecting duct

this molecule that contributes to the high solute concentration of the lowest portion of the inner medulla.

Because of the osmotic gradient within the renal medulla, water leaves the descending limb along its entire length. There is a higher concentration of water at the top of the descending limb, and so it takes a lesser amount of solute in the medulla to pull it out. The remaining fluid within the descending limb encounters an even greater osmotic concentration of solute as it moves along; therefore, water continues to leave the descending limb from the top to the bottom. Such a mechanism is called a countercurrent mechanism.

At the top of the ascending limb, any remaining water enters the collecting duct. Surprisingly, the fluid inside the nephron is still not hypertonic—the net effect of reabsorption of salt and water so far is the production of a fluid that has the same tonicity as blood plasma. However, the collecting duct also encounters the same osmotic gradient as did the descending limb of the loop of the nephron (Fig. 16.7). Therefore, water diffuses out of the collecting duct into the renal

medulla, and the urine within the collecting duct becomes hypertonic to blood plasma.

Antidiuretic Hormone (ADH) ADH released by the posterior lobe of the pituitary plays a role in water reabsorption at the collecting duct. In order to understand the action of this hormone, consider its name. *Diuresis* means flow of urine, and *antidiuresis* means against a flow of urine. When ADH is present, more water is reabsorbed (blood volume and pressure rise), and a decreased amount of urine results. In practical terms, if an individual does not drink much water on a certain day, the posterior lobe of the pituitary releases ADH, causing more water to be reabsorbed and less urine to form. On the other hand, if an individual drinks a large amount of water and does not perspire much, ADH is not released. In that case, more water is excreted, and more urine forms.

Reabsorption of Electrolytes

As previously discussed, the osmolarity of body fluids is dependent upon the concentration of particular electrolytes within the fluids. **Electrolytes** are compounds and molecules that are able to ionize and, thus, carry an electrical current. The kidneys regulate electrolyte excretion and therefore help control blood composition.

The Electrolytes The most common electrolytes in the plasma are sodium (Na^+), potassium (K^+), and bicarbonate ion (HCO_3^-). Na^+ and K^+ are termed *cations* because they are positively charged, and HCO_3^- is termed an *anion* because it is negatively charged.

Sodium The movement of Na^+ across an axon membrane, you will recall, is necessary to the formation of a nerve impulse and muscle contraction. The concentration of Na^+ in the blood is also the best indicator of the blood's osmolarity.

Potassium The movement of K^+ across an axon membrane is also necessary to the formation of a nerve impulse and muscle contraction. Abnormally low K^+ concentrations in the blood, as might occur if diuretics are abused, can lead to cardiac arrest.

Bicarbonate Ion HCO_3^- is the form in which carbon dioxide is carried in the blood. The bicarbonate ion has the very important function of helping maintain the pH of the blood, as will be discussed later in this section.

Other Ions The plasma contains many other ions. For example, calcium ions (Ca^{2+}) and phosphate ions (HPO_4^{2-}) are important to bone formation and cellular metabolism. Their absorption from the intestine and excretion by the kidneys is regulated by hormones, as discussed in Chapter 10.

The Kidneys More than 99% of sodium (Na^+) filtered at the glomerulus is returned to the blood. Most sodium (67%) is reabsorbed at the proximal convoluted tubule, and a sizable amount (25%) is actively transported from the tubule by the

Figure 16.8 Juxtaglomerular apparatus. This drawing shows that the afferent arteriole and the distal convoluted tubule usually lie next to each other. The juxtaglomerular apparatus occurs where they touch. The juxtaglomerular apparatus secretes renin, a substance that leads to the release of aldosterone by the adrenal cortex. Reabsorption of sodium ions followed by water then occurs. Therefore, blood volume and blood pressure increase.

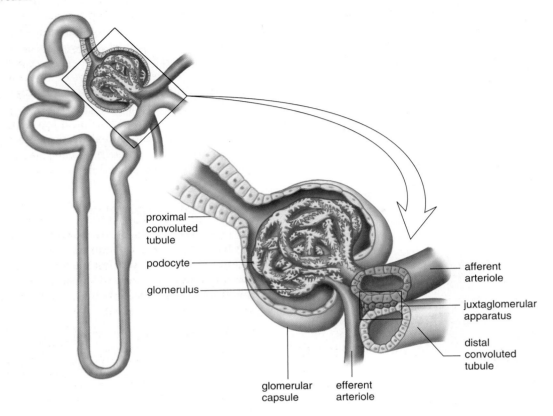

proximal convoluted tubule

podocyte

glomerulus

afferent arteriole

juxtaglomerular apparatus

distal convoluted tubule

glomerular capsule

efferent arteriole

ascending limb of the loop of the nephron. The rest is reabsorbed from the distal convoluted tubule and collecting duct.

Aldosterone Hormones control the reabsorption of sodium at the distal convoluted tubule. **Aldosterone,** a hormone secreted by the adrenal cortex, promotes the excretion of potassium ions (K^+) and the reabsorption of sodium ions (Na^+). The release of aldosterone is set in motion by the kidneys themselves. The **juxtaglomerular apparatus** is a region of contact between the afferent arteriole and the distal convoluted tubule (Fig. 16.8). When blood volume, and therefore blood pressure, is not sufficient to promote glomerular filtration, the juxtaglomerular apparatus secretes renin. **Renin** is an enzyme that changes angiotensinogen (a large plasma protein produced by the liver) into angiotensin I. Later, angiotensin I is converted to angiotensin II, a powerful vasoconstrictor that also stimulates the adrenal cortex to release aldosterone. The reabsorption of sodium ions is followed by the reabsorption of water. Therefore, blood volume and blood pressure increase.

Atrial natriuretic hormone (ANH) ANH is a hormone secreted by the atria of the heart when cardiac cells are stretched due to increased blood volume. ANH inhibits the secretion of renin by the juxtaglomerular apparatus and the secretion of aldosterone by the adrenal cortex. Its effect, therefore, is to promote the excretion of Na^+, called *natriuresis*. When Na^+ is excreted, so is water, and therefore blood volume and blood pressure decrease.

Diuretics

Diuretics are chemicals that increase the flow of urine. Drinking alcohol causes diuresis because it inhibits the secretion of ADH. The dehydration that follows is believed to contribute to the symptoms of a hangover. Caffeine is a diuretic because it increases the glomerular filtration rate and decreases the tubular reabsorption of Na^+. Diuretic drugs developed to counteract high blood pressure inhibit active transport of Na^+ at the loop of the nephron or at the distal convoluted tubule into the blood. A decrease in water reabsorption and a decrease in blood volume follow.

Acid-Base Balance

The pH scale, as discussed in Chapter 2, can be used to indicate the basicity (alkalinity) or the acidity of body fluids. A basic solution has a lesser hydrogen ion concentration $[H^+]$ than the neutral pH of 7.0. An acidic solution has a greater $[H^+]$ than neutral pH. The normal pH for body fluids is about 7.4. This is the pH at which our proteins, such as cellular enzymes, function properly. If the blood pH rises above 7.4, a person is said to have **alkalosis**, and if the blood pH decreases below 7.4, a person is said to have **acidosis**. Alkalosis and acidosis are abnormal conditions that may need medical attention.

The foods we eat add basic or acidic substances to the blood, and so does metabolism. For example, cellular respiration adds carbon dioxide that combines with water to form carbonic acid, and fermentation adds lactic acid. The pH of body fluids stays at just about 7.4 via several mechanisms, primarily acid-base buffer systems, the respiratory center, and the kidneys.

Acid-Base Buffer Systems

The pH of the blood stays near 7.4 because the blood is buffered. A **buffer** is a chemical or a combination of chemicals that can take up excess hydrogen ions (H^+) or excess hydroxide ions (OH^-). One of the most important buffers in the blood is a combination of carbonic acid (H_2CO_3) and bicarbonate ions (HCO_3^-). Carbonic acid is a weak acid that minimally dissociates and re-forms in the following manner:

$$H_2CO_3 \underset{\text{re-forms}}{\overset{\text{dissociates}}{\rightleftharpoons}} H^+ + HCO_3^-$$

carbonic acid   hydrogen ion   bicarbonate ion

When hydrogen ions (H^+) are added to blood, the following reaction occurs:

$$H^+ + HCO_3^- \rightarrow H_2CO_3$$

When hydroxide ions (OH^-) are added to blood, this reaction occurs:

$$OH^- + H_2CO_3 \rightarrow HCO_3^- + H_2O$$

These reactions temporarily prevent any significant change in blood pH. A blood buffer, however, can be overwhelmed unless some more permanent adjustment is made. The next adjustment to keep the pH of the blood constant occurs at pulmonary capillaries.

Respiratory Center

As discussed in Chapter 14, the respiratory center in the medulla oblongata increases the breathing rate if the hydrogen ion concentration of the blood rises. Increasing the breathing rate rids the body of hydrogen ions because the following reaction takes place in pulmonary capillaries:

$$H^+ + HCO_3^- \rightleftharpoons H_2CO_3 \rightleftharpoons H_2O + CO_2$$

In other words, when carbon dioxide is exhaled, the amount of carbonic acid that dissociates to give hydrogen ions is reduced.

It is important to have the correct proportion of carbonic acid and bicarbonate ions in the blood. Breathing readjusts this proportion so that this particular acid-base buffer system can continue to absorb both H^+ and OH^- as needed.

The Kidneys

As powerful as the acid-base buffer and the respiratory center mechanisms are, only the kidneys can rid the body of a wide range of acidic and basic substances and otherwise adjust the pH. The kidneys are slower acting than the other two mechanisms, but they have a more powerful effect on pH. For the sake of simplicity, we can think of the kidneys as reabsorbing bicarbonate ions and excreting hydrogen ions as needed to maintain the normal pH of the blood (Fig. 16.9). If the blood is acidic, hydrogen ions are excreted and bicarbonate ions are reabsorbed. If the blood is basic, hydrogen ions are not excreted and bicarbonate ions are not reabsorbed. Because the urine is usually acidic, it follows that an excess of hydrogen ions is usually excreted. Ammonia (NH_3) provides a means for buffering these hydrogen ions in urine: $(NH_3 + H^+ \rightarrow NH_4^+)$. Ammonia (whose presence is quite obvious in the diaper pail or kitty litter box) is produced in tubule cells by the deamination of amino acids. Phosphate provides another means of buffering hydrogen ions in urine.

The importance of the kidneys' ultimate control over the pH of the blood cannot be overemphasized. As mentioned, the enzymes of cells cannot continue to function if the internal environment does not have near-normal pH.

Figure 16.9 Acid-base balance. In the kidneys, bicarbonate ions (HCO_3^-) are reabsorbed and hydrogen ions (H^+) are excreted as needed to maintain the pH of the blood. Excess hydrogen ions are buffered, for example, by ammonia (NH_3), which becomes ammonium (NH_4^+). Ammonia is produced in tubule cells by the deamination of amino acids.

Illnesses Detected by Urinalysis

Urinalysis, or examination of the urine, indicates whether any abnormal substances are present in the urine. The presence of glucose in the urine usually indicates that the individual has diabetes mellitus, a condition in which either the liver fails to store glucose as glycogen or the cells fail to take up glucose. In both cases, the blood glucose level is abnormally high. This makes the filtrate level of glucose high, and because the proximal convoluted tubule cannot absorb all of it, glucose appears in the urine.

The presence of albumin and/or blood cells in the urine indicates that the glomerulus is more permeable than usual, as occurs in renal disease. When plasma proteins are excreted in the urine, the blood's osmotic pressure is reduced, and capillaries fail to take up water. Tissue fluid accumulates, and edema, particularly in the abdomen, occurs. As blood volume, and therefore blood pressure, decreases, the kidneys absorb more salt and water, but this, in the end, serves only to increase the edema. The best treatment is to cure the underlying cause of the edema.

Insufficient urine suggests kidney failure, which leads to **uremia,** or a very high blood urea nitrogen level (BUN). Death from kidney failure, however, is not due to the buildup of nitrogenous wastes; rather, it is due to an imbalance of electrolytes. Studies have shown that if urea is high but can be stabilized at normal levels, the patient usually recovers from the symptoms of uremia. An electrolyte imbalance, however, particularly the accumulation of potassium in the blood, interferes with the heartbeat and leads to heart failure.

16.4 Problems with Kidney Function

The composition of normal urine is given in Table 16.3. Water accounts for almost all of the volume of urine (95%). The remaining 5% consists of electrolytes and various solutes, including nitrogenous end products and substances derived from drugs. Notice that urine is typically free of proteins and blood cells because they are not filtered at the glomerulus.

Urinalysis is an examination of the physical, chemical, and microscopic properties of the urine. A urinalysis is done to help determine the state of the body. As discussed in the Medical Focus on this page, the composition of the urine changes if disease has altered body metabolism or if kidney function is abnormal. Abnormal substances in urine and abnormal quantities of normal constituents are both matters of concern.

Many types of illnesses, especially diabetes, hypertension, and inherited conditions, cause progressive renal disease and renal failure. Infections of the urinary tract are fairly common, particularly in females because the urethra is considerably shorter than that of the male. If the infection is localized in the urethra, it is called **urethritis.** If the infection invades the urinary bladder, it is called **cystitis.** Finally, if the kidneys are affected, the infection is called **pyelonephritis.**

Glomerular damage sometimes leads to blockage of the glomeruli so that glomerular filtration either does not occur or allows large substances to pass through. This is detected when a urinalysis is done. If the glomeruli are too permeable, albumin, white blood cells, or even red blood cells appear in the urine. A trace amount of protein in the urine is not a matter of concern, however.

Table 16.3	Composition of Urine
Water	95%
Solids	5%
Organic nitrogenous wastes (per 1,500 ml of urine)	
Urea	30 g
Creatinine	1–2 g
Ammonia	1–2 g
Uric acid	1 g
Electrolytes	25 g

Positive	Negative
Sodium (Na^+)	Chlorides (Cl^-)
Potassium (K^+)	Sulfates (SO_4^{2-})
Magnesium (Mg^{2+})	Phosphates (PO_4^{3-})
Calcium (Ca^{2+})	

When glomerular damage is so extensive that more than two-thirds of the nephrons are inoperative, urea and other waste substances accumulate in the blood. As mentioned in the Medical Focus on page 334, this condition is called uremia. Although nitrogenous wastes can cause serious damage, the retention of water and salts is of even greater concern. The latter causes edema, fluid accumulation in the body tissues. Imbalance in the ionic composition of body fluids can lead to loss of consciousness and to heart failure.

Hemodialysis

Patients with renal failure can undergo **hemodialysis,** utilizing either an artificial kidney machine or continuous ambulatory peritoneal dialysis (CAPD). *Dialysis* is defined as the diffusion of dissolved molecules through a semipermeable natural or synthetic membrane having pore sizes that allow only small molecules to pass through. In an artificial kidney machine (Fig. 16.10), the patient's blood is passed through a membranous tube, which is in contact with a dialysis solution, or **dialysate.** Substances more concentrated in the blood diffuse into the dialysate, and substances more concentrated in the dialysate diffuse into the blood. The dialysate is continuously replaced to maintain favorable concentration gradients. In this way, the artificial kidney can be utilized either to extract substances from blood, including waste products or toxic chemicals and drugs, or to add substances to blood—for example, bicarbonate ions (HCO_3^-) if the blood is acidic. In the course of a three- to six-hour hemodialysis, from 50 to 250 grams of urea can be removed from a patient, which greatly exceeds the amount excreted by normal kidneys. Therefore, a patient needs to undergo treatment only about twice a week.

CAPD is so named because the peritoneal lining of the peritoneal (abdominal) cavity is the dialysis membrane. A fresh amount of dialysate is introduced directly into the abdominal cavity from a bag that is temporarily attached to a permanently implanted plastic tube. The dialysate flows into the peritoneal cavity by gravity. Waste and salt molecules pass from the blood vessels in the abdominal wall into the dialysate before the fluid is collected four or eight hours later. The solution is drained into a bag from the abdominal cavity by gravity, and then it is discarded. One advantage of CAPD over an artificial kidney machine is that the individual can go about his or her normal activities during CAPD.

Replacing a Kidney

Patients with renal failure sometimes undergo a kidney transplant operation during which a functioning kidney from a donor is received. As with all organ transplants, there is the possibility of organ rejection. Receiving a kidney from a close relative has the highest chance of success. The current one-year survival rate is 97% if the kidney is received from a relative and 90% if it is received from a nonrelative. As discussed in the What's New reading on page 9, it's possible that kidneys from pigs will eventually be available or that tissue engineering will produce kidneys for transplant in the laboratory.

Figure 16.10 An artificial kidney machine. As the patient's blood is pumped through dialysis tubing, it is exposed to a dialysate (dialysis solution). Wastes exit from blood into the solution because of a preestablished concentration gradient. In this way, blood is not only cleansed, but its water-salt and acid-base balances can also be adjusted.

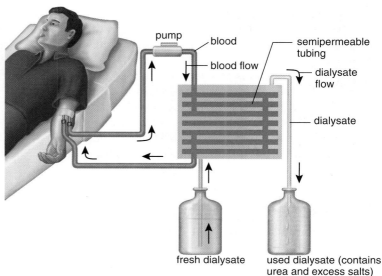

16.5 Effects of Aging

Urinary disorders are significant causes of illness and death among the elderly. Total renal function in an elderly individual may be only 50% of that of the young adult. With increasing age, the kidneys decrease in size and have significantly fewer nephrons. However, vascular changes may play a more significant role in declining renal efficiency than renal tissue loss. Microscopic examination shows many degenerate glomeruli through which blood no longer flows and many other glomeruli that are completely destroyed.

Kidney stones occur more frequently with age, possibly as a result of improper diet, inadequate fluid intake, and kidney infections. Infections of the urethra, bladder, ureters, and kidneys increase in frequency among the elderly. Enlargement of the prostate occurs in males and, as is discussed in the Medical Focus on page 338, this can lead to urine retention and kidney disease. Cancer of the prostate and bladder are the most common cancers of the urogenital system.

The involuntary loss of urine, called **incontinence**, increases with age. The bladder of an elderly person has a capacity of less than half that of a young adult and often contains residual urine. Therefore, urination is more urgent and frequent.

16.6 Homeostasis

The illustration in Human Systems Work Together on page 337 tells how the urinary system works with the other systems of the body to help maintain homeostasis.

Recall that excretion means to rid the body of a metabolic waste. Using this definition, it is possible to classify three other organs in addition to the kidneys as excretory organs:

1. The sweat glands in the skin excrete perspiration, which is a solution of water, salt, and some urea. Although perspiration is a form of excretion, we perspire not so much to rid the body of wastes as to cool it. In times of kidney failure, urea is excreted by the sweat glands and forms a so-called urea frost on the skin.
2. The liver breaks down hemoglobin and excretes bile pigments, which are derived from heme. Bile pigments are incorporated into bile, a substance stored in the gallbladder before it passes into the small intestine by way of ducts.

   The yellow pigment found in urine, called urochrome, also is derived from the breakdown of heme, but this pigment is deposited in blood and is subsequently excreted by the kidneys. As you know, the liver also produces urea—our main nitrogenous end product—which is excreted by the kidneys.
3. The lungs excrete carbon dioxide. The process of exhalation not only removes carbon dioxide, but also

results in the loss of water. The air we exhale contains moisture, as demonstrated by breathing onto a cool mirror.

The kidneys are the primary organs of excretion. They excrete almost all of our nitrogenous wastes, namely urea, creatinine, and uric acid. The liver makes urea, and muscles make creatinine. Urea is the end product of protein metabolism, and creatinine is a breakdown product of creatine phosphate, a molecule that stores energy in muscles. Uric acid is produced by cells when they break down nucleotides. Nitrogenous wastes are carried by the cardiovascular system to the kidneys. In this way, the cardiovascular system and the kidneys work together to clear the blood of nitrogenous end products. The excretion of nitrogenous wastes may not be as critical as maintaining the water-salt and the acid-base balances, but it is still necessary because urea is a toxic substance.

The kidneys are primary organs of homeostasis because they maintain the water-salt (electrolyte) and the acid-base balance of the blood. If blood does not have the usual water-salt balance, blood volume and blood pressure are affected. Without adequate blood pressure, exchange across capillary walls cannot take place, nor is glomerular filtration possible in the kidneys themselves. The kidneys and the endocrine system work together to help maintain blood pressure. The production of renin by the kidneys and subsequently the renin-angiotensin-aldosterone sequence help ensure that the sodium (Na^+) concentration of the blood, and therefore osmolarity and blood pressure, stay normal. The lymphatic system assists the urinary system because it makes a significant contribution to blood pressure by picking up excess tissue fluid and returning it to the cardiovascular veins.

Aside from producing renin, the kidneys assist the endocrine system and also the cardiovascular system by producing erythropoietin. Erythropoietin stimulates red bone marrow to produce red blood cells. The kidneys assist the skeletal, nervous, and muscular systems by helping to regulate the amount of calcium ions (Ca^{2+}) in the blood. The kidneys convert vitamin D to its active form needed for Ca^{2+} absorption by the digestive tract, and they regulate the excretion of electrolytes, including Ca^{2+}. The kidneys also regulate the sodium (Na^+) and potassium (K^+) content of the blood. These ions are necessary to the contraction of the heart and other muscles in the body, and are also needed for nerve conduction.

We have already described how the kidneys work with the cardiovascular system and the respiratory system to maintain the acid-base balance (page 333). This is a critical function to prevent the occurrence of alkalosis, or acidosis, which are life-threatening conditions. This function must be performed by a machine when people undergo hemodialysis. So, while we tend to remember that the kidneys excrete urea, we must also keep in mind all the other functions of the kidneys that are absolutely essential to homeostasis.

Integumentary System

Kidneys compensate for water loss due to sweating; activate vitamin D precursor made by skin.

Skin helps regulate water loss; sweat glands carry on some excretion.

Skeletal System

Kidneys provide active vitamin D for Ca^{2+} absorption and help maintain blood level of Ca^{2+}, needed for bone growth and repair.

Bones provide support and protection.

Muscular System

Kidneys maintain blood levels of Na^+, K^+, and Ca^{2+}, which are needed for muscle innervation, and eliminate creatinine, a muscle waste.

Smooth muscular contraction assists voiding of urine; skeletal muscles support and help protect urinary organs.

Nervous System

Kidneys maintain blood levels of Na^+, K^+, and Ca^{2+}, which are needed for nerve conduction.

Brain controls nerves, which innervate muscles that permit urination.

Endocrine System

Kidneys keep blood values within normal limits so that transport of hormones continues.

ADH and aldosterone, and atrial natriuretic hormone regulate reabsorption of Na^+ by kidneys.

How the Urinary System works with other body systems

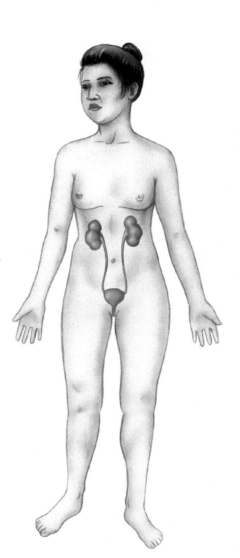

Cardiovascular System

Kidneys filter blood and excrete wastes; maintain blood volume, pressure, and pH; produce renin and erythropoietin.

Blood vessels deliver waste to be excreted; blood pressure aids kidney function; heart produces atrial natriuretic hormone.

Lymphatic System/Immunity

Kidneys control volume of body fluids, including lymph.

Lymphatic system picks up excess tissue fluid, helping to maintain blood pressure for kidneys to function; immune system protects against infections.

Respiratory System

Kidneys compensate for water lost through respiratory tract; work with lungs to maintain blood pH.

Lungs excrete carbon dioxide, provide oxygen, and convert angiotensin I to angiotensin II, leading to kidney regulation.

Digestive System

Kidneys convert vitamin D to active form needed for Ca^{2+} absorption; compensate for any water loss by digestive tract.

Liver synthesizes urea; digestive tract excretes bile pigments from liver and provides nutrients.

Reproductive System

Semen is discharged through the urethra in males; kidneys excrete wastes and maintain electrolyte levels for mother and child.

Penis in males contains the urethra and performs urination; prostate enlargement hinders urination.

Prostate Enlargement and Cancer

The prostate gland, which is part of the male reproductive system, surrounds the urethra at the point where the urethra leaves the urinary bladder (Fig. 16A). The prostate gland produces and adds a fluid to semen as semen passes through the urethra within the penis. At about age 50, the prostate gland often begins to enlarge, growing from the size of a walnut to that of a lime or even a lemon. This condition is called **benign prostatic hyperplasia (BPH).** As it enlarges, the prostate squeezes the urethra, causing urine to back up—first into the bladder, then into the ureters, and finally, perhaps, into the kidneys.

The treatment for BPH can involve (1) taking a drug that is expected to shrink the prostate and/or improve urine flow, or (2) a more invasive procedure to reduce the size of the prostate. Prostate tissue can be destroyed by applying microwaves to a specific portion of the prostate. In many cases, however, a physician may decide that prostate tissue should be removed surgically. In some cases, rather than performing abdominal surgery, which requires an incision in the abdomen, the physician gains access to the prostate via the urethra. This operation, called transurethral resection of the prostate (TURP), requires careful consideration because one study found that the death rate during the 5 years following TURP is much higher than that following abdominal surgery.

Prostate enlargement is due to a prostate enzyme (5a-reductase) that acts on the male sex hormone testosterone, converting it into a substance that promotes prostate growth. That growth is fine during puberty, but continued growth in an adult is undesirable. Two substances, one a nutrient supplement and the other a prescription drug, interfere with the action of this enzyme. Saw palmetto, which is sold in tablet form as an over-the-counter nutrient supplement, is derived from a plant of the same name. This drug should not be taken unless the need for it is confirmed by a physician, but it is particularly effective during the early stages of prostate enlargement. Finasteride, a prescription drug, is a more powerful inhibitor of the enzyme, but patients complain of erectile dysfunction and loss of libido while on the drug.

Two other medications have a different mode of action. Nafarelin prevents the release of luteinizing hormone, which leads to testosterone production. When it is administered, approximately half of the patients report relief of urinary symptoms even after drug treatment is halted. However, again, the patients experience erectile dysfunction and other side effects, such as hot flashes. The drug terazosin, which is on the market for hypertension because it relaxes arterial walls, also relaxes muscle tissue in the prostate. Improved urine flow was experienced by 70% of the patients taking this drug. However, the drug has no effect on the prostate's overall size.

Many men are concerned that BPH may be associated with prostate cancer, but the two conditions are not necessarily related. BPH occurs in the inner zone of the prostate, while cancer tends to develop in the outer area. If prostate cancer is suspected, blood tests and a biopsy, in which a tiny sample of prostate tissue is surgically removed, will confirm the diagnosis.

Although prostate cancer is the second most common cancer in men, it is not a major killer. Typically, prostate cancer is so slow growing that the survival rate is about 98% if the condition is detected early.

Figure 16A Longitudinal section of a male urethra leaving the bladder. Note the position of the prostate gland, which can enlarge to obstruct urine flow.

Selected New Terms

Basic Key Terms

aldosterone (al-dos′ter-ōn), p. 332

antidiuretic hormone (an″tĭ-di″yū-ret′ik hor′mōn), p. 331

atrial natriuretic hormone (a′tre-al na″tre-yū-ret′ik hor′mōn), p. 332

buffer (buf′er), p. 333

collecting duct (kuh-lek′ting dukt), p. 327

creatinine (kre-at′ĭ-nēn), p. 324

distal convoluted tubule (dis′tal kon′vo-lūt-ed tu′byūl), p. 327

electrolytes (e-lek′tro-lītz), p. 331

erythropoietin (ĕ-rith″ro-poy′ĕ-tin), p. 324

excretion (ek-skre′shun), p. 324

glomerular capsule (glo-měr′yū-ler kap′sul), p. 326

glomerular filtrate (glo-měr′yū-ler fil′trāt), p. 329

glomerular filtration (glo-měr′yū-ler fil-tra′shun), p. 329

glomerulus (glo-měr′yū-lus), p. 326

juxtaglomerular apparatus (juks″tuh-glo-měr′yū-ler ap″uh-ra′tus), p. 332

kidney (kid′ne), p. 325

micturition (mik″tu-rish′un), p. 325

nephron (nef′ron), p. 326

peritubular capillary network (per″ĭ-tu′byū-ler kap′ĭ-lār″e net′werk), p. 326

proximal convoluted tubule (prok′sĭ-mal kon′vo-lū-ted tu′byūl), p. 326

renal cortex (re′nul kor′teks), p. 326

renal medulla (re′nul mě-du′luh), p. 326

renal pelvis (re′nul pel′vis), p. 326

renin (re′nin), p. 332

tubular reabsorption (tu′byū-ler re″ab-sorp′shun), p. 329

tubular secretion (tu′byū-ler sě-kre′shun), p. 329

urea (yū-re′uh), p. 324

ureters (yū-re′terz), p. 325

urethra (yū-re′thruh), p. 325

uric acid (yū-rik as′id), p. 324

urinary bladder (yūr′in-ār-e blad′er), p. 325

Clinical Key Terms

acidosis (as″ĭ-do′sis), p. 333

alkalosis (al″kuh-lo′sis), p. 333

benign prostatic hyperplasia (bĭ-nīn′ prahs-tat′ik hi″per-pla′ze-uh), p. 338

cystitis (sis′ti′tis), p. 334

diuretic (di-yū-ret′ik), p. 332

floating kidney (flōt′ing kid′ne), p. 325

gout (gowt), p. 324

hemodialysis (he-mo-di-al′ĭ-sis), p. 335

incontinence (in-con′tin-ents), p. 336

pyelonephritis (pi-lo-nef-ri′tis), p. 334

uremia (yū-re′me-uh), p. 334

urethritis (yū-re-thri′tis), p. 334

urinalysis (yū-rĭ-nal′ĭ-sis), p. 334

Summary

16.1 Urinary System

A. The kidneys excrete nitrogenous wastes, including urea, uric acid, and creatinine. They maintain the normal water-salt balance and the acid-base balance of the blood, as well as influencing the secretion of certain hormones.

B. The kidneys produce urine, which is conducted by the ureters to the bladder, where it is stored before being released by way of the urethra.

16.2 Anatomy of the Kidney and Excretion

A. Macroscopically, the kidneys are divided into the renal cortex, renal medulla, and renal pelvis. Microscopically, they contain the nephrons.

B. Each nephron has its own blood supply; the afferent arteriole approaches the glomerular capsule and divides to become the glomerulus, a knot of capillaries. The efferent arteriole leaves the capsule and immediately branches into the peritubular capillary network.

C. Each region of the nephron is anatomically suited to its task in urine formation. The spaces between the podocytes of the glomerular capsule allow small molecules to enter the capsule from the glomerulus. The cuboidal epithelial cells of the proximal convoluted tubule have many mitochondria and microvilli to carry out active transport (following passive transport) from the tubule to the blood. In contrast, the cuboidal epithelial cells of the distal convoluted tubule have numerous mitochondria but lack microvilli. They carry out active transport from the blood to the tubule.

D. The steps in urine formation are glomerular filtration, tubular reabsorption, and tubular secretion.

16.3 Regulatory Functions of the Kidneys

A. The kidneys regulate the fluid and electrolyte balance of the body. Water is reabsorbed from certain parts of the tubule, and the loop of the nephron establishes an osmotic gradient that draws water from the descending loop of the nephron and also from the collecting duct. The permeability of the collecting duct is under the control of the hormone ADH. The reabsorption of salt increases blood volume and pressure because more water is also reabsorbed. Two other hormones, aldosterone and ANH, control the kidneys' reabsorption of sodium (Na^+).

B. The kidneys regulate the acid-base balance of the blood. Before the work of the kidneys begins, the acid-base buffer systems of the blood have functioned to keep the pH temporarily under control; also, the respiratory center has regulated the breathing rate to control the excretion of carbon dioxide at pulmonary capillaries. The kidneys largely function by excreting hydrogen ions and reabsorbing bicarbonate ions as needed.

16.4 Problems with Kidney Function
Various types of problems, including repeated urinary infections, can lead to renal failure, which necessitates receiving a kidney from a donor or undergoing hemodialysis by utilizing a kidney machine or CAPD.

16.5 Effects of Aging
Kidney function declines with age. Also, kidney stones, infections, and urination problems are more common.

16.6 Homeostasis
The urinary system works with the other systems of the body to maintain homeostasis in the ways described in the Human Systems Work Together on page 337.

Study Questions

1. List and explain four functions of the urinary system. (p. 324)
2. Trace the path of urine, and describe the function of each organ mentioned. (pp. 324–25)
3. Explain how urination is controlled. (p. 325)
4. Describe the detailed anatomy of a kidney. (pp. 326–28)
5. Trace the path of blood about a nephron. (pp. 328–29)
6. Name the parts of a nephron, and tell how the structure of the convoluted tubules suits their respective functions. (pp. 326–27)
7. State and describe the three steps of urine formation. (pp. 328–29)
8. Where in particular are salt and water reabsorbed along the length of the nephron? Describe the contribution of the loop of the nephron. (pp. 328–29)
9. Name and describe the action of anti-diuretic hormone (ADH), the renin-aldosterone connection, and atrial natriuretic hormone (ANH). (pp. 331–32)
10. How do the kidneys maintain the pH of the blood within normal limits? (p. 333)
11. Explain how the artificial kidney machine works. (p. 335)

Objective Questions

Fill in the blanks.

1. The lungs are organs of excretion because they rid the body of _____.
2. The capillary tuft inside the glomerular capsule is called the _____.
3. Urine leaves the bladder in the _____.
4. _____ is a substance that is found in the filtrate, is reabsorbed, and is present in urine.
5. Tubular secretion takes place at the _____, a portion of the nephron.
6. The primary nitrogenous end product of humans is _____.
7. _____ is a substance that is found in the filtrate, is not reabsorbed, and is concentrated in urine.
8. In addition to excreting nitrogenous wastes, the kidneys adjust the _____, _____, and _____ balance of the blood.
9. Reabsorption of water from the collecting duct is regulated by the hormone _____.
10. A _____ is a chemical that can combine with either hydrogen ions or hydroxide ions, depending on the pH of the solution.
11. The accumulation of uric acid crystals in a joint cavity produces a condition called _____.
12. Urine is carried from the kidneys to the urinary bladder by a pair of organs called _____.
13. The outer granulated layer of the kidney is the renal _____, whereas the inner striated layer is the renal _____.

Medical Terminology Reinforcement Exercise

Consult Appendix B for help in pronouncing and analyzing the meaning of the terms that follow.

1. hematuria (hem″uh-tu-re′uh)
2. oliguria (ol″ĭ-gu′re-uh)
3. polyuria (pol″e-yū′re-uh)
4. extracorporeal shock wave lithotripsy (ESWL) (eks″truh-kor-po′re-al lith″o-trip′se)
5. antidiuretic (an″tī-di″yū-ret′ik)
6. urethratresia (yū-re″thruh-tre′ze-uh)
7. cystopyelonephritis (sis″to-pi″e-lo-ně-fri′tis)
8. nocturia (nok-tu′re-uh)
9. glomerulonephritis (glo-měr″yū-lo-ně-fri′tis)
10. ureterovesicostomy (yū-re″ter-o-ves″ĭ-kos′to-me)

Website Link

Visit the Student Edition of the Online Learning Center at http://www.mhhe.com/maderap5 for additional quizzes, interactive learning exercises, and other study tools.

The Reproductive System

Sperm (blue) are produced in seminiferous tubules. The threadlike tails of sperm are clearly visible as hairlike masses in the tubules.

chapter outline & learning objectives

After you have studied this chapter, you should be able to:

Part V

17.1 Human Life Cycle

Unlike the other systems of the body, which are the same in males and females, the reproductive system is quite different in males and females. The reproductive system does not begin to fully function until **puberty,** when sexual maturity occurs between the ages of 11 and 13 in girls and 14 and 16 in boys. Following puberty, the individual is capable of producing offspring.

The reproductive organs (**genitals**) have the following functions:

1. Males produce sperm within testes, and females produce eggs within ovaries.
2. Males nurture and transport the sperm in ducts until they exit the penis, and females transport the eggs in uterine tubes to the uterus.
3. The male penis functions to deliver sperm to the female vagina, which functions to receive the sperm. The vagina also transports menstrual fluid to the exterior and is the birth canal.
4. The uterus of the female allows the fertilized egg to develop within her body. After birth, the female breast provides nourishment in the form of milk.
5. The testes and ovaries produce the sex hormones that maintain the testes and ovaries and have a profound effect on the body because they bring about masculinization and feminization of various features.

Meiosis

We studied the type of cell division called mitosis in Chapter 3 and learned that mitosis occurs during growth and repair of the body's tissues. As a result of mitosis, the chromosome number stays constant, and every cell in your body has 46 chromosomes.

The human life cycle (Fig. 17.1) includes mitosis and a type of cell division called **meiosis.** During meiosis, the chromosome number is reduced from 46 chromosomes to 23 chromosomes, called the n number of chromosomes. During meiosis, chromosomes of the same shape and size, called homologous pairs of chromosomes, align, and only one member of each pair goes into the daughter cells. Meiosis only takes place in the testes of males during the production of sperm and in the ovaries of females during the production of eggs.

A **zygote,** the first cell of a new human being, forms following fertilization, when a sperm joins with an egg. Because the sperm has 23 chromosomes and the egg has 23 chromosomes, the zygote has 23 pairs of homologous chromosomes, or 46 chromosomes altogether. Without meiosis, the chromosome number in each generation of human beings would double, and cells would no longer be able to function. The zygote undergoes mitosis during development to produce the many cells of a newborn, and mitosis also occurs as a child becomes an adult.

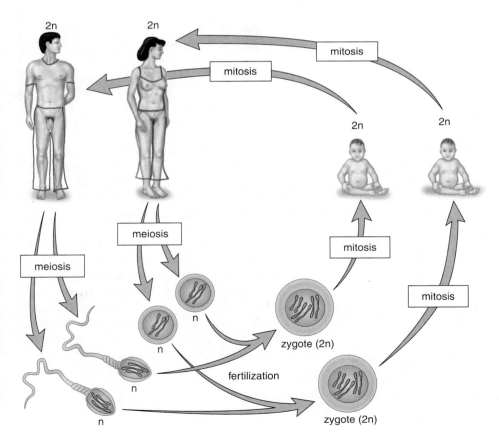

Figure 17.1 The human life cycle has two types of cell divisions: mitosis, in which the chromosome number stays constant, and meiosis, in which the chromosome number is reduced. Meiosis only occurs in the testes of males during the production of sperm and in the ovaries of females during the production of eggs. In human beings, the egg and sperm have 23 chromosomes each, called the n number. Following fertilization, the new individual has 46 chromosomes, called the 2n number.

Figure 17.2 The male reproductive system. The testes produce sperm. The seminal vesicles, the prostate gland, and the bulbourethral glands provide a fluid medium for the sperm, which move from a testis to an epididymis to a vas deferens and through the ejaculatory duct to the urethra in the penis. The foreskin (prepuce) is removed when a penis is circumcised.

17.2 Male Reproductive System

The male reproductive system includes the organs depicted in Figure 17.2. The *primary sex organs* of a male are the paired testes (sing., **testis**), which are suspended within the sacs of the **scrotum**. The testes are the primary sex organs because they produce sperm and the male sex hormones (**androgens**).

The other organs depicted in Figure 17.2 are the *accessory* (or secondary) *sex organs* of a male. Sperm produced by the testes are stored within the **epididymis** (pl., epididymides). Then they enter a **vas deferens** (pl., vasa deferentia), which transports them to an **ejaculatory duct**. The ejaculatory ducts enter the **urethra**. (The urethra in males is a part of both the urinary system and the reproductive system.) The urethra passes through the penis and transports sperm to outside the body.

At the time of **ejaculation**, sperm leave the penis in a fluid called **semen** (seminal fluid). The seminal vesicles, the prostate gland, and the bulbourethral glands (Cowper glands) add secretions to seminal fluid. The **seminal vesicles** lie lateral to the vas deferens, and their ducts join to form an ejaculatory duct. The **prostate gland** is a single, donut-shaped gland that surrounds the upper portion of the urethra just inferior to the bladder. **Bulbourethral glands** are pea-sized organs that lie inferior to the prostate on either side of the urethra.

Each component of seminal fluid seems to have a particular function. Sperm are more viable in a basic solution, and seminal fluid, which is milky in appearance, has a slightly basic pH (about 7.5). Swimming sperm require energy, and seminal fluid contains the sugar fructose, which presumably serves as an energy source. Semen also contains prostaglandins, chemicals that cause the uterus to contract. Uterine contractions help propel the sperm toward the egg.

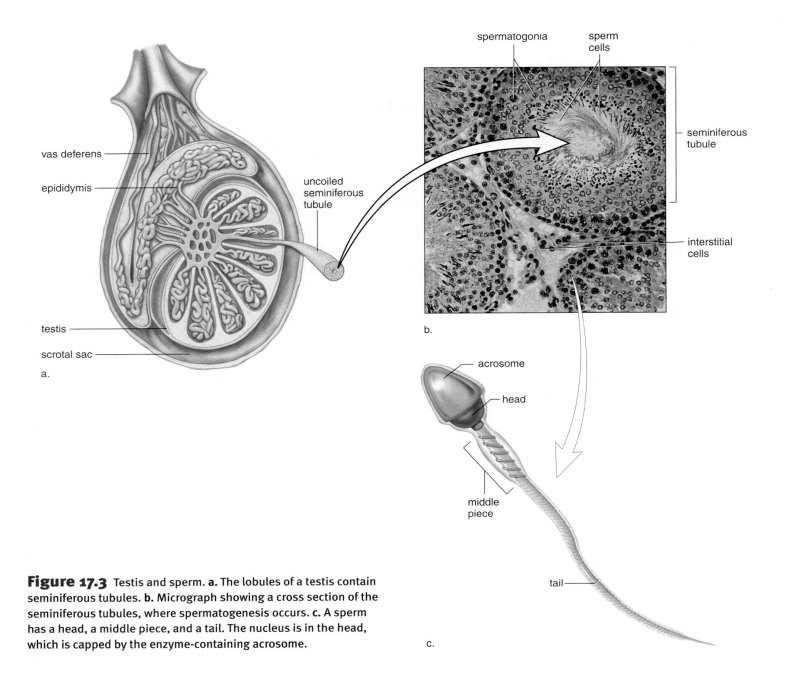

Figure 17.3 Testis and sperm. **a.** The lobules of a testis contain seminiferous tubules. **b.** Micrograph showing a cross section of the seminiferous tubules, where spermatogenesis occurs. **c.** A sperm has a head, a middle piece, and a tail. The nucleus is in the head, which is capped by the enzyme-containing acrosome.

The Testes

The testes, which produce sperm and also the male sex hormones, lie outside the abdominal cavity of the male within the scrotum. The testes begin their development inside the abdominal cavity but descend into the scrotal sacs during the last two months of fetal development. If, by chance, the testes do not descend and the male is not treated or operated on to place the testes in the scrotum, sterility—the inability to produce offspring—usually follows. This is because the internal temperature of the body is too high to produce viable sperm. A subcutaneous muscle along with an adjoining muscle raise the scrotum during sexual excitement and when a higher temperature is need to warm the testes.

Anatomy of a Testis

A sagittal section of a testis shows that it is enclosed by a tough, fibrous capsule. The connective tissue of the capsule extends into the testis, forming septa that divide the testis into compartments called lobules. Each lobule contains one to three tightly coiled **seminiferous tubules** (Fig. 17.3*a*). Altogether, these tubules have a combined length of approximately 250 m. A microscopic cross section of a seminiferous tubule reveals that it is packed with cells undergoing spermatogenesis (Fig. 17.3*b*), the production of sperm.

Delicate connective tissue surrounds the seminiferous tubules. Cells that secrete the male sex hormones, the androgens, are located here between the seminiferous tubules.

Figure 17.4 Spermatogenesis.

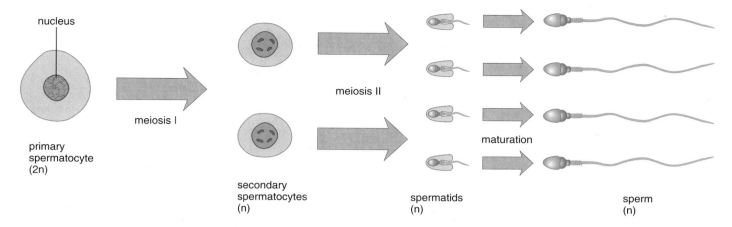

nucleus

primary
spermatocyte
(2n)

meiosis I

secondary
spermatocytes
(n)

meiosis II

maturation

spermatids
(n)

sperm
(n)

Therefore, these endocrine cells are called **interstitial cells.** The most important of the androgens is **testosterone,** whose functions are discussed later in this section.

Testicular cancer, or cancer of the testes, is one type of cancer that can be detected by self-examination, as explained in the Medical Focus on page 357.

Spermatogenesis

Spermatogenesis, the production of sperm, includes the process of meiosis as the sperm form. Before puberty, the testes, including the seminiferous tubules, are small and nonfunctioning. At the time of puberty, the interstitial cells become larger and start producing androgens. Then, the seminiferous tubules also enlarge, and they start producing sperm.

The seminiferous tubules contain two types of cells: germ cells, which are involved in spermatogenesis, and sustentacular (Sertoli) cells. Sustentacular cells are large; they extend from the capsule to the lumen of the seminiferous tubule. The sustentacular cells support, nourish, and regulate the development of cells undergoing spermatogenesis.

The germ cells near the capsule are called spermatogonia. The spermatogonia divide, producing more cells by mitosis. Some of these cells remain as spermatogonia, and some are **primary spermatocytes** (Fig. 17.4). The spermatocytes start the process of meiosis, which requires two divisions. Following meiosis I, cells called **secondary spermatocytes** have the reduced, or n, number of chromosomes (i.e., 23 chromosomes). Following meiosis II, there are four spermatids. **Spermatids** then differentiate into sperm.

Mature **sperm,** or spermatozoa, have three distinct parts: a head, a middle piece, and a tail (see Fig. 17.3c). Mitochondria in the middle piece provide energy for the movement of the tail, which has the structure of a flagellum. The head contains a nucleus covered by a cap called the **acrosome,** which stores

enzymes needed to penetrate the egg. Notice in Figure 17.3b, that the sperm are situated so that their tails project into the lumen of the seminiferous tubules.

When formed, the sperm are transported to the epididymis because the seminiferous tubules unite to form a complex network of channels that join, forming ducts. When the ducts join, an epididymis is formed.

The ejaculated semen of a normal human male contains several hundred million sperm, but only one sperm normally enters an egg. Sperm usually do not live more than 48 hours in the female genital tract.

Male Internal Accessory Organs

Table 17.1 lists and Figure 17.5 depicts the internal accessory organs, as well as the other reproductive organs, of the male. Sperm are, transported to the urethra by a series of ducts. Along the way, various glands add secretions to seminal fluid.

Table 17.1	**Male Internal Accessory Organs**
Organ	**Function**
Epididymides	Ducts where sperm mature and some sperm are stored
Vas deferentia	Transport and store sperm
Seminal vesicles	Contribute nutrients and fluid to semen
Ejaculatory ducts	Transport sperm
Prostate gland	Contributes basic fluid to semen
Urethra	Transports sperm
Bulbourethral glands	Contribute mucoid fluid to semen

Figure 17.5 Male reproductive system, posterior view. This view shows the duct system that transports sperm from each testis to the urethra, which continues in the penis.

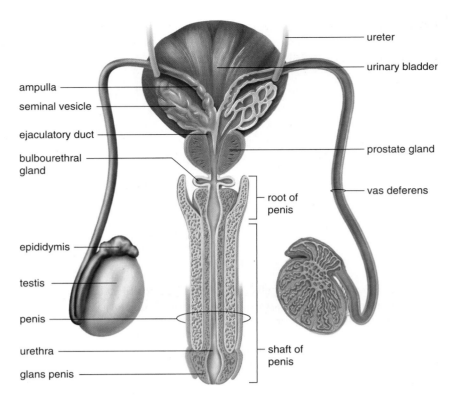

ureter
urinary bladder
ampulla
seminal vesicle
ejaculatory duct
prostate gland
bulbourethral gland
vas deferens
root of penis
epididymis
testis
penis
shaft of penis
urethra
glans penis

Epididymides

Each epididymis is a tightly coiled, threadlike tube that would stretch about 6 meters if uncoiled. A epididymis runs posteriorly down along a testis and becomes a vas deferens that ascends a testis medially.

The lining of an epididymis consists of pseudostratified columnar epithelium with long cilia. Sperm are stored in the epididymides, and the lining secretes a fluid that supports them. The wall of an epididymis contains a thin layer of smooth muscle. Peristaltic contractions move the sperm along as they mature. By the time the sperm leave the epididymides, they are capable of fertilizing an egg even though they do not "swim" until they enter the vagina.

Vas Deferens

Each vas deferens is a continuation of an epididymis. As the vas deferens ascends into the abdomen, it passes through an inguinal canal. This is the passageway by which a testis descended from the abdomen into the scrotum. The canal contains the *spermatic cords*, which consist of connective tissue and muscle fibers that enclose a vas deferens, blood vessels, and nerves. The inguinal canal remains a weak point in the adominal wall. As such, it is frequently a site of hernias. A **hernia** is an opening or separation of some part of the abdominal wall through which a portion of an internal organ, usually the intestine, protrudes.

After the vas deferens enters the abdomen, it crosses over to reach the posterior side of the urinary bladder. The vas deferens is lined by pseudostratified columnar epithelium that is ciliated at the testicular end. A vas deferens has an expanded portion called the ampulla, but it is slender again when it joins with the duct of a seminal vesicle to form an ejaculatory duct. The ejaculatory ducts pass through the prostate gland to join the urethra.

Seminal Vesicles

The seminal vesicles lie lateral to the vas deferens on the posterior side of the bladder. They are coiled, membranous pouches about 5 cm long. The glandular lining of the seminal vesicles secretes an alkaline fluid that contains fructose and prostaglandins into an ejaculatory duct. The pH of the fluid helps modify the pH of seminal fluid; the fructose provides energy for sperm; and the prostaglandins promote muscular contractions of the female genital tract that help move sperm along.

Prostate

The prostate gland encircles the urethra just inferior to the bladder. The donut-shaped gland is about 4 cm across, 2 cm thick, and 3 cm in length. The fibrous connective tissue of its capsule extends inward to divide the gland into lobes, each of which contains about 40 to 50 tubules. The epithelium lining the tubules secretes a fluid that is thin, milky, and alkaline. In addition to adjusting the pH of seminal fluid, prostatic fluid enhances the motility of sperm. The secretion of the prostate gland enters the urethra when the smooth muscle in its capsular wall contracts.

As discussed in the Medical Focus on page 338, the prostate gland is a frequent site for cancer.

Figure 17.6 Penis anatomy. **a.** Beneath the skin and the connective tissue lies the urethra, surrounded by erectile tissue. This tissue expands to form the glans penis, which in uncircumcised males is partially covered by the foreskin (prepuce). **b.** Two other columns of erectile tissue in the penis are located posteriorly.

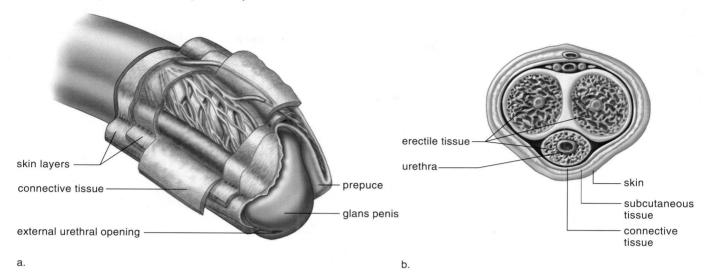

a.

b.

Bulbourethal Glands

The bulbourethral glands (Cowper glands) are two small glands about the size of peas. They are located inferior to the prostate gland and enclosed by fibers of the external urethral sphincter. These glands also contain many tubules that secrete a mucuslike fluid. This fluid lubricates the end of the penis preparatory to sexual intercourse.

Male Sexual Response

The **external genitals** are the sex organs that can be easily observed because they are located outside the body. The **penis** and the scrotum are the external genitals of the male. The penis is the male organ of sexual intercourse by which sperm are introduced into the female reproductive tract.

The penis has an internal root and an external shaft (see Fig. 17.5). At the glans penis, the skin folds back on itself to form the *prepuce*, or foreskin (Fig. 17.6*a*). This is the structure that is removed in the surgical procedure called **circumcision.** Internally, it contains three cylindrical bodies of erectile tissue; the urethra passes though one of them. These three columns are supported by fibrous connective tissue, and the whole is covered with a thin, loose skin (Fig. 17.6*b*).

The erectile tissues contain distensible blood spaces. During sexual arousal, autonomic nerve impulses lead to the production of cGMP (cyclic guanosine monophosphate), causing the smooth muscle walls of incoming arteries to relax and the erectile tissue to fill with blood. The veins that take blood away from the penis are compressed, and the penis becomes erect. **Erectile dysfunction** (formerly called impotency) exists when the erectile tissue doesn't expand enough to compress the veins. The drug Viagra inhibits an enzyme that breaks down cGMP, ensuring that a full erection will take place. However, vision problems may occur when taking Viagra because the same enzyme occurs in the retina.

Orgasm (climax) in males is marked by ejaculation, which has two phases: emission and expulsion. During emission, sperm enter the urethra from each ejaculatory duct, and the prostate, seminal vesicles, and bulbourethral glands contribute secretions to the seminal fluid. Once seminal fluid is in the urethra, rhythmic muscle contractions cause seminal fluid to be expelled from the penis in spurts. During ejaculation, a sphincter closes off the bladder so that no urine enters the urethra. (Notice that the urethra carries either urine or semen at different times.)

Male orgasm includes expulsion of seminal fluid from the penis but also the physiological and psychological sensations that occur at the climax of sexual stimulation. The psychological sensation of pleasure is centered in the brain, but the physiological reactions involve the genital organs and associated muscles, as well as the entire body. Marked muscular tension is followed by contraction and relaxation.

Following ejaculation and/or loss of sexual arousal, the penis returns to its normal flaccid state. After ejaculation, a male typically experiences a period of time, called the refractory period, during which stimulation does not bring about an erection. The length of the refractory period increases with age.

There may be in excess of 400 million sperm in the 3.5 ml of semen expelled during ejaculation. The sperm count can be much lower than this, however, and fertilization of the egg by a sperm can still take place.

Regulation of Male Hormone Levels

At the time of puberty, the sex organs mature, and then changes occur in the physique of males. The cause of puberty is related to the level of sex hormones in the body, as regulated by the negative feedback system described in Figure 17.7. We now know that this feedback system functions long before puberty, but the level of hormones is low because the hypothalamus is supersensitive to feedback control. At the start of puberty, the hypothalamus becomes less sensitive to feedback control and begins to increase its production of gonadotropin-releasing hormone (GnRH), which stimulates the anterior pituitary to produce the gonadotropic hormones. Two gonadotropic hormones, **FSH (follicle-stimulating hormone)** and **LH (luteinizing hormone),** are named for their function in females but exist in both sexes, stimulating the appropriate organs in each. FSH promotes spermatogenesis in the seminiferous tubules, and LH promotes androgen (e.g., testosterone) production in the interstitial cells. LH in males is also called interstitial cell-stimulating hormone (ICSH).

Negative Feedback Mechanisms

As mentioned, the hypothalamus, anterior pituitary, and testes are involved in a negative feedback system. The system maintains testosterone production at a fairly constant level. When the amount of testosterone in the blood rises to a certain level, it causes the hypothalamus and anterior pituitary to decrease their respective secretion of GnRH and LH. As the level of testosterone begins to fall, the hypothalamus increases its secretion of GnRH, and the anterior pituitary increases its secretion of LH; thus, stimulation of the interstitial cells occurs. Only minor fluctuations of the testosterone level occur in the male, and the feedback mechanism in this case acts to maintain testosterone at a normal level.

A similar feedback mechanism maintains the continuous production of sperm. The sustentacular cells in the wall of the seminiferous tubules produce a hormone called **inhibin** that blocks GnRH and FSH secretion when appropriate.

Testosterone

The male sex hormone, testosterone, has many functions. It is essential for normal development and function of the sex organs in males. For example, greatly increased testosterone secretion at the time of puberty stimulates maturation of the penis and the testes.

Secondary Sex Characteristics Testosterone also brings about and maintains the male **secondary sex characteristics,** which develop at the time of puberty and visibly distinguish males from females. These characteristics include a pattern of male hair growth, activity of cutaneous glands, pitch of the voice, and muscle strength.

Figure 17.7 Negative feedback. Regulation of testosterone secretion involves negative feedback (reverse arrows) by testosterone on GnRH and LH. Regulation of sperm production involves negative feedback by inhibin on GnRH and FSH.

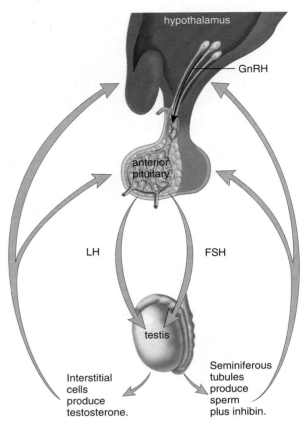

At puberty, males experience growth of a beard, axillary (underarm) hair, and pubic hair. In males, pubic hair tapers toward the navel. A side effect of testosterone activity is baldness. Genes for baldness are probably inherited by both sexes, but baldness is seen more often in males because of the presence of testosterone. This makes baldness a sex-influenced trait.

Testosterone also causes oil and sweat glands in the skin to secrete, thereby contributing to acne and body odor. The larynx and vocal cords enlarge, causing the voice to change. The "Adam's apple" is a part of the larynx, and it is usually more prominent in males than in females.

Testosterone is responsible for the greater muscular strength of males, which is why some athletes take a supplemental anabolic steroid, which is either testosterone or a related chemical. The disadvantages of anabolic steroid use are discussed in a Medical Focus in Chapter 10, page 199.

17.3 Female Reproductive System

The female reproductive system includes the organs depicted in Figure 17.8. The primary sex organs of a female are the paired **ovaries** that lie in shallow depressions, one on each side of the upper pelvic cavity. The ovaries are the primary sex organs because they produce eggs and the female sex hormones, estrogen and progesterone.

The other organs depicted in Figure 17.8 are the accessory (or secondary) sex organs of a female. When an egg leaves an ovary, it is usually swept into a uterine (fallopian) tube by the combined action of the fimbriae (fingerlike projections of a uterine tube) and the beating of cilia that line the uterine tube.

Once in a uterine tube, the egg is transported toward the uterus. Fertilization, and therefore zygote formation, usually takes place in the uterine tube. The developing embryo normally arrives at the **uterus** several days later, and then **implantation** occurs as the embryo embeds in the uterine lining, which has been prepared to receive it.

Development of the embryo and fetus normally takes place in the uterus. The lining of the uterus, called the **endometrium**, participates in the formation of the placenta (see Chapter 18, page 378), which supplies nutrients needed for embryonic and fetal development.

The uterine tubes join the uterus at its upper end, while at its lower end, the **cervix** enters the vagina nearly at a right angle. A small opening in the cervix leads from the uterus to the vagina.

The **vagina** is the birth canal and organ of sexual intercourse in females. The vagina also acts as an exit for menstrual flow. If fertilization and implantation do not occur, the endometrium is sloughed off during menstruation.

The external genital organs of the female are known collectively as the **vulva.** The vulva is recognized by two folds of skin, the labia majora and the labia minora. The cleft between the labia minora contains the openings of the urethra and the vagina.

Notice that the urinary and reproductive systems in the female are entirely separate. For example, the urethra carries only urine, and the vagina has functions that pertain only to reproduction.

Figure 17.8 The female reproductive system. The ovaries release one egg per month. Fertilization occurs in the uterine tube, and development occurs in the uterus. The vagina is the birth canal as well as the organ of sexual intercourse.

visual focus

uterine tube

ovary

uterus

vagina

1. Primary follicles contain oocyte and begin producing the sex hormone estrogen.

2. Secondary follicles contain secondary oocyte and produce the sex hormones estrogen and some progesterone.

3. Vesicular (Graafian) follicle develops.

primary follicles

secondary follicles

vesicular (Graafian) follicle

oocyte

6. Corpus luteum degenerates.

secondary oocyte

corpus luteum

4. Ovulation: The secondary oocyte is released.

5. Corpus luteum produces the sex hormones progesterone and some estrogen.

Figure 17.9 Anatomy of ovary and follicle. As a follicle matures, the oocyte enlarges and is surrounded by layers of follicular cells and fluid. The micrograph shows the mature vesicular (Graafian) follicle. Eventually, ovulation occurs, the mature follicle ruptures, and the secondary oocyte is released. A single follicle actually goes through all the stages in one place within the ovary.

Figure 17.10 Oogenesis in an ovary. Oogenesis involves meiosis I, during which the chromosome number is reduced, and meiosis II, which results in a single egg. Meiosis II takes place after a sperm enters the secondary oocyte. At the end of oogenesis, there are also at least two polar bodies, nonfunctional cells that later disintegrate.

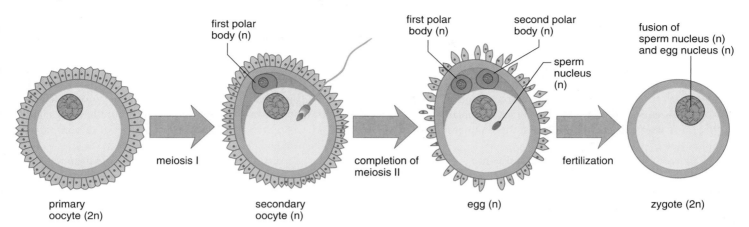

primary oocyte (2n) → meiosis I → secondary oocyte (n) → completion of meiosis II → egg (n) → fertilization → zygote (2n)

first polar body (n)

first polar body (n)   second polar body (n)   sperm nucleus (n)

fusion of sperm nucleus (n) and egg nucleus (n)

The Ovary

The ovaries are paired, oval bodies about 3 to 4 cm in length by 2 cm in width and less than 1 cm thick. They lie to either side of the uterus on the lateral walls of the pelvic cavity.

Several ligaments hold the ovaries in place (see Fig. 17.11). The largest of these, the broad ligament, is also attached to the uterine tubes and the uterus. The suspensory ligament holds the upper end of the ovary to the pelvic wall, and the ovarian ligament attaches the lower end of the ovary to the uterus.

A sagittal section through an ovary shows that it is made up of an outer cortex and an inner medulla. In the cortex are many **follicles,** each one containing an immature egg, called an **oocyte** (Fig. 17.9). A female is born with as many as 2 million follicles, but the number is reduced to 300,000–400,000 by the time of puberty. Only a small number of follicles (about 400) ever mature because a female usually produces only one egg per month during her reproductive years. Because oocytes are present at birth, they age as the woman ages. This may be one reason older women are more likely to produce children with genetic defects.

Cancer of an ovary, or ovarian cancer, which is discussed in the Medical Focus on page 352, causes more deaths than cervical and uterine cancer.

Oogenesis

Oogenesis, the production of an egg, includes the process of meiosis. Similar to spermatogenesis, oogenesis begins with a primary oocyte that undergoes meiosis I to become a secondary oocyte having 23 chromosomes. The secondary oocyte undergoes meiosis II to produce an egg.

Oogenesis begins within a follicle. As the follicle matures, it develops from a primary follicle to a secondary follicle to a **vesicular (Graafian) follicle** (see Fig. 17.9). The epithelium of a primary follicle surrounds a primary oocyte. Pools of follicular fluid surround the oocyte in a secondary follicle. In a vesicular follicle, a fluid-filled cavity increases to the point that the follicle wall balloons out on the surface of the ovary.

Figure 17.10 traces the steps of oogenesis. As a follicle matures, the primary oocyte divides, producing two cells. One cell is a secondary oocyte, and the other is a polar body. A **polar body** is a nonfunctioning cell that occurs only during oogenesis. The vesicular follicle bursts, releasing the secondary oocyte surrounded by a clear membrane and attached follicular cells. This process is referred to as **ovulation.**

The secondary oocyte, often called an egg for convenience, enters a uterine tube. If fertilization occurs, a sperm enters the secondary oocyte, which then completes meiosis II. An egg with 23 chromosomes and a second polar body result. When the sperm nucleus unites with the egg nucleus, a zygote with 46 chromosomes is produced.

A follicle that has lost its egg develops into a **corpus luteum,** a glandlike structure. If implantation does not occur, the corpus luteum begins to degenerate after about 10 days. The remains of a corpus luteum is a white scar called the **corpus albicans.** If implantation does occur, the corpus luteum continues for about six months and produces hormones that help keep the uterine lining intact.

Although a number of follicles grow during each month, only one reaches full maturity and ruptures to release a secondary oocyte. Presumably the ovaries alternate in producing functional ova. The number of secondary oocytes produced by a female during her lifetime is minuscule compared to the number of sperm produced by a male.

Ovarian Cancer

Ovarian cancer is often "silent," showing no obvious signs or symptoms until late in its development. The most common sign is enlargement of the abdomen, which is caused by the accumulation of fluid. Rarely is there abnormal vaginal bleeding. In women over 40, vague digestive disturbances (stomach discomfort, gas, distention) that persist and cannot be explained by any other cause may indicate the need for a thorough evaluation for ovarian cancer.

The risk for ovarian cancer increases with age. The highest rates are for women over age 60. Women who have never had children are twice as likely to develop ovarian cancer as those who have. Early age at first pregnancy, early menopause, and the use of oral contraceptives, which reduces ovulation frequency, appear to be protective against ovarian cancer. If a woman has had breast cancer, her chances of developing ovarian cancer double. Certain rare genetic disorders are associated with increased risk. The highest incidence rates are reported in the more industrialized countries, with the exception of Japan.

Early detection requires periodic, thorough pelvic examinations. The Pap smear, useful in detecting cervical cancer, does not reveal ovarian cancer. Women over age 40 should have a cancer-related checkup every year. Testing for the level of tumor marker CA-125, a protein antigen, is helpful.

Surgery, radiation therapy, and drug therapy are treatment options. Surgery usually includes the removal of one or both ovaries **(oophorectomy)**, the uterus **(hysterectomy)**, and the uterine tubes **(salpingectomy)**. In some very early tumors, only the involved ovary is removed, especially in young women. In advanced disease, an attempt is made to remove all intra-abdominal cancerous tissue to enhance the effect of chemotherapy.

Female Internal Accessory Organs

Table 17.2 lists and Figure 17.11 depicts the internal accessory organs, as well as the other reproductive organs, of a female.

Uterine Tubes

The **uterine tubes,** also called fallopian tubes or oviducts, extend from the uterus to the ovaries. Usually the secondary oocyte enters a uterine tube because the **fimbriae** sweep over the ovary at the time of ovulation, and the beating of the cilia that line uterine tubes creates a suction effect. Once in the uterine tube, the egg is propelled slowly toward the uterus by action of the cilia and by muscular contractions in the wall of the uterine tubes.

Fertilization, the completion of oogenesis, and zygote formation normally occur in the upper one-third of a uterine tube. The developing embryo usually does not arrive at the uterus for several days, and then it embeds itself in the uterine lining, which has been prepared to receive it.

Occasionally, the embryo becomes embedded in the wall of a uterine tube, where it begins to develop. Tubular pregnancies cannot succeed because the tubes are not anatomically capable of allowing full development to occur. Any pregnancy that occurs outside the uterus is called an **ectopic pregnancy.**

Uterus

The *uterus* is a thick-walled, muscular organ about the size and shape of an inverted pear. Normally, it lies above and is tipped over the urinary bladder. The uterus has three sections. The *fundus* is the region superior to the entrance of the uterine tubes. The *body* of the uterus is the major region. The *cervix* is the narrow end of the uterus that projects into the vagina. A cervical orifice leads to the lumen of the vagina.

Development of the embryo normally takes place in the uterus. This organ, sometimes called the womb, is approximately 5 cm wide in its usual state but is capable of stretching to over 30 cm to accommodate the growing baby. The lining of the uterus, called the *endometrium,* participates in the formation of the placenta (see Chapter 18), which supplies nutrients needed for embryonic and fetal development. In the nonpregnant female, the endometrium varies in thickness during a monthly menstrual cycle, discussed later in this chapter.

Cancer of the cervix is a common form of cancer in women. Early detection is possible by means of a **Pap smear,** which entails the removal of a few cells from the region of the cervix for microscopic examination. If the cells are cancerous, a hysterectomy (the removal of the uterus) may be recommended. Removal of the ovaries in addition to the uterus is termed an

Table 17.2	Female Internal Accessory Organs
Organ	**Function**
Uterine tubes (fallopian tubes, oviducts)	Transport egg; location of fertilization
Uterus (womb)	Houses developing fetus
Cervix	Contains opening to uterus
Vagina	Receives penis during sexual intercourse; serves as birth canal and as an exit for menstrual flow

Figure 17.11 Female reproductive system, posterior view.

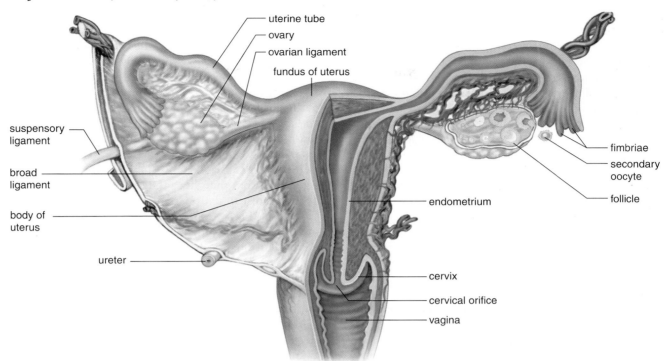

- uterine tube
- ovary
- ovarian ligament
- fundus of uterus
- suspensory ligament
- broad ligament
- body of uterus
- ureter
- fimbriae
- secondary oocyte
- follicle
- endometrium
- cervix
- cervical orifice
- vagina

ovariohysterectomy. Because the vagina remains intact, the woman can still engage in sexual intercourse.

Vagina

The vagina is a tube that makes a 45° angle with the small of the back. The mucosal lining of the vagina lies in folds that extend when the fibromuscular wall stretches. This capacity to extend is especially important when the vagina serves as the birth canal, and it can also facilitate intercourse, when the vagina receives the penis.

External Genitals

The female external genitals (Fig. 17.12) are known collectively as the vulva. The vulva includes two large, hair-covered folds of skin called the **labia majora** (sing., labium majus). They extend posteriorly from the **mons pubis,** a fatty prominence underlying the pubic hair. The **labia minora** (sing., labium minus) are two small folds of skin lying just inside the labia majora. They extend forward from the vaginal opening to encircle and form a foreskin for the **clitoris,** an organ that is homologous to the penis. Although quite small, the clitoris has a shaft of erectile tissue and is capped by a pea-shaped glans. The clitoris also has sensory receptors that allow it to function as a sexually sensitive organ.

The **vestibule,** a cleft between the labia minora, contains the orifices of the urethra and the vagina. The vagina can be partially closed by a ring of tissue called

the hymen. The hymen ordinarily is ruptured by initial sexual intercourse; however, it can also be disrupted by other types of physical activities. If the hymen persists after sexual intercourse, it can be surgically ruptured.

The urinary and reproductive systems in the female are entirely separate: The urethra carries only urine, and the vagina serves only as the birth canal and as the organ for sexual intercourse.

Figure 17.12 External genitals of the female. At birth, the opening of the vagina is partially blocked by a membrane called the hymen. Physical activities and sexual intercourse disrupt the hymen.

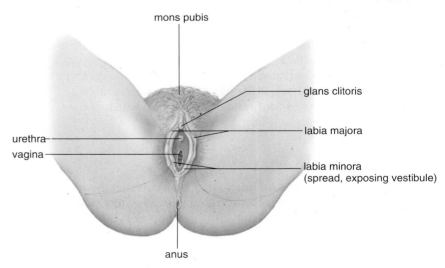

- mons pubis
- glans clitoris
- labia majora
- urethra
- vagina
- labia minora (spread, exposing vestibule)
- anus

Female Sexual Response

Upon sexual stimulation, the labia minora, the vaginal wall, and the clitoris become engorged with blood. The breasts also swell, and the nipples become erect. The labia majora enlarge, redden, and spread away from the vaginal opening.

The vagina expands and elongates. Blood vessels in the vaginal wall release small droplets of fluid that seep into the vagina and lubricate it. Mucus-secreting glands beneath the labia minora on either side of the vagina also provide lubrication for entry of the penis into the vagina. Although the vagina is the organ of sexual intercourse in females, the clitoris plays a significant role in the female sexual response. The extremely sensitive clitoris can swell to two or three times its usual size. The thrusting of the penis and the pressure of the pubic symphyses of the partners act to stimulate the clitoris.

Orgasm occurs at the height of the sexual response. Blood pressure and pulse rate rise, breathing quickens, and the walls of the uterus and uterine tubes contract rhythmically. A sensation of intense pleasure is followed by relaxation when organs return to their normal size. Females have no refractory period, and multiple orgasms can occur during a single sexual experience.

Regulation of Female Hormone Levels

At the time of puberty in females, the hypothalamus increases its secretion of GnRH, and the anterior pituitary releases larger amounts of the gonadotropins, FSH and LH. These hormones stimulate the ovaries to produce eggs and elevated estrogen and progesterone levels.

Estrogen and Progesterone

In particular, estrogen stimulates the growth of the uterus and the vagina. **Estrogen** is also necessary for egg maturation and the onset of the menstrual cycle, as well as for the development of the secondary sex characteristics in females.

Secondary Sex Characteristics These characteristics include the female pattern of body hair and fat distribution. In general, females have a more rounded appearance than males because of a greater accumulation of fat beneath the skin. Also, the pelvic girdle enlarges in females so that the pelvic cavity has a larger relative size compared to that of males; this means that females have wider hips. Both estrogen and **progesterone** are required for breast development, which is discussed on page 356.

Menstrual Cycle

The **menstrual cycle** is a monthly series of events that involve the ovaries and uterus plus the hormones already mentioned. The cycle is about 28 days long, but it can be as short as 18 days or as long as 40 days (Fig. 17.13).

Pre-Ovulation Events

Under the influence of follicle-stimulating hormone (FSH) from the anterior pituitary, several follicles begin developing in the ovary. Therefore, this period of time (days 1–14) is called the *follicular phase* of the ovary (Fig. 17.13). Although several follicles begin growing, only one follicle continues developing, and it secretes increasing amounts of estrogen. This particular follicle becomes more and more sensitive to FSH and then LH. Eventually, the very high level of estrogen exerts *positive feedback control* over the hypothalamus so that it secretes ever greater amounts of GnRH. GnRH induces a surge in FSH and LH secretion by the pituitary. The LH level rises to a greater extent than does the FSH level. Under the influence of so much stimulation, ovulation occurs.

While the ovary is experiencing its follicular phase, first menstruation and then the proliferative phase occur in the uterus. During menstruation (days 1–5), a low level of female sex hormones in the body causes the endometrial tissue to disintegrate and its blood vessels to rupture. A flow of blood and tissues, known as the **menses,** passes out of the vagina during menstruation, also called the menstrual period.

Under the influence of estrogen released by the new follicle, the endometrium thickens and becomes vascular and glandular. This is the *proliferative phase* of the uterus, which ends when ovulation occurs.

Post-Ovulation Events

Under the influence of LH, the ovulated follicle becomes the corpus luteum. Therefore, this period of time (days 15–28) is known as the *luteal phase* of the ovary (Fig. 17.13). The corpus luteum secretes progesterone and some estrogen. As the blood level of progesterone rises, it exerts *negative feedback control* over the anterior pituitary's secretion of LH so that the corpus luteum in the ovary begins to degenerate. If fertilization of the egg does occur, the corpus luteum persists for reasons that will be discussed shortly.

Under the influence of progesterone secreted by the corpus luteum, a secretory phase (days 15–28) begins in the uterus. During the *secretory phase* of the uterus, the endometrium of the uterus doubles or even triples in thickness (from 1 mm to 2–3 mm), and the uterine glands mature, producing a thick, mucoid secretion. The endometrium is now prepared to receive the pre-embryo. If implantation of a pre-embryo does not take place, the corpus luteum disintegrates, and menstruation occurs.

If fertilization occurs and is followed by implantation, the developing placenta produces **human chorionic gonadotropin (HCG),** which maintains the corpus luteum in the ovary until the placenta begins to produce progesterone and estrogen. The placental hormones shut down the anterior pituitary so that no new follicle in the ovaries matures, and they maintain the endometrium so that the corpus luteum in the ovary is no longer needed. Usually, no menstruation occurs during pregnancy.

Figure 17.13 During the menstrual cycle, FSH and LH are released by the anterior pituitary. FSH promotes the maturation of a follicle in the ovary. The follicle produces increasing levels of estrogen, which cause the endometrium to thicken during the proliferative phase in the uterus. An LH surge causes ovulation. After ovulation, LH promotes the development of the corpus luteum. This structure produces increasing levels of progesterone, which causes the endometrial lining to become secretory. Menses due to the breakdown of the endometrium begins when progesterone production declines to a low level due to corpus luteum disintegration.

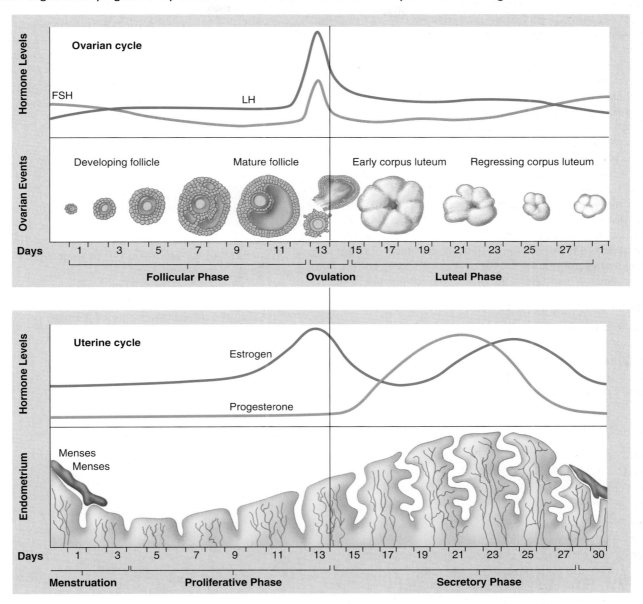

Menopause

Menopause, the period in a woman's life during which the menstrual cycle ceases, is likely to occur between ages 45 and 55. The ovaries are no longer responsive to the gonadotropic hormones produced by the anterior pituitary, and the ovaries no longer secrete estrogen or progesterone. At the onset of menopause, the uterine cycle becomes irregular, but as long as menstruation occurs, it is still possible for a woman to conceive. Therefore, a woman is usually not considered to have completed menopause until menstruation has been absent for a year.

The hormonal changes during menopause often produce physical symptoms, such as "hot flashes" (caused by circulatory irregularities), dizziness, headaches, insomnia, sleepiness, and depression. These symptoms may be mild or even absent. If they are severe, medical attention should be sought. Women sometimes report an increased sex drive following menopause. It has been suggested that this may be due to androgen production by the adrenal cortex.

Female Breast and Lactation

Early growth of the female breasts during puberty is referred to as *budding* of the breasts. Budding is followed by development of lobes, the functional portions of the breast, and deposition of adipose tissue, which gives breasts their adult shape.

A breast contains 15 to 25 lobules, each with a milk duct that begins at the nipple. The nipple is surrounded by a pigmented area called the **areola.** Hair and glands are absent from the nipples and areola, but glands are present that secrete a saliva-resisting lubricant to protect the nipples, particularly during nursing. Smooth muscle fibers in the region of the areola may cause the nipple to become erect in response to sexual stimulation or cold.

Within each lobe, the mammary duct divides into numerous alveolar ducts that end in blind sacs called alveoli (Fig. 17.14). The alveoli are made up of the cells that can produce milk. Estrogen and progesterone are required for lobe development. It is believed that estrogen causes proliferation of ducts and that both estrogen and progesterone bring about alveolar development. The abundance of these hormones during pregnancy means that the alveoli proliferate at this time. A nonlactating breast has ducts but few alveoli, while a lactating breast has many ducts and alveoli.

During pregnancy, the breasts enlarge as the ducts and alveoli increase in number and size. The same hormones that affect the mother's breasts can also affect the child's. Some newborns, including males, even secrete a small amount of milk for a few days.

Usually, no milk is produced during pregnancy. The hormone prolactin is needed for lactation to begin, and the production of this hormone is suppressed because of the feedback control that the increased amount of estrogen and progesterone during pregnancy has on the pituitary. Once the baby is delivered, however, the pituitary begins secreting prolactin. It takes a couple of days for milk production to begin, and in the meantime, the breasts produce **colostrum,** a thin, yellow, milky fluid rich in protein, including antibodies.

The continued production of milk requires a suckling child. When a breast is suckled, the nerve endings in the areola are stimulated, and a nerve impulse travels along neural pathways from the nipples to the hypothalamus, which directs the pituitary gland to release the hormone oxytocin. When this hormone arrives at the breast, it causes the lobules to contract so that milk flows into the ducts (called milk letdown), where it may be drawn out of the nipple by the suckling child.

Breast cancer is one of the few types of cancer that can be detected by the female herself. The Medical Focus on page 357 tells how to do a shower check for breast cancer.

Figure 17.14 Structure of the female breast and mammary glands. **a.** Sagittal section. **b.** Anterior view.

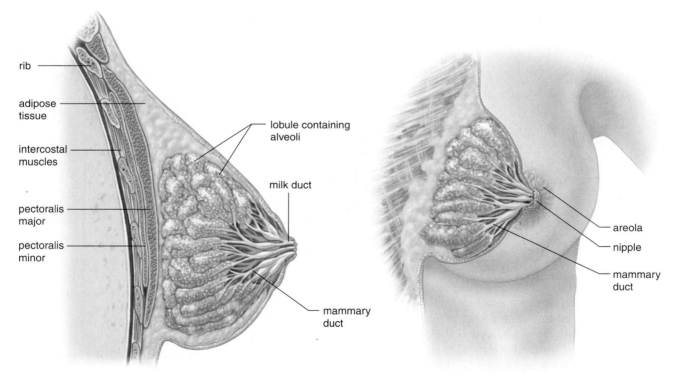

rib

adipose tissue

intercostal muscles

pectoralis major

pectoralis minor

lobule containing alveoli

milk duct

mammary duct

areola

nipple

mammary duct

a.

b.

Medical Focus

Shower Check for Cancer

The American Cancer Society urges women to do a breast self-exam and men to do a testicle self-exam every month. Breast cancer and testicular cancer are far more curable if found early, and we must all take the responsibility of checking for one or the other.

Breast Self-Exam for Women

1. Check your breasts for any lumps, knots, or changes about one week after your period.
2. Place your right hand behind your head. Move your *left* hand over your *right* breast in a circle. Press firmly with the pads of your fingers (Fig. 17A). Also check the armpit.
3. Now place your left hand behind your head and check your *left* breast with your *right* hand in the same manner as before. Also check the armpit.
4. Check your breasts while standing in front of a mirror right after you do your shower check. First, put your hands on your hips and then raise your arms above your head (Fig. 17B). Look for any changes in the way your breasts look: dimpling of the skin, changes in the nipple, or redness or swelling.

5. If you find any changes during your shower or mirror check, see your doctor right away.

You should know that the best check for breast cancer is a mammogram. When your doctor checks your breasts, ask about getting a mammogram.

Testicle Self-Exam for Men

1. Check your testicles once a month.
2. Roll each testicle between your thumb and finger as shown in Figure 17C. Feel for hard lumps or bumps.
3. If you notice a change or have aches or lumps, tell your doctor right away so he or she can recommend proper treatment.

Cancer of the testicles can be cured if you find it early. You should also know that prostate cancer is the most common cancer in men. Men over age 50 should have an annual health checkup that includes a prostate examination.

Information provided by the American Cancer Society. Used by permission.

Figure 17A Shower check for breast cancer.

Figure 17B Mirror check for breast cancer.

Figure 17C Shower check for testicular cancer.

17.4 Control of Reproduction and Sexually Transmitted Diseases

Birth Control Methods

The most reliable method of birth control is abstinence—that is, not engaging in sexual intercourse. This form of birth control has the added advantage of preventing transmission of a sexually transmitted disease. Table 17.3 lists other means of birth control used in the United States, and rates their effectiveness. For example, with natural family planning, one of the least effective methods given in the table, we expect that within a year, 70 out of 100, or 70%, of sexually active women will not get pregnant, while 30 women will get pregnant.

Figure 17.15 features some of the most effective and commonly used means of birth control. Oral contraception **(birth control pills)** often involves taking a combination of estrogen and progesterone on a daily basis. The estrogen and progesterone in the birth control pill effectively shut down the pituitary's production of both FSH and LH so that no follicle begins to develop in the ovary; since ovulation does not occur, pregnancy cannot take place. Because of possible side effects, women taking birth control pills should see a physician regularly.

An **intrauterine device (IUD)** is a small piece of molded plastic that is inserted into the uterus by a physician. IUDs are believed to alter the environment of the uterus and uterine tubes so that fertilization probably will not occur—but if fertilization should occur, implantation cannot take place. The type of IUD featured in Figure 17.15b has copper wire wrapped around the plastic.

The **diaphragm** is a soft latex cup with a flexible rim (Fig. 17.15c) that lodges behind the pubic bone and fits over the cervix. Each woman must be properly fitted by a physician, and

Figure 17.15 Various birth control devices. **a.** Oral contraception (birth control pills). **b.** Intrauterine device. **c.** Spermicidal jelly and diaphragm. **d.** Female condom. **e.** Contraceptive implants. **f.** Contraceptive injection.

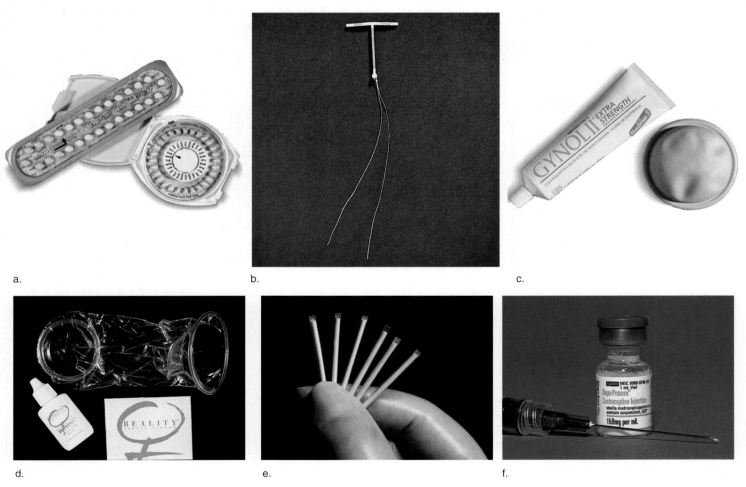

a.

b.

c.

d.

e.

f.

the diaphragm can be inserted into the vagina no more than two hours before sexual relations. Also, it must be used with spermicidal jelly or cream and should be left in place at least six hours after sexual relations. The *cervical cap* is a minidiaphragm.

There has been a revival of interest in barrier methods of birth control, because these methods offer some protection against sexually transmitted diseases. A female **condom,** now available, consists of a large polyurethane tube with a flexible ring that fits onto the cervix (Fig. 17.15*d*). The open end of the tube has a ring that covers the external genitals. A male condom is most often a latex sheath that fits over the erect penis. The ejaculate is trapped inside the sheath, and thus does not enter the vagina. When used in conjunction with a spermicide, protection is better than with the condom alone.

Contraceptive implants utilize a synthetic progesterone to disrupt the events of the menstrual cycle. The older version

of the implant (Fig. 17.15*e*) consists of six match-size release tubes that are implanted under the skin of a woman's upper arm. The newest version consists of a single tube that remains effective for about three years.

Contraceptive injections are available as progesterone only (Fig. 17.15*f*) or a combination of estrogen and progesterone. The length of time between injections can vary from three months to a few weeks.

Contraceptive vaccines are now being developed. For example, a vaccine intended to immunize women against HCG, the hormone so necessary to maintaining the implantation of the embryo, was successful in a limited clinical trial. Because HCG is not normally present in the body, no untoward autoimmune reaction is expected, but the immunization does wear off with time. Others believe that it would also be possible to develop a safe antisperm vaccine that could be used in women.

Table 17.3	Common Birth Control Methods			
Name	**Procedure**	**Methodology**	**Effectiveness**	**Risk**
Abstinence	Refrain from sexual intercourse	No sperm in vagina	100%	None
Vasectomy	Vasa deferentia are cut and tied	No sperm in seminal fluid	Almost 100%	Irreversible sterility
Tubal ligation	Oviducts cut and tied	No eggs in oviduct	Almost 100%	Irreversible sterility
Oral contraception	Hormone medication taken daily	Anterior pituitary does not release FSH and LH	Almost 100%	Thromboembolism, especially in smokers
Contraceptive implants	Tubes of progestin (form of progesterone) implanted under skin	Anterior pituitary does not release FSH and LH	More than 90%	Presently none known
Contraceptive injections	Injections of hormones	Anterior pituitary does not release FSH and LH	About 99%	Breast cancer? Osteoporosis?
Intrauterine device (IUD)	Plastic coil inserted into uterus by physician	Prevents implantation	More than 90%	Infection (pelvic inflammatory disease, PID)
Diaphragm	Latex cup inserted into vagina to cover cervix before intercourse	Blocks entrance of sperm to uterus	With jelly, about 90%	Latex, spermicide allergy
Cervical cap	Latex cap held by suction over cervix	Delivers spermicide near cervix	Almost 85%	UTI[1], latex or spermicide allergy
Male condom	Latex sheath fitted over erect penis	Traps sperm and prevents STDs	About 85%	Latex allergy
Female condom	Polyurethane liner fitted inside vagina	Blocks entrance of sperm to uterus and prevents STDs	About 85%	Latex allergy
Coitus interruptus	Penis withdrawn before ejaculation	Prevents sperm from entering vagina	About 75%	Presently none known
Jellies, creams, foams	These spermicidal products inserted before intercourse	Kill a large number of sperm	About 75%	UTI[1], vaginitis, allergy
Natural family planning	Day of ovulation determined by record keeping, various methods of testing	Intercourse avoided on certain days of the month	About 70%	Presently none known
Douche	Vagina cleansed after intercourse	Washes out sperm	Less than 70%	Presently none known

[1]UTI = urinary tract infection

Morning-After Pills

A morning-after, pill, or emergency contraception, refers to a medication that will prevent pregnancy after unprotected intercourse. The expression is a misnomer in that medication can begin one to several days after unprotected intercourse.

One type, a kit called Preven, contains four synthetic progesterone pills; two are taken up to 72 hours after unprotected intercourse, and two more are taken 12 hours later. The medication upsets the normal uterine cycle, making it difficult for an embryo to implant itself in the endometrium. A recent study estimated that the medication was 85% effective in preventing unintended pregnancies.

Mifepristone, better known as RU-486, is a pill that is presently used to cause the loss of an implanted embryo by blocking the progesterone receptor proteins of endometrial cells. Without functioning receptors for progesterone, the endometrium sloughs off, carrying the embryo with it. When taken in conjunction with a prostaglandin to induce uterine contractions, RU-486 is 95% effective. It is possible that some day this medication will also be a "morning-after pill," taken when menstruation is late without evidence that pregnancy has occurred.

Infertility

Infertility is the failure of a couple to achieve pregnancy after one year of regular, unprotected intercourse. The American Medical Association estimates that 15% of all couples are infertile. The cause of infertility can be attributed to the male (40%), the female (40%), or both (20%).

Causes of Infertility

The most frequent cause of infertility in males is low sperm count and/or a large proportion of abnormal sperm, which can be due to environmental influences. The public is particularly concerned about endocrine-disrupting contaminants, discussed in the What's New reading on page 361. But thus far, it appears that a sedentary lifestyle coupled with smoking and alcohol consumption most often leads to male infertility. When males spend most of the day sitting in front of a computer or the TV or driving, the testes temperature remains too high for adequate sperm production.

Body weight appears to be the most significant factor in causing female infertility. In women of normal weight, fat cells produce a hormone called leptin that stimulates the hypothalamus to release GnRH. In overweight women, the ovaries often contain many small follicles, and the woman fails to ovulate. Other causes of infertility in females are blocked uterine tubes due to pelvic inflammatory disease (see page 363) and endometriosis. **Endometriosis** is the presence of uterine tissue outside the uterus, particularly in the uterine tubes and on the abdominal organs. Backward flow of menstrual fluid allows living uterine cells to establish themselves in the abdominal cavity, where they go through the usual uterine cycle, causing pain and structural abnormalities that make it more difficult for a woman to conceive.

Sometimes the causes of infertility can be corrected by medical intervention so that couples can have children. If no obstruction is apparent and body weight is normal, it is possible to give females fertility drugs, which are gonadotropic hormones that stimulate the ovaries and bring about ovulation. Such hormone treatments may cause multiple ovulations and multiple births.

When reproduction does not occur in the usual manner, many couples adopt a child. Others sometimes try one of the assisted reproductive technologies discussed in the following paragraphs.

Assisted Reproductive Technologies

Assisted reproductive technologies (ART) consist of techniques used to increase the chances of pregnancy. Often, sperm and/or eggs are retrieved from the testes and ovaries, and fertilization takes place in a clinical or laboratory setting.

Artificial Insemination During **artificial insemination,** sperm are placed in the vagina by a physician. Sometimes a woman is artificially inseminated by her partner's sperm. This is especially helpful if the partner has a low sperm count, because the sperm can be collected over a period of time and concentrated so that the sperm count is sufficient to result in fertilization. Often, however, a woman is inseminated by sperm acquired from a donor who is a complete stranger to her. At times, a combination of partner and donor sperm is used.

During *intrauterine insemination (IUI)*, fertility drugs are given to stimulate the ovaries, and then the donor's sperm is placed in the uterus rather than in the vagina.

If the prospective parents wish, sperm can be sorted into those believed to be X-bearing or Y-bearing to increase the chances of having a child of the desired sex.

In Vitro Fertilization During **in vitro fertilization (IVF),** conception occurs in laboratory glassware. Ultrasound machines can now spot follicles in the ovaries that hold immature eggs; therefore, the latest method is to forgo the administration of fertility drugs and retrieve immature eggs by using a needle. The immature eggs are then brought to maturity in glassware before concentrated sperm are added. After about two to four days, the embryos are ready to be transferred to the uterus of the woman, who is now in the secretory phase of her uterine cycle. If desired, preimplantation genetic analysis can be done and only embryos found to be free of genetic disorders are used. If implantation is successful, development is normal and continues to term.

Intracytoplasmic Sperm Injection In **intracytoplasmic sperm injection (ICSI),** a highly sophisticated procedure, a single sperm is injected into an egg. This method is used effectively when a man has severe infertility problems.

Endocrine-Disrupting Contaminants

Rachel Carson's book *Silent Spring*, published in 1962, predicted that pesticides would have a deleterious effect on animal life. Soon thereafter, it was found that pesticides caused the eggshells of bald eagles to become so thin that their eggs broke and the chicks died. Additionally, populations of terns, gulls, cormorants, and lake trout declined after they ate fish contaminated by high levels of environmental toxins. The concern was so great that the United States Environmental Protection Agency (EPA) came into existence. The efforts of this agency and civilian environmental groups have brought about a reduction in pollutant release and a cleaning up of emissions. Even so, we are now aware of more subtle effects that pollutants can have.

Hormones influence nearly all aspects of physiology and behavior in animals, including tissue differentiation, growth, and reproduction. Therefore, when wildlife in contaminated areas began to exhibit certain types of abnormalities, researchers began to think that certain pollutants can affect the endocrine system. In England, male fish exposed to sewage developed ovarian tissue and produced a metabolite normally found only in females during egg formation. In California, western gulls displayed abnormalities in gonad structure and nesting behaviors. Hatchling alligators in Florida possessed abnormal gonads and hormone concentrations linked to nesting.

At first, such effects seemed to indicate only the involvement of the female hormone estrogen, and researchers therefore called the contaminants ecoestrogens. However, further study brought more information to light. Many of the contaminants interact with hormone receptors, and in that way cause developmental effects. Others bind directly with sex hormones such as testosterone and estradiol. Still others alter the physiology of the growth hormones and neurotransmitters responsible for brain development

and behavior. Therefore, the preferred term today for these pollutants is endocrine-disrupting contaminants (EDCs).

Many EDCs are chemicals used as pesticides and herbicides in agriculture, and some are associated with the manufacture of various other synthetic organic compounds such as PCBs (polychlorinated biphenyls). Some chemicals shown to influence hormones are found in plastics, food additives, and personal hygiene products. In mice, phthalate esters, which are plastic components, affect neonatal development when present in the part-per-trillion range. It is, therefore, of great concern that EDCs have been found at levels one thousand times greater than this—even in amounts comparable to functional hormone levels in the human body. Furthermore, it is not surprising that EDCs are affecting the endocrine systems of a wide range of organisms (Fig. 17D).

Scientists and those representing industrial manufacturers continue to debate whether EDCs pose a health risk to humans. Some suspect that EDCs lower sperm counts, reduce male and female fertility, and increase the rates of certain cancers (breast, ovarian, testicular, and prostate). Additionally, some studies suggest that EDCs contribute to learning deficits and behavioral problems in children. Laboratory and field research continues to identify chemicals that have the ability to influence the endocrine system. Millions of tons of potential EDCs are produced annually in the United States, and the EPA is under pressure to certify these compounds as safe. The European Economic Community has already restricted the use of certain EDCs, and has banned the production of specific plastic components that are found in items intended for use by children, specifically toys. Only through continued scientific research and the cooperation of industry can we identify the risks that EDCs pose to the environment, wildlife, and humans.

Figure 17D Exposure to endocrine-disrupting contaminants. Various types of wildlife, as well as humans, are exposed to endocrine-disrupting contaminants that can seriously affect their health and reproductive abilities.

Preventing Transmission of STDs

It is wise to protect yourself from getting a sexually transmitted disease (STD). Some of the STDs, such as gonorrhea, syphilis, and chlamydia, can be cured by taking an antibiotic, but medication for the ones transmitted by viruses is much more problematic. In any case, it is best to prevent the passage of STDs from person to person so that treatment becomes unnecessary.

Sexual Activities Transmit STDs

Abstain from sexual intercourse or develop a long-term monogamous (always the same partner) *sexual relationship* with a partner who is free of STDs.

Refrain from multiple sex partners or having relations with someone who has multiple sex partners. If you have sex with two other people and each of these has sex with two people and so forth, the number of people who are relating is quite large.

Remember that, although the prevalence of AIDS is presently higher among homosexuals and bisexuals, the highest rate of increase is now occurring among heterosexuals. The lining of the uterus is only one cell thick, and it does allow infected cells from a sexual partner to enter.

Be aware that having relations with an intravenous drug user is risky because the behavior of this group risks hepatitis and an HIV infection. Be aware that anyone who already has another sexually transmitted disease is more susceptible to an HIV infection.

Uncircumcised males are more likely to become infected with an STD than circumcised males because vaginal secretions can remain under the foreskin for a long period of time.

Avoid anal-rectal intercourse (in which the penis is inserted into the rectum) because the lining of the rectum is thin and cells infected with HIV can easily enter the body there.

Unsafe Sexual Practices Transmit STDs

Always use a latex condom during sexual intercourse if you do not know for certain that your partner has been free of STDs for some time. Be sure to follow the directions supplied by the manufacturer. Use of a water-based spermicide containing nonoxynol-9 in addition to the condom can offer further protection because nonoxynol-9 immobilizes viruses and virus-infected cells.

Avoid fellatio (kissing and insertion of the penis into a partner's mouth) *and cunnilingus* (kissing and insertion of the tongue into the vagina) because they may be a means of transmission. The mouth and gums often have cuts and sores that facilitate the entrance of infected cells.

Be cautious about using alcohol or any drug that may prevent you from being able to control your behavior.

Drug Use Transmits Hepatitis and HIV

Stop, if necessary, or do not start the habit of injecting drugs into your veins. Be aware that hepatitis and HIV can be spread by blood-to-blood contact.

Always use a new, sterile needle for injection or one that has been cleaned in bleach if you are a drug user and cannot stop your behavior.

Figure 17E Sexual activities transmit STDs.

Figure 17F Sharing needles transmits STDs.

Sexually Transmitted Diseases

Sexually transmitted diseases (STDs) are caused by organisms ranging from viruses to arthropods; however, we will discuss only certain STDs caused by viruses and bacteria. Unfortunately, for unknown reasons, humans cannot develop effective immunity to any STDs. Therefore, any person exposed to an STD should seek prompt medical treatment. To prevent the spread of STDs, a latex condom can be used; the concomitant use of a spermicide containing nonoxynol-9 gives added protection.

Among those STDs caused by viruses, treatment is available for AIDS and genital herpes. Only STDs caused by bacteria (e.g., chlamydia, gonorrhea, and syphilis) are treatable with antibiotics.

Genital Warts

Genital warts are caused by the human papillomaviruses (HPVs). Many times, carriers either do not have any sign of warts or merely have flat lesions. When present, the warts commonly are seen on the penis and foreskin of men and near the vaginal opening in women. A newborn can become infected while passing through the birth canal.

Presently, there is no cure for an HPV infection, but it can be treated effectively by surgery, freezing, application of an acid, or laser burning, depending on severity. If visible warts are removed, they may recur. Genital warts are associated with cancer of the cervix, as well as tumors of the vulva, the vagina, the anus, and the penis. Some researchers believe that the viruses are involved in 90–95% of all cases of cancer of the cervix.

Genital Herpes

Genital herpes is caused by herpes simplex virus. Type 1 usually causes cold sores and fever blisters, while type 2 more often causes genital herpes.

Persons usually get infected with herpes simplex virus type 2 when they are adults. Some people exhibit no symptoms; other may experience a tingling or itching sensation before blisters appear on the genitals. Once the blisters rupture, they leave painful ulcers that may take as long as three weeks or as little as five days to heal. The blisters may be accompanied by fever, pain on urination, swollen lymph nodes in the groin, and in women, a copious discharge. At this time, the individual has an increased risk of acquiring an HIV infection.

After the ulcers heal, the disease is only latent, and blisters can recur, although usually at less frequent intervals and with milder symptoms. Fever, stress, sunlight, and menstruation are associated with recurrence of symptoms. Exposure to herpes in the birth canal can cause an infection in the newborn, which leads to neurological disorders and even death. Birth by cesarean section prevents this possibility.

Hepatitis

Hepatitis infects the liver and can lead to liver failure, liver cancer, and death. There are several types of hepatitis, and some of them are sexually transmitted. The type of hepatitis and the virus that causes it are designated by the same letter. Hepatitis A is usually acquired from sewage-contaminated drinking water, but this infection can also be sexually transmitted through oral/anal contact. Hepatitis B, which is spread in the same manner as AIDS, is even more infectious. Fortunately, a vaccine is now available for hepatitis B. Hepatitis C is called post-transfusion hepatitis.

Chlamydia

Chlamydia is named for the tiny bacterium that causes it (*Chlamydia trachomatis*). The incidence of new chlamydia infections has steadily increased since 1984.

Chlamydia infections of the lower reproductive tract are usually mild or asymptomatic, especially in women. About 18 to 21 days after infection, men may experience a mild burning sensation on urination and a mucoid discharge. Women may have a vaginal discharge along with the symptoms of a urinary tract infection. Chlamydia also causes cervical ulcerations, which increase the risk of acquiring HIV.

If the infection is misdiagnosed or if a woman does not seek medical help, there is a particular risk of the infection spreading from the cervix to the uterine tubes so that **pelvic inflammatory disease (PID)** results. This very painful condition can result in blockage of the uterine tubes with the possibility of sterility and infertility. If a baby comes in contact with chlamydia during birth, inflammation of the eyes or pneumonia can result.

Gonorrhea

Gonorrhea is caused by the bacterium *Neisseria gonorrhoeae.* Diagnosis in the male is not difficult, since typical symptoms are pain upon urination and a thick, greenish-yellow urethral discharge. In males and females, a latent infection leads to pelvic inflammatory disease (PID), which can also cause sterility in males. If a baby is exposed during birth, an eye infection leading to blindness can result. All newborns are given eyedrops to prevent this possibility.

Gonorrhea proctitis, an infection of the anus characterized by anal pain and blood or pus in the feces, also occurs in patients. Oral/genital contact can cause infection of the mouth, throat, and tonsils. Gonorrhea can spread to internal parts of the body, causing heart damage or arthritis. If, by chance, the person touches infected genitals and then touches his or her eyes, a severe eye infection can result. Up to now, gonorrhea was curable by antibiotic therapy, but resistance to antibiotics is becoming more and more common, and 40% of all strains are now known to be resistant to therapy.

Syphilis

Syphilis is caused by a bacterium called *Treponema pallidum*. As with many other bacterial diseases, penicillin is an effective antibiotic. Syphilis has three stages, often separated by latent periods, during which the bacteria are resting before multiplying again. During the *primary stage*, a hard chancre (ulcerated sore with hard edges) indicates the site of infection. The chancre usually heals spontaneously, leaving little scarring. During the *secondary stage*, the victim breaks out in a rash that does not itch and is seen even on the palms of the hands and the soles of the feet. Hair loss and infectious gray patches on the mucous membranes may also occur. These symptoms disappear of their own accord.

During the *tertiary stage*, which lasts until the patient dies, syphilis may affect the cardiovascular system by causing aneurysms, particularly in the aorta. In other instances, the disease may affect the nervous system, resulting in psychological disturbances. Also, gummas, large destructive ulcers, may develop on the skin or within the internal organs.

Congenital syphilis is caused by syphilitic bacteria crossing the placenta. The child is born blind and/or with numerous anatomical malformations. Control of syphilis depends on prompt and adequate treatment of all new cases; therefore, it is crucial for all sexual contacts to be traced so they can be treated. Diagnosis of syphilis can be made by blood tests or by microscopic examination of fluids from lesions.

17.5 Effects of Aging

Sex hormone levels decline with age in both men and women. Menopause, the period in a woman's life during which menstruation ceases, is likely to occur between the ages of 45 and 55. The ovaries are no longer responsive to gonadotropic hormones, and they stop producing eggs and the female sex hormones. At the onset of menopause, the menstrual cycle becomes irregular and then eventually ceases. Hormonal imbalance often produces physical symptoms, such as dizziness, headaches, insomnia, sleepiness, depression, and "hot flashes" that are caused by circulatory irregularities. Menopausal symptoms vary greatly among women, and some symptoms may be absent altogether.

Following menopause, atrophy of the uterus, vagina, breasts, and external genitals is likely. The lack of estrogen also promotes changes in the skin (e.g., wrinkling; see Chapter 5) and in the skeleton (e.g., osteoporosis; see Chapter 6).

In men, testosterone production diminishes steadily after age 50, which may be responsible for the enlargement of the prostate gland. Sperm production declines with age, yet men can remain fertile well into old age. With age, however, the chance of erectile dysfunction due to degenerative vascular changes in the penis increases.

Sexual desire and activity need not decline with age, and many older men and women enjoy sexual relationships. Men are likely to experience reduced erection until close to ejaculation, and women may experience a drier vagina.

17.6 Homeostasis

Regulation of sex hormone blood level is an example of homeostatic control. Figure 17.7 shows how the blood level of testosterone is maintained within normal limits. Negative feedback results in a self-regulatory mechanism that maintains the appropriate level of these hormones in the blood.

The illustration in Human Systems Work Together on page 365 shows how the reproductive system works with the other systems of the body to maintain homeostasis. Usually we stress that the function of sex hormones produced not only by the gonads but also by the adrenal glands is to foster the maturation of the reproductive organs and to maintain the secondary sex characteristics. However, these functions of sex hormones have nothing to do with homeostasis. Why? Because homeostasis pertains to the constancy of the internal environment of cells. Other activities of the sex hormones do affect the internal environment. For example, estrogen promotes fat deposition, which serves as a source of energy for cells and also helps the body maintain a normal temperature because of its insulating effect.

In recent years, it's been discovered that the sex hormones perform other activities that affect homeostasis even more directly. We are just now beginning to discover the role that estrogen and androgens play in the metabolism of cells and therefore their role in homeostasis in general. Estrogen induces the liver to produce many types of proteins that transport substances in the blood. These include proteins that bind iron and copper and lipoproteins that transport cholesterol. Iron and copper are enzyme cofactors necessary to cellular metabolism. Although we associate cholesterol with cardiovascular diseases, in fact, it is also a substance that contributes to the functioning of the plasma membrane.

Estrogen also induces synthesis of bone matrix proteins and counteracts the loss of bone mass. At menopause, when the rate of estrogen secretion is drastically reduced, osteoporosis (decrease in bone density) may develop. Nevertheless, long-term estrogen therapy is no longer recommended. The National Institutes of Health conducted a study of 16,608 healthy women who were taking both estrogen and progesterone—that is, hormone replacement therapy (HRT)—or a placebo. The study was halted after 5.2 years because physicians concluded that the risks for the group on HRT outweighed the benefits. The women on HRT had a small but significant increased risk for breast cancer, coronary heart disease, stroke, and blood clots. The benefits of HRT included lower risk of hip fractures and colon cancer.

Similarly, besides the action of androgens (e.g., testosterone) on the sexual organs and functions of males, androgens play a metabolic role in cells. They stimulate synthesis of structural proteins in skeletal muscles and bone, and they also affect the activity of various enzymes in the liver and kidneys. For example, in the kidney, androgens stimulate synthesis of erythropoietin, the protein that signals the bone marrow to increase the production of red blood cells.

Human Systems Work Together

Integumentary System

Androgens activate oil glands; sex hormones stimulate fat deposition, affect hair distribution in males and females.

Skin receptors respond to touch; modified sweat glands produce milk; skin stretches to accommodate growing fetus.

How the Reproductive System works with other body systems

Cardiovascular System

Sex hormones influence cardiovascular health; sexual activities stimulate cardiovascular system.

Blood vessels transport sex hormones; vasodilation causes genitals to become erect; blood services the reproductive organs.

Skeletal System

Sex hormones influence bone growth and density in males and females.

Bones provide support and protection of reproductive organs.

Lymphatic System/Immunity

Sex hormones influence immune functioning; acidity of vagina helps prevent pathogen invasion of body; milk passes antibodies to newborn.

Immune system does not attack sperm or fetus, even though they are foreign to the body.

Muscular System

Androgens promote growth of skeletal muscle.

Muscle contraction occurs during orgasm and moves gametes; abdominal and uterine muscle contractions occur during childbirth.

Respiratory System

Sexual activity increases breathing; pregnancy causes breathing rate and vital capacity to increase.

Gas exchange increases during sexual activity.

Nervous System

Sex hormones masculinize or feminize the brain, exert feedback control over the hypothalamus, and influence sexual behavior.

Brain controls onset of puberty; nerves are involved in erection of penis and clitoris, movement of gametes along ducts, and contraction of uterus.

Digestive System

Pregnancy crowds digestive organs and promotes heartburn and constipation.

Digestive tract provides nutrients for growth and repair of organs and for development of fetus.

Endocrine System

Gonads produce the sex hormones.

Hypothalamic, pituitary, and sex hormones control sex characteristics and regulate reproductive processes.

Urinary System

Penis in males contains the urethra and performs urination; prostate enlargement hinders urination.

Semen is discharged through the urethra in males; kidneys excrete wastes and maintain electrolyte levels for mother and child.

Selected New Terms

Basic Key Terms

acrosome (ak'ro-sōm), p. 345

assisted reproductive technologies (uh-sis'ted re"pro-duk'tiv tek-nah'lo-jēz), p. 360

bulbourethral gland (bul"bo-yū-re'thral gland), p. 343

cervix (ser'viks), p. 349

clitoris (klĭ'to-ris), p. 353

colostrum (ko-los'trum), p. 356

corpus albicans (kor'pus al'bĭ-kanz), p. 351

corpus luteum (kor'pus lu'te-um), p. 351

ejaculation (e-jak"yū-la'shun), p. 343

ejaculatory duct (e-jak'yū-luh-to"re dukt), p. 343

endometrium (en-do-me'tre-um), p. 349

epididymis (ep"ĭ-did'ĭ-mis), p. 343

estrogen (es'tro-jen), p. 354

external genitals (eks-ter'nal jen'ĭ-talz), p. 347

fimbriae (fim'bre-e), p. 352

follicle (fol'ĭ-kl), p. 351

FSH (follicle-stimulating hormone) (fol'ĭ-kl stim'yū-la-ting hor'mōn), p. 348

hernia (her'ne-uh), p. 346

human chorionic gonadotropin (hyū'man ko"re-on'ik go'nad-o-tro'pin), p. 354

implantation (im"plan-ta'shun), p. 349

infertility (in-fer-til'ĭ-te), p. 360

interstitial cell (in"ter-stish'ul sel), p. 345

labia majora (la'be-uh muh-jor'uh), p. 353

labia minora (la'be-uh mi-nor'uh), p. 353

LH (luteinizing hormone) (lu'te-ĭ-nīz-ing hor'mōn), p. 348

meiosis (mi-o'sis), p. 342

menopause (men'o-pawz), p. 355

menstrual cycle (men"stru-ăl), p. 354

oocyte (o'o-sīt), p. 351

oogenesis (o"o-jen'ĕ-sis), p. 351

ovary (o'vuh-re), p. 349

ovulation (ov'yū-la'shun), p. 351

penis (pe'nis), p. 347

progesterone (pro-jes'ter-ōn), p. 354

prostate gland (pros'tāt gland), p. 343

puberty (pyū'ber-te), p. 342

scrotum (skro'tum), p. 343

semen (se'men), p. 343

seminiferous tubule (se"mĭ-nif'er-us tu'byūl), p. 344

sperm (sperm), p. 345

spermatogenesis (sper"muh-to-jen'ĕ-sis), p. 345

testis (tes'tis), p. 343

urethra (yū-re'thruh), p. 343

uterine tube (yū'ter-in tūb), p. 352

vagina (vuh-ji'nuh), p. 349

vas deferens (vas def'er-ens), p. 343

vesicular (Graafian) follicle (ves-ik'yū-ler [graf'e-un] fol'ĭ-kl), p. 351

vulva (vul'vuh), p. 349

zygote (zi'gōt), p. 342

Clinical Key Terms

artificial insemination by donor (ar"tĭ-fĭ'shul in-sem-ĭ-na'shun), p. 360

chlamydia (kluh-mĭ'de-uh), p. 363

circumcision (ser"kum-sizh'un), p. 347

ectopic pregnancy (ek-top'ik preg'nun-se), p. 352

endometriosis (en-do-me"tre-o'sis), p. 360

erectile dysfunction (e-rek'tīl dis-funk'shun), p. 347

genital herpes (jen'ĭ-tal her'pēz), p. 363

genital warts (jen'ĭ-tal worts), p. 363

gonorrhea (gon-o-re'uh), p. 363

hernia (her'ne-uh), p. 346

hysterectomy (his"ter-ek'to-me), p. 352

infertility (in-fer-til'ĭ-te), p. 360

oophorectomy (o-ahf-or-ek'to-me), p. 352

ovarian cancer (o-vā're-un can'ser), p. 352

ovariohysterectomy (o-vār"e-o-his-ter-ek'to-me), p. 353

Pap smear (pap smēr), p. 352

salpingectomy (sal-pin-jek'to-me), p. 352

sexually transmitted disease (sek'shu-ah-le tranz-mit'ed dĭ-zēz'), p. 363

Summary

17.1 Human Life Cycle
The life cycle of humans requires two types of nuclear division: mitosis and meiosis. Meiosis is involved in sperm production in males and egg production in females.

17.2 Male Reproductive System
A. In males, spermatogenesis, occurring in seminiferous tubules of the testes, produces sperm that mature and are stored in the epididymides. Sperm may also be stored in the vasa deferentia before entering the urethra, along with secretions produced by the seminal vesicles, prostate gland, and bulbourethral glands. Sperm and these secretions are called semen, or seminal fluid.

B. The external genitals of males are the penis, the organ of sexual intercourse, and the scrotum, which contains the testes. Orgasm in males is a physical and emotional climax during sexual intercourse that results in ejaculation of semen from the penis.

C. Hormonal regulation, involving secretions from the hypothalamus, the anterior pituitary, and the testes, maintains testosterone, produced by the interstitial cells of the testes, at a fairly constant level. FSH from the anterior pituitary promotes spermatogenesis in the seminiferous tubules, and LH promotes testosterone production by the interstitial cells.

17.3 Female Reproductive System
A. In females, oogenesis occurring within the ovaries typically produces one mature follicle each month. This follicle balloons out of the ovary and bursts, releasing an egg, which enters a uterine tube. The uterine tubes lead to the uterus, where implantation and development occur. The external genital area includes the vaginal opening, the clitoris, the labia minora, and the labia majora.

B. The vagina is the organ of sexual intercourse and the birth canal in females. The vagina and the external genitals, especially the clitoris, play an active role in orgasm, which culminates in uterine and uterine tube contractions.

C. Hormonal regulation in females involves the production of FSH and LH by the anterior pituitary and also production of estrogen and progesterone by the ovaries.

D. The menstrual cycle is a monthly series of events that can be divided into the pre-ovulation events and the post-ovulation events. Before ovulation, FSH from the anterior pituitary causes an estrogen-producing follicle to begin developing in the ovary. Meanwhile in the uterus, menstruation occurs before the proliferation phase occurs. During the proliferation phase, estrogen causes the uterine lining to thicken.

Ovulation is caused by a positive feedback cycle in which an abundance of estrogen brings about an FSH and LH surge. After ovulation, the corpus luteum in the ovary secretes primarily progesterone that causes the uterine lining to become secretory. If the egg is fertilized, it implants itself in the uterine lining and the corpus luteum does not disintegrate.

E. If fertilization takes place, the pre-embryo implants itself in the thickened endometrium. If fertilization and implantation occur, the corpus luteum in the ovary is maintained because of HCG production by the placenta, and therefore progesterone production does not cease. Menstruation usually does not occur during pregnancy.

17.4 Control of Reproduction and Sexually Transmitted Diseases
A. Numerous birth control methods and devices, such as the birth control pill, diaphragm, and condom, are available for those who wish to prevent pregnancy.

A morning-after pill can be taken before there is any indication of pregnancy and mifepristone is available when menstruation is late.

B. Some couples are infertile, and if so, they may use assisted reproductive technologies in order to have a child. Artificial insemination and in vitro fertilization have been followed by more sophisticated techniques such as intracytoplasmic sperm injection.

17.5 Effects of Aging
Menopause occurs between the ages of 45 and 55 in women. Following menopause, atrophy of the genitals is likely. In men, testosterone production decreases after age 50, and the incidence of erectile dysfunction increases.

17.6 Homeostasis
The reproductive system works with the other systems of the body in the ways described in Human Systems Work Together on page 365.

Study Questions

1. Outline the path of sperm. What glands contribute fluids to semen? (p. 343)
2. Discuss the anatomy and physiology of the testes. Describe the structure of sperm. (pp. 344–45)
3. Name the endocrine glands involved in maintaining the sex characteristics of males and the hormones produced by each. (p. 348)
4. Describe the organs of the female genital tract. Where do fertilization and implantation occur? Name two functions of the vagina. (p. 349–53)
5. Name and describe the external genitals in females. (p. 353)
6. Discuss the anatomy and the physiology of the ovaries. (p. 351)
7. Describe the pre- and post-ovulation events of the menstrual cycle. In what way is menstruation prevented if pregnancy occurs? (p. 354)
8. Name three functions of the female sex hormones. (p. 354)
9. Discuss the various means of birth control and their relative effectiveness in preventing pregnancy. (pp. 358–60)
10. Describe how in vitro fertilization is carried out. (p. 360)

Objective Questions

Fill in the blanks.

1. In tracing the path of sperm, the structure that follows the epididymis is the _____.
2. The prostate gland, the bulbourethral glands, and the _____ all contribute to seminal fluid.
3. An erection is caused by the entrance of _____ into erectile tissue of the penis.
4. The primary male sex hormone is _____.
5. In the female reproductive system, the uterus lies between the uterine tubes and the _____.
6. The female sex hormones are _____ and _____.
7. In the menstrual cycle, once each month a _____ produces an egg, and the _____ is prepared to receive the pre-embryo.
8. The most frequent causes of male infertility are _____ and _____.
9. Spermatogenesis occurs within the _____ of the testes.
10. Androgens are secreted by the _____ cells that lie between seminiferous tubules.
11. Once a vesicular follicle has released an egg, it develops into a glandlike structure called a _____.
12. The release of an egg from a vesicular follicle is called _____.
13. Whereas AIDS and genital herpes are caused by _____, gonorrhea and chlamydia are caused by _____.

Medical Terminology Reinforcement Exercise

Consult Appendix B for help in pronouncing and analyzing the meaning of the terms that follow.

1. orchidopexy (or"kĭ-do-pek'se)
2. transurethral resection of prostate (TURP) (trans"yū-re'thral re-sek'shun ov pros'tāt)
3. gonadotropic (go"nad-o-trōp'ik)
4. contraceptive (kon"truh-sep'tiv)
5. gynecomastia (jin"ĕ-ko-mas'te-uh)
6. hysterosalpingo-oophorectomy (his"ter-o-sal-ping'go-o"ahf-or-ek'to-me)
7. colporrhaphy (kol-por'uh-fe)
8. menometrorrhagia (men'o-me-tro-ra-je-uh)
9. multipara (mul-tip'uh-ruh)
10. balanitis (bal"uh-ni'tis)
11. seminoma (sem'ĭ-no'muh)
12. genitourinary (jen'ĭ-to-yū'rĭ-nār'e)
13. prostatic hypertrophy (pros-tat'ik hy'per-tro'fe)
14. azoospermia (ā-zo'o-sper'me-uh)

Website Link

Visit the Student Edition of the Online Learning Center at http://www.mhhe.com/maderap5 for additional quizzes, interactive learning exercises, and other study tools.

Human Development and Birth

chapter 18

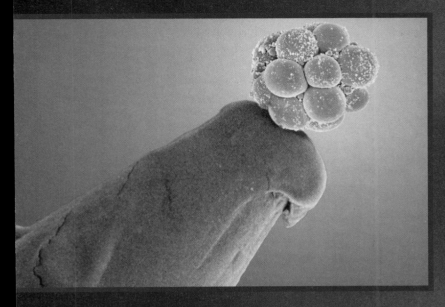

Human embryo at an early stage on the point of a pin (SEM).

chapter outline & learning objectives

After you have studied this chapter, you should be able to:

18.1 Fertilization (p. 370)
- Explain the events of fertilization and the conversion of the egg into a zygote.

18.2 Development (p. 371)
- Discuss the processes of development.
- Name the four extraembryonic membranes, and give a function for each.
- Describe the events that occur during pre-embryonic and embryonic development.

- Describe the structures and functions of the placenta and the umbilical cord.
- Describe the events that occur during fetal development.

18.3 Birth (p. 384)
- Describe the three stages of birth.
- In general, describe the physical and physiological changes in the mother during pregnancy.

Medical Focus
Premature Babies (p. 380)
Preventing Birth Defects (pp. 382–83)

What's New
Therapeutic Cloning (p. 374)

18.1 Fertilization

Fertilization, which results in a **zygote**, requires that the sperm and egg interact. Figure 18.1 shows the manner in which an egg is fertilized by a sperm in humans.

Sperm and Egg Anatomy

A sperm has three distinct parts: a head, a middle piece, and a tail. The tail is a flagellum, which allows the sperm to swim toward the egg, and the middle piece contains energy-producing mitochondria. The head contains a nucleus and is capped by a membrane-bounded acrosome. Notice that only the nucleus from the sperm head fuses with the egg nucleus. Therefore, the zygote receives cytoplasm and organelles only from the mother.

The plasma membrane of the egg is surrounded by an extracellular matrix termed the zona pellucida. In turn, the zona pellucida is surrounded by a few layers of adhering follicular cells, collectively called the corona radiata. These cells nourished the egg when it was in a follicle of the ovary.

Steps of Fertilization

During fertilization, (1) several sperm penetrate the corona radiata, (2) several sperm attempt to penetrate the zona pellucida, and (3) one sperm enters the egg. The acrosome plays a role in allowing sperm to penetrate the zona pellucida. After a sperm head binds tightly to the zona pellucida, the acrosome releases digestive enzymes that forge a pathway for the sperm through the zona pellucida. When a sperm binds to the egg, their plasma membranes fuse, and this sperm (the head, the middle piece, and usually the tail) enters the egg. Fusion of the sperm nucleus and the egg nucleus follows.

To ensure proper development, only one sperm should enter an egg. Prevention of polyspermy (entrance of more than one sperm) depends on changes in the egg's plasma membrane and in the zona pellucida. As soon as a sperm touches an egg, the egg's plasma membrane depolarizes (from -65 mV to 10 mV), and this prevents the binding of any other sperm. Then the egg releases substances that lead to a lifting of the zona pellucida away from the surface of the egg. Now sperm cannot bind to the zona pellucida either.

Figure 18.1 Fertilization. **a.** During fertilization, a single sperm enters the egg. **b.** The head of a sperm has a membrane-bounded acrosome filled with enzymes. When released, these enzymes digest a pathway for the sperm through the zona pellucida. After it binds to the plasma membrane of the egg, a sperm enters the egg. When the sperm nucleus fuses with the egg nucleus, fertilization is complete.

18.2 Development

Before we discuss the stages of development, you will want to become familiar with the processes of development and the names and functions of the extraembryonic membranes.

Processes of Development

As a human being develops, these processes occur:

Cleavage Immediately after fertilization, the zygote begins to divide so that there are first 2, then 4, 8, 16, and 32 cells, and so forth. Increase in size does not accompany these divisions (see Fig. 18.3). Cell division during cleavage is mitotic, and each cell receives a full complement of chromosomes and genes.

Growth During embryonic development, cell division is accompanied by an increase in size of the daughter cells.

Morphogenesis Morphogenesis refers to the shaping of the embryo and is first evident when certain cells are seen to move, or migrate, in relation to other cells. By these movements, the embryo begins to assume various shapes.

Differentiation When cells take on a specific structure and function, differentiation occurs. The first system to become visibly differentiated is the nervous system.

Extraembryonic Membranes

The **extraembryonic membranes** are not part of the embryo and fetus; instead, as implied by their name, they are outside the embryo (Fig. 18.2). The names of the extraembryonic membranes in humans are strange to us because they are named for their function in shelled animals! In shelled animals, the chorion lies next to the shell and carries on gas exchange. The amnion contains the protective amniotic fluid, which bathes the developing embryo. The allantois collects nitrogenous wastes, and the yolk sac surrounds the yolk, which provides nourishment.

The functions of the extraembryonic membranes are different in humans because humans develop inside the uterus. The extraembryonic membranes have these functions in humans:

1. **Chorion.** The chorion develops into the fetal half of the **placenta,** the organ that provides the embryo/fetus with nourishment and oxygen and takes away its waste.
2. **Yolk sac.** The yolk sac has little yolk and is the first site of blood cell formation.
3. **Allantois.** The allantois blood vessels become the umbilical blood vessels.
4. **Amnion.** The amnion contains fluid to cushion and protect the embryo, which develops into a fetus.

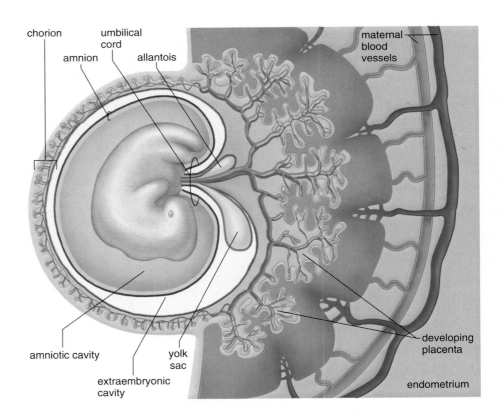

Figure 18.2 The extraembryonic membranes. The chorion and amnion surround the embryo. The two other extraembryonic membranes, the yolk sac and allantois, contribute to the umbilical cord.

Table 18.1 Human Development

Time	Events for Mother	Events for Baby
Pre-embryonic Development		
First week	Ovulation occurs.	Fertilization occurs. Cell division begins and continues. Chorion appears.
Embryonic Development		
Second week	Symptoms of early pregnancy (nausea, breast swelling and tenderness, fatigue) are present. Blood pregnancy test is positive.	Implantation occurs. Amnion and yolk sac appear. Embryo has tissues. Placenta begins to form.
Third week	First menstruation is missed. Urine pregnancy test is positive. Symptoms of early pregnancy continue.	Nervous system begins to develop. Allantois and blood vessels are present. Placenta is well formed.
Fourth week		Limb buds form. Heart is noticeable and beating. Nervous system is prominent. Embryo has tail. Other systems form.
Fifth week	Uterus is the size of a hen's egg. Mother feels frequent need to urinate due to pressure of growing uterus on bladder.	Embryo is curved. Head is large. Limb buds show divisions. Nose, eyes, and ears are noticeable.
Sixth week	Uterus is the size of an orange.	Fingers and toes are present. Skeleton is cartilaginous.
Two months	Uterus can be felt above the pubic bone.	All systems are developing. Bone is replacing cartilage. Facial features are becoming refined. Embryo is about 38 mm ($1\frac{1}{2}$ in.) long.
Fetal Development		
Third month	Uterus is the size of a grapefruit.	Gender can be distinguished by ultrasound. Fingernails appear.
Fourth month	Fetal movement is felt by a mother who has previously been pregnant.	Skeleton is visible. Hair begins to appear. Fetus is about 150 mm (6 in.) long and weighs about 170 g (6 oz).
Fifth month	Fetal movement is felt by a mother who has not previously been pregnant. Uterus reaches up to level of umbilicus, and pregnancy is obvious.	Protective cheesy coating, called vernix caseosa, begins to be deposited. Heartbeat can be heard.
Sixth month	Doctor can tell where baby's head, back, and limbs are. Breasts have enlarged, nipples and areolae are darkly pigmented, and colostrum is produced.	Body is covered with fine hair called lanugo. Skin is wrinkled and reddish.
Seventh month	Uterus reaches halfway between umbilicus and rib cage.	Testes descend into scrotum. Eyes are open. Fetus is about 300 mm (12 in.) long and weighs about 1,350 g (3 lb).
Eighth month	Weight gain is averaging about a pound a week. Standing and walking are difficult because center of gravity is thrown forward.	Body hair begins to disappear. Subcutaneous fat begins to be deposited.
Ninth month	Uterus is up to rib cage, causing shortness of breath and heartburn. Sleeping becomes difficult.	Fetus is ready for birth. It is about 530 mm ($20\frac{1}{2}$ in.) long and weighs about 3,400 g ($7\frac{1}{2}$ lb).

Stages of Development

Development encompasses the events that occur from fertilization to birth. In humans, this **gestation** period is usually calculated by adding 280 days to the start of the last menstruation, a date that is usually known. However, only about 5% of babies actually arrive on the predicted date.

Pre-Embryonic Development

Table 18.1 shows that we can subdivide development into pre-embryonic, embryonic, and fetal development. **Pre-embryonic development** encompasses the events of the first week, as shown in Figure 18.3.

Immediately after fertilization, the zygote divides repeatedly as it passes down the uterine tube to the uterus. A **morula** is a compact ball of embryonic cells that becomes a **blastocyst**.

The many cells of the blastocyst arrange themselves so that there is an **inner cell mass** surrounded by a layer of cells, the **trophoblast.** The trophoblast will become the *chorion*. The early appearance of the chorion emphasizes the complete dependence of the developing embryo on this extraembryonic membrane. The inner cell mass will become the embryo.

Each cell within the morula and blastocyst has the genetic capability of becoming any tissue. This recognition has recently led to a new procedure called therapeutic cloning, as discussed in the What's New reading on page 374. Sometimes during development, the cells of the morula separate, or the inner cell mass splits, and two pre-embryos are present rather than one. If all goes well, these two pre-embryos will be *identical twins* because they have inherited exactly the same chromosomes. *Fraternal twins*, who arise when two different eggs are fertilized by two different sperm, do not have identical chromosomes.

Figure 18.3 Pre-embryonic development. At ovulation, the egg leaves the ovary. Fertilization occurs in the upper one-third of the uterine tube. The zygote is termed a pre-embryo when cell division (cleavage) begins. When the pre-embryo begins implanting itself into the endometrium, it becomes an embryo.

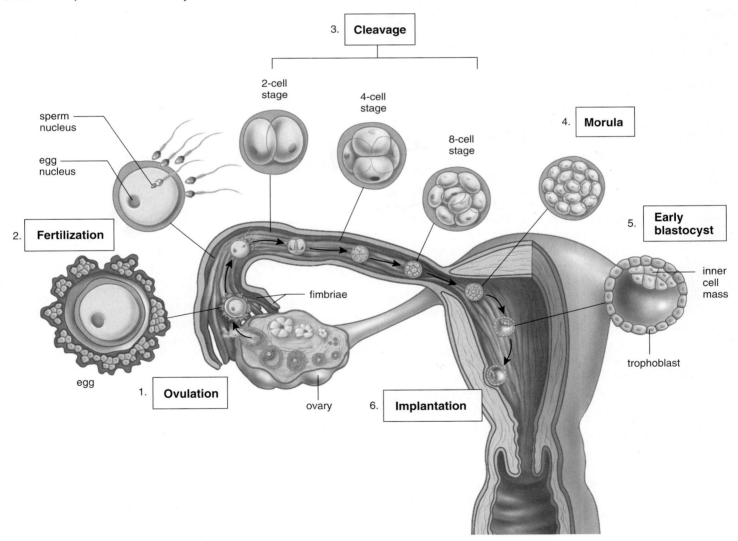

Therapeutic Cloning

The term *cloning* means making exact multiple copies of genes, a cell, or an organism. For example, identical twins are clones of a single zygote. The cloning of human beings may some day be possible. The procedure would begin as described in Figure 18A. In other words, the person being cloned need not contribute sperm or an egg to the process. Instead, a 2n nucleus from, say, a fibroblast can be placed in an enucleated egg, and that egg begins developing. The pre-embryo (blastocyst) would be implanted in the uterus of a surrogate mother where it would develop until birth. Although subject to environmental influences, the clone would be expected to closely resemble its "parent."

Therapeutic cloning is not the same as cloning a human being because the cells of the pre-embryo are separated and treated to become particular tissues, which can be used to treat the patient. The separated cells of a pre-embryo are called stem cells because they divide repeatedly and can become various tissues, as shown in Figure 18A. The tissues resulting from this procedure will not be subject to rejection by the patient because they bear the same surface molecules as the patient's cells. However, there is another way to carry out therapeutic cloning. Fertility clinics store extra pre-embryos prepared by in vitro fertilization but not used. These pre-embryos could be a source of stem cells to make tissues that could be stored and used when needed by any patient, if they were stripped of rejection-causing surface molecules.

So far, therapeutic cloning is experimental and has not been perfected. However, one day it may provide insulin-secreting cells for diabetic patients, nerve cells for stroke patients or those with Parkinson disease, cardiac cells for heart patients, and so forth. The United States is opposed to the use of embryonic stem cells regardless of their source—even if they are obtained from countries where the work is permitted. Why? Because a pre-embryo is potentially a living, breathing human being!

Because of the controversy over the cloning of stem cells derived from pre-embryos, some researchers have begun searching for other sources. It turns out that the adult body has not only blood stem cells, but also neural stem cells in the brain. It has even been possible to coax blood stem cells and neural stem cells to become other types of human tissues in the body. Another potential source of blood stem cells is a baby's umbilical cord, and umbilical blood can now be stored for future use. Once researchers have the know-how, they may be able to use any type of stem cell to cure many of the disorders afflicting human beings.

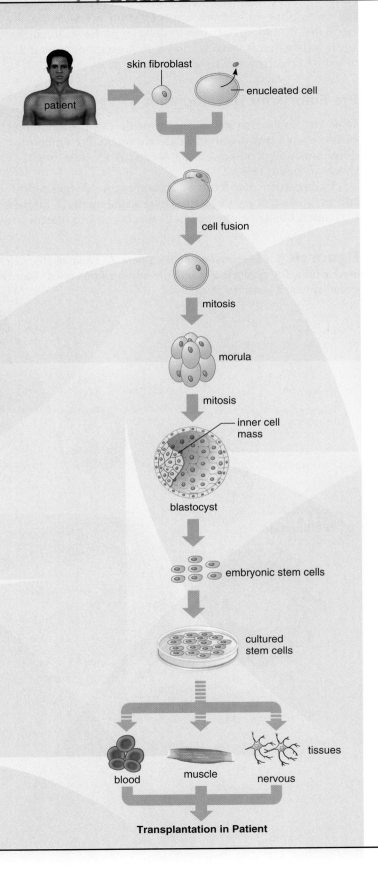

Figure 18A Therapeutic cloning is a process by which tissues are obtained from embryonic stem cells. One method of obtaining embryonic stem cells begins when a nucleus from the patient is placed in an enucleated egg.

Embryonic Development

Embryonic development begins with the second week and lasts until the end of the second month of development.

Second Week

At the end of the first week, the **embryo** usually begins the process of implanting itself in the wall of the uterus. If **implantation** is successful, the woman is clinically pregnant. On occasion, it happens that the embryo implants itself in a location other than the uterus—most likely, the uterine tube. Such a so-called **ectopic pregnancy** cannot succeed because a uterine tube is unable to support it.

During implantation, the trophoblast secretes enzymes to digest away some of the tissue and blood vessels of the endometrium of the uterus. The trophoblast also begins to secrete **human chorionic gonadotropin (HCG)**, the hormone that is the basis for the pregnancy test. HCG acts like luteinizing hormone (LH) in that it serves to maintain the corpus luteum past the time it normally disintegrates. Because it is being stimulated, the corpus luteum secretes progesterone, the endometrium is maintained, and the expected menstruation does not occur.

The embryo is now about the size of the period at the end of this sentence. As the week progresses, the inner cell mass detaches itself from the trophoblast and becomes the **embryonic disk,** and two more extraembryonic membranes form (Fig. 18.4a). The yolk sac is the first site of blood cell formation. The amniotic cavity surrounds the embryo (and then the fetus) as it develops. In humans, amniotic fluid acts as an insulator against cold and heat and also absorbs shock, such as that caused by the mother exercising.

Figure 18.4 Embryonic development. **a.** At first, no organs are present in the embryo, only tissues. The amniotic cavity is above the embryonic disk, and the yolk sac is below. **b.** The chorion develops villi, the structures so important to exchange between mother and child. **c, d.** The allantois and yolk sac, two more extraembryonic membranes, are positioned inside the body stalk as it becomes the umbilical cord. **e.** At 35+ days, the embryo has a head region and a tail region. The umbilical cord takes blood vessels between the embryo and the chorion (placenta).

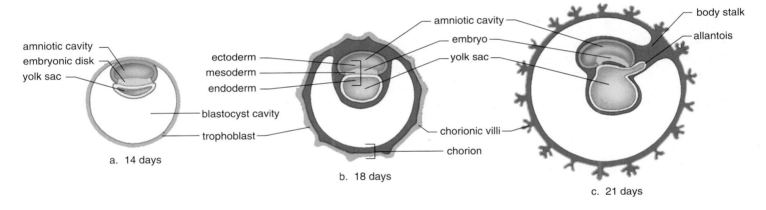

a. 14 days

b. 18 days

c. 21 days

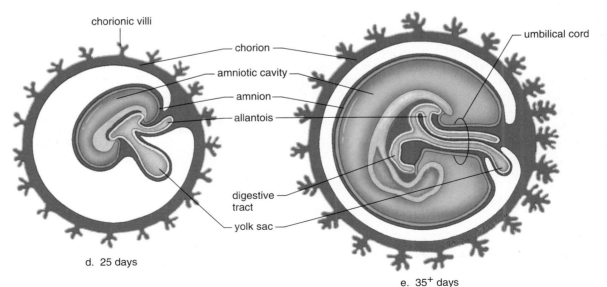

d. 25 days

e. 35+ days

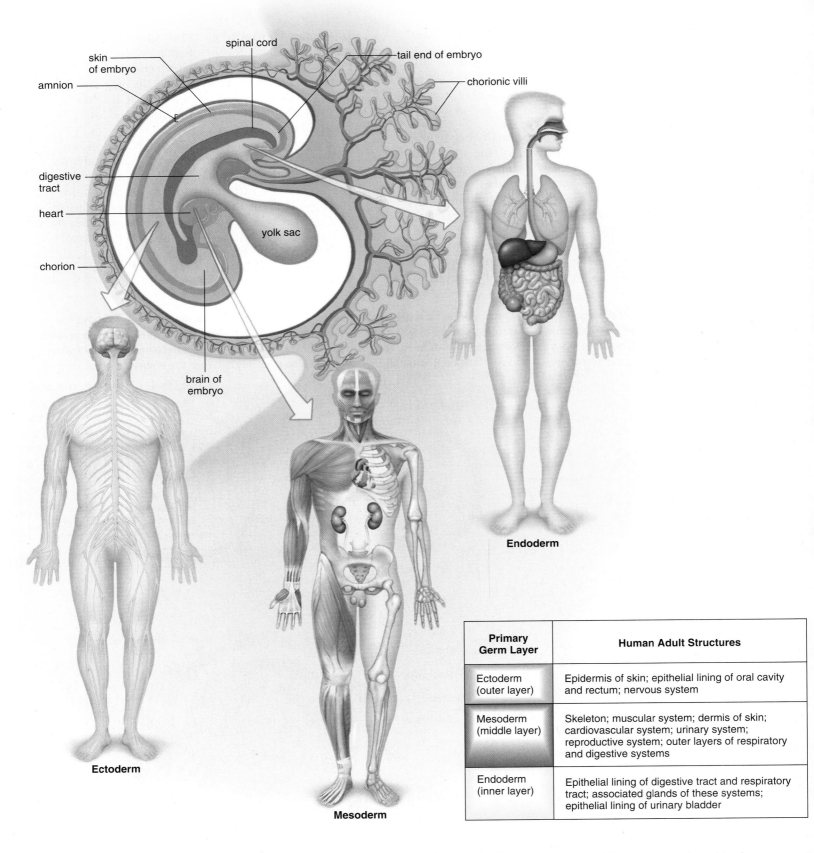

Primary Germ Layer	Human Adult Structures
Ectoderm (outer layer)	Epidermis of skin; epithelial lining of oral cavity and rectum; nervous system
Mesoderm (middle layer)	Skeleton; muscular system; dermis of skin; cardiovascular system; urinary system; reproductive system; outer layers of respiratory and digestive systems
Endoderm (inner layer)	Epithelial lining of digestive tract and respiratory tract; associated glands of these systems; epithelial lining of urinary bladder

Figure 18.5 An embryo has three primary germ layers: ectoderm, mesoderm, and endoderm. Organs and tissues can be traced back to a particular germ layer as indicated in this illustration.

Primary Germ Layers With the start of the major event called **gastrulation,** the inner cell mass becomes the embryonic disk. Gastrulation is an example of morphogenesis (see page 371) during which cells move or migrate, in this case to become tissue layers called the **primary germ layers.** By the time gastrulation is complete, the embryonic disk has become an embryo with three primary germ layers: ectoderm, mesoderm, and endoderm. Figure 18.5 shows the significance of the primary germ layers—all the organs of an individual can be traced back to one of the primary germ layers. Notice also that when the trophoblast is reinforced by mesoderm, it becomes the chorion (see Fig. 18.4*b*).

Third Week

Two important organ systems make their appearance during the third week. The nervous system is the first organ system to be visually evident. At first, a thickening appears along the entire posterior length of the embryo, and then invagination occurs as neural folds appear. When the neural folds meet at the midline, the neural tube, which later develops into the brain and the spinal cord, is formed.

Development of the heart begins in the third week and continues into the fourth week. At first, there are right and left heart tubes; when these fuse, the heart begins pumping blood, even though the chambers of the heart are not fully formed. The veins enter posteriorly, and the arteries exit anteriorly from this largely tubular heart, but later the heart twists so that all major blood vessels are located anteriorly.

Fourth and Fifth Weeks

At four weeks, the embryo is barely larger than the height of this print. A body stalk connects the caudal (tail) end of the embryo with the chorion, which has treelike projections called **chorionic villi** (see Fig. 18.4*c,d*). The fourth extraembryonic membrane, the allantois, lies within the body stalk, and its blood vessels become the umbilical blood vessels. The head and the tail then lift up, and the body stalk moves anteriorly by constriction. Once this process is complete, the **umbilical cord,** which connects the developing embryo to the placenta, is fully formed (see Fig. 18.4*e*).

Little flippers called limb buds appear (Fig. 18.6); later, the arms and the legs develop from the limb buds, and even the hands and the feet become apparent. At the same time— during the fifth week—the head enlarges and the sense organs become more prominent. It is possible to make out the developing eyes and ears, and even the nose.

Sixth Through Eighth Weeks

During the sixth through eighth weeks of development, the embryo changes to a form that is easily recognized as a human being. Concurrent with brain development, the head achieves its normal relationship with the body as a neck region develops. The nervous system is developed well enough to permit reflex actions, such as a startle response to touch. At the end of this period, the embryo is about 38 mm (1.5 in.) long and weighs no more than an aspirin tablet, even though all organ systems have been established.

Figure 18.6 Human embryo at beginning of fifth week. **a.** Scanning electron micrograph. **b.** The embryo is curled so that the head touches the region of the heart and liver. The organs of the gastrointestinal tract are forming, and the arms and the legs develop from the bulges called limb buds. The tail is an evolutionary remnant; its bones regress and become those of the coccyx (tailbone).

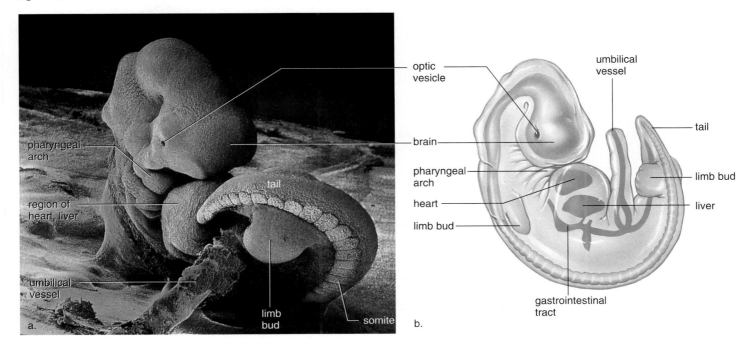

Placenta

The placenta is shaped like a pancake, measuring 15 to 20 cm in diameter and 2.5 cm thick. The placenta is normally fully formed and functional by the end of the embryonic period and before the fetal period begins. The placenta is expelled as the afterbirth following the birth of an infant.

The placenta has two portions, a fetal portion composed of chorionic tissue and a maternal portion composed of uterine tissue. Chorionic villi cover the entire surface of the chorion until about the eighth week when they begin to disappear, except in one area. These villi are surrounded by maternal blood, and it is here that exchanges of materials take place across the placental membrane. The **placental membrane** consists of the epithelial wall of an embryonic capillary and the epithelial wall of a chorionic villus. Maternal blood rarely mingles with fetal blood. Instead, oxygen and nutrient molecules, such as glucose and amino acids, diffuse from maternal blood across the placental membrane into fetal blood, and carbon dioxide and other wastes, such as urea, diffuse out of fetal blood into maternal blood.

Note that the digestive system, lungs, and kidneys do not function in the fetus. The functions of these organs are not needed because the placenta supplies the fetus with its nutritional and excretory needs.

The umbilical cord transports fetal blood to and from the placenta (Fig. 18.7; see Fig. 12.22). The umbilical cord is the fetal lifeline because it contains the umbilical arteries and vein, which transport waste molecules (carbon dioxide and urea) to the placenta for disposal and oxygen and nutrient molecules from the placenta to the rest of the fetal circulatory system.

As mentioned, the chorion and then the placenta produce HCG, the hormone detected by a pregnancy test. HCG prevents the normal degeneration of the corpus luteum and, instead, stimulates it to secrete even larger quantities of progesterone. Later, the placenta begins to produce progesterone and estrogen, and the corpus luteum degenerates—it is no longer needed. Placental estrogen and progesterone maintain the endometrium and have a negative feedback effect on the anterior pituitary so that it ceases to produce gonadotropic hormones during pregnancy. Menstruation does not occur during the length of pregnancy.

Figure 18.7 The placenta. Blood vessels within the umbilical cord lead to the placenta, where exchange takes place between fetal blood and maternal blood.

amniotic fluid

umbilical cord

placenta

uterine wall

umbilical vein
umbilical arteries

chorionic villi

maternal blood vessels

Placenta

Fetal Development and Birth

Fetal development includes the third through the ninth months of development. At this time, the fetus looks human (Fig. 18.8).

Third and Fourth Months

At the beginning of the third month, the fetal head is still very large, the nose is flat, the eyes are far apart, and the ears are well formed. Head growth now begins to slow down as the rest of the body increases in length. Epidermal refinements, such as fingernails, nipples, eyelashes, eyebrows, and hair on the head, appear.

Cartilage begins to be replaced by bone as ossification centers appear in most of the bones. Cartilage remains at the ends of the long bones, and ossification is not complete until age 18 or 20 years. The skull has six large membranous areas called **fontanels,** which permit a certain amount of flexibility as the head passes through the birth canal and allow rapid growth of the brain during infancy. Progressive fusion of the skull bones causes the fontanels to close, usually by 2 years of age.

Sometime during the third month, it is possible to distinguish males from females. Researchers have discovered a series of genes on the X and Y chromosomes that cause the differentiation of gonads into testes and ovaries. Once these have differentiated, they produce the sex hormones that influence the differentiation of the genital tract.

At this time, either testes or ovaries are located within the abdominal cavity, but later, in the last trimester of fetal development, the testes descend into the scrotal sacs (scrotum). Sometimes the testes fail to descend, and in that case, an operation may be done later to place them in their proper location.

During the fourth month, the fetal heartbeat is loud enough to be heard when a physician applies a stethoscope to the mother's abdomen. By the end of this month, the fetus is about 152 mm (6 in.) in length and weighs about 171 g (6 oz).

Fifth Through Seventh Months

During the fifth through seventh months (Fig. 18.8), the mother begins to feel movement. At first, there is only a fluttering sensation, but as the fetal legs grow and develop, kicks and jabs are felt. The fetus, though, is in the fetal position, with the head bent down and in contact with the flexed knees.

The wrinkled, translucent, pink-colored skin is covered by a fine down called **lanugo.** This in turn is coated with a white, greasy, cheeselike substance called **vernix caseosa,** which probably protects the delicate skin from the amniotic fluid. The eyelids are now fully open.

At the end of this period, the fetus's length has increased to about 300 mm (12 in.), and it weighs about 1,380 g (3 lb). It is possible that, if born now, the baby will survive.

Figure 18.8 Five- to seven-month-old fetus.

Eighth Through Ninth Months

As the end of development approaches, the fetus usually rotates so that the head is pointed toward the cervix. However, if the fetus does not turn, a **breech birth** (rump first) is likely. It is very difficult for the cervix to expand enough to accommodate this form of birth, and asphyxiation of the baby is more likely to occur. Thus, a **cesarean section** may be prescribed for delivery of the fetus (incision through the abdominal and uterine walls).

At the end of nine months, the fetus is about 530 mm (20½ in.) long and weighs about 3,400 g (7½ lb). Weight gain is due largely to an accumulation of fat beneath the skin. Full-term babies have the best chance of survival; as discussed in the Medical Focus on page 380, premature babies are subject to various challenges.

Premature Babies

About 7% of all newborns in the United States weigh less than 5½ pounds. Most of these are **premature babies** who face the following difficulties:

Respiratory distress syndrome (hyaline membrane disease) The lungs do not produce enough of a chemical surfactant that helps the alveoli stay open. Therefore, the lungs tend to collapse, instead of expanding to be filled with air.

Retinopathy of prematurity The high level of oxygen needed to ensure adequate gas exchange by the immature lungs can lead to proliferation of blood vessels within the eyes, with ensuing blindness.

Intracranial hemorrhage The delicate blood vessels in the brain are apt to break, causing swelling and inflammation of the brain. If not fatal, this can lead to brain damage.

Jaundice The immature liver fails to excrete the waste product bilirubin, which instead builds up in the blood, possibly causing brain damage.

Infections The level of antibodies in the body is low, and the various medical procedures performed could possibly introduce germs. Also, bowel infection is common, along with perforation, bleeding, and shock.

Circulatory disorders Fetal circulation, discussed in Chapter 12, has two features: (1) the oval opening between the atria, and (2) the arterial duct that allows blood to bypass the lungs. If these features persist in the newborn, oxygen-rich blood will mix with oxygen-poor blood, and blood circulation will be impaired, perhaps leading to the delivery of a "blue baby"—that is, a baby with cyanosis, a bluish cast to the skin. Heart failure can also result from these conditions.

Researchers have investigated the reasons for premature birth, and have concluded that prenatal care, including good nutrition and the willingness to refrain from drinking alcohol and smoking cigarettes, could reduce the incidence of premature birth and/or low birth weight.

Development of Male and Female Sex Organs

The sex of an individual is determined at the moment of fertilization. Both males and females have 23 pairs of chromosomes; in males, one of these pairs is an X and Y, while females have two X chromosomes. During the first several weeks of development, it is impossible to tell by external inspection whether the unborn child is a boy or a girl. Gonads don't start developing until the seventh week of development. The tissue that gives rise to the gonads is called indifferent because it can become testes or ovaries depending on the action of hormones. Genes on the Y chromosome cause the production of testosterone, and then the indifferent tissue becomes testes.

In Figure 18.9*a*, notice that at six weeks both males and females have the same types of ducts. During this indifferent stage, an embryo has the potential to develop into a male or a female. If a Y chromosome is present, testosterone stimulates the wolffian ducts to become male genital ducts. The wolffian ducts enter the urethra, which belongs to both the urinary and reproductive systems in males. The testes secrete an anti-müllerian hormone that causes the müllerian ducts to regress.

In the absence of a Y chromosome, ovaries develop instead of testes from the same indifferent tissue. Now the wolffian ducts regress, and the müllerian ducts develop into the uterus and uterine tubes. A developing vagina also extends from the uterus. There is no connection between the urinary and genital systems in females.

At fourteen weeks, both the primitive testes and ovaries are located deep inside the abdominal cavity. An inspection of the interior of the testes would show that sperm are even now starting to develop, and similarly, the ovaries already contain large numbers of tiny follicles, each having an ovum. Toward the end of development, the testes descend into the scrotal sac; the ovaries remain in the abdominal cavity.

Figure 18.9*b* shows the development of the external genitals. These tissues are also indifferent at first—they can develop into either male or female genitals. At six weeks, a small bud appears between the legs; this can develop into the male penis or the female clitoris, depending on the presence or absence of the Y chromosome and testosterone. At nine weeks, a urogenital groove bordered by two swellings appears. By fourteen weeks, this groove has disappeared in males, and the scrotum has formed from the original swellings. In females, the groove persists and becomes the vaginal opening. Labia majora and labia minora are present instead of a scrotum.

Figure 18.9 Male and female organs. **a.** Development of gonads and ducts. **b.** Development of external genitals.

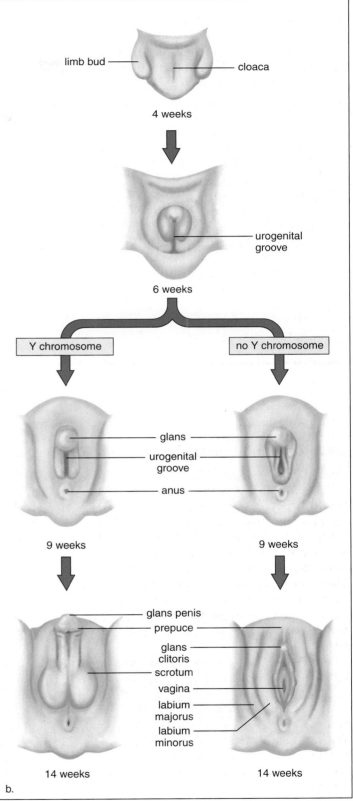

Medical Focus

Preventing Birth Defects

While some **congenital (birth) defects** are not preventable, certain ones are, and therefore all females of childbearing age are advised to take everyday precautions to protect any future and/or presently developing embryos and fetuses from these defects. For example, it is best if a woman has a physical exam even before she becomes pregnant. At that time, it can be determined if she has been immunized against **rubella (German measles).** Depending on exactly when a pregnant woman has the disease, rubella can cause blindness, deafness, mental retardation, heart malformations, and other serious problems in an unborn child. A vaccine to prevent the disease can be given to a woman before she gets pregnant, but cannot be given to a woman who is already pregnant because it contains live viruses. Also, the presence of HIV (the causative agent for AIDS) should be tested for because preventative therapies are available to improve maternal and infant health.

Good health habits are a must during pregnancy, including proper nutrition, adequate rest, and exercise. Moderate exercise can usually continue throughout pregnancy and hopefully will contribute to ease of delivery. Basic nutrients are required in adequate amounts to meet the demands of both fetus and mother. A growing number of studies confirm that small, thin newborns are more likely to develop certain chronic diseases, such as diabetes and high blood pressure, when they become adults than are babies who are born heavier. An increased amount of minerals, such as calcium for bone growth and iron for red blood cell formation, and certain vitamins, such as vitamin B_6 for proper metabolism and folate (folic acid), are required. Pregnant women need more folate (folic acid) a day to meet an increased rate of cell division and DNA synthesis in their own bodies and that of the developing child. A maternal deficiency of folate has been linked to development of neural tube defects in the fetus. These defects include **spina bifida** (spinal cord or spinal fluid bulge through the back) and **anencephaly** (absence of a brain). Perhaps as many as 75% of these defects could be avoided by adequate folate intake even before pregnancy occurs. Consuming fortified breakfast cereals is a good way to meet folate needs, because they contain a more absorbable form of folate.

Good health habits include avoiding substances that can cross the placenta and harm the fetus (Table 18A). Cigarette smoke poses a serious threat to the health of a fetus because it contains not only carbon monoxide but also other fetotoxic chemicals. Children born to smoking mothers have a greater chance of a cleft lip or palate, increased incidence of respiratory diseases, and later on, more reading disorders than those born to mothers who did not smoke during their pregnancy.

Alcohol easily crosses the placenta, and even one drink a day appears to increase the chance of a spontaneous abortion. The more alcohol consumed, the greater are the chances of physical abnormalities if the pregnancy continues. Heavy consumption of alcohol puts a fetus at risk of a mental defect because alcohol enters the brain of the fetus. Babies born to heavy drinkers are apt to undergo **delirium tremens** after birth—shaking, vomiting, and extreme irritability—and to have **fetal alcohol syndrome (FAS).** Babies with FAS have decreased weight, height, and head size, with malformation of the head and face (Fig. 18B). Later, mental retardation is common, as are numerous other physical malformations.

Certainly, illegal drugs, such as marijuana, cocaine, and heroin, should be completely avoided during pregnancy. *Cocaine babies* now make up 60% of drug-affected babies. Cocaine use causes severe fluctuations in a mother's blood pressure that temporarily deprive the developing fetus's brain of oxygen. Cocaine babies have visual problems, lack coordination, and are mentally retarded.

Children born to women who received X-ray treatment during pregnancy for, say, cancer are apt to have birth defects and/or to develop leukemia later. It takes a lower amount of X rays to cause mutations in a developing embryo or fetus than in an adult. Dental and other diagnostic X rays that result in only a small amount of radiation are probably safe. Still, a woman should be sure a physician knows that she is or may be pregnant. Similarly, toxic chemicals, such as pesticides, and many organic industrial chemicals, such as vinyl chloride, formaldehyde, asbestos, and benzenes, are mutagenic and can cross the placenta, resulting in abnormalities. Lead circulating in a pregnant woman's blood can cause a child to be mentally retarded. Agents that produce abnormalities during development are called **teratogens.**

A woman has to be very careful about taking medications while pregnant. Excessive vitamin A, sometimes used to treat acne, may damage an embryo. In the 1950s and 1960s, DES (diethylstilbestrol), a synthetic hormone related to the natural female hormone estrogen, was given to pregnant women to prevent cramps, bleeding, and threatened miscarriage. But in the 1970s

Table 18A Behaviors Harmful to the Unborn
Drinking alcohol
Smoking cigarettes
Taking illegal drugs
Taking any medication not approved by a physician

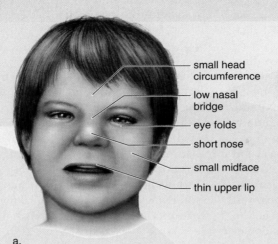

small head circumference

low nasal bridge

eye folds

short nose

small midface

thin upper lip

a.

b.

c.

d.

Figure 18B Fetal alcohol syndrome is characterized by certain features. a. These features include malformations of the head and face. b–d. Photos of children who have fetal alcohol syndrome.

and 1980s, some adolescent girls and young women whose mothers had been treated with DES showed various abnormalities of the reproductive organs and an increased tendency toward cervical cancer. Other sex hormones, including birth control pills, can possibly cause abnormal fetal development, including abnormalities of the sex organs. The drug thalidomide was a popular tranquilizer during the 1950s and 1960s in many European countries and to a degree in the United States. The drug, which was taken to prevent nausea in pregnant women, arrested the development of arms and legs in some children and also damaged heart and blood vessels, ears, and the digestive tract. Some mothers of affected children report that they took the drug for only a few days. Because of such experiences, physicians are generally very cautious about prescribing drugs during pregnancy, and no pregnant woman should take any drug—even ordinary cold remedies—without checking first with her physician.

Unfortunately, immunization for sexually transmitted diseases is not possible. The HIV virus can cross the placenta and cause mental retardation. As mentioned, proper medication can greatly reduce the chance of this happening. When a mother has herpes, gonorrhea, or chlamydia, newborns can become infected as they pass through the birth canal. Blindness and other physical and mental defects may develop. Birth by cesarean section could prevent these occurrences.

An Rh-negative woman who has given birth to an Rh-positive child should receive an Rh immunoglobulin injection within 72 hours to prevent her body from producing Rh antibodies. She will start producing these antibodies when some of the child's Rh-positive red blood cells enter her bloodstream, possibly before but particularly at birth. Rh antibodies can cause nervous system and heart defects in a fetus. The first Rh-positive baby is not usually affected. But in subsequent pregnancies, antibodies created at the time of the first birth cross the placenta and begin to destroy the blood cells of the fetus, thereby causing anemia and other complications.

The birth defects we have been discussing are particularly preventable because they are not due to inheritance of an abnormal number of chromosomes or any other genetic abnormality. More women are having babies after the age of 35, and first births among women older than 40 have increased by 50% since 1980. The chance of an older woman bearing a child with a birth defect unrelated to genetic inheritance is no greater than that of a younger woman. However, as discussed in Chapter 19, there is a greater risk of an older woman having a child with a chromosomal abnormality leading to premature delivery, cesarean section, a low birth weight, or certain syndromes. Some chromosomal and other genetic defects can be detected in utero so that therapy for these disorders can begin as soon as possible.

Now that physicians and laypeople are aware of the various ways birth defects can be prevented, it is hoped that the incidence of birth defects will decrease in the future.

18.3 Birth

The uterus has contractions throughout pregnancy. At first, these are light, lasting about 20–30 seconds and occurring every 15–20 minutes. Near the end of pregnancy, the contractions may become stronger and more frequent so that a woman thinks she is in labor. "False-labor" contractions are called **Braxton Hicks contractions.** However, the onset of true labor is marked by uterine contractions that occur regularly every 15–20 minutes and last for 40 seconds or longer.

A positive feedback mechanism can explain the onset and continuation of labor. Uterine contractions are induced by a stretching of the cervix, which also brings about the release of oxytocin from the posterior pituitary gland. Oxytocin stimulates the uterine muscles, both directly and through the action of prostaglandins. Uterine contractions push the fetus downward, and the cervix stretches even more. This cycle keeps repeating itself until birth occurs.

Prior to or at the first stage of **parturition,** which is the process of giving birth to an offspring, there can be a "bloody show" caused by expulsion of a mucous plug from the cervical canal. This plug prevents bacteria and sperm from entering the uterus during pregnancy.

Stage 1

During the first stage of labor, the uterine contractions of labor occur in such a way that the cervical canal slowly disappears as the lower part of the uterus is pulled upward toward the baby's head. This process is called effacement, or "taking up the cervix." With further contractions, the baby's head acts as a wedge to assist cervical dilation (Fig. 18.10b). If the amniotic membrane has not already ruptured, it is apt to do so during this stage, releasing the amniotic fluid, which leaks out the vagina (an event sometimes referred to as "breaking water"). The first stage of parturition ends once the cervix is dilated completely.

Stage 2

During the second stage of parturition, the uterine contractions occur every 1–2 minutes and last about one minute each. They are accompanied by a desire to push, or bear down.

Figure 18.10 Three stages of parturition (birth). **a.** Position of fetus just before birth begins. **b.** Dilation of cervix. **c.** Birth of baby. **d.** Expulsion of afterbirth.

placenta

pubic symphysis
urethra
urinary bladder
vagina
cervix
rectum

a. 9-month-old fetus

ruptured amniotic sac

b. First stage of birth: cervix dilates

placenta

c. Second stage of birth: baby emerges

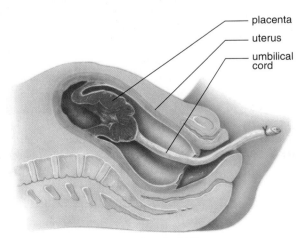

placenta
uterus
umbilical cord

d. Third stage of birth: expelling afterbirth

As the baby's head gradually descends into the vagina, the desire to push becomes greater. When the baby's head reaches the exterior, it turns so that the back of the head is uppermost (Fig. 18.10c). Since the vaginal orifice may not expand enough to allow passage of the head, an **episiotomy** is often performed. This incision, which enlarges the opening, is sewn together later. As soon as the head is delivered, the baby's shoulders rotate so that the baby faces either to the right or the left. At this time, the physician may hold the head and guide it downward, while one shoulder and then the other emerges. The rest of the baby follows easily.

Once the baby is breathing normally, the umbilical cord is cut and tied, severing the child from the placenta. The stump of the cord shrivels and leaves a scar, which is the umbilicus.

Stage 3

The placenta, or **afterbirth,** is delivered during the third stage of parturition (Fig. 18.10d). About 15 minutes after delivery of the baby, uterine muscular contractions shrink the uterus and dislodge the placenta. The placenta then is expelled into the vagina. As soon as the placenta and its membranes are delivered, the third stage of parturition is complete.

Effects of Pregnancy on the Mother

Major changes take place in the mother's body during pregnancy. When first pregnant, the mother may experience nausea and vomiting, loss of appetite, and fatigue. These symptoms subside, and some mothers report increased energy levels and a general sense of well-being despite an increase in weight. During pregnancy, the mother gains weight due to breast and uterine enlargement, weight of the fetus, amount of amniotic fluid, size of the placenta, her own increase in total body fluid; and an increase in storage of proteins, fats, and minerals. The increased weight can lead to lordosis (swayback) and lower back pain.

Table 18.2 — Effect of Placental Hormones on Mother

Hormone	Chief Effects
Progesterone	Relaxation of smooth muscle; reduced uterine motility; reduced maternal immune response to fetus
Estrogen	Increased uterine blood flow; increased renin-angiotensin-aldosterone activity; increased protein biosynthesis by the liver
Peptide hormones	Increased insulin resistance

Source: Moore, Thomas R., Gestation Encyclopedia of Human Biology, Vol. 7, 7th edition. Copyright © 1997 Academic Press.

Aside from an increase in weight, many of the physiological changes in the mother are due to the presence of the placental hormones that support fetal development (Table 18.2). Progesterone decreases uterine motility by relaxing smooth muscle, including the smooth muscle in the walls of arteries. The arteries expand, and this leads to a low blood pressure that sets in motion the renin-angiotensin-aldosterone mechanism, which is promoted by estrogen. Aldosterone activity promotes sodium and water retention, and blood volume increases until it reaches its peak sometime during weeks 28–32 of pregnancy. Altogether, blood volume increases from 5 liters to 7 liters—a 40% rise. An increase in the number of red blood cells follows. With the rise in blood volume, cardiac output increases by 20–30%. Blood flow to the kidneys, placenta, skin, and breasts rises significantly. Smooth muscle relaxation also explains the common gastrointestinal effects of pregnancy. The heartburn experienced by many is due to relaxation of the esophageal sphincter and reflux of stomach contents into the esophagus. Constipation is caused by a decrease in intestinal tract motility.

Of interest is the increase in pulmonary valves in a pregnant woman. The bronchial tubes relax, but this alone cannot explain the typical 40% increase in vital capacity and tidal volume. The increasing size of the uterus from a nonpregnant weight of 60–80 g to 900–1,200 g contributes to an improvement in respiratory functions. The uterus comes to occupy most of the abdominal cavity, reaching nearly to the xiphoid process of the sternum. This increase in size not only pushes the intestines, liver, stomach, and diaphragm superiorly, but it also widens the thoracic cavity. Compared to nonpregnant values, the maternal oxygen level changes little, but blood carbon dioxide levels fall by 20%, creating a concentration gradient favorable to the flow of carbon dioxide from fetal blood to maternal blood at the placenta.

The enlargement of the uterus does result in some problems. In the pelvic cavity, compression of the ureters and urinary bladder can result in stress incontinence. Compression of the inferior vena cava, especially when lying down, decreases venous return, and the result is edema and varicose veins.

Aside from the steroid hormones progesterone and estrogen, the placenta also produces some peptide hormones. One of these makes cells resistant to insulin, and the result can be pregnancy-induced diabetes. Some of the integumentary changes observed during pregnancy are also due to placental hormones. **Striae gravidarum,** commonly called "stretch marks," typically form over the abdomen and lower breasts in response to increased steroid hormone levels rather than stretching of the skin. Melanocyte activity also increases during pregnancy. Darkening of the areolae, skin in the line from the navel to the pubis, areas of the face and neck, and vulva is common.

Changes in breast anatomy and the occurrence of lactation are discussed in Chapter 17, page 356.

Basic Key Terms

afterbirth (af'ter-berth), p. 385

allantois (uh-lan'to-is), p. 371

amnion (am'ne-on), p. 371

blastocyst (blas'to-sist), p. 373

chorion (ko're-on), p. 371

chorionic villi (ko"re-on'ik vil'ī), p. 377

cleavage (klēv'ij), p. 371

differentiation (dif'er-en"she-a'shun), p. 371

embryo (em'bre-o), p. 375

embryonic development (em"bre-on'ik de-vel'op-ment), p. 375

embryonic disk (em"bre-on'ik disk), p. 375

extraembryonic membrane (eks"truh-em"bre-on'ik mem'brān), p. 371

fertilization (fer'tĭ-lĭ-za'shun), p. 370

fetal development (fe'tal de-vel'op-ment), p. 379

fontanel (fon"tuh-nel'), p. 379

gastrulation (gas'tru-la'shun), p. 377

gestation (jes-ta'shun), p. 373

growth (grōth), p. 371

human chorionic gonadotropin (hyū'man ko"re-on'ik go-nad'o-tro'pin), p. 375

implantation (im"plan-ta'shun), p. 375

inner cell mass (in'er sel mas), p. 373

lanugo (luh-nu'go), p. 379

morphogenesis (morf-o-jen'ĕ-sis), p. 371

morula (mor'u-luh), p. 373

parturition (par"tu-rish'un), p. 384

placenta (pluh-sen'tuh), p. 371

trophoblast (trof'o-blast), p. 373

umbilical cord (um-bil'ĭ-kl kord), p. 377

vernix caseosa (ver'niks ka"se-o'suh), p. 379

yolk sac (yōk sak), p. 371

zygote (zi'gōt), p. 370

Clinical Key Terms

anencephaly (an'en-sef'uh-le), p. 382

Braxton Hicks contraction (braks'ton hiks con-trak'shun), p. 384

breech birth (brēch berth), p. 379

cesarean section (sĭ-zār'e-un sek'shun), p. 379

congenital defect (kon-jen'ĭ-tul de'fekt), p. 382

delirium tremens (de-lēr'e-um tre'mens), p. 382

ectopic pregnancy (ek-top'ik preg'nun-se), p. 375

episiotomy (e-piz"e-ot'o-me), p. 385

fetal alcohol syndrome (fe'tal al'cuh-hol sin'drōm), p. 382

premature baby (pre-mah-tyūr' ba'be), p. 380

rubella (German measles) (ru-bel'uh), p. 382

spina bifida (spi'nuh bif'ĭ-duh), p. 382

teratogen (ter-ah'to-jen), p. 382

Summary

18.1 Fertilization

During fertilization, a sperm nucleus fuses with the egg nucleus. The resulting zygote begins to develop into a mass of cells, which travels down the uterine tube and embeds itself in the endometrium. Cells surrounding the embryo produce HCG, the hormone whose presence indicates that the female is pregnant.

18.2 Development

A. The extraembryonic membranes, placenta, and umbilical cord allow humans to develop internally within the uterus. These structures protect the embryo and allow it to exchange waste for nutrients with the mother's blood.

B. At the end of the embryonic period, all organ systems are established, and there is a mature and functioning placenta. The embryo is only about 38 mm (1 1/2 in.) long.

C. Fetal development extends from the third through the ninth months. During the third and fourth months, the skeleton is becoming ossified. The sex of the fetus becomes distinguishable.

D. During the fifth through the ninth months, the fetus continues to grow and to gain weight. Babies born after six or seven months may survive, but full-term babies have a better chance of survival.

E. During pregnancy, the mother's uterus enlarges greatly, resulting in weight gain, standing and walking difficulties, and general discomfort.

18.3 Birth

A. During stage 1 of parturition, the cervix dilates. During stage 2, the child is born. During stage 3, the afterbirth is expelled.

B. During pregnancy, the mother gains weight as the uterus comes to occupy most of the abdominal cavity with resultant annoyances such as incontinence. Many of the complaints of pregnancy, such as constipation, heartburn, darkening of certain skin areas, and diabetes of pregnancy, are due to the presence of the placental hormones.

Study Questions

1. Describe the process of fertilization and the events immediately following it. (p. 370)
2. Name the four extraembryonic membranes, and give a function for each. (p. 371)
3. Label the diagram below to review the events that occur during pre-embryonic development. (p. 373)
4. What is the basis of the pregnancy test? (p. 375)
5. Specifically, what events normally occur during embryonic development? What events normally occur during fetal development? (pp. 375–79)
6. Describe the structure and function of the umbilical cord. (p. 378)
7. Describe the structure and function of the placenta. (p. 378)
8. What are the three stages of birth? Describe the events of each stage. (pp. 384–85)
9. In general, describe the physical changes in the mother during pregnancy. (p. 385)

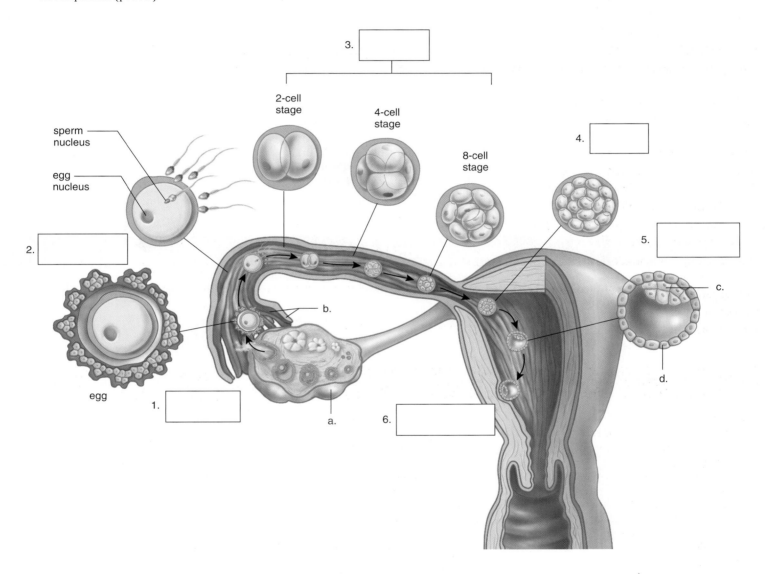

3.

2-cell stage

4-cell stage

8-cell stage

sperm nucleus

egg nucleus

4.

5.

2.

c.

b.

egg

d.

1.

a.

6.

Fill in the blanks.

1. Fertilization occurs when the _____ nucleus fuses with the _____ nucleus.
2. The _____ membranes include the chorion, the _____, the yolk sac, and the allantois.
3. During development, the nutrient needs of the developing embryo (fetus) are served by the _____.

4. The zygote divides as it passes down a uterine tube. This process is called _____.
5. When cells take on a specific structure and function, _____ occurs.
6. Once the blastocyst arrives at the uterus, it begins to _____ itself in the endometrium.
7. During embryonic development, all major _____ form.

8. Fetal development begins at the end of the _____ month.
9. In most deliveries, the _____ appear(s) before the rest of the body.
10. During pregnancy, constipation, darkening of certain areas of the skin, and diabetes are all due to _____ produced by the placenta.

Medical Terminology Reinforcement Exercise

Consult Appendix B for help in pronouncing and analyzing the meaning of the terms that follow.

1. morphogenesis (mor″fo-jen′ĕ-sis)
2. neonatologist (ne″o-na-tol′o-jist)
3. prenatal (pre-na′tal)
4. hyperemesis gravidarum (hi″per-em′ĕ-sis grav-id-ar′um)
5. dysmenorrhea (dis″men-o-re′uh)
6. pseudocyesis (su″do-si′ĕ-sis)
7. primigravida (pri″mĭ-grav′ĭ-duh)
8. cryptorchidism (krip-tor′kĭ-dizm)
9. oligospermia (ol″i-go-sper′me-uh)
10. perineorrhaphy (per″i-ne-or′uh-fe)
11. abruptio placentae (ab-rup′she-o pluh-sen′te)
12. dystocia (dis-to′se-uh)
13. galactostasis (gal″ak-tos′tuh-sis)
14. polyhydramnios (pol″e-hi-dram′ne-os)
15. amniorrhea (am′ne′-o-re′uh)
16. placenta previa (pla-se′n′tuh pre′ve-uh)

Website Link

Visit the Student Edition of the Online Learning Center at http://www.mhhe.com/maderap5 for additional quizzes, interactive learning exercises, and other study tools.

Human Genetics

chapter 19

In individuals with the genetic disorder sickle-cell trait, red blood cells can become sickle-shaped.

chapter outline & learning objectives

After you have studied this chapter, you should be able to:

19.1 Chromosomal Inheritance (p. 390)

- Explain the normal chromosomal inheritance of humans.
- Describe how a karyotype is prepared and two ways to obtain fetal chromosomes.
- Explain how nondisjunction results in inheritance of an abnormal chromosome number.
- Describe Down syndrome and various syndromes that result from the inheritance of an abnormal sex chromosome number.

19.2 Genetic Inheritance (p. 395)

- Explain autosomal dominant and recessive allele inheritance.

- Explain X-linked inheritance and why males have more X-linked disorders than females.
- Relate the inheritance of an allele to protein synthesis.
- Tell how a genetic counselor could help a couple who are carriers for cystic fibrosis.

19.3 DNA Technology (p. 399)

- Explain how gene therapy is being used to treat genetic disorders.
- Discuss genomics, including how genomics might lead to better treatments for illnesses.

Medical Focus

Living with Klinefelter Syndrome (p. 394)
New Cures on the Horizon (p. 400)

What's New

Preimplantation Genetic Studies (p. 398)

19.1 Chromosomal Inheritance

Normally, both males and females have 23 pairs of chromosomes, for a total of 46 chromosomes. Twenty-two pairs are **autosomes** (nonsex chromosomes), and one pair is the **sex chromosomes**, so called because they differ between the sexes. In humans, males have a **Y chromosome** and an X chromosome. Females have two **X chromosomes.**

Various human disorders result from the inheritance of an abnormal chromosome number. Such a disorder may be a **syndrome,** which is a group of symptoms that always occur together. Table 19.1 lists several syndromes that are due to an abnormal chromosome number. It is possible to view an individual's chromosomes by constructing a **karyotype,** a display of the chromosomes arranged by size, shape, and banding pattern. Doing a karyotype will reveal whether an individual has inherited an abnormal chromosome number.

Karyotyping

Any cell in the body except red blood cells, which lack a nucleus, can be a source of chromosomes for karyotyping. In adults, it is easiest to use white blood cells separated from a blood sample for this purpose. The chromosomes of fetuses are often obtained by either amniocentesis or chorionic villi sampling.

During **amniocentesis,** a sample of amniotic fluid is withdrawn from the uterus of a pregnant woman. Blood tests and the age of the mother are used to determine whether the procedure should be done. Amniocentesis is not usually performed until about the fourteenth to the seventeenth week of pregnancy. A long needle is passed through the abdominal and uterine walls to obtain a small amount of fluid, which also contains fetal cells (Fig. 19.1*a*). Testing the cells and karyotyping the chromosomes may be delayed as long as four weeks so that the cells can be cultured to increase their number. As many as 400 chromosomal and biochemical problems can be detected by testing the cells and the amniotic fluid.

The risk of spontaneous abortion increases by about 0.3% due to amniocentesis, and doctors only use the procedure if it is medically warranted.

Chorionic villi sampling (CVS) is a procedure for obtaining chorionic cells in the region where the placenta will develop. This procedure can be done as early as the fifth week of pregnancy. A long, thin suction tube is inserted through the vagina into the uterus (Fig. 19.1*b*). Ultrasound, which gives a picture of the uterine contents, is used to place the tube between the uterine lining and the chorionic villi. Then a sample of chorionic cells is withdrawn by suction. The cells do not have to be cultured, and karyotyping can be done immediately. This sampling procedure does not gather any amniotic fluid, so the biochemical tests done on the amniotic fluid following amniocentesis are not possible. Also, CVS carries a greater risk of spontaneous abortion than amniocentesis—0.8% compared to 0.3%. The advantage of CVS is that the results of karyotyping are available at an earlier date.

Preparing the Karyotype

After a sample of cells has been obtained, the cells are stimulated to divide in a culture medium. A chemical is used to stop mitosis during metaphase when chromosomes are the most highly compacted and condensed. The cells are then spread on a microscope slide and dried. Stains are applied to the slides, and the cells are photographed. Staining produces dark and light cross-bands of varying widths, and these can be used in addition to size and shape to help pair up the chromosomes. Today, a computer is used to arrange the chromosomes in pairs. It is possible to photograph the nucleus of a cell that is about to divide (the chromosomes are more visible then), so that a picture of the chromosomes is obtained. The picture may be entered into a computer, and the chromosomes electronically arranged by pairs (Fig. 19.1*c*). The resulting display of chromosomes is the karyotype. Figure 19.1*d,e* compares a normal karyotype with that of a person who has Down syndrome, the most common autosomal abnormality.

Table 19.1		Syndromes from Abnormal Chromosome Numbers				
Syndrome	**Sex**	**Disorder**	**Chromosome Number**		**Frequency**	
					SPONTANEOUS ABORTIONS	**LIVE BIRTHS**
Down	M or F	Trisomy 21	47		1/40	1/800
Poly-X	F	XXX (or XXXX)	47 or 48		0	1/1,500
Klinefelter	M	XXY (or XXXY)	47 or 48		1/300	1/800
Jacobs	M	XYY	47		?	1/1,000
Turner	F	XO	45		1/18	1/2,500

Figure 19.1 Human karyotype preparation. A karyotype is an arrangement of an individual's chromosomes into numbered pairs according to their size, shape, and banding pattern. **a.** Amniocentesis and **(b)** chorionic villi sampling provide cells for karyotyping to determine if the unborn child has a chromosomal abnormality. **c.** After cells are treated as described in the text, a computer constructs the karyotype. **d.** Karyotype of a normal male. **e.** Karyotype of a male with Down syndrome. A Down syndrome karyotype has three number 21 chromosomes.

amniotic cavity

a. During amniocentesis, a long needle is used to withdraw amniotic fluid containing fetal cells.

b. During chorionic villi sampling, a suction tube is used to remove cells from the chorion, where the placenta will develop.

c. Cells are microscopically examined and photographed. Computer arranges the chromosomes into pairs.

d. Normal male karyotype with 46 chromosomes

e. Down syndrome karyotype with an extra chromosome 21

Nondisjunction

An abnormal chromosomal makeup in an individual can be due to nondisjunction. **Nondisjunction** occurs during meiosis I when both members of a homologous pair go into the same daughter cell or during meiosis II when the sister chromatids fail to separate and both daughter chromosomes go into the same gamete (Fig. 19.2). If an egg with 24 chromosomes is fertilized with a normal sperm, the result is a *trisomy*, so called because one type of chromosome is present in three copies. If an egg with 22 chromosomes is fertilized with a normal sperm, the result is a *monosomy*, so called because one type of chromosome is present in a single copy.

Figure 19.2 Nondisjunction during oogenesis. Nondisjunction can occur **(a)** during meiosis I if homologous chromosomes fail to separate or **(b)** during meiosis II if the sister chromatids fail to separate completely. In either case, abnormal gametes have an extra chromosome or lack a chromosome.

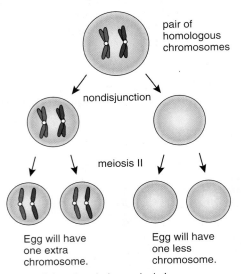

pair of homologous chromosomes

nondisjunction

meiosis II

Egg will have one extra chromosome.

Egg will have one less chromosome.

a. Nondisjunction during meiosis I

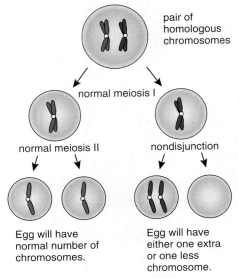

pair of homologous chromosomes

normal meiosis I

normal meiosis II

nondisjunction

Egg will have normal number of chromosomes.

Egg will have either one extra or one less chromosome.

b. Nondisjunction during meiosis II

Down Syndrome

Down syndrome is also called trisomy 21 because the individual usually has three copies of chromosome 21. In most instances, the egg had two copies instead of one of this chromosome. (In 23% of the cases studied, however, the sperm had the extra chromosome 21.)

Down syndrome (Fig. 19.3) is easily recognized by these characteristics: short stature, an eyelid fold, stubby fingers, a wide gap between the first and second toes, a large, fissured tongue, a round head, a palm crease (the so-called simian line), and unfortunately, mental retardation, which can sometimes be severe.

The chance of a woman having a Down syndrome child increases rapidly with age, starting at about age 40. The frequency of Down syndrome is 1 in 800 births for mothers under 40 years of age and 1 in 80 for mothers over 40 years of age. Most Down syndrome babies are born to women younger than age 40, however, because this is the age group having the most babies. Amniocentesis followed by karyotyping can detect a Down syndrome child.

It is known that the genes that cause Down syndrome are located on the bottom third of chromosome 21, and extensive investigative work has been directed toward discovering the specific genes responsible for the characteristics of the syndrome. One day it might be possible to control the expression of these genes even before birth, so that the symptoms of Down syndrome do not appear.

Figure 19.3 Down syndrome. Down syndrome occurs when the egg or the sperm has an extra chromosome 21 due to nondisjunction in either meiosis I or meiosis II. Characteristics include a wide, rounded face and narrow, slanting eyelids. Mental retardation to varying degrees is usually present.

Sex Chromosome Inheritance

As stated, the sex chromosomes in humans are called X and Y. Because women are XX, an egg always bears an X, but since males are XY, a sperm can bear an X or a Y. Therefore, the sex of the newborn child is determined by the father. If a Y-bearing sperm fertilizes the egg, then the XY combination results in a male. On the other hand, if an X-bearing sperm fertilizes the egg, the XX combination results in a female. All factors being equal, there is a 50% chance of having a girl or a boy.

♀＼♂	X	Y
X	XX	XY

Nondisjunction also occurs with regard to the sex chromosomes. Eggs or sperm with too many or too few sex chromosomes can occur. Therefore, nondisjunction accounts for the birth of individuals with too few or too many sex chromosomes.

Too Many/Too Few Sex Chromosomes

From birth, an XO individual with **Turner syndrome** has only one sex chromosome, an X; the O signifies the absence of a second sex chromosome. Turner females are short, with a broad chest and a webbed neck. The ovaries, uterine tubes, and uterus are very small and nonfunctional. Turner females do not undergo puberty or menstruate, and their breasts do not develop (Fig. 19.4*a*). They are usually of normal intelligence and can lead fairly normal lives. Some Turner females have even given birth following in vitro fertilization using donor eggs.

A male with **Klinefelter syndrome** has two or more X chromosomes in addition to a Y chromosome, and is sterile. The testes and prostate gland are underdeveloped, and the individual has no facial hair. Also, some breast development may occur (Fig. 19.4*b*). Affected individuals have large hands and feet and very long arms and legs. They are usually slow to learn but not mentally retarded unless they inherit more than two X chromosomes. The Medical Focus on the next page suggests that much can be done to help a person with Klinefelter syndrome lead a normal life.

Figure 19.4 Syndromes due to an abnormal sex chromosome number. **a.** A female with Turner (XO) syndrome has a short thick neck, short stature, and lack of breast development. **b.** A male with Klinefelter (XXY) syndrome has immature sex organs and some development of the breasts.

a.

b.

A **poly-X female** has more than two X chromosomes. Females with three X chromosomes have no distinctive phenotype aside from a tendency to be tall and thin. Although some exhibit delayed motor and language development, most poly-X females are not mentally retarded. Some may have menstrual difficulties, but many menstruate regularly and are fertile. Their children usually have a normal karyotype.

Females with more than three X chromosomes occur rarely. Unlike XXX females, XXXX females are usually tall and severely retarded. Various physical abnormalities are seen, but they may menstruate normally.

XYY males with **Jacobs syndrome** can only result from nondisjunction during spermatogenesis. This is because only males have a Y chromosome. Affected males are usually taller than average, suffer from persistent acne, and tend to have speech and reading problems. At one time, it was suggested that these men were likely to be criminally aggressive, but it has since been shown that the incidence of such behavior among them may be no greater than among XY males.

Notice that there are no YO males. This shows that at least one X chromosome is needed for survival. However, XXY individuals are males, not females.

Medical Focus

Living with Klinefelter Syndrome

In 1996, at the age of 25, I was diagnosed with Klinefelter syndrome (KS). Being diagnosed has changed my life for the better.

I was a happy baby, but when I was still very young, my parents began to believe that there was something wrong with me. I knew something was different about me, too, as early on as five years old. I was very shy and had trouble making friends. One minute I'd be well behaved, and the next I'd be picking fights and flying into a rage. Many psychologists, therapists, and doctors tested me because of school and social problems and severe mood changes. Their only diagnosis was "learning disabilities" in such areas as reading comprehension, abstract thinking, word retrieval, and auditory processing. In the seventh grade, a psychologist told me that I was stupid and lazy, I would probably live at home for the rest of my life, and I would never amount to anything. For the next five years, he was basically right, and I barely graduated from high school.

I believe, though, that I have succeeded because I was told that I would fail. When I enrolled at a community college, I decided I could figure things out on my own and did not need tutoring. I received an associate degree there, then transferred to a small liberal arts college. However, I never had a semester below a 3.0, and I graduated with two B.S. degrees. I was accepted into a graduate program but decided instead to accept a job as a software engineer even though I did not have an educational background in this field. As I later learned, many KS'ers excel in computer skills. I had been using a computer for many years and had learned everything I needed to know on my own, through trial and error.

Around the time I started the computer job, I went to my physician for a physical. He sent me for blood tests because he noticed that my testes were smaller than usual. The results were conclusive: Klinefelter syndrome with sex chromosomes XXY. I initially felt denial, depression, and anger, even though I now had an explanation for many of the problems I had experienced all my life. But then I decided to learn as much as I could about the condition and the treatments available. I now give myself a testosterone injection once every two weeks, and it has made me a different person, with improved learning abilities and stronger thought processes in addition to a more outgoing personality.

I found, though, that the best possible path I could take was to help others live with the condition. I attended my first support group meeting four months after I was diagnosed. I had decided to work diligently to help people with KS forever. I have been very involved in KS conferences and have helped start support groups in the U.S., Spain, and Australia.

Since my diagnosis, it has been my dream to have a son with KS, although when I was diagnosed, I found out it was unlikely that I could have biological children. Through my work with KS, I had the opportunity to meet my fiancee, Chris. She has two wonderful children: a daughter, and a son who has the same condition that I do. There are a lot of similarities between my stepson and me, and I am happy I will be able to help him get the head start in coping with KS that I never had. I also look forward to many more years of helping other people seek diagnosis and live a good life with Klinefelter syndrome.

Stefan Schwarz
stefan13@mail.ptd.net

19.2 Genetic Inheritance

Genes, which are sections of chromosomes, control body traits, such as height, eye color, or type of earlobe. Recall that as described in Chapter 17, page 342, each cell contains homologous pairs of chromosomes. Alternate forms of a gene having the same position (locus) on a pair of homologous chromosomes and affecting the same trait are called **alleles.** It is customary to designate an allele by a letter, which represents the specific characteristic it controls; a **dominant allele** is assigned an uppercase (capital) letter, while a **recessive allele** is given the same letter but in lowercase. In humans, for example, unattached (free) earlobes are dominant over attached earlobes, so a suitable key would be *E* for unattached earlobes and *e* for attached earlobes.

Inheritance of Genes on Autosomal Chromosomes

An individual normally has two alleles for an autosomal trait. Just as one member of each pair of chromosomes is inherited from each parent, so too is one of each pair of alleles inherited from each parent.

The term **genotype** refers to the genes of the individual. Figure 19.5 shows three possible fertilizations and the resulting genotype of the individual for earlobe attachment. In the first instance, the chromosomes of both the sperm and the egg carry an *E*. Consequently, the zygote and subsequent individual have the alleles *EE*, which may be called a **homozygous dominant** genotype. A person with genotype *EE* obviously has unattached earlobes. The physical appearance of the individual—in this case, unattached earlobes—is called the **phenotype.**

In the second fertilization, the zygote has received two recessive alleles (*ee*), and the genotype is called **homozygous recessive.** An individual with this genotype has the recessive phenotype, which is attached earlobes. In the third fertilization, the resulting individual has the alleles *Ee*, which is called a **heterozygous** genotype. A heterozygote shows the dominant characteristic; therefore, the phenotype of this individual is unattached earlobes.

How many dominant alleles does an individual need to inherit to have a dominant phenotype? These examples show that a dominant allele contributed from only one parent can bring about a particular dominant phenotype. How many recessive alleles does an individual need to inherit to have the recessive phenotype? A recessive allele must be received from both parents to bring about the recessive phenotype.

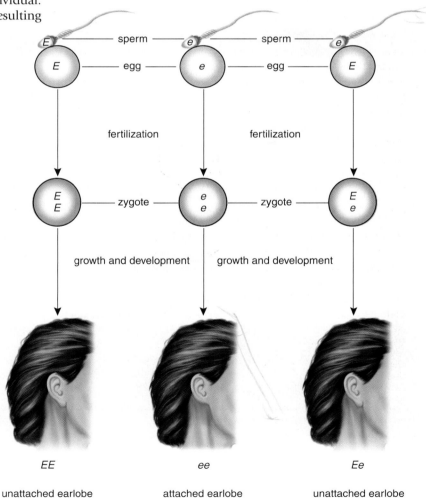

Figure 19.5 Genetic inheritance. Individuals inherit a minimum of two alleles for every characteristic of their anatomy and physiology. The inheritance of a single dominant allele (*E*) causes an individual to have unattached earlobes; two recessive alleles (*ee*) cause an individual to have attached earlobes. Notice that each individual receives one allele from the father (by way of a sperm) and one allele from the mother (by way of an egg).

EE
unattached earlobe

ee
attached earlobe

Ee
unattached earlobe

Sex-Linked Inheritance

The sex chromosomes contain genes just as the autosomal chromosomes do. Some of these genes determine whether the individual is a male or a female. Investigators have now discovered a series of genes on the Y chromosome that determine the development of male genitals, and at least one on the X chromosome that seems to be necessary for the development of female genitals.

Some traits controlled by alleles on the sex chromosomes have nothing to do with the sex of individual. These traits are said to be **sex-linked**. An allele that is only on the X chromosome is **X-linked** and an allele that is only on the Y chromosome is Y-linked. Most sex-linked traits are controlled by alleles on the larger X chromosome, and the smaller Y chromosome is blank for these.

It would be logical to suppose that a sex-linked trait is passed from father to son or from mother to daughter, but this is not the case. A male always receives a sex-linked condition from his mother, from whom he inherited an X chromosome. *The Y chromosome from his father does not carry an allele for the trait.* Therefore, males need receive only one recessive allele to have the X-linked disorder. If a mother is a carrier, males have a 50% chance of inheriting the disease. On the other hand, a female must receive two recessive X-linked alleles, one from each parent, before she has a recessive condition. The inheritance of a dominant allele from either her mother or her father can offset the inheritance of a recessive X-linked allele. If a mother is a carrier and the father is normal, females have a 50% chance of also being a carrier.

Genetic Counseling

A genetic counselor helps determine whether an unborn child will have a genetic disorder. In order to understand genetic counseling, we will consider the inheritance of cystic fibrosis. **Cystic fibrosis (CF)** is the most common lethal genetic disorder among Caucasians in the United States. A **carrier** is an individual who is heterozygous for a recessive genetic disorder and therefore has no symptoms. About one in 20 Caucasians is a carrier for CF, and about one in 3,000 newborns has the disorder. In children with CF, the mucus in the bronchial tubes and pancreatic ducts is particularly thick and viscous, interfering with the function of the lungs and pancreas. In the past few years, new treatments have raised the life expectancy for CF patients to as much as 35 years of age.

Normal individuals have at least one dominant allele for a plasma membrane channel protein. Figure 19.6 shows the

Table 19.2	Inheritance of Some Genetic Disorders		
Dominant	**Recessive**	**X-Linked**	**Multiple Genes**
Examples of dominantly inherited disorders include:	Examples of recessive inherited disorders include:	Examples of X-linked disorders include:	Examples of multifactorial inheritance include:
• Neurofibromatosis—benign tumors in skin or deeper	• Cystic fibrosis—disorder affecting function of mucous and sweat glands	• Agammaglobulinemia—lack of immunity to infections	• Cleft lip and/or palate
• Achondroplasia—a form of dwarfism	• Galactosemia—inability to metabolize milk sugar	• Color blindness—inability to distinguish certain colors	• Clubfoot
• Chronic simple glaucoma (some forms)—a major cause of blindness if untreated	• Phenylketonuria—essential liver enzyme deficiency	• Hemophilia (some forms)—defect in blood-clotting mechanisms	• Congenital dislocation of the hip
• Huntington disease—progressive nervous system degeneration	• Sickle-cell disease—blood disorder primarily affecting blacks	• Muscular dystrophy (some forms)—progressive wasting of muscles	• Spina bifida—open spine
• Familial hypercholesterolemia—high blood cholesterol levels, propensity to heart disease	• Thalassemia—blood disorder primarily affecting persons of Mediterranean ancestry	• Spinal ataxia (some forms)—spinal cord degeneration	• Hydrocephalus (with spina bifida)—water on the brain
• Polydactyly—extra fingers or toes	• Tay-Sachs disease—lysosomal storage disease leading to nervous system destruction		• Pyloric stenosis—narrowed or obstructed opening from stomach into small intestine

Source: Data from the National Foundation/March of Dimes.

relationship between inheritance of a normal CF allele on a chromosome (chromosome 7) and development of the channel protein. The illustration emphasizes that alleles are actually a segment of DNA and that alleles cause the production of certain proteins in a cell.

As shown in Figure 19.7a, if a genetic counselor knows the genotype of the potential parents, the counselor can predict the chances that a couple will have a child having a recessive autosomal disorder such as CF. If the parents are both carriers, each offspring has a 25% chance of receiving two recessive alleles and having CF.

If the counselor does not know the inheritance pattern of a disorder, it is sometimes possible to deduce it by studying a pedigree. A **pedigree** is a diagram that depicts the inheritance of a particular trait: Circles are females, and squares are males; shaded-in symbols represent those who have a trait; half-shaded symbols represent carriers; and roman numerals indicate generations. Notice that the pedigree in Figure 19.7b has to be for a recessive disorder because unaffected parents have a child with the disorder. This can only happen when a condition is recessive. If the condition were dominant, one of the parents would be affected!

Figure 19.6 A person with cystic fibrosis has an abnormal allele, and the result is an abnormal channel protein in the plasma membrane. Chloride ions cannot exit the cell, resulting in a very thick mucus, particularly in the bronchial tubes and pancreatic duct.

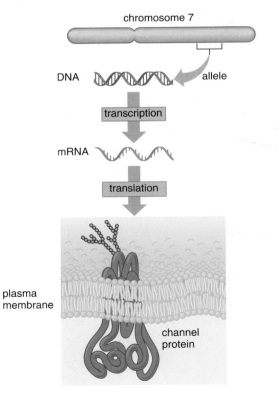

Prenatal Testing for Genetic Disorders

Commonly inherited genetic disorders are listed in Table 19.2. Several of these disorders do not appear unless multiple abnormal genes are inherited. The inheritance of these conditions, listed in the "Multiple Genes" column in Table 19.2, is complex.

Sometimes parents want to improve their chances of having a child free of a particular genetic disorder that runs in their families. Until recently, the best that could be done was to test for a genetic disorder following amniocentesis or chorionic villi sampling. If the embryo had the disorder, the parents could consider an abortion. Now it is possible to retrieve eggs from the ovary to make sure the egg does not carry an abnormal allele prior to in vitro fertilization or to screen morulas following in vitro fertilization. The What's New reading on page 398 discusses the latter technique. In the future, it might be possible to use gene therapy to cure any genetic defects found in an egg or embryo.

Figure 19.7 Inheritance pattern for CF, an autosomal recessive disorder. **a.** The figures below the parents show four possible combinations of inherited alleles; therefore, each offspring has a 25% chance of inheriting two recessive alleles and having CF.

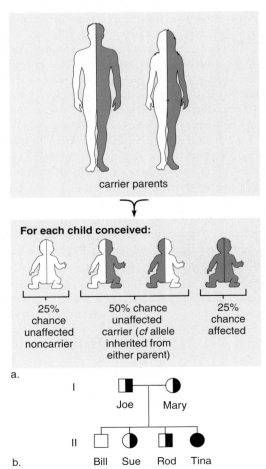

Preimplantation Genetic Studies

We have already seen that in vitro fertilization can lead to therapeutic cloning (see page 374) for the production of various tissues. Now, we will consider the medical implications of the fact that each cell of the pre-embryo is totipotent, meaning that each cell can become a complete embryo because the cells have not become specialized yet. Not surprisingly, then, if a single cell is removed from an eight-celled cleavage pre-embryo, the seven-celled pre-embryo will still go on and develop into a normal newborn (Figure 19A). Researchers are using this knowledge to allow them to carry out preimplantation genetic analysis.

Consider that a woman might have one of the autosomal dominant genetic disorders listed in Table 19.2 or be a carrier for one of the recessive disorders. Her partner might have one of the autosomal dominant genetic disorders, be a carrier for one of the recessive autosomal disorders, or have an X-linked recessive disorder. As potential parents, wouldn't they want the assurance that the pre-embryo is free of genetic disorders and will develop into a normal adult? In some instances, it is possible to perform in vitro fertilization and then **preimplantation genetic diagnosis (PGD)** in order to determine the genotype of the pre-embryo with regard to particular genetic disorders. Then, only a normal pre-embryo is implanted in the female. So far, about 500 children free of genetic disorders that run in their families have been born worldwide following PGD. In the future, it is possible that PGD might be coupled with gene therapy so that any pre-embryo would be suitable for implantion.

PGD has another benefit. Sometimes a woman has a **miscarriage** (loss of an embryo and termination of pregnancy) because the embryo has inherited an abnormal chromosome. Such miscarriages might happen repeatedly, but this unhappy situation can be halted by PGD because PGD makes it possible to implant only normal pre-embryos. However, it must be recognized that any technology that alters the normal way offspring are conceived is considered immoral by some. And the use of PGD to prevent defects could eventually be followed by selection of pre-embryos simply for preferred traits regarding intelligence and physical appearance or gene therapy for the same purpose.

Figure 19A One cell from an eight-celled pre-embryo can be tested for abnormal alleles; if all tested alleles are normal, the seven-celled pre-embryo can complete normal development.

1 cell removed for genetic analysis

7 cells can complete normal development.

19.3 DNA Technology

Previously, you studied the structure of DNA and how it replicates and carries out protein synthesis. **DNA technology** includes our ability to work directly with DNA to determine the relatedness of individuals, to assist forensics in determining whether a person has committed a crime, and to develop new treatments for human illnesses, called gene therapy.

Gene Therapy

Gene therapy is the insertion of genetic material into human cells for the treatment of a disorder. It includes procedures that give a patient healthy genes to make up for faulty genes and also includes the use of genes to treat various other human illnesses, such as cancer and cardiovascular disease. Currently, approximately 1,000 patients are enrolled in nearly 200 approved gene therapy trials in the United States.

Children with SCID (severe combined immunodeficiency syndrome) lack an enzyme called adenosine deaminase (ADA) that is involved in the maturation of T and B cells. Therefore, they are subject to life-threatening infections. In the latest gene therapy treatment for this disorder, bone marrow stem cells are removed from the blood and infected with a virus that carries a normal gene for the enzyme. Then the cells are returned to the patient. Bone marrow stem cells are preferred for this procedure because they divide to produce more cells with the same genes. Patients who have undergone this procedure do show a significant improvement in immune function associated with a sustained rise in the level of ADA enzyme activity in their blood.

Among the many gene therapy trials, one is for the treatment of familial hypercholesterolemia, a condition that develops when liver cells lack a receptor for removing cholesterol from the blood. The high levels of blood cholesterol make the patient subject to fatal heart attacks at a young age. In a newly developed procedure, a small portion of the liver is surgically excised and infected with a virus containing a normal gene for the receptor. Several patients have experienced lowered serum cholesterol levels following this procedure.

Cystic fibrosis patients have an abnormal gene for a transmembrane carrier of the chloride ion. Patients often die due to numerous infections of the respiratory tract. In a newly developed procedure, liposomes—microscopic vesicles that spontaneously form when lipoproteins are put into a solution—have been coated with the gene needed to cure cystic fibrosis, and then the liposomes have been delivered to the lower respiratory tract.

Genes are also being used to treat medical conditions other than the known genetic disorders. VEGF (vascular endothelial growth factor) can cause the growth of blood vessels. The gene that codes for this growth factor can be injected alone or within a virus into the heart to stimulate branching of coronary blood vessels. Coronary patients report that they have less chest pain and can run longer on a treadmill.

Gene therapy is increasingly used as part of cancer therapy. Genes are being used to make healthy cells more tolerant of, and tumors more vulnerable to, chemotherapy. The gene *p53* brings about the death of cells, and there is much interest in introducing it into cancer cells, and in that way killing them off.

Genomics

Genomics is the molecular analysis of a **genome,** which is all the genetic information in all the chromosomes of an individual. Recall from Chapter 2, Figure 2.17, that the two DNA strands of a double helix are held together by bonding between their bases, designated as A, T, G, and C. Base A is always paired with base T, and base G is always paired with base C. In a worldwide effort known as the Human Genome Project, researchers set out to map the human chromosomes in two ways: (1) by constructing a map that shows the sequence of base pairs along all the human chromosomes, and (2) by constructing a map that shows the sequence of genes along the human chromosomes.

The Base Sequence Map

Researchers have now completed the first goal. They know the sequence of the three billion base pairs, one after the other, along the lengths of the human chromosomes. It took some 15 years for researchers to complete this monumental task. As discussed in the Medical Focus on page 400, researchers expect this knowledge to result in many new medicines, development of medicines suited to the genotype of the individual, a longer life span, and the ability to shape the genotypes of offspring.

The Genetic Map

The genetic map tells the location of genes along each chromosome. Although the location of many genes has been determined, we still do not know the sequence of all the genes on any particular chromosome. Completing the genetic map should accelerate now that the base sequence map is done. Researchers need only know a short sequence of bases in a gene of interest in order for the computer to search the genome for a match. Then, the computer indicates where this gene is located.

Many ethical questions arise regarding how we should use our knowledge of the human genome. Therefore, it is imperative that you be knowledgeable about the human genome so that you can help decide these issues.

New Cures on the Horizon

Now that we know the sequence of the bases in the DNA of all the human chromosomes, biologists all over the world believe this knowledge will result in rapid medical advances for ourselves and our children.

First prediction: Many new medicines will be available.

Most drugs are proteins or small chemicals that are able to interact with proteins. Today's drugs were usually discovered in a hit-or-miss fashion, but now researchers will be able to take a more systematic approach to finding effective medicines. In a recent search for a medicine that makes wounds heal, researchers cultured skin cells with 14 proteins (found by chance) that can cause skin cells to grow. Only one of these proteins made skin cells grow and did nothing else. They expect this protein to become an effective drug for conditions such as venous ulcers, which are skin lesions that affect many thousands of people in the United States. Tests leading to effective medicines can be carried out with many more proteins that scientists will discover by scanning the human genome.

Second prediction: Medicines will be safer due to genome scans.

Genome scans are expected to make drugs safer to take. As you know, many drugs potentially have unwanted side effects. Why do some people and not others have one or more of the side effects? Most likely, this is because people have different genotypes. It is expected that a physicians will be able to match patients to drugs that are safe for them on the basis of their genotypes.

A more carefree life is predicted for us because of the Human Genome Project.

The use of a gene chip will quickly and efficiently provide knowledge of your genotype. A gene chip is an array of thousands of genes on one or several glass slides packaged together. After a gene chip contains an individual's DNA, a technician can note any mutant sequences present in the individual's genes.

One study found that various combinations of mutations can lead to the development of asthma. A particular drug, called albuterol, is effective and safe for patients with certain combinations of mutations and not others. This example and others show that many diseases are polygenic, and that only a genome scan is able to detect which mutations are causing an individual to have a disease, and how it should be properly treated.

Third prediction: A longer and healthier life will be yours.

Pre-embryonic gene therapy may become routine once we discover the genes that contribute to a longer and healthier life. We know that the presence of free radicals causes cellular molecules to become unstable and cells to die. Certain genes are believed to code for antioxidant enzymes that detoxify free radicals. It could be that human beings with particular forms of these genes have more efficient antioxidant enzymes, and therefore live longer. If so, researchers will no doubt be able to locate these genes and also others that promote a longer, healthier life.

Perhaps certain genotypes allow some people to live far beyond the normal life span. Researchers may be able to find which genes allow individuals to live a long time and make them available to the general public. Then, many more people would live longer and healthier lives.

Fourth prediction: You will be able to design your children.

Genome sequence data will be used to identify many more mutant genes that cause genetic disorders than are presently known. In the future, it may be possible to cure genetic disorders before the child is born by adding a normal gene to any egg that carries a mutant gene. Or an artificial chromosome, constructed to carry a large number of corrective genes, could automatically be placed in eggs. In vitro fertilization would have to be utilized in order to take advantage of such measures for curing genetic disorders before conception.

Genome sequence data can also be used to identify polygenic genes for traits such as height, intelligence, or behavioral characteristics. A couple could decide on their own which genes they wish to use to enhance a child's phenotype. In other words, the sequencing of the human genome may bring about a genetically just society, in which all types of genes would be accessible to all parents.

Selected New Terms

Basic Key Terms

allele (uh-lēl'), p. 395

amniocentesis (am"ne-o-sen-te'sis), p. 390

autosome (aw'to-sōm), p. 390

carrier (kār'e-er), p. 396

chorionic villi sampling (ko-re-on'ik vil'ī sam'pling), p. 390

dominant allele (dom'ĭ-nant uh-lēl'), p. 395

gene (jēn), p. 395

genome (je'nōm), p. 399

genotype (je'-no-tīp), p. 395

heterozygous (het-er-o-zi'gus), p. 395

homozygous dominant (ho-mo-zi'gus dom'ĭ-nant), p. 395

homozygous recessive (ho-mo-zi'gus re-ses'iv), p. 395

karyotype (kār'e-o-tīp), p. 390

nondisjunction (non"dis-junk'shun), p. 392

pedigree (ped-ĭ-gre), p. 397

phenotype (fe'no-tīp), p. 395

recessive allele (re-ses'iv uh-lēl'), p. 395

sex chromosome (seks kro'mo-sōm), p. 390

sex-linked (seks-linkt), p. 396

syndrome (sin'drōm), p. 390

X chromosome (x kro'mo-sōm), p. 390

X-linked (x-linkt), p. 396

Y chromosome (y kro'mo-sōm), p. 390

Clinical Key Terms

cystic fibrosis (sis'tik fi-bro'sis), p. 396

Down syndrome (down sin'drōm), p. 392

gene therapy (jēn thĕr'uh-pe), p. 399

Jacobs syndrome (ja'kubs sin'drōm), p. 393

Klinefelter syndrome (klīn'fel-ter sin'drōm), p. 393

poly-X female (pah'le-x fe'māl), p. 394

Turner syndrome (tur'ner sin'drōm), p. 393

XYY male (xyy māl), p. 394

Summary

19.1 Chromosomal Inheritance

A. Normally, an individual inherits 22 pairs of autosomal chromosomes and one pair of sex chromosomes. Females are XX and males are XY.

B. Amniocentesis and chorionic villi sampling are used to provide cell samples for karyotyping fetal chromosomes.

C. Nondisjunction during oogenesis or spermatogenesis explains the inheritance of an abnormal number of chromosomes.

D. The most common autosomal abnormality is Down syndrome, which is due to the inheritance of an extra chromosome 21.

E. Abnormal combinations of sex chromosomes include XO (Turner syndrome), XXX (poly-X), XXY (Klinefelter syndrome), and XYY (Jacobs syndrome).

19.2 Genetic Inheritance

A. Genes control human traits. Uppercase letters designate dominant alleles; lowercase letters designate recessive alleles.

B. The genotype represents the genes of an individual, and the phenotype refers to the appearance. A homozygous dominant individual inherited two dominant alleles and has the dominant phenotype; a heterozygous individual inherited one dominant and one recessive allele and has the dominant phenotype; a homozygous recessive individual inherited two recessive alleles and has the recessive phenotype.

C. The inheritance of X-linked alleles differs in males and females. Males require only one recessive allele to have an X-linked trait; females require two recessive alleles. This means that males are more likely to inherit an X-linked disorder.

D. Genetic counselors help couples determine the chances of having children with a genetic disorder, such as cystic fibrosis. They can also determine the pattern of inheritance from studying a family's pedigree.

19.3 DNA Technology

A. Gene therapy, which involves replacing defective genes with healthy genes, is now a reality. Researchers are envisioning various applications aimed at curing human genetic disorders, as well as many other types of illnesses.

B. Genomics is an actively growing field. Because the sequence of base pairs along the human chromosomes has now been determined, new treatments for genetic disorders are expected.

Study Questions

1. What is the normal chromosome inheritance of humans? (p. 390)
2. How is a karyotype prepared? What are the possible sources for cell samples in an adult? In the fetus? (pp. 390–91)
3. What is nondisjunction, and when does nondisjunction occur during meiosis? (p. 392)
4. What are the characteristics of a person with Down syndrome? (p. 392)
5. What are the characteristics of the most common human conditions resulting from inheritance of abnormal numbers of sex chromosomes? (pp. 393–94)
6. Explain autosomal dominant and recessive genetic inheritance. (p. 395)
7. Explain X-linked allele inheritance in humans. (p. 396)
8. What type of information does a genetic counselor give parents who might pass on a genetic disorder? (pp. 396–98)
9. Give examples of dominant, recessive, and X-linked genetic disorders in humans. (p. 396)
10. Describe the function of an allele using the CF allele as an example. (p. 397)
11. What is gene therapy, and what types of genetic disorders have been treated thus far? (p. 399)
12. What is a genome? What is genomics, and what might be the benefits of genomics in the future? (pp. 399–400)

Objective Questions

Fill in the blanks.

1. The genes are on the _____ .
2. A karyotype shows the individual's _____ .
3. The sex chromosomes of a male are labeled _____ .
4. A person with Down syndrome has inherited _____ copies of chromosome 21.
5. A person with Klinefelter syndrome has the chromosomes _____ .
6. A dominant autosomal genetic disorder only requires the inheritance of _____ (one or two) abnormal gene(s).
7. A male with an X-linked recessive disorder inherited a _____ allele for the disorder.
8. If a person inherits an autosomal genetic disorder and both parents are unaffected by the disorder, the disorder is _____ .
9. Replacing defective genes with healthy genes is the goal of _____ .
10. The molecular analysis of a genome is called _____ .

Medical Terminology Reinforcement Exercise

Consult Appendix B for help in pronouncing and analyzing the meaning of the terms that follow.

1. neogenesis (ne″o-jen′ĕ-sis)
2. regeneration (re-jen″er-a′shun)
3. fetoscope (fe′to-skōp)
4. chromosome (kro′mo-sōm)
5. polydysplasia (pol″e-dis-pla′ze-uh)
6. congenital (kon-jen′ĭ-tal)
7. autosome (aw′to-sōm)

Website Link

Visit the Student Edition of the Online Learning Center at http://www.mhhe.com/maderap5 for additional quizzes, interactive learning exercises, and other study tools.

Appendix A
Reference Figures
THE HUMAN ORGANISM

The following series of reference figures show the major organs of the human torso. The first plate illustrates the anterior surface and reveals the superficial muscles on one side. Each subsequent plate exposes deeper organs, including those in the thoracic, abdominal, and pelvic cavities.

Chapters 5–17 of this textbook describe the organ systems of the human organism in detail. As you read them, you may want to refer to these plates to help visualize the locations of organs and the three-dimensional relationships among them.

Plate 1 Anterior view of the human torso with the superficial muscles exposed. (m. = muscles; v. = vein.)

sternocleidomastoid m.

trapezius m.

clavicle

deltoid m.

pectoralis major m.

mammary gland

areola

serratus anterior m.

rectus abdominis m.

external oblique m.

sartorius m.

femoral v.

great saphenous v.

nipple

breast

umbilicus

anterior superior iliac spine

mons pubis

Plate 2 The torso, with the deep muscles exposed. (m. = muscle; n. = nerve; a. = artery; v. = vein.)

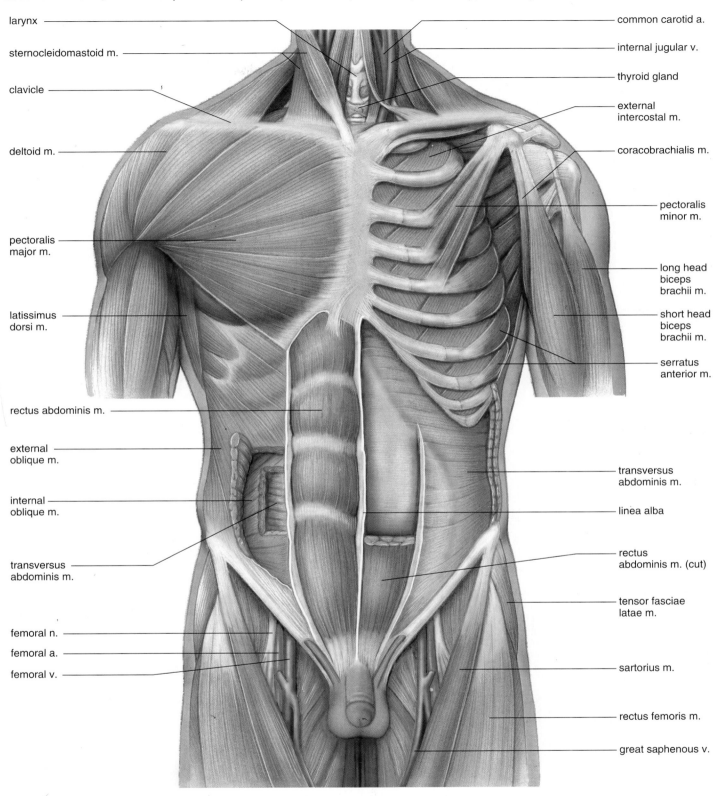

larynx

sternocleidomastoid m.

clavicle

deltoid m.

pectoralis major m.

latissimus dorsi m.

rectus abdominis m.

external oblique m.

internal oblique m.

transversus abdominis m.

femoral n.

femoral a.

femoral v.

common carotid a.

internal jugular v.

thyroid gland

external intercostal m.

coracobrachialis m.

pectoralis minor m.

long head biceps brachii m.

short head biceps brachii m.

serratus anterior m.

transversus abdominis m.

linea alba

rectus abdominis m. (cut)

tensor fasciae latae m.

sartorius m.

rectus femoris m.

great saphenous v.

Plate 3 The torso, with the anterior abdominal wall removed to expose the abdominal viscera. (a. = artery; v. = vein; m. = muscle; n. = nerve.)

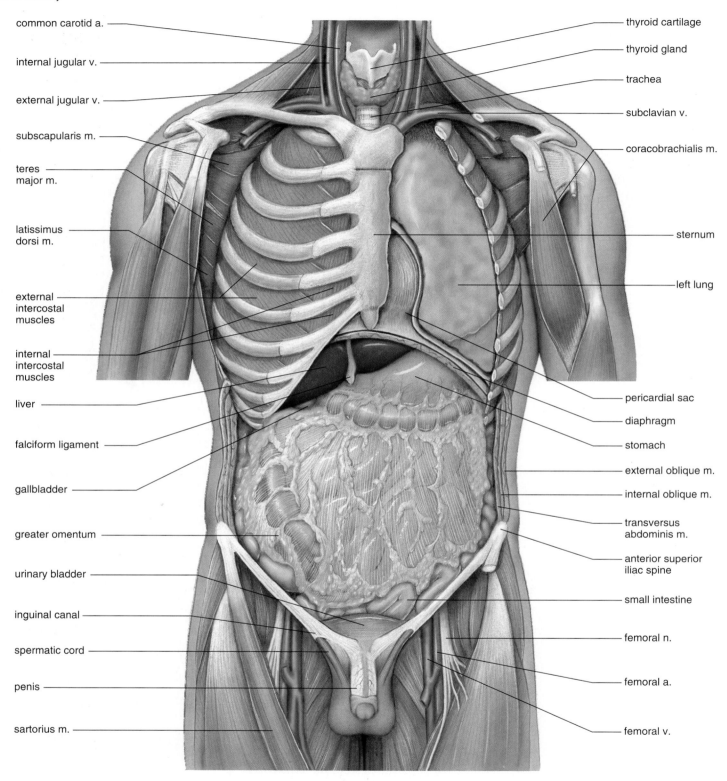

common carotid a.

internal jugular v.

external jugular v.

subscapularis m.

teres major m.

latissimus dorsi m.

external intercostal muscles

internal intercostal muscles

liver

falciform ligament

gallbladder

greater omentum

urinary bladder

inguinal canal

spermatic cord

penis

sartorius m.

thyroid cartilage

thyroid gland

trachea

subclavian v.

coracobrachialis m.

sternum

left lung

pericardial sac

diaphragm

stomach

external oblique m.

internal oblique m.

transversus abdominis m.

anterior superior iliac spine

small intestine

femoral n.

femoral a.

femoral v.

Plate 4 The torso, with the anterior thoracic wall removed to expose the thoracic viscera. (a. = artery; m. = muscle; n. = nerve; v. = vein.)

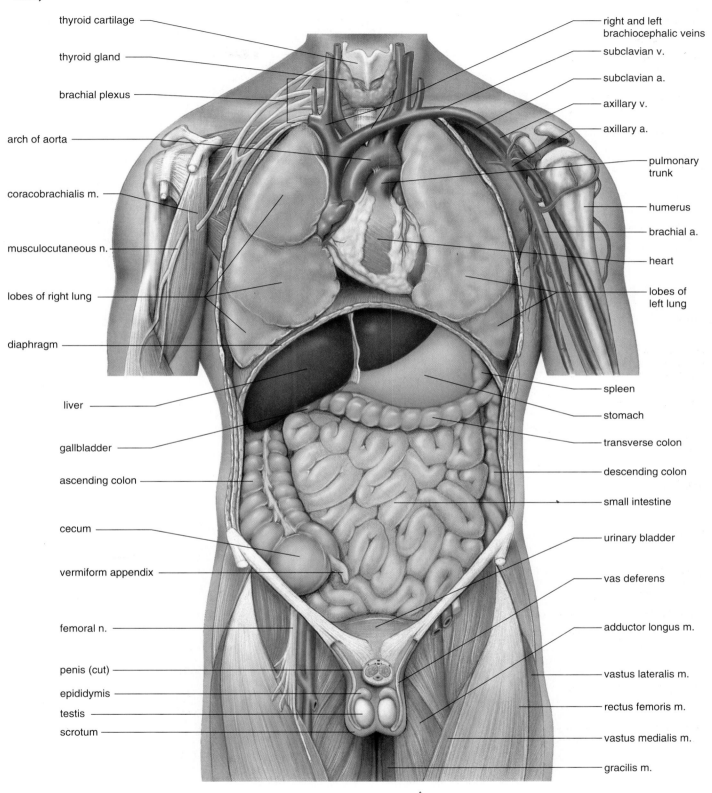

thyroid cartilage

thyroid gland

brachial plexus

arch of aorta

coracobrachialis m.

musculocutaneous n.

lobes of right lung

diaphragm

liver

gallbladder

ascending colon

cecum

vermiform appendix

femoral n.

penis (cut)

epididymis

testis

scrotum

right and left brachiocephalic veins

subclavian v.

subclavian a.

axillary v.

axillary a.

pulmonary trunk

humerus

brachial a.

heart

lobes of left lung

spleen

stomach

transverse colon

descending colon

small intestine

urinary bladder

vas deferens

adductor longus m.

vastus lateralis m.

rectus femoris m.

vastus medialis m.

gracilis m.

Plate 5 The torso as viewed with the thoracic viscera sectioned in a coronal plane; the abdominal viscera as viewed with most of the small intestine removed. (a. = artery; m. = muscle; v. = vein.)

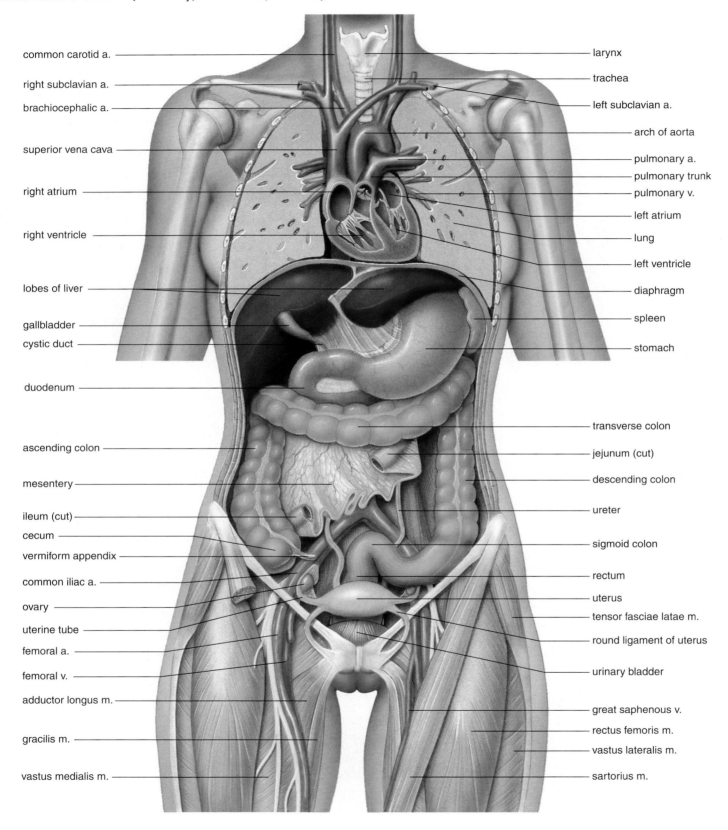

common carotid a.

right subclavian a.

brachiocephalic a.

superior vena cava

right atrium

right ventricle

lobes of liver

gallbladder

cystic duct

duodenum

ascending colon

mesentery

ileum (cut)

cecum

vermiform appendix

common iliac a.

ovary

uterine tube

femoral a.

femoral v.

adductor longus m.

gracilis m.

vastus medialis m.

larynx

trachea

left subclavian a.

arch of aorta

pulmonary a.

pulmonary trunk

pulmonary v.

left atrium

lung

left ventricle

diaphragm

spleen

stomach

transverse colon

jejunum (cut)

descending colon

ureter

sigmoid colon

rectum

uterus

tensor fasciae latae m.

round ligament of uterus

urinary bladder

great saphenous v.

rectus femoris m.

vastus lateralis m.

sartorius m.

Plate 6 The torso as viewed with the heart, liver, stomach, and portions of the small and large intestines removed. (a. = artery; m. = muscle; v. = vein.)

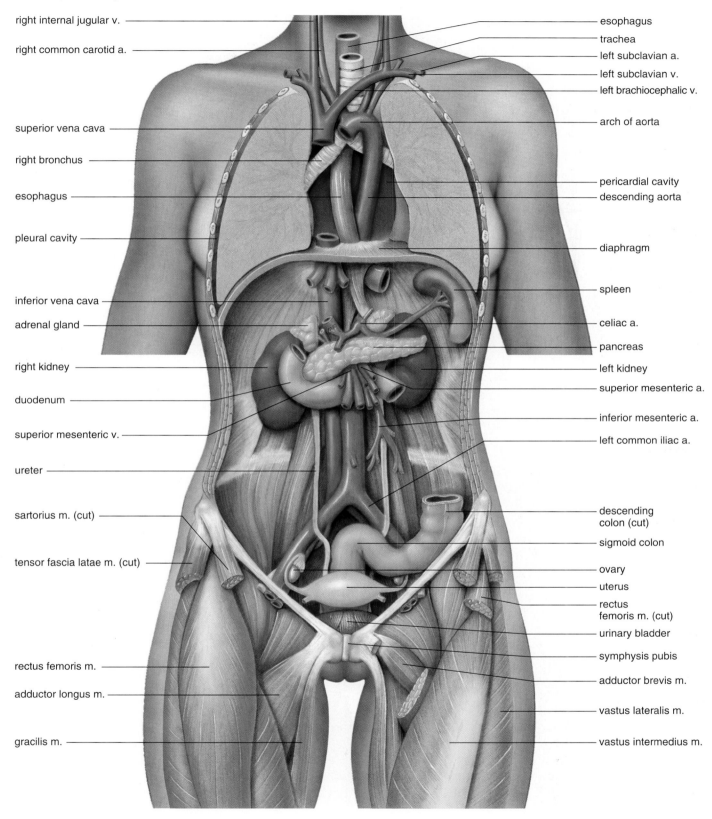

right internal jugular v.

right common carotid a.

superior vena cava

right bronchus

esophagus

pleural cavity

inferior vena cava

adrenal gland

right kidney

duodenum

superior mesenteric v.

ureter

sartorius m. (cut)

tensor fascia latae m. (cut)

rectus femoris m.

adductor longus m.

gracilis m.

esophagus

trachea

left subclavian a.

left subclavian v.

left brachiocephalic v.

arch of aorta

pericardial cavity

descending aorta

diaphragm

spleen

celiac a.

pancreas

left kidney

superior mesenteric a.

inferior mesenteric a.

left common iliac a.

descending colon (cut)

sigmoid colon

ovary

uterus

rectus femoris m. (cut)

urinary bladder

symphysis pubis

adductor brevis m.

vastus lateralis m.

vastus intermedius m.

Plate 7 The torso, with the anterior thoracic and abdominal walls removed, along with the viscera, to expose the posterior walls and body cavities. (a. = artery; m. = muscle.)

esophagus

right subclavian a.

brachiocephalic a.

thoracic cavity

rib

external intercostal m.

diaphragm

abdominal cavity

inferior vena cava

quadratus lumborum m.

intervertebral disc

iliac crest

iliacus m.

psoas major m.

gluteus medius m.

symphysis pubis

femur

adductor longus m.

gracilis m.

left common carotid a.

arch of aorta

internal intercostal m.

descending aorta

esophagus

diaphragm

abdominal aorta

transversus abdominis m.

fifth lumbar vertebra

anterior superior iliac spine

pelvic sacral foramen

sacrum

rectum

vagina

urethra

obturator foramen

adductor magnus m.

Appendix B

Understanding Medical Terminology

Learning Objectives

Upon completion of this section, you should be able to:

1. Discuss the importance of medical terminology and how it can be incorporated into the study of the human body.
2. Differentiate between a root word, a prefix, a suffix, and a compound word.
3. Link word parts to form medical terms.
4. Differentiate between singular and plural endings of medical terms.
5. Pronounce medical words.
6. Separate compound medical words into parts, and analyze their meaning.
7. Recognize root words, prefixes, and suffixes commonly used in medical terminology.

Introduction to Medical Terminology

As students of medical science, we have inherited a wealth of knowledge from scholars of the past. This knowledge was nurtured largely in the atmospheres of European universities, in which Latin and Greek were the languages of lecture and writing. Past scientists sought to define a universal language in which to communicate their findings. Latin and Greek, studied throughout Europe, became the languages of choice for university scholars whose native tongues were English, German, French, Spanish, and so on. Many important early works in medicine were first written in Latin, and their vocabularies remain to this day.

Anatomy and physiology, like many other scientific disciplines, have their own particular language. As the language was developed, names for each new structure to be described were created from existing words. Words were then combined, until they approximated an acceptable description. Medical terminology is simply a catalog of parts that allows us to take apart and reassemble the special language of medicine. The study of medical terminology is easier than it first seems. Relax; you won't need to walk around with a medical dictionary to make sense of medical terminology!

Medical words have three basic parts: a root word, a prefix, and a suffix. The **root word** is the main part of each medical term. Most describe parts of the body, using a Latin or Greek term. Mastering the list of root words in this appendix is an important first step in successfully translating medical terminology. Many of these words will be familiar to you from everyday language: For example, the root word *pyr-* for fire, shows up in the word *pyrotechnics* (fireworks), and the root word for produce, *gen-* , is familiar from the word *generate*.

A **prefix** comes before a root word and alters its meaning. For example, the prefix *hyper-* means over or above. Hyper/kinetic means overactive, hyper/esthesia is overly sensitive, hyper/tension is high blood pressure, and hyper/trophy is overdevelopment.

A **suffix** is attached to the end of a root word and also changes the meaning of the word. For example, the suffix *-itis* means inflammation. Inflammation can occur at almost any part of the body, so *-itis* can be added to root words to make hundreds of words. Dermat/itis is inflammation of the skin, rhin/itis is inflammation of the nose, gastr/itis is inflammation of the stomach, and so on.

Once the root word is known for each part of the anatomy, the prefixes and suffixes can be used to analyze and/or build many medical words. For example, the root word for heart is *cardi*. A few terms in which *cardi* appears are: cardi/algia (pain in the heart), cardio/megaly (enlarged heart), brady/cardia (slow heart), and peri/cardio/centesis (puncture to aspirate fluid from around the heart).

Many medical words have, in addition to a prefix and/or a suffix, more than one root word. These are called **compound words,** and can be analyzed by breaking them into parts. For example, hysterosalpingo-oophorectomy is made up of three root words and a suffix. *Hyster* is the root word for uterus, *salping* is the root word for tube, *oophor* is the root word for ovary, and *-ectomy* is the suffix for cut out. Now we know that hysterosalpingo-oophorectomy means the surgical removal of the uterus, uterine (fallopian) tube, and ovary. (A woman with uterine or ovarian cancer might undergo such a surgery.)

To facilitate pronunciation, word parts need to be linked together. The linkage for word parts is o, which may be referred to as a **combining form.** For example, linking the root *cardi* with the suffix *-pathy* would produce a word that would be difficult to pronounce; therefore, an *o* is used to link the root word with the suffix. The complete word is written *cardiopathy* and pronounced kar"de-op'uh-the; the combining form is cardi/o.

When a word is only a root or ends with a root, the word ending depends on whether the word is a noun or an adjective. For example, duodenum (noun) is a part of the small intestine, while duodenal (adjective) is related to the duodenum (for example, duodenal ulcer).

Accurate spelling of each word part is essential:

1. Changing one letter may change the word part. For example, *ileum* is a part of the small intestine, whereas *ilium* is a pelvic bone.

2. Finding a word in the dictionary requires a knowledge of spelling—at least of the beginning of the word. For example, *pneumonia* and *psychology* have a silent *p*, *rhinitis* (inflammation of the nose) has a silent *h*, and *eupnea* (easy breathing) has an initial silent *e*.

Plural Endings

In many English words, the plurals are formed by adding *s* or *es*, but in Greek and Latin, the plural may be designated by changing the ending:

Singular Ending	Plural Ending	Examples
-a	-ae	aorta—aortae
-ax	-aces	thorax—thoraces
-en	-ina	lumen—lumina
-ex	-ices	cortex—cortices
-ix	-ices	appendix—appendices
-is	-es	testis—testes
-on	-a	phenomenon—phenomena
-um	-a	medium—media
-ur	-ora	femur—femora
-us	-i	bronchus—bronchi
-x	-ces	calyx—calyces
-y	-ies	anomaly—anomalies
-ma	-mata	adenoma—adenomata

If a word ends in *s* and the vowel in the last syllable is short, the word is singular. If the word ends in *s* and the vowel in the last syllable is long, the word is plural. Any word ending in a consonant is singular (for example, *-urn*, *-us*, *-at*).

Pronunciation Key

1. Words are made up of syllables.
2. Syllables are made up of letters—consonants and the vowels *a,e,i,o,u*.
3. Diacritical marks are placed over a vowel to help you understand how to pronounce that syllable. The two diacritical marks you should know are the macron (-) and the breve (˘). The macron designates a long vowel sound, and the breve indicates a short vowel sound. Examples are given below.
4. In this book, vowels standing alone at the end of a syllable with no diacritical mark above are understood to have the "long" sound:

a as in "day"	(matrix = ma′triks)
e as in "be"	(amino = uh-me′no)
i as in "hi"	(ion = i′on)
o as in "no"	(acidosis = as-i-do′sis)
u as in "blue"	(nucleus = nu′kle-us)

5. Vowels embedded within a syllable with no diacritical mark above are understood to have the "short" sound:

a as in "cat"	(lateral = lat′er-al)
e as in "yes"	(pelvic = pel′vik)
i as in "sit"	(distal = dis′tal)
o as in "not"	(abdominal = ab-dom′i-nal)
u as in "cut"	(buffer = buf′er)

6. Vowels in other positions are marked as long (-) or short (˘) with diacritical marks:
   membrane = mem′brān
   feedback = fēd′bak
   peptide = pep′tīd
   disease = di-zēz′
   cytokinesis = si′to-kĭ-ne′sis
   vesicle = ves′ĭ-kl
   centriole = sen′tre-ōl
   ribosome = ri′bo-sōm

7. Other vowel sounds are expressed as follows:
   ah the sound of **a** as in "father"
   aw the sound of **a** as in "fall"
   ar as in "large" (sarcoma = sar-ko′muh)
   ār as in bare (larynx = lār′inks; paranasal = pār-uh-na′zal)
   uh the sound of **a** as in "about" (anatomy = uh-nat′o-me; negative = neg′uh-tiv)
   er as in "her"
   ĕr as in "very" (therapy = thĕr′uh-pe; glomerulus = glo-mĕr′yū-lus)
   ēr as in peer (delirium = de-lēr′e-um; sarcomere = sar′ko-mĕr)
   ow as in "cow"
   oy as in "boy"
   yū the sound of **u** as in "cute" (mucus = myū′kus; tuberculosis = tu-ber-kyū-lo′sis)

8. The primary accent in a word is indicated by a single accent mark; for example, ostomy (os′to-me).
9. The secondary accent is indicated by a double accent; for example, duodenostomy (du″o-dĕ-nos′to-me).
10. The accent on medical terms is generally on the third from the last syllable.

Practice pronouncing the following words:

1. hematemesis (hem″uh-tem′ĕ-sis), vomiting blood
2. hysterosalpingo-oophorectomy (his″ter-o-sal-ping″go-o′ of-or-ek′to-me), surgical excision of the uterus, uterine tube, and ovary
3. phrenohepatic (fren″o-he-pat′ik), pertaining to the diaphragm and liver
4. gastropathy (gas″trop′uh-the), disease of the stomach
5. metatarsus (met″uh-tar′sus), part of the foot between the tarsus (ankle) and toes

Commonly Used Prefixes

Prefix	Meaning	Example
a-, an-, in-	without, negative	a/men/orrhea, without a monthly flow
ab-	from, away from	ab/normal, away from normal
ad-, ac-, as-, at-	to, toward	ad/duct, carry toward
allo-	other	allo/graft, grafted tissue donated from one person to another
amphi-	both sides, surrounding	amphi/arthrosis, union between two bones at a joint
aniso-	unequal	an/iso/cyt/osis, abnormal condition of unequal cells
ante-, pre-	before	anterior, front; pre/natal, before birth
anti-, ant-, ob-	against	anti/pyre/tic, agent used against fever
bi-	two	bi/lateral, two sides
bio-	life	bio/logy, study of life
brachy-	short	brachy/dactyl/ism, short fingers and toes
brady-	slow	brady/cardia, slow heart rate
cata-	down	cata/bolism, breakdown of nutrients
cent-	hundred	centi/meter, 1/100 of a meter
chem-	chemical	chemo/therapy, chemical treatment for cancer
chlor-	green	chlor/opsia, green vision, as in certain cases of poisoning
circum-	around	circum/cis/ion, to cut around
co-, com-, con-	with, together	con/genital, born with
contra-	against	contra/indicated, against indication
cyano-	blue	cyano/sis, blue color to skin
de-	away from	de/hydrate, loss of water
dextr-	right	dextr/o/cardia, heart displaced to the right
dia-	through	dia/rrhea, flow through
diplo-	double, twofold	diplo/pia, double vision
dis-	apart	dis/sect, to cut apart
dys-	bad, difficult	dys/pnea, difficult breathing
e-, ex-	out, out from	ex/cise, to cut out
ect-, exo-, extra-	outside	extra/corporeal, outside the body
en-	in, on	en/capsulated, in a capsule
end-	within	endo/scopy, visualization within
epi-	upon	epi/dermis, upon the skin
eu-	good	eu/phonic, good sound
eury-	broad, wide	eury/gnathous, having a wide jaw
gero-, geronto-	old, elderly	geronto/logy, study of diseases of the elderly
hem-, semi-	half	hemi/gastr/ectomy, surgical removal of half of the stomach
hydro-	water	hydro/cephalus, water on the brain
hyper-	over, above	hyper/kinetic, overactive
hypo-	under, below	hypo/glossal, under the tongue
immun-	free, exempt	immun/ity, exempt from the effects of specific disease-causing agents
in-	not	in/soluble, not able to dissolve
infra-	beneath	infra/mammary, beneath the breast
inter-	between	inter/cellular, between the cells
intra-	within	intra/cranial, within the cranium
iso-	same	iso/coria, pupils of equal size
kil-	thousand	kilo/gram, 1,000 grams
leio-	smooth	leio/myoma, smooth muscle tumor
lepto-	high, thin	lepto/cephaly, having a long, thin head and neck
levo-	left	levo/duction of eye, movement of eye to the left

lys-	dissolution, disintegration	lyso/some, organelle that degrades worn cell parts
macr-	large	macro/cyte, large cell
mal-	bad	mal/nutrition, bad nourishment
mes-	middle	mes/entery, middle of intestine
meta-	after, beyond	meta/carpals, beyond the carpals (wrist)
micr-	small	micro/cephal/ic, having a small head
milli-	one-thousandth	milli/liter, 1/1,000 of a liter
multi-	many	multi/para, one who has many children
neo-	new	neo/plasm, new growth
normo-	normal	normo/cyte, normal, healthy red blood cell
olig-	scanty, few	olig/uria, scanty amount of urine
onc-	tumor	onc/ology, study of tumors
opistho-	behind, backward	opistho/tonos, bending backward
pachy-	thick	pachy/derma, thick skin
per-	through	per/cutaneous, through the skin
peri-	around	peri/tonsillar, around the tonsil
photo-	light	photo/phobia, avoidance of light
pleur-	rib, side	pleur/al membranes, serous membranes that enclose the lungs
poly-	much, many	poly/cystic, many cysts
post-	after	post/mortem, after death
pre-	before	pre/natal, before birth
presby-	old	presby/opia, old vision
primi-	first	primi/gravida, first pregnancy
pro-	before	pro/gnosis, prediction of the probable outcome of a disease
re-	back, again	re/generate, produce, develop again
retr-, retro-	behind	retro/sternal, behind the sternum
rhod-	red	rhod/opsin, visual pigment in the eye
semi-	half	semi/comatose, in a partial comatose state; semiconscious
sub-	under	sub/lingual, under the tongue
super-, supra-	above	supra/spinal, above the vertebral column
syn- , sym-	with, together	syn/ergism, working together
tachy-	fast	tachy/phasia, fast speech
un-	not	un/conscious, not conscious

Commonly Used Suffixes

Suffix	Meaning	Example
-algia	pain	dent/algia, pain in the tooth
-ase	suffix for an enzyme	protein/ase, protein-digesting enzyme
-atresia	without an opening	proct/atresia, rectum without an opening
-blast	immature cell form	erythro/blast, immature red blood cell
-cele	hernia	omphalo/cele, umbilical hernia
-centesis	puncture to aspirate fluid	arthro/centesis, puncture to aspirate fluid from a joint
-cept	take, receive	re/cept/or, something that receives again
-cide	kill	bacteri/cidal, able to kill bacteria
-cis	cut	circum/cis/ion, cutting around
-cyte	cell	erythro/cyte, red cell
-denia	pain	cephalo/denia, pain in the head
-desis	fusion	arthro/desis, fusion of a joint
-ectasia	expansion	cor/ectasis, expanding or dilating pupil
-ectomy	cut out, excise	nephr/ectomy, surgically remove kidney

-edema	swelling	cephal/edema, swelling of head
-emesis	vomiting	hyper/emesis, excessive vomiting
-emia	blood	hyper/glyc/emia, elevated blood sugar
-gen	precursor of	terato/gen, agent that causes a malformed fetus
-gnosis	knowledge	dia/gnosis, knowledge through examination (determining cause of disease)
-gram	record	myelo/gram, X ray of the spinal cord
-graphy	making a record	angio/graphy, making a record of vessels
-iasis	condition	chole/lith/iasis, condition of gallstones
-ism	condition, disease	alcohol/ism, addiction to alcohol
-ist	one who	opto/metr/ist, one who measures vision
-itis	inflammation	aden/itis, inflammation of a gland
-lepsy	seizures	narco/lepsy, seizures of numbness
-lexy	speech, words	dys/lexia, difficulty in reading words
-logist	one who specializes	ophthalmo/logist, one specializing in eyes
-logy	study of	bio/logy, study of life
-lysis, -lytic, -lyze	break down, dissolve	teno/lysis, destruction of tendons
-lyt	dissolvable	electro/lyte, substance that ionizes in water solution
-malacia	abnormal softening	osteo/malacia, abnormal softening of bone
-mania	madness	pyro/mania, irresistible urge to set fires
-megaly	enlargement	spleno/megaly, enlargement of spleen
-meter	measure	thermo/meter, instrument to measure temperature
-oid	resembling	muc/oid, resembling mucus
-oma	tumor	neur/oma, nerve tumor
-opia	vision	ambly/opia, dim vision
-osis	abnormal condition	nephr/osis, abnormal condition of kidney
-osme, -osmia	smell	an/osmia, inability to smell
-ostomy	create an opening	col/ostomy, create an opening in the colon
-otia	ear	macr/otia, large ear
-pathy	disease	encephalo/pathy, disease of the brain
-penia	deficiency, poor	leuko/cyto/penia, deficiency of white cells
-pepsia	digestion	dys/pepsia, bad digestion
-pexy	surgical fixation	nephro/pexy, surgical fixation of kidney
-phasia	speak, say	a/phasia, without ability to speak
-philia	love, attraction	chromo/philic, attracted to color
-phobia	abnormal fear	agora/phobia, abnormal fear of crowds
-plasia	formation	hyper/plasia, excessive formation
-plasm	substance	proto/plasm, original substance
-plasty	make, shape	rhino/plasty, to shape the nose
-plegia	paralysis	hemi/plegia, paralysis of one half of body
-pnea	breath	tachy/pnea, fast breathing
-ptosis	prolapse, dropping	hystero/ptosis, prolapse of uterus
-rrhagia	burst forth	metro/rrhagia, hemorrhage from uterus
-rrhaphy	suture, sew	hernio/rrhaphy, suture a hernia
-rrhea	flow, discharge	oto/rrhea, discharge from ear
-rrhexis	rupture	spleno/rrhexis, rupture of the spleen
-scope	instrument for viewing	oto/scope, instrument to look in ears
-scopy	visualization	laryngo/scopy, visualization of larynx
-some, -soma	body	lyso/some, body that lyses or dissolves
-spasm	twitching	blepharo/spasm, twitching of eyelid
-stasis	stop, control	hemo/stasis, control bleeding
-therapy	treatment	hydro/therapy, treatment with water

Commonly Used Suffixes continued

-tome	instrument to cut	osteo/tome, instrument to cut bone
-tomy	to cut	laparo/tomy, to cut into the abdomen
-tripsy	crushing	nephro/litho/tripsy, crushing stone in kidney
-trophy, -trophic, -trophin	development	hyper/trophy, overdevelopment
-uria	urine	hemat/uria, blood in the urine

Commonly Used Root Words*

Root	Meaning	Example
acro-	extremity, peak	acro/megaly, enlarged extremities; acro/phobia, abnormal fear of heights
aden-	gland	adeno/pathy, disease of a gland
adip-	fat, lipid	adip/ose tissue
aer-, aero-	air	aero/phagia, swallowing air
andro-	man, male	andro/gen, agent that causes male development
angi-	vessel	angi/oma, tumor of a vessel
arthr-	joint	arthr/algia, pain in the joint
athero-	soft, pasty material	athero/sclerosis, pasty hardening of an artery
balano-	penis	balano/plasty, surgical repair of penis
blast-	bud, growing thing	neuro/blast, growing nerve cell
blephar-	eyelid	blephar/op/tosis, drooping eyelid
brachi-	arm	brachi/al, pertaining to the arm
bronch-	windpipe	bronch/us, a branch of the trachea (windpipe)
bucco-	cheek	bucco/labial, referring to cheek and lip
calcaneo-	heel	calcaneo/dynia, painful heel
carcin-	cancer	adeno/carcin/oma, cancerous tumor of a gland
cardi-	heart	myo/cardi/tis, inflammation of heart muscle
carp-	wrist	flexor carp/i, muscle to bend wrist
caud-	tail	caud/al, pertaining to tail
celio-	abdomen	celio/tomy, incision of the abdomen
cephal-	head	cephalo/dynia, pain in the head
cervic-	neck, cervix	cervic/itis, inflammation of the neck of uterus
cheil-	lip	cheilo/plasty, shaping the lip
cheir-, chir-	hand	chiro/megaly, large hands
chol-	bile, gall	chole/cyst/ectomy, surgical removal of the gallbladder
chondr-	cartilage	chondro/malacia, softening of cartilage
chrom-	color	poly/chromatic, having many colors
chron-	time	syn/chron/ous, occurring at the same time
cleid-	clavicle	cleido/costal, referring to clavicle and ribs
col-	colon	mega/colon, enlarged colon
colp-	vagina	colp/orrhaphy, suture of vagina
core-	pupil	core/pexy, suturing the iris to change the pupil
cost-	ribs	inter/costal, between the ribs
crani-	skull	crani/otomy, incision into the skull
cry-	cold	cryo/philic, cold loving
crypt-	hidden	crypt/orchid/ism, hidden (undescended) testicle
cutan-, cut-	skin	sub/cutaneous, below the skin
cyan-	blue	acro/cyan/osis, abnormal condition of blueness of extremities
cyst-	bladder	cysto/cele, bladder hernia
cyt-	cell	thrombo/cyte, clotting cell (platelet)

dacry-	tear	dacryo/rrhea, flow of tears
dactyl-	fingers, toes	poly/dactyl/ism, too many fingers and toes
dent-, -odont	teeth	peri/odontal, around the teeth; dent/algia, toothache
derm-, dermat-	skin	intra/dermal, within the skin
desmo-	ligament	desmo/dentium, ligament anchoring tooth
dextr-	right	dextro/cardia, heart displaced to the right
dips-	thirst	poly/dipsia, excessive thirst
dors-	back	dors/al, pertaining to the back
duct-	carry	ovi/duct, tube to carry ova (eggs)
encephal-	brain	encephalo/cele, hernia of the brain
enter-	intestine	gastro/enter/itis, inflammation of stomach and intestine
erg-	work	en/ergy, working with
erthyr-	red	erythro/cyto/penia, deficiency of red cells
esthe-	sensation	an/esthe/tic, agent to eliminate sensation
esthen-	weakness	my/esthenia, muscle weakness
facio-	facial, the face	facio/plasty, plastic surgery on the face
febr-	fever	a/febrile, without a fever
flex-	bend	dorsi/flex, bend backward
gastr-	stomach	gastro/scopy, visualization of the stomach
gen-	produce	patho/genic, agent that produces disease
gingiv-	gums	gingiv/ectomy, removal of gums
gloss-	tongue	hypo/glossal, under the tongue
glyc-, glu-	sugar	hypo/glyc/emia, low blood sugar
gnath-	jaw	micro/gnath/ism, small jaw
gonado-	sex organs	gonado/trophin, causes development of sex organs
grav-	heavy, pregnancy	secundi/gravida, second pregnancy
gynec-	female	gyneco/logy, study of female conditions
hem-, hemat-	blood	hemat/emesis, vomiting blood
hepat-	liver	hepato/megaly, enlarged liver
heter-	different	hetero/genous, different origins
hidr-	perspiration	hidro/rrhea, flow of perspiration
hist-	tissue	histo/logy, study of tissue
home-, hom-	same	homeo/stasis, stay same, equilibrium
hydro, hydra-	water	de/hydra/tion, process of losing water
hyster-	uterus	hyster/ectomy, removal of the uterus
iatr-	physician	iatro/genic, produced by the physician
irid-	iris	irid/ectomy, surgical removal of iris
is-	equal	iso/tonic, equal in pressure
kary-	nut, nucleus	mega/karyo/cyte, cell with large nucleus
kerat-	cornea	kerato/plasty, repair of cornea
kin-	move	kinesio/logy, study of movement
labio-	lips	labio/gingival, refers to lips and gums
lacrim-	tear	lacrima/tion, crying
lact-, galact-	milk	lacto/genic, milk-producing
lapar-	abdomen	laparo/rrhaphy, suture of the abdomen
laryng-	larynx	laryngo/scopy, visualization of larynx
later-	side	bi/lateral, two sides
leuk-, leuc-	white	leuko/rrhea, white discharge
lingu-	tongue	sub/lingual, under the tongue
lip-	fat	lip/oma, tumor of fat
lith-	stone	litho/tripsy, crushing a stone

lymphadeno-	lymph node	lymphadeno/pathy, disease affecting lymph nodes
lymphangio-	lymph vessel	lymphangio/graphy, X rays of lymph vessels and nodes
mast-, mammo-	breast	mast/itis, inflammation of the breast; mammo/gram, X ray of breast
melan-	black	melan/oma, black tumor
men-	monthly, menstrual	dys/meno/rrhea, difficult monthly flow
mening-	membrane	mening/es, membranes that cover the brain and spinal cord
metr-	uterus	endo/metr/ium, lining of uterus
morph-	shape, form	poly/morphic, pertaining to many shapes
my-	muscle	myo/metr/itis, inflammation of muscle of uterus
myc-	fungus	onycho/myc/osis, fungus condition of the nails
myel-	marrow, spinal cord	myelo/gram, X-ray record of spinal cord
myring-	eardrum	myringo/tomy, opening into eardrum
nas-	nose	naso/pharyng/eal, pertaining to nose and throat
nat-	to be born	pre/nat/al, before birth
necr-	dead	necr/opsy, examining dead bodies; autopsy
nephr-, -ren	kidney	hydro/nephr/osis, abnormal condition of water in the kidney
neur-	nerve	neur/algia, nerve pain
noct-, -nyct	night	noct/uria, voiding at night
nucle-	kernel	nucle/us, dense core (kernel) of an atom
null-	none	nulli/gravida, woman who has had no pregnancies
ocul-	eye	mon/ocul/ar, pertaining to one eye
omphal-	umbilicus	omphalo/rrhea, discharge from the navel
onych-	nail	onycho/crypt/osis, condition of hidden nail (ingrown)
oo-	ova, egg	oo/genesis, producing eggs
oophor-	ovary	oophoro/cyst/ectomy, removal of cyst from ovary
ophthalm-	eye	ex/ophthalmos, condition of protruding eyes
or-	mouth	oro/pharyngeal, pertaining to mouth and throat
orchid-	testis	orchid/ectomy, removal of testis
orexis-	appetite	an/orexis, absence of appetite
orth-	straight	orth/odont/ist, one who straightens teeth
oste-, oss-	bone	osteo/chondr/oma, tumor of bone and cartilage
ot-, aur-	ear	ot/itis, inflammation of the ear; post/auricular, behind the ear
para-	to bear	primi/para, to bear first child.
path-	disease	patho/physio/logy, study of effects of disease on body functioning
pect-	chest	pecto/ralis, chest muscle
ped-	child	ped/iatrician, doctor who specializes in children
peps-	digest	dys/pepsia, bad digestion
phag-	swallow, eat	a/phagia, inability to swallow
phallo-	penis	phallo/dynia, pain in the penis
pharmac-	drug	pharmaco/logy, study of drugs
pharyng-	throat	pharyng/itis, inflammation of the throat
phas-	speak, say	tachy/phasia, speaking rapidly
phleb-	vein	phlebo/thromb/osis, abnormal condition of clot in vein
phon-	voice	a/phonic, absence of voice
phren-	diaphragm	phreno/hepatic, pertaining to the diaphragm and liver
pil-, trich-	hair	tricho/glossia, hairy tongue
pleur-	lining of lung, thorax	pleur/isy, inflammation of the pleura
pneum-	air, breath	pneumo/thorax, air in the chest
pneumon-	lung	pneumon/ectomy, surgical removal of the lung
pod-	foot	pod/iatrist, one who specializes in foot problems

proct-	rectum	procto/scopy, visualization of the rectum
pseud-	false	pseudo/cyesis, false pregnancy
psych-	mind	psycho/somatic, pertaining to the mind and the body
pulmon-	lung	cardio/pulmonary, pertaining to heart and lungs
py-	pus	pyo/rrhea, flow of pus
pyel-	kidney	pyelo/nephr/itis, inflammation of the kidney
pyl-	door, orifice	pyl/oric sphincter, ring of muscle that controls food entry into duodenum
pyr-	fire, fever	anti/pyretic, agent used against fever
quadri-	four	quadri/plegia, paralysis of all four extremities
rhin-	nose	rhino/plasty, revision of the nose
salping-	tube	salping/itis, inflammation of the uterine tube
sanguin-	blood	ex/sanguina/tion, process of bleeding out (bleed to death)
sarc-, sarco-	flesh, striated muscle	sarco/lemma, cell membrane of a muscle fiber
scler-	hard	arterio/scler/osis, condition of hardening of arteries
scot-	dark	scot/oma, blind spot in the visual field
sect-	cut	dis/section, cutting apart
sept-	contamination	anti/septic, agent used against contamination
sial-	saliva	sialo/rrhea, excessive salivation
spondyl-	vertebra	spondyl/itis, inflammation of the vertebrae
steato-	fat, lipid	steato/rrhea, fat in the fecal material
sten-	narrow, constricted	pyloric sten/osis, narrowing of pylorus
stomat-	mouth	stomat/itis, inflammation of the mouth
strict-	draw tight	vaso/con/strict/or, agent that compresses vessels
tax-	order, arrange	a/taxic, uncoordinated
ten-	tendon	teno/rrhaphy, suture a tendon
terato-	malformed fetus	terato/gen, agent that can harm a fetus
therm-	heat	hyper/thermia, raising body heat
thorac-	chest	thoraco/centesis, puncture to aspirate fluid from chest
thromb-	clot	thrombo/cyte, clotting cell
tox-	poison	tox/emia, poison in the blood
trache-	windpipe	tracheo/malacia, softening of tracheal cartilages
trachel-	neck	trachel/orrhaphy, suture of cervix (neck of uterus)
traumat-	wound	traumat/ology, study of trauma
tri-	three	tri/geminal, having three beginnings
trop-	turn	ec/tropion, turned out
ur-	urine	ur/emia, urine constituents in the blood
vas-	vessel	vaso/constriction, narrowing of a vessel
veni-	vein	veni/puncture, puncture of a vein
vert-	turn	retro/vert/ed, turned backward
vesic-	bladder	vesico/cele, hernia of the bladder
viscer-	internal organs	e/viscera/tion, process of viscera protruding from abdominal wall
vita-	life	vital, necessary for life

*Words that are the same as anatomical terms used in English (for example, pancreas, tonsil, and so on) have been omitted.

Now you are ready to apply your knowledge! Each time you find a new word in the text, try to analyze its meaning. Break each word into its parts: root, prefix, and suffix. You'll be able to translate the words without using a dictionary. At the end of each chapter, in the Medical Terminology Reinforcement Exercise, you are given an opportunity to reinforce your knowledge. Pronounce the words, and dissect them into parts to arrive at a meaning. You can also begin to build medical words and use them in your everyday conversation. You will be amazed at how rapidly your vocabulary will grow, and how your study of the human body will become easier and more enjoyable.

Glossary

A

abdominal cavity Portion of the body between the diaphragm and the pelvis. 7

abdominopelvic cavity Pertaining to the abdominal and pelvic regions. 6

abduction Movement of a body part away from the midline. 106

acetabulum Socket in the lateral surface of the hipbone into which the head of the femur articulates. 101

acetylcholine (ACh) Neurotransmitter secreted at the ends of many neurons; responsible for the transmission of a nerve impulse across a synaptic cleft. 145

acetylcholinesterase (AChE) Enzyme in the membrane of postsynaptic cells that breaks down acetylcholine; this enzymatic reaction inactivates the neurotransmitter. 145

ACh See *acetylcholine*. 145

AChE See *acetylcholinesterase*. 145

acid Solution in which pH is less than 7; substance that contributes or liberates hydrogen ions in a solution; opposite of *base*. 23

acidosis Excessive accumulation of acids in body fluids. 23, 197, 333

acne vulgaris Inflammation of sebaceous glands; the common form of acne. 73

acquired immunodeficiency syndrome See *AIDS*. 264, 362

acromegaly Condition resulting from an increase in growth hormone production after adult height has been achieved. 190

acrosome Covering on the tip of a sperm cell's nucleus that is believed to contain enzymes necessary for fertilization. 345

ACTH See *adrenocorticotropic hormone*. 188

actin One of the two major proteins of muscle; makes up thin myofilaments in myofibrils of muscle cells. See *myosin*. 42, 116

action potential Change in potential propagated along the membrane of a neuron; the nerve impulse. 143

active immunity Resistance to disease due to the immune system's response to a microorganism or a vaccine. 266

active transport Transfer of a substance into or out of a cell against a concentration gradient by a process that requires a plasma membrane carrier protein and an expenditure of energy. 44

acute bronchitis Infection of the primary and secondary bronchi. 286

acute disease Sudden in onset and severe. 12

acute lymphoblastic leukemia (ALL) Cancer of the blood in which immature lymphocytes proliferate in bone marrow, the thymus, and lymph nodes. 213

Addison disease Condition resulting from a deficiency of adrenal cortex hormones. 195

adduction Movement of a body part toward the midline. 106

adenosine diphosphate (ADP) Molecule produced when the terminal phosphate is lost from a molecule of adenosine triphosphate; ADP. 32

adenosine triphosphate (ATP) Molecule used by cells when energy is needed. 32

ADH See *antidiuretic hormone*. 188

adhesion junction Junction between cells in which the adjacent plasma membranes do not touch but are held together by intercellular filaments attached to buttonlike thickenings. 65

ADP See *adenosine diphosphate*. 32

adrenal cortex Outer portion of the adrenal gland. 193

adrenal gland Endocrine gland located on the superior portion of each kidney. 193

adrenaline See *epinephrine*. 193

adrenal medulla Inner portion of the adrenal gland. 193

adrenocorticotropic hormone (ACTH) Hormone secreted by the anterior lobe of the pituitary gland that stimulates the adrenal cortex to produce cortisol. 188

afterbirth Placenta and the extraembryonic membranes, which are delivered (expelled) during the third stage of parturition. 385

agglutination Clumping of cells, particularly in reference to red blood cells involved in an antigen-antibody reaction. 218

agranular leukocyte White blood cell with poorly visible cytoplasmic granules. 212

AID See *artificial insemination by donor*. 360

AIDS (acquired immunodeficiency syndrome) Disease caused by a retrovirus and transmitted via body fluids; characterized by failure of the immune system. 264, 362

albinism Genetic disorder characterized by a defect in pigment production. 71

albumin Plasma protein that helps the osmotic concentration of blood. 209

aldosterone Hormone secreted by the adrenal cortex that functions in regulating sodium and potassium excretion by the kidneys. 194, 332

alimentary canal Tubular portion of the digestive tract. 296

alkalosis Excessive accumulation of bases in body fluids. 23, 333

ALL See *acute lymphoblastic leukemia*. 213

allantois Extraembryonic membrane that serves as a source of blood vessels for the umbilical cord. 371

allele Different forms of a gene. 395

allergen Foreign substance capable of stimulating an allergic reaction. 268

allergy Immune response to substances that usually are not recognized as foreign. 268

all-or-none law Law that states that muscle fibers either contract maximally or not at all, and that neurons either conduct a nerve impulse completely or not at all. 122

alopecia Loss of hair. 72

alveolus Air sac of a lung (pl., *alveoli*). 279

Alzheimer disease Brain disorder characterized by a general loss of mental abilities. 145

amino acid Unit of a protein that takes its name from the fact that it contains an amino group ($-NH_2$) and an acid group ($-COOH$). 28

amniocentesis Method of retrieving fetal cells for genetic testing in which a long needle is used to withdraw a sample of amniotic fluid. 390

amnion One of the extraembryonic membranes; a fluid-filled sac around the embryo. 371

ampulla Expansion at the end of each semicircular canal that contains receptors for rotational equilibrium. 181

anabolic steroid Synthetic steroid that mimics the effect of testosterone. 197

anaphase Stage in mitosis when replicated chromosomes separate and move to opposite poles of the cell. 50

anaphylactic shock Severe systemic form of anaphylaxis involving bronchiolar constriction, impaired breathing, vasodilation, and a rapid drop in blood pressure with a threat of circulatory failure. 268

anatomy Branch of science dealing with the form and structure of body parts. 2

androgen Male sex hormone. 197, 343

anemia Condition characterized by a deficiency of red blood cells or hemoglobin. See also *iron deficiency anemia, pernicious anemia*. 214

anencephaly Congenital absence of the cranial vault, with cerebral hemispheres completely missing or reduced to small masses attached to the base of the skull. 382

aneurysm Saclike expansion of a blood vessel wall. 239

angina pectoris Condition characterized by thoracic pain resulting from occluded coronary arteries; precedes a heart attack. 228

ankle-jerk reflex Automatic, involuntary response initiated by tapping the Achilles tendon just above its attachment to the calcaneus (heel bone). 155

anorexia nervosa Eating disorder caused by the fear of becoming obese; includes loss of appetite and inability to maintain a normal minimum body weight. 319

antagonist Muscle that acts in opposition to a prime mover. 124

anterior Pertaining to the front; the opposite of *posterior*. 3

anterior pituitary Front lobe of the pituitary gland. 188

antibody Protein produced in response to the presence of some foreign substance in the blood or tissues. 212

antibody-mediated immunity Resistance to disease-causing agents resulting from the production of specific antibodies by B lymphocytes; humoral immunity. 261

antibody titer Amount of antibody present in a sample of blood serum. 266

anticodon Three contiguous nucleotides of a transfer RNA molecule that are complementary to a specific mRNA codon. 48

antidiuretic hormone (ADH) Hormone released from the posterior lobe of the pituitary gland that enhances water conservation by the kidneys; sometimes called vasopressin. 188

antigen Foreign substance, usually a protein, that stimulates the immune system to produce antibodies. 212, 260

antigen-presenting cell (APC) The cell that displays the antigen to the cells of the immune system so they can defend the body against that particular antigen. 262

antigen receptor Receptor proteins in the plasma membrane of immune system cells whose shape allows them to combine with a specific antigen. 260

anus Outlet of the alimentary canal. 304

aorta Major systemic artery that receives blood from the left ventricle. 242

aortic body Receptor in the aortic arch sensitive to oxygen content, carbon dioxide content, and blood pH. 283

aplastic anemia Insufficient number of red blood cells brought on by damage to the red bone marrow due to radiation or chemicals. 213

apnea Temporary cessation of breathing. 284

apoptosis Programmed cell death. 46, 260

appendicitis Infected swelling of the appendix. 307

appendicular portion Pertaining to the upper limbs (arm) and lower limbs (legs). 4

appendicular skeleton Part of the skeleton forming the upper limbs, pectoral girdle, lower limbs, and pelvic girdle. 97

appendix Small, tubular appendage that extends outward from the cecum of the large intestine; see also *vermiform appendix*. 257

aqueous humor Watery fluid that fills the anterior cavity of the eye. 171

arachnoid Weblike middle covering (one of the three meninges) of the central nervous system. 146

areola Dark, circular area surrounding the nipple of the breast. 356

arrector pili Smooth muscle in the skin associated with a hair follicle. 72

arrhythmia Abnormal heart rhythm. 20, 231

arterial duct See *ductus arteriosus*. 246

arteriole Branch from an artery that leads into a capillary. 234

arteriosclerosis Thickening and hardening of arterial walls. 234

artery Vessel that takes blood away from the heart; characteristically possesses thick elastic walls. 234

articular cartilage Hyaline cartilaginous covering over the articulating surface of the bones of synovial joints. 84

articulation Joining together of bones at a joint. 84

artificial insemination by donor (AID) Placement of donated sperm in the vagina so that fertilization followed by pregnancy might occur. 360

ascending colon Portion of the large intestine that travels superiorly as it extends from the entry of the small intestine to the transverse colon. 304

assisted reproductive technologies (ART) Medical techniques, sometimes performed in vitro, that are done to increase the chances of pregnancy. 360

association area Region of the cerebral cortex related to memory, reasoning, judgment, and emotional feelings. 149

aster Short, radiating fibers about the centrioles at the poles of a spindle. 49

asthma Condition in which bronchioles constrict and cause difficulty in breathing. 268, 288

astigmatism Visual defect due to errors in refraction caused by abnormal curvatures in the surface of the cornea or lens. 177

atherosclerosis Condition in which fatty substances accumulate abnormally beneath the inner linings of the arteries. 228

athlete's foot Skin disease caused by fungal infection, usually of the toes and soles of the foot. 74

atlas First cervical vertebra; it supports and balances the head. 95

atom Smallest unit of matter. 2, 18

ATP See *adenosine triphosphate*. 32

atria Referring to the chambers of the heart. 226

atrial natriuretic hormone (ANH) Substance secreted by the atria of the heart that accelerates sodium excretion so that blood volume decreases. 194, 238, 332

atrioventricular (AV) bundle Part of the cardiac conduction system that extends from the AV node to the bundle branches. 230

atrioventricular (AV) node Small region of neuromuscular tissue located near the septum of the heart that transmits impulses from the SA node to the ventricular walls. 230

atrioventricular (AV) valve Valve located between the atrium and the ventricle. 226

atrium Chamber; particularly an upper chamber of the heart that lies above the ventricles (pl., *atria*). 226

atrophy Wasting away or decrease in size of an organ or tissue. 123

auditory canal Tube in the outer ear that leads to the tympanic membrane. 178

auditory (eustachian) tube Air tube that connects the pharynx to the middle ear. 178

autoimmune disease Disease that results when the immune system mistakenly attacks the body's own tissues. 269

autonomic system Sympathetic and parasympathetic portions of the nervous system that function to control the actions of the visceral organs and skin. 152, 155

autosome Chromosome other than a sex chromosome. 390

AV bundle See *atrioventricular bundle*. 230

AV node See *atrioventricular node*. 230

AV valve See *atrioventricular valve*. 226

axial portion Pertaining to the body's axis. 4

axial skeleton Portion of the skeleton that supports and protects the organs of the head, neck, and trunk. 89

axis Second cervical vertebra upon which the atlas rotates, allowing the head to turn. 95

axon Process of a neuron that conducts nerve impulses away from the cell body. 142

B

ball-and-socket joint The most freely movable type of joint (for example, the shoulder or hip joint). 105

balloon angioplasty Procedure for treating a blocked coronary artery: A flexible guide wire is pushed into the coronary artery, and a miniature balloon catheter is pushed down the wire to the blockage; repeated inflations of the balloon decrease or relieve the blockage. 229

basal body Cytoplasmic structure that is located at the base of and may organize cilia or flagella. 42

basal cell carcinoma Form of skin cancer that begins in the epidermis and rarely metastasizes but has the capacity to invade local tissues. 74

basal nuclei Mass of gray matter located deep within a cerebral hemisphere of the brain. 151

base Solution in which pH is more than 7; a substance that contributes or liberates hydroxide ions in a solution; alkaline; opposite of *acid*. 23

basophil Leukocyte with a granular cytoplasm and that is able to be stained with a basic dye. 212

benign prostatic hyperplasia (BPH) Enlargement of the prostate gland. 338

benign tumor Mass of cells derived from a single mutated cell that has repeatedly undergone cell division but remained at the site of origin. 80

bicarbonate ion The form in which carbon dioxide is carried in the blood; HCO_3^-. 285

bicuspid valve Atrioventricular valve between the left atrium and the left ventricle; also known as the mitral valve. 226

bile Secretion of the liver that is temporarily stored in the gallbladder before being released into the small intestine, where it emulsifies fat. 302

biopsy Removal of sample tissue by plungerlike devices to diagnose a disease. 66

birth control pill Oral contraception containing estrogen and progesterone. 358

blastocyst Early stage of embryonic development that consists of a hollow ball of cells. 373

blind spot Area where the optic nerve passes through the retina and where vision is not possible due to the lack of rod cells and cone cells. 173

blood Connective tissue composed of cells separated by plasma. 61

blood pressure Force of blood against a blood vessel wall. 236

blood transfusion Introduction of whole blood or a blood component directly into the bloodstream. 218

B lymphocyte Type of lymphocyte that is responsible for antibody-mediated immunity. 212, 260

bolus Small lump of food that has been chewed and swallowed. 298

bone Connective tissue having a hard matrix of calcium salts deposited around protein fibers. 61

brachiocephalic Pertaining to the arm and head, as in the brachiocephalic artery and vein. 242

bradycardia Slow heart rate, characterized by fewer than 60 heartbeats per minute. 231

brain stem Portion of the brain that includes the midbrain, pons, and medulla oblongata. 151

Braxton Hicks contractions Strong, late-term uterine contractions prior to cervical dilation; also called false labor. 384

breech birth Birth in which the baby is positioned rump first. 379

bronchiole Smaller air passages in the lungs. 279

bronchus One of the two major divisions of the trachea; leads to the lungs (pl., *bronchi*). 279

buffer Substance or compound that prevents large changes in the pH of a solution. 23, 333

bulbourethral gland Gland located in the pelvic cavity that adds secretions to seminal fluid within the urethra. 343

bulimia nervosa Eating disorder characterized by binge eating followed by purging. 318

bursa Saclike, fluid-filled structure, lined with synovial membrane, that occurs near a joint (pl., *bursae*). 104

bursitis Inflammation of any of the friction-easing sacs called bursae within the knee joint. 104

C

calcaneus Heel bone. 103

calcitonin Hormone secreted by the thyroid gland that helps regulate the level of blood calcium level. 192

capillary Microscopic vessel located in the tissues connecting arterioles to venules; molecules either exit or enter the blood through the thin walls of capillaries. 235

carbaminohemoglobin Hemoglobin carrying carbon dioxide. 285

carbohydrate Organic compounds with the general formula $(CH_2O)_n$, including sugars and glycogen. 24

carcinogen Any agent that causes cancer. 80

carcinoma Cancer arising in epithelial tissue. 66

cardiac cycle Series of myocardial contractions that constitutes a complete heartbeat. 232

cardiac muscle Heart muscle (myocardium) consisting of striated muscle cells that interlock. 63, 114

cardiac vein Blood vessel that returns blood from the venules of the myocardium to the coronary sinus. 228

cardioregulatory center Portion of the medulla oblongata that regulates the heartbeat rate. 233

caries Destruction of tooth enamel by oral bacteria. 297

carotid artery Either of two arteries branching off the aortic arch and supplying blood to the head and neck. 242

carotid body Structure located at the branching of the carotid arteries; contains chemoreceptors. 283

carpals Bones of the wrist. 100

carrier Molecule that combines with a substance and actively transports it through the plasma membrane. 396

cartilaginous joint Two or more bones joined by cartilage. 104

cataract Opaqueness of the lens of the eye, making the lens incapable of transmitting light. 171

CCK See *cholecystokinin*. 304

cecum Blind pouch, such as the one below where the small intestine enters the large intestine. 304

cell Structural and functional unit of an organism; smallest structure capable of performing all the functions necessary for life. 2

cell body Portion of a nerve cell that includes a cytoplasmic mass and a nucleus, and from which the nerve fibers extend. 142

cell cycle Life cycle of a cell consisting of G_1 (growth), S (DNA synthesis), G_2 (growth), and mitosis (division). 46

cell-mediated immunity Immunological defense provided by killer T cells, which destroy virus-infected cells, foreign cells, and cancer cells. 263

cellular respiration Process that releases energy from organic compounds in cells. 41

cellulose Polysaccharide very abundant in plant tissues that human enzymes cannot break down. 25

central Situated at the center of the body or an organ. 3

central canal Tube within the spinal cord that is continuous with the ventricle of the brain and contains cerebrospinal fluid. 146

central nervous system (CNS) Brain and spinal cord. 141

centriole Short, cylindrical organelle that contains microtubules in a 9 + 0 pattern and is associated with the formation of the spindle during cell division. 42

cerebellum Part of the brain that controls muscular coordination. 151

cerebral cortex Outer layer of the cerebrum. 149

cerebral hemisphere One of the large, paired structures that together constitute the cerebrum of the brain. 149

cerebral palsy Spastic weakness of the arms and legs due to damage to the motor areas of the cerebral cortex. 149

cerebrospinal fluid (CSF) Fluid found within the ventricles of the brain and surrounding the CNS in association with the meninges. 146

cerebrovascular accident (CVA) Condition resulting when an arteriole in the brain bursts or becomes blocked by an embolism; stroke. 239

cerebrum Main portion of the vertebrate brain that is responsible for consciousness. 148

cervix Narrow end of the uterus that projects into the vagina. 349

cesarean section Birth by surgical incision of the abdomen and uterus. 379

chemotherapy Use of drugs to kill cancer cells. 80

Cheyne-Stokes respiration Type of respiration characterized by alternate periods of deep, labored breathing and no breathing at all. 284

chlamydia Sexually transmitted disease caused by the bacterium *Chlamydia trachomatis*; often causes painful urination and swelling of the testes in men; is usually symptomless in women but can cause inflammation of the cervix or uterine tubes. 363

chloride shift Movement of chloride ions from the blood plasma into red blood cells as bicarbonate ions diffuse out of the blood cells into the plasma. 285

cholecystokinin (CCK) Hormone secreted by the small intestine that stimulates the release of pancreatic juice from the pancreas and bile from the gallbladder. 304

chordae tendineae Tough bands of connective tissue that attach the papillary muscles to the atrioventricular valves within the heart. 226

chorion Extraembryonic membrane that forms an outer covering around the embryo and contributes to the formation of the placenta. 371

chorionic villi Projections from the chorion that appear during implantation and that in one area contribute to the development of the placenta. 377

chorionic villi sampling (CVS) Method of retrieving fetal cells for genetic testing in which a long, thin tube is passed through the vagina into the uterus, and suction is used to obtain a sample of chorionic villi cells. 390

choroid Vascular, pigmented middle layer of the wall of the eye. 170

chromatids Two identical parts of a chromosome following replication of DNA. 47

chromatin Threadlike network in the nucleus that condenses to become the chromosomes just before cell division. 39

chromosome Rod-shaped body in the nucleus, particularly during cell division, that contains the hereditary units, or genes. 39

chronic bronchitis Obstructive pulmonary disorder that tends to recur, marked by inflamed airways filled with mucus, and degenerative changes in the bronchi, including loss of cilia. 287

chronic disease Long and continued but not acute. 12

chronic obstructive pulmonary disease (COPD) Continued interference with airflow in the lungs due to chronic bronchitis or emphysema. 287

chyme Semifluid food mass leaving the stomach. 301

cilia Membrane-bounded microtubular structures that project from a cell, and in multicellular animals facilitate the flow of materials over the cell surface. 42

ciliary body Structure associated with the choroid layer of the eye that secretes aqueous humor and contains the ciliary muscle. 170

ciliary muscle Muscle that controls the curvature of the lens of the eye. 170

cilium Short, hairlike projection from the plasma membrane, occurring usually in large numbers. 42

circadian rhythm Pattern of repeated behavior associated with the cycles of night and day. 200

circle of Willis Arterial ring located on the ventral surface of the brain. 246

circular fold Permanent transverse folds of the luminal surface of the small intestine, involving the mucosa and the submucosa. 302

circulation Movement of the blood through the heart and blood vessels. 236

circumcision Removal of the prepuce (foreskin) of the penis. 347

circumduction Conelike movement of a body part, such that the distal end moves in a circle, while the proximal portion remains relatively stable. 106

cirrhosis Chronic, irreversible injury to liver tissue; commonly caused by frequent alcohol consumption. 310

clavicle Bone extending from the sternum to the scapula. 97

cleavage Early, successive divisions of the blastocyst cells into smaller and smaller cells. 371

cleavage furrow Site of cell division of the fertilized egg that is unaccompanied by growth. Numerous small cells result. 50

clitoris Small, erectile, female organ located in the vulva; homologous to the penis. 353

clonal selection theory States that the antigen selects which lymphocyte will undergo clonal expansion and produce more lymphocytes bearing the same type of receptor. 260

CNS See *central nervous system*. 141

coagulation Blood clotting. 214

coccyx Caudal end of the vertebral column formed by the fusion of four vertebrae; tailbone. 95

cochlea Portion of the inner ear that contains the receptors for hearing. 178

cochlear canal Canal within the cochlea that bears small hair cells that function as hearing receptors. 179

cochlear implant Prosthetic device used to help persons with severe hearing impairment; the device converts sound to an electrical impulse that directly stimulates the auditory nerve. 182

cochlear nerve Either of two cranial nerves that carry nerve impulses from the spiral organ to the brain; auditory nerve. 179

codon Set of three nucleotides of a messenger RNA molecule corresponding to a particular amino acid. 48

collecting duct Tube that receives urine from several distal convoluted tubules. 324

colon Large intestine. 304, 327

color vision Ability to detect the color of an object, dependent on three kinds of cone cells. 172

colostomy Attachment of a shortened colon to a surgical opening in the abdominal wall. 306

colostrum First secretion of a woman's mammary glands after she gives birth. 356

compact bone Hard bone consisting of osteons cemented together. 61, 84

complement system Group of proteins in plasma that aid the general defense of the body by destroying bacteria; often called complement. 259

compound Chemical substance having two or more different elements in fixed ratio. 20

concha Shell-shaped structure, such as that seen in the bones of the nasal cavity (pl., *conchae*). 277

condom For males, a latex sheath used to cover the penis during sexual intercourse; for females, a large polyurethane tube with a flexible ring that fits onto the cervix. Both male and female condoms function as contraceptives and help minimize the risk of transmitting infection. 359

conduction deafness Hearing impairment due to fusion of the ossicles or other damage to the middle ear, thereby restricting the ability to transmit and magnify sound. 182

conduction system of the heart Neuromuscular tissue and fibers that control the cardiac cycle; includes the SA node, the AV node, the AV bundle and its branches, and the Purkinje fibers. 230

condyle Large, rounded surface at the end of a bone. 87

condyloid joint Bone with an oval-shaped projection at one end joined with a bone possessing a complementary elliptical cavity. 105

cone cell Color receptor located in the retina of the eye. 172

congenital defect Body abnormality arising from birth and due to hereditary factors. 382

congestive heart failure Inability of the heart to maintain adequate circulation, especially of the venous blood returned to it. 239

connective tissue Type of tissue characterized by cells separated by a matrix; often contains fibers. 58

constipation Infrequent, difficult defecation caused by insufficient water in the feces. 306

COPD See *chronic obstructive pulmonary disease.* 287

cornea Transparent, anterior portion of the outer layer of the eyeball. 170

coronal suture Line of junction of the frontal bone with the two parietal bones. 104

coronary artery Artery that supplies blood to the wall of the heart (myocardium). 228

coronary bypass operation Therapy for blocked coronary arteries in which part of a blood vessel from another part of the body is grafted around the obstructed artery. 229

coronary sinus Large vessel on the posterior surface of the heart into which the cardiac veins drain. 228

corpus albicans White, fibrous tissue that replaces the regressing corpus luteum in the ovary in the latter half of pregnancy. 351

corpus callosum Mass of white matter within the brain, composed of nerve fibers connecting the right and left cerebral hemispheres. 149

corpus luteum Structure that forms from the tissues of a ruptured ovarian follicle and functions to secrete female hormones. 351

cortisol Glucocorticoid secreted by the adrenal cortex. 194

covalent bond Chemical bond created by the sharing of electrons between atoms. 21

coxal bone Bone of the pelvic girdle. 100

cranial cavity Hollow space in the cranium containing the brain. 6

cranial nerve Nerve that arises from the brain. 152

creatine phosphate Muscle biochemical that stores energy. 120

creatinine Nitrogenous waste, the end product of creatine phosphate metabolism. 324

crenation Shrinking of red blood cells often caused by osmotic conditions. 43

cretinism Condition resulting from a lack of thyroid hormone in an infant. 191

CSF See *cerebrospinal fluid.* 146

Cushing syndrome Condition characterized by thin arms and legs and a "moon face;" accompanied by high blood glucose and sodium levels due to hypersecretion of cortical hormones. 195

cutaneous membrane Pertaining to the skin. 66, 70

cyanosis Bluish cast to the skin due to an increased amount of deoxyhemoglobin in the blood; sometimes due to a defective atrial septum, which incompletely closes the foramen ovale after birth. 247

cyclic AMP Derivative of ATP that responds to messages entering a cell and triggers the cell's response; also known as cAMP. 201

cystic fibrosis (CF) Generalized, autosomal recessive disorder of infants and children, in which there is widespread dysfunction of the exocrine glands. 396

cystitis Inflammation of the urinary bladder. 334

cytokine Type of protein secreted by a T lymphocyte that attacks viruses, virally infected cells, and cancer cells. 262

cytokinesis Division of the cytoplasm following mitosis and meiosis. 46

cytoplasm Ground substance of cells located between the nucleus and the plasma membrane. 36

cytoskeleton System of microtubules and filaments that reinforces a cell's three-dimensional form; maintains cell shape and allows movement of cell and its contents. 36

cytotoxic T cell T lymphocyte that attacks and kills antigen-bearing cells. 263

D

dandruff Skin disorder characterized by flaking, itchy scalp; caused by accelerated keratinization of the scalp. 74

daughter cell Cell that arises from a parental cell by mitosis or meiosis. 49

decubitus ulcer Skin sore due to restricted blood flow to the area in bedridden patients; also called a bedsore. 71

deep Located away from the surface of the body or an organ. 3

defecation Discharge of feces from the rectum through the anus. 304

dehydration reaction Anabolic process that joins small molecules; synthesis. 24

delayed allergic response Allergic response initiated at the site of the allergen by sensitized T cells, involving macrophages and regulated by cytokines. 268

delirium tremens Alcohol withdrawal. 382

denaturation Loss of normal shape by an enzyme so that it no longer functions; caused by a less than optimal pH or temperature. 28

dendrite Process of a neuron, typically branched, that conducts nerve impulses toward the cell body. 142

dense connective tissue Type of tissue containing many collagen fibers packed together; found in tendons and ligaments, for example. 59

deoxyhemoglobin Hemoglobin not carrying oxygen. 211

deoxyribonucleic acid (DNA) Nucleic acid; the genetic material found in the nucleus of a cell. 31

depolarization Loss in polarization, as when a nerve impulse occurs. 143

depression Movement of a synovial joint that lowers a body part. 106

dermis Thick skin layer that lies beneath the epidermis. 71

descending colon That portion of the large intestine that travels inferiorly as it extends from the transverse colon to the sigmoid colon. 304

diabetes insipidus Condition characterized by an abnormally large production of urine, due to a deficiency of antidiuretic hormone. 188

diabetes mellitus Condition characterized by a high blood glucose level and the appearance of glucose in the urine, due to a deficiency of insulin. 25, 197

diagnosis Decision based on an examination to determine the nature of a diseased condition. 66

dialysate Material that passes through the membrane in dialysis. 335

diaphragm Sheet of muscle that separates the thoracic cavity from the abdominopelvic cavity; also, a birth control device inserted in front of the cervix in females. 6, 128, 358

diaphysis Shaft of a long bone. 84

diarrhea Frequent, watery defecation, often caused by digestive infection or stress. 306

diastole Relaxation of heart chambers. 232

diastolic pressure Arterial blood pressure during the diastolic phase of the cardiac cycle. 239

diencephalon Portion of the brain in the region of the third ventricle that includes the thalamus and hypothalamus. 151

differential white blood cell count Microscopic examination of a blood sample in which each type of white blood cell is counted. 213

differentiation Process by which a cell becomes specialized for a particular function. 371

diffusion Passive movement of molecules from an area of greater concentration to an area of lesser concentration. 43

disaccharide Sugar that contains two units of a monosaccharide; for example, maltose. 25

disease Any abnormal condition considered harmful to the body; an illness or disorder. 12, 255

distal Further from the midline or origin; opposite of *proximal*. 3

distal convoluted tubule Highly coiled region of a nephron that is distant from the glomerular capsule. 327

diuretic Drug used to counteract hypertension by inhibiting Na^+ reabsorption so that less water is reabsorbed in the nephron. 332

diverticulosis Presence of diverticula, or saclike pouches, in the colon. 307

DNA See *deoxyribonucleic acid*. 31

dominant allele Hereditary factor that expresses itself even when there is only one copy in the genotype. 395

dorsal Pertaining to the back or posterior portion of a body part; opposite of *ventral*. 3

Down syndrome Human congenital disorder associated with an extra chromosome 21. 392

ductus arteriosus Fetal connection between the pulmonary artery and the aorta; venous artery. 246

ductus venosus Fetal connection between the umbilical vein and the inferior vena cava; also called venous duct. 246

duodenum First portion of the small intestine into which ducts from the gallbladder and pancreas enter. 302

duplicated chromosome Chromosome having two sister chromatids held together by a centromere. 47

dura mater Tough outer layer of the meninges; membranes that protect the brain and spinal cord. 146

E

ECG See *electrocardiogram*. 231

ectopic pregnancy Implantation of the embryo in a location other than the uterus, most often in a uterine tube. 352, 375

eczema Form of noncontagious dermatitis that begins with itchy red patches that thicken and crust over. 74

edema Swelling due to tissue fluid accumulation in the intercellular spaces. 217, 254

ejaculation Ejection of seminal fluid. 343

ejaculatory duct Tube, formed by the joining of the vas deferens and the tube from the seminal vesicle, that transports sperm to the urethra. 343

EKG See *electrocardiogram*. 231

elastic cartilage Cartilage composed of elastic fibers, allowing greater flexibility. 61

electrocardiogram (ECG) Recording of the electrical activity that accompanies the cardiac cycle. 231

electroencephalogram (EEG) Graphic recording of the brain's electrical activity. 151

electrolyte Any substance that ionizes and conducts electricity; electrolytes are present in the body fluids and tissues. 23, 331

electron Small, negatively charged particle that revolves around the nucleus of an atom. 18

element The simplest of substances, consisting of only one type of atom (for example, carbon, hydrogen, oxygen). 18

elephantiasis Swelling of the arms, legs, or external genitalia due to failure of the lymphatic system to remove excess fluid. 257

elevation Movement of a synovial joint that raises a body part. 106

embolus Moving blood clot that is carried through the bloodstream. 214

embryo Organism in its early stages of development; in humans, the organism in its second week to two months of development. 375

embryonic development Period of development from the second through eighth weeks. 375

embryonic disk Flattened area between the amniotic cavity and the yolk sac from which the embryo arises. 375

emphysema Lung impairment caused by deterioration of the bronchioles, which traps air in alveoli. 287

emulsification Breaking up of fat globules into smaller droplets by the action of bile salts. 26

endocardium Inner layer of the heart wall. 226

endochondral ossification Ossification that begins as hyaline cartilage that is subsequently replaced by bone tissue. 86

endocrine gland Gland that secretes hormones directly into the bloodstream or body fluids. 186

endocytosis Process in which a vesicle is formed at the plasma membrane to bring a substance into the cell. 44

endomembrane system Collection of membranous structures involved in transport within the cell. 40

endometriosis Implantation of uterine endometrial tissue in the abdominal cavity, possibly as a result of irregular menstrual flow. 360

endometrium Lining of the uterus that becomes thickened and vascular during the menstrual cycle. 349

endoplasmic reticulum (ER) Complex system of tubules, vesicles, and sacs in cells; sometimes has attached ribosomes. 40

enzyme Protein catalyst that speeds a specific reaction or a specific type of reaction. 29

eosinophil Granular leukocyte capable of being stained with the dye eosin. 212

epicardium Visceral portion of the pericardium on the surface of the heart. 226

epidermis Organism's outer layer of cells. 70

epididymis Coiled tubules next to the testes where sperm mature and may be stored for a short time. 343

epidural hematoma Bleeding between the dura mater and the bone, as a result of a head injury. 146

epiglottis Structure that covers the glottis during the process of swallowing. 278, 298

epinephrine Hormone produced by the adrenal medulla that stimulates "fight-or-flight" reactions; also called adrenaline. 193

epiphyseal plate Cartilaginous layer within the epiphysis of a long bone that functions as a growing region. 86

epiphysis End segment of a long bone, separated from the diaphysis early in life by an epiphyseal plate, but later becoming part of the larger bone. 84

episiotomy Surgical procedure performed during childbirth in which the opening of the vagina is enlarged to avoid tearing. 385

epithelial tissue Type of tissue that lines the body's internal cavities and covers the body's external surface. 55

erectile dysfunction Failure of the penis to achieve erection. 347

erythrocyte Nonnucleated, hemoglobin-containing blood cell capable of carrying oxygen; red blood cell. 211

erythropoietin Kidney hormone that promotes red blood cell formation. 211, 324

esophagus Tube that transports food from the mouth to the stomach. 299

essential amino acid Amino acid that is necessary in the diet because the body is unable to manufacture it. 314

essential fatty acid Fatty acid that is necessary in the diet because the body is unable to manufacture it. 314

estrogen Female sex hormone secreted by the ovaries that, along with progesterone, promotes the development and maintenance of the primary and secondary female sex characteristics. 197

eupnea Easy or normal respiration. 284

eversion Movement of the foot in which the sole is turned outward. 106

excretion Elimination of metabolic wastes. 324

exocrine gland Particular glands with ducts, such as salivary glands, whose secretions are deposited into cavities. 186

exocytosis Process in which an intracellular vesicle fuses with the plasma membrane so that the vesicle's contents are released outside the cell. 44

exophthalmic goiter Enlargement of the thyroid gland, accompanied by an abnormal protrusion of the eyes. 191

expiration Process of expelling air from the lungs; exhalation. 276

expiratory reserve volume Volume of air that can be forcibly exhaled after normal exhalation. 281

extension Movement that increases the angle between parts at a joint. 106

external auditory meatus Opening through the temporal bone that connects with the tympanum and the middle ear chamber and through which sound vibrations pass. 92

external genitals Sex organs that occur outside the body. 347

external respiration Exchange of oxygen and carbon dioxide between alveoli and blood. 285

extraembryonic membranes Membranes that are not a part of the embryo but that are necessary to the embryo's continued existence and health. 371

extrinsic muscle Muscle that anchors and moves the eye. 169

F

facilitated transport Use of a plasma membrane carrier protein to move a substance into or out of a cell from higher to lower concentration; no energy required. 44

fascia Tough sheet of fibrous tissue that binds the skin to underlying muscles; also supports and separates muscles. 115

fascicle Small bundle of muscle fibers. 114

fat Organic molecule that the body uses for long-term energy storage. 26, 71

fatigue Failure of a muscle fiber to continue to contract, due to exhaustion of ATP. 122

fatty acid Molecule that contains a hydrocarbon chain and ends with an acid group. 26

feces Indigestible wastes expelled from the digestive tract; excrement. 307

femur Thighbone located in the upper leg. 102

fertilization Union of a sperm nucleus and an egg nucleus, which creates a zygote with the diploid number of chromosomes. 370

fetal alcohol syndrome (FAS) Babies born with decreased weight, height, and head size and with malformation of the head and face due to the mothers' consumption of alcohol during pregnancy. 382

fetal development Period of human development from the ninth week through birth. 379

fetus Human in its later developmental stages (from three months to term), following the embryonic stage. 379

fiber Dendrites and axons of neurons. 304

fibrillation Rapid but uncoordinated heartbeat. 231

fibrin Insoluble protein threads formed from fibrinogen during blood clotting. 214

fibrinogen Plasma protein that is converted into fibrin threads during blood coagulation. 214

fibroblast Cell that produces fibers and other intercellular materials in connective tissues. 59

fibrocartilage Cartilage with a matrix of strong collagenous fibers. 61

fibrous connective tissue Tissue composed mainly of closely packed collagenous fibers and found in tendons and ligaments. 59

fibrous joint Two or more bones joined by connective tissue containing many fibers. 104

fibrous pericardium External layer of the pericardium, consisting of fibrous tissue. 226

fibula Long, slender bone located on the lateral side of the tibia. 102

filament Protein molecule that makes up part of a myofibril. 116

filtration Passage of fluid through a membrane because of mechanical pressure, as when blood pressure forces water out of a capillary. 43

fimbria Fingerlike extension from the uterine tube near the ovary (pl., *fimbriae*). 352

flagellum Slender, long process used for locomotion—for example, by sperm (pl., *flagella*). 42

flexion Bending at a joint so that the angle between bones is decreased. 106

floating kidney Kidney that has been dislodged from its normal position. 325

focus Bending of light rays by the cornea, lens, and humors so that they converge and create an image on the retina. 171

follicle Structure in the ovary that produces the egg and particularly the female sex hormone estrogen. 351

follicle-stimulating hormone (FSH) Hormone secreted by the anterior pituitary gland that stimulates the development of an ovarian follicle in a female or the production of sperm cells in a male. 348

fontanel Membranous region located between certain cranial bones in the skull of a fetus or infant. 90, 379

foramen Opening, usually in a bone or membrane (pl., *foramina*). 87

foramen ovale Oval-shaped opening between the atria in the fetal heart. 246

foreskin Skin covering the glans penis in uncircumcised males. 347

formed element Cellular constituent of blood. 209

fovea centralis Region of the retina that consists of densely packed cones and is responsible for the greatest visual acuity. 171

fracture A break in a bone. 87

free radicals Atoms or molecules with an unpaired electron in their outermost shell; linked to several diseases and play a role in the aging process. 315

frontal lobe Area of the cerebrum responsible for voluntary movements and higher intellectual processes. 149

frontal plane Plane or section that divides a structure lengthwise into anterior and posterior portions; pertaining to the region of the forehead. 5

FSH See *follicle-stimulating hormone*. 348

G

gallbladder Saclike organ associated with the liver that stores and concentrates bile. 310

ganglion Collection of neuron cell bodies outside the central nervous system (pl., *ganglia*). 152

gap junction Junction between cells formed by the joining of two adjacent plasma membranes; it lends strength and allows ions, sugars, and small molecules to pass between cells. 65

gastric gland Gland within the stomach wall that secretes gastric juice. 301

gastrulation Formation of a gastrula from a blastula; characterized by an invagination of the cell layers to form a caplike structure. 377

gene Unit of heredity located on a chromosome. 395

gene therapy Method of replacing a defective gene with a healthy gene. 399

genital Pertaining to the genitalia (internal and external organs of reproduction). 342

genital herpes Sexually transmitted disease caused by herpes simplex virus and sometimes accompanied by painful ulcers on the genitals. 363

genital wart Raised growth on the genitals due to a sexually transmitted disease caused by human papillomavirus. 363

genome All of the DNA in a cell of an organism. 399

genotype Combination of genes present within a zygote or within the cells of an individual. 395

gestation Period of development, from the start of the last menstrual cycle until birth; in humans, typically 280 days. 373

GH See *growth hormone*. 188

gingivitis Inflammation of the gums. 297

gland Epithelial cell or group of epithelial cells that are specialized to secrete a substance. 65

glaucoma Increasing loss of field of vision, caused by blockage of the ducts that drain the aqueous humor, creating pressure buildup and nerve damage. 171

gliding joint Two bones with nearly flat surfaces joined together. 105

globulin Type of protein in blood plasma. There are alpha, beta, and gamma globulins. 209

glomerular capsule Double-walled cup that surrounds the glomerulus at the beginning of the kidney tubule; also known as Bowman's capsule. 326

glomerular filtrate Liquid that passes out of the glomerular capillaries in the kidney into the glomerular capsules. 329

glomerular filtration Process whereby blood pressure forces liquid through the glomerular capillaries in the kidney into the glomerular capsule. 329

glomerulus Cluster of capillaries surrounded by the glomerular capsule in a kidney nephron. 326

glottis Slitlike opening between the vocal cords. 278

glucagon Hormone secreted by the pancreatic islets that causes the release of glucose from glycogen. 196

glucocorticoid Any one of a group of hormones secreted by the adrenal cortex that influences carbohydrate, fat, and protein metabolism. 193

glucose Blood sugar that is broken down in cells to acquire energy for ATP production. 24

glycerol Three-carbon molecule that joins with fatty acids to form fat. 26

glycogen Polysaccharide that is the principal storage compound for sugar in animals. 25

glycosuria Presence of glucose in the urine, typically indicative of a kidney disease, diabetes mellitus, or other endocrine disorder. 197

Golgi apparatus Organelle that consists of concentrically folded membranes and that functions in the packaging and secretion of cellular products. 40

gonad Organ that produces sex cells: the ovary, which produces eggs, and the testis, which produces sperm. 197

gonadotropic hormone Type of hormone that regulates the activity of the ovaries and testes; principally, follicle-stimulating hormone and luteinizing hormone. 188

gonorrhea Sexually transmitted disease caused by the bacterium *Neisseria gonorrhoeae* that causes painful urination and swollen testes in men and is usually symptomless in women, but can cause inflammation of the cervix and uterine tubes. 363

gout Joint inflammation caused by accumulation of uric acid. 324

granular leukocyte White blood cell with prominent granules in the cytoplasm. 212

Graves disease Autoimmune disease with swollen throat due to an enlarged, hyperactive thyroid gland; patients often have protruding eyes and are underweight, hyperactive, and irritable. 191

gravitational equilibrium Maintenance of balance when the head and body are motionless. 181

gray matter Nonmyelinated nerve fibers in the central nervous system. 146

greater sciatic notch Indentation in the posterior coxal bone through which pass the blood vessels and the large sciatic nerve to the lower leg. 100

growth Increase in the number of cells and/or the size of these cells. 371

growth factor Chemical signal that regulates mitosis and differentiation of cells that have receptors for it; important in such processes as fetal development, tissue maintenance and repair, and hematopoiesis; sometimes a contributing factor in cancer. 200

growth hormone (GH) Hormone released by the anterior lobe of the pituitary gland that promotes the growth of the organism; also known as somatotropin. 188

gyrus Convoluted elevation or ridge (pl., *gyri*). 149

H

hair Consists of a cylindrical shaft and a root, which is contained in a flasklike depression (hair follicle) in the dermis and subcutaneous tissue. The base of the root is expanded into the hair bulb, which rests upon and encloses the hair papilla. 72

hair cell Mechanoreceptor in the inner ear that lies between the basilar membrane and the tectorial membrane and triggers action potentials in fibers of the auditory nerve. 178

hair follicle Tubelike depression in the skin in which a hair develops. 72

hard palate Anterior portion of the roof of the mouth that contains several bones. 296

hay fever Seasonal variety of allergic reaction to a specific allergen. Characterized by sudden attacks of sneezing, swelling of nasal mucosa, and often asthmatic symptoms. 268

hCG See *human chorionic gonadotropin.* 354, 375

head Pertaining to the skeleton, an enlargement on the end of a bone. 102

heart Muscular organ located in the thoracic cavity that is responsible for maintenance of blood circulation. 225

heart attack See *myocardial infarction.* 228

heart block Impairment of conduction of an impulse in heart excitation. 231

heartburn Burning pain in the chest occurring when part of the stomach contents escapes into the esophagus. 299

heart murmur Clicking or swishing sounds often due to leaky valves. 232

heart valve Valve found between the chambers of the heart or between a chamber and a vessel leaving the heart. 227

helper T cell Secretes lymphokines, which stimulate all kinds of immune cells. 263

hematopoiesis Production of blood cells. 84, 210

heme Iron-containing portion of a hemoglobin molecule. 211

hemodialysis Mechanical way to remove nitrogenous wastes and to regulate blood pH when the kidneys are unable to perform these functions. 45, 335

hemoglobin Pigment of red blood cells responsible for oxygen transport. 211, 285

hemolysis Bursting of red blood cells with the release of hemoglobin; can be caused by osmotic conditions. 211

hemolytic anemia Insufficient number of red blood cells caused by an increased rate of red blood cell destruction. 213

hemolytic disease of the newborn Destruction of a fetus's red blood cells by the mother's immune system, caused by differing Rh factors between mother and fetus. 213

hemophilia Most common of the severe clotting disorders caused by the absence of a blood clotting factor. 214

hemorrhagic bleeding Escape of blood from blood vessels. 214

hemorrhoids Abnormally dilated blood vessels of the rectum. 235

hemostasis Stoppage of bleeding. 214

hepatic portal system Portal system that begins at the villi of the small intestine and ends at the liver. 245

hepatic portal vein Vein leading to the liver and formed by the merging blood vessels of the small intestine. 245

hepatitis Inflammation of the liver; often due to a serious infection by any of a number of viruses. 310

hernia Protrusion of an organ through an abnormal opening, such as the intestine through the abdominal wall near the scrotum (inguinal hernia) or the stomach through the diaphragm (hiatal hernia). 346

herniated disk Fibrous ring of cartilage between two vertebrae that has ruptured. 94

heterozygous Different alleles in a gene pair. 395

hexose Six-carbon sugar. 24

hinge joint Type of joint characterized by a convex surface of one bone fitting into a concave surface of another so that movement is confined to one place, such as in the knee or interphalangeal joint. 105

hirsutism Excessive body and facial hair in women. 72

histamine Substance produced by basophil-derived mast cells in connective tissue that causes capillaries to dilate; causes many of the symptoms of allergy. 259

HLA (human leukocyte-associated) antigen Protein in a plasma membrane that identifies the cell as belonging to a particular individual and acts as an antigen in other organisms. 262

Hodgkin disease Cancer of the lymph glands that is normally localized in the neck region. 257

homeostasis Constancy of conditions, particularly the environment of body cells: constant temperature, blood pressure, pH, and other body conditions. 10

homozygous dominant Possessing two identical alleles, such as *AA*, for a particular trait. 395

homozygous recessive Possessing two identical alleles, such as *aa*, for a particular trait. 395

hormone Substance secreted by an endocrine gland that is transmitted in the blood or body fluids. 186, 304

human chorionic gonadotropin (HCG) Hormone produced by the placenta that helps maintain pregnancy and is the basis for the pregnancy test. 354, 375

human immunodeficiency virus (HIV) Virus responsible for AIDS. 264

humerus Heavy bone that extends from the scapula to the elbow. 98

Huntington disease Genetic disease marked by progressive deterioration of the nervous system due to deficiency of a neuro-transmitter. 145

hyaline cartilage Cartilage composed of very fine collagenous fibers and a matrix of a glassy, white, opaque appearance. 61

hydrocephalus Enlargement of the brain due to abnormal accumulation of cerebrospinal fluid. 146

hydrogen bond Weak attraction between a partially positive hydrogen and a partially negative oxygen or nitrogen some distance away; found in proteins and nucleic acids. 22

hydrolysis reaction Splitting of a bond by the addition of water. 24

hydrolytic enzyme Enzyme that catalyzes a reaction in which the substrate is broken down by the addition of water. 311

hydrophilic Type of molecule that interacts with water by dissolving in water and/or forming hydrogen bonds with water molecules. 22

hydrophobic Type of molecule that does not interact with water because it is nonpolar. 22

hyperglycemia Excessive glucose in the blood. 197

hyperopia Inability to see nearby objects. 177

hyperpnea Deep and labored breathing. 284

hypertension Elevated blood pressure, particularly the diastolic pressure. 20, 239

hyperthermia Abnormally high body temperature. 78

hypertonic solution Solution that has a higher concentration of solute and a lower concentration of water than the cell. 43

hypertrophy Increase in the size of an organ, usually by an increase in the size of its cells. 123

hypodermic needle Slender, hollow instrument for introducing material into or removing material from or below the skin. 71

hypodermis Mainly composed of fat, this loose layer is directly beneath the dermis; subcutaneous. 70

hypoglycemia Insufficient amount of glucose in the blood. 197

hypothalamic-inhibiting hormone One of many hormones produced by the hypothalamus that inhibits the secretion of an anterior pituitary hormone. 188

hypothalamic-releasing hormone One of many hormones produced by the hypothalamus that stimulates the secretion of an anterior pituitary hormone. 188

hypothalamus Region of the brain; the floor of the third ventricle that helps maintain homeostasis. 151, 188

hypothermia Abnormally low body temperature. 78

hypotonic solution Solution that has a lower concentration of solute and a higher concentration of water than the cell. 43

hysterectomy Surgical removal of the uterus. 352

I

ileum Lower portion of the small intestine. 302

ilium One of the bones of a coxal bone or hipbone. 100

immediate allergic response Allergic response that occurs within seconds of contact with an allergen; caused by the attachment of the allergen to IgE antibodies. 268

immune system All the cells in the body that protect the body against foreign organisms and substances, and also against cancerous cells. 255

immunity Resistance to disease-causing organisms. 255

immunization Strategy for achieving artificial immunity to the effects of specific disease-causing agents. 266

immunoglobulin (Ig) Globular plasma proteins that function as antibodies. 261

immunosuppressive Inactivating the immune system to prevent organ rejection, usually via a drug. 269

impetigo Contagious skin disease caused by bacteria in which vesicles erupt and crust over. 74

implantation Attachment and penetration of the embryo to the lining (endometrium) of the uterus. 349, 375

incontinence Involuntary loss of urine. 336

incus The middle of three ossicles of the ear; serves with the malleus and the stapes to conduct vibrations from the tympanic membrane to the oval window of the inner ear. 178

infant respiratory distress syndrome Condition in newborns, especially premature ones, in which the lungs collapse because of a lack of surfactant lining the alveoli. 279

inferior Situated below something else; pertaining to the lower surface of a part. 3

inferior vena cava Large vein that enters the right atrium from below and carries blood from the trunk and lower extremities. 242

infertility Inability to have as many children as desired. 360

inflammatory reaction Tissue response to injury that is characterized by dilation of blood vessels and accumulation of fluid in the affected region. 259

inhibin Hormone secreted by seminiferous tubules that inhibits the release of follicle-stimulating hormone from the anterior pituitary. 348

inner cell mass An aggregation of cells at one pole of the blastocyte, which is destined to form the embryo proper. 373

inner ear Portion of the ear, consisting of a vestibule, semicircular canals, and the cochlea, where balance is maintained and sound is transmitted. 178

inorganic molecule Type of molecule that is not an organic molecule; not derived from a living organism. 22

insertion End of a muscle that is attached to a movable part. 124

inspiration The act of breathing in; inhalation. 276

inspiratory reserve volume Volume of air that can be forcibly inhaled after normal inhalation. 281

insulin Hormone produced by the pancreas that regulates glucose storage in the liver and glucose uptake by cells. 196

insulin-dependent diabetes mellitus (IDDM) Type 1 diabetes mellitus characterized by abrupt onset of symptoms, dependence on exogenous insulin, and a tendency to develop ketoacidosis. 197

integration Summing up of excitatory and inhibitory signals by a neuron or by some part of the brain. 145

integument Pertaining to the skin. 70

integumentary system Pertaining to the skin and accessory organs. 8, 70

interatrial septum Wall between the atria of the heart. 226

intercalated disk Membranous boundary between adjacent cardiac muscle cells. 63

interferon Protein formed by a cell infected with a virus that can increase the resistance of other cells to the virus. 259

interleukin Class of immune system chemicals (cytokines) having varied effects on the body. 263

internal respiration Exchange of oxygen and carbon dioxide between blood and tissue fluid. 285

interneuron Neuron found within the central nervous system that takes nerve impulses from one portion of the system to another. 142

interstitial cell Hormone-secreting cell located between the seminiferous tubules of the testes. 345

intervertebral disk Layer of cartilage located between adjacent vertebrae. 94

intramembranous ossification Bone that forms from membranelike layers of primitive connective tissue. 86

intrauterine device Solid object placed in the uterine cavity for purposes of contraception; IUD. 358

intrauterine insemination (IUI) Process of achieving pregnancy in which donated sperm are deposited in the uterus. 360

inversion Movement of the foot so that the sole is turned inward. 106

in vitro fertilization (IVF) Process of achieving pregnancy in which eggs retrieved from an ovary are fertilized in a laboratory; viable embryos are then placed into the woman's uterus. 360

ion A charged atom. 20

ionic bond Chemical attraction between a positive ion and a negative ion. 20

iris Muscular ring that surrounds the pupil and regulates the passage of light through this opening. 170

iron deficiency anemia Abnormally low amount of red blood cells or hemoglobin, due to a lack of iron in the diet. 213

ischemic heart disease Insufficient oxygen delivery to the heart, usually caused by partially blocked coronary arteries. 228

ischial spine Projection of the coxal bone into the pelvic cavity. 100

isotonic solution Solution that contains the same concentration of solutes and water as does the cell. 43

isotope One of two or more atoms with the same atomic number that differs in the number of neutrons and, therefore, in weight. 19

IVF See *in vitro fertilization*. 360

IVI See *intrauterine insemination*. 360

J

jaundice Yellowish tint to the skin caused by an abnormal amount of bilirubin in the blood, indicating liver malfunction. 310

jejunum Middle portion of the small intestine. 302

joint Union of two or more bones; an articulation. 104

jugular Any of four veins that drain blood from the head and neck. 245

juxtaglomerular apparatus Structure located in the walls of arterioles near the glomerulus that regulates renal blood flow. 332

K

karyotype Arrangement of all the chromosomes from a nucleus by pairs in a fixed order. 390

keratin Insoluble protein present in the epidermis and in epidermal derivatives, such as hair and nails. 71

ketonuria Abnormal presence of acidic molecules called ketones in the urine. 198

kidney Organ in the urinary system that forms, concentrates, and excretes urine. 325

Klinefelter syndrome Condition caused by the inheritance of XXY chromosomes. 393

knee-jerk reflex Automatic, involuntary response initiated by tapping the ligaments just below the patella (kneecap). 155

kyphosis Increased roundness in the thoracic curvature of the spine; also called "hunchback." 94

L

labia majora Two large, hairy folds of skin of the female external genitalia. 353

labia minora Two small folds of skin inside the labia majora and encircling the clitoris. 353

lacrimal apparatus Structures that provide tears to wash the eye, consisting of the lacrimal gland and the lacrimal sac with its ducts. 168

lactation Production and secretion of milk by the mammary glands. 356

lacteal Lymph vessel in a villus of the wall of the small intestine. 302

lacuna Small pit or hollow cavity, as in bone or cartilage, where a cell or cells are located (pl., *lacunae*). 61

lambdoidal suture Line of junction between the occipital and parietal bones. 104

Langerhans cells Specialized epidermal cells that assist the immune system. 71

lanugo Short, fine hair that is present during the later portion of fetal development. 379

large intestine Portion of the digestive tract that extends from the small intestine to the anus. 304

laryngitis Inflammation of the larynx. 286

laryngopharynx Lower portion of the pharynx near the opening to the larynx. 278

larynx Structure that contains the vocal cords; also known as the voice box. 278

lateral Pertaining to the side. 3

lateral malleolus Rounded protuberance on the lateral surface of the ankle joint. 103

lens Clear, membranelike structure that is found in the eye behind the iris and that brings objects into focus. 170

leptin Hormone produced by adipose tissue that acts on the hypothalamus to signal satiety. 200

leukemia Form of cancer characterized by uncontrolled production of leukocytes in red bone marrow. 213

leukocytes Several types of colorless, nucleated blood cells that, among other functions, resist infection; white blood cells. 212

leukocytosis Abnormally large increase in the number of white blood cells. 213

leukopenia Abnormally low number of leukocytes in the blood. 213

LH See *luteinizing hormone*. 348

ligament Strong connective tissue that joins bone to bone. 59, 104

limbic system System that involves many different centers of the brain and that is concerned with visceral functioning and emotional responses. 151

lipase Enzyme secreted by the pancreas that digests or breaks down fats. 308

lipid Group of organic compounds that are insoluble in water—notably, fats, oils, and steroids. 26

liver Largest organ in the body, located in the abdominal cavity below the diaphragm; performs many vital functions that maintain homeostasis of blood. 308

loop of the nephron Portion of a nephron between the proximal and distal convoluted tubules; functions in water reabsorption. 327

loose connective tissue Tissue that is composed mainly of fibroblasts separated by collagenous and elastin fibers and that is found beneath epithelium. 59

lordosis Exaggerated lumbar curvature of the spine; also called "swayback." 94

lumen Space within a tubular structure such as a blood vessel or intestine. 299

lung Internal respiratory organ containing moist surfaces for gas exchange. 279

lunula Pale, half-moon–shaped area at the base of nails. 73

luteinizing hormone (LH) Hormone produced by the anterior pituitary that stimulates the development of the corpus luteum in females and the production of testosterone in males. 348

lymph Fluid having the same composition as tissue fluid; carried in lymph vessels. 217, 254

lymphadenitis Infection of the lymph nodes. 257

lymphangitis Infection of the lymphatic vessels. 257

lymphatic organ Organ other than a lymphatic vessel that is part of the lymphatic system; includes lymph nodes, tonsils, spleen, thymus gland, and bone marrow. 255

lymphatic system Vascular system that takes up excess tissue fluid and transports it to the bloodstream. 8, 254

lymphatic vessel Vessel that carries lymph. 217, 254

lymph node Mass of lymphatic tissue located along the course of a lymphatic vessel. 257

lymphocyte Type of white blood cell characterized by agranular cytoplasm; lymphocytes usually constitute 20–25% of the white cell count. 212

lymphoma Cancer of lymphatic tissue (reticular connective tissue). 257

lysosome Organelle involved in intracellular digestion; contains powerful digestive enzymes. 40

M

macromolecule Large molecule composed of smaller molecules. 2

macrophage Enlarged monocyte that ingests foreign material and cellular debris. 212, 259

macular degeneration Disruption of the macula lutea, a central part of the retina, causing blurred vision. 174

malignant The power to threaten life; cancerous. 80

malleolus Rounded projection from a bone. 103

malleus First of three ossicles of the ear; serves with the incus and stapes to conduct vibrations from the tympanic membrane to the oval window of the inner ear. 178

maltase Enzyme that catalyzes conversion of maltose into glucose. 311

mammary gland Milk-secreting gland that develops within the breast in pregnancy and lactation; only minimally developed in the breast of a nonpregnant or nonlactating woman. 73

mast cell Cell to which antibodies, formed in response to allergens, attach, bursting the cell and releasing allergy mediators, which cause symptoms. 259

mastoiditis Inflammation of the mastoid sinuses of the skull. 90

matrix Secreted basic material or medium of biological structures, such as the matrix of cartilage or bone. 58

medial Toward or near the midline. 3

mediastinum Tissue mass located between the lungs. 6

medulla oblongata Lowest portion of the brain; concerned with the control of internal organs. 151

medullary cavity Within the diaphysis of a long bone, cavity occupied by yellow marrow. 84

megakaryocyte Large bone marrow cell that gives rise to blood platelets. 214

meiosis Type of cell division in which the daughter cells have 23 chromosomes; occurs during spermatogenesis and oogenesis. 342

melanin Pigment found in the skin and hair of humans that is responsible for coloration. 71

melanocyte Melanin-producing cell. 71

melanocyte-stimulating hormone (MSH) Substance that causes melanocytes to secrete melanin in lower vertebrates. 188

melanoma Deadly form of skin cancer that begins in the melanocytes, pigment cells present in the epidermis. 74

melatonin Hormone, secreted by the pineal gland, that is involved in biorhythms. 200

memory B cell Cells derived from B lymphocytes that remain within the body for some time and account for active immunity. 260

meninges Protective membranous coverings around the brain and spinal cord (sing., *meninx*). 6, 66, 146

meniscus Piece of fibrocartilage that separates the surfaces of bones in the knee (pl., *menisci*). 104

menopause Termination of the menstrual cycle in older women. 355

menses (menstruation) Loss of blood and tissue from the uterus. 354

menstrual cycle Female reproductive cycle characterized by regularly occurring changes in the uterine lining. 354

mesentery Fold of peritoneal membrane that attaches an abdominal organ to the abdominal wall. 66

messenger RNA (mRNA) Nucleic acid (ribonucleic acid) complementary to genetic DNA; has codons that direct cell protein synthesis at the ribosomes. 39

metabolism All of the chemical changes that occur within cells. 29

metacarpal Bone of the hand between the wrist and the finger bones. 100

metaphase Stage in mitosis when chromosomes align in the center of the cell. 50

metastasis Mechanism of cancer spread in which cancer cells break off from the initial tumor, enter the blood vessels or lymphatic vessels, and start new tumors elsewhere in the body. 80

metatarsal bones Bones found in the foot between the ankle and the toes. 103

microtubule Hollow rod of the protein tubulin in the cytoplasm. 42

microvillus Cylindrical process that extends from some epithelial cell membranes and increases the membrane surface area (pl., *microvilli*). 302

micturition Emptying of the bladder; urination. 325

midbrain Small region of the brain stem located between the forebrain and the hindbrain; contains tracts that conduct impulses to and from the higher parts of the brain. 151

middle ear Portion of the ear consisting of the tympanic membrane, the oval and round windows, and the ossicles, where sound is amplified. 178

mineral Inorganic substance; certain minerals must be in the diet for normal metabolic functioning of cells. 315

mineralocorticoid Hormones the adrenal cortex secretes that influence the concentrations of electrolytes in body fluids. 193

mitochondrion Organelle in which cellular respiration produces the energy molecule ATP. 41

mitosis Type of cell division in which two daughter cells receive 46 chromosomes; occurs during growth and repair. 46

mixed nerve Nerve that contains both the long dendrites of sensory neurons and the long axons of motor neurons. 152

mole Raised growth on the skin due to an overgrowth of melanocytes. 74

molecule Smallest quantity of a substance that retains its chemical properties. 2, 20

monoclonal antibody Antibody of one type that is produced by cells derived from a lymphocyte that has fused with a cancer cell. 268

monocyte Type of white blood cell that functions as a phagocyte. 212

mononucleosis Viral disease characterized by an increase in atypical lymphocytes in the blood. 213

monosaccharide Simple sugar; a carbohydrate that cannot be decomposed by hydrolysis. 24

mons pubis The rounded, fleshy prominence over the pubic symphysis. 353

morphogenesis Establishment of shape and structure in an organism. 371

morula Early stage in development in which the embryo consists of a mass of cells, often spherical. 373

motor neuron Neuron that takes nerve impulses from the central nervous system to an effector; also known as an efferent neuron. 142

motor unit Motor neuron and all the muscle fibers it innervates. 122

mouth Opening through which food enters the body. 296

MS See *multiple sclerosis*. 269

mucous membrane Membrane lining a cavity or tube that opens to the outside of the body; also called mucosa. 66

multiple sclerosis (MS) Disease in which the outer, myelin layer of nerve fiber insulation becomes scarred, interfering with normal conduction of nerve impulses. 269

muscle fiber Muscle cell. 114, 116

muscle twitch Contraction of a whole muscle in response to a single stimulus. 122

muscular dystrophy Progressive muscle weakness and atrophy caused by deficient dystrophin protein. 136

muscular tissue Major type of tissue that is adapted to contract; the three kinds of muscle are cardiac, smooth, and skeletal. 62

myalgia Pain in a muscle or muscles. 136

myasthenia gravis Muscle weakness due to an inability to respond to the neurotransmitter acetylcholine. 136, 168, 269

myelin sheath Fatty plasma membranes of Schwann cells that cover long neuron fibers and give them a white, glistening appearance. 64, 142

myocardial infarction Damage to the myocardium due to blocked circulation in the coronary arteries; a heart attack. 228

myocardium Heart (cardiac) muscle consisting of striated muscle cells that interlock. 226

myofibril Contractile portion of muscle fibers. 116

myoglobin Pigmented compound in muscle tissue that stores oxygen. 116

myopia Inability to see distant objects clearly. 177

myosin Thick myofilament in myofibrils that is made of protein and is capable of breaking down ATP; see also *actin*. 116

myxedema Condition resulting from a deficiency of thyroid hormone in an adult. 191

N

nasal cavity Space within the nose. 277

nasopharynx Portion of the pharynx associated with the nasal cavity. 298

natural killer cell (NK) Lymphocyte that causes an infected or cancerous cell to burst. 259

negative feedback Mechanism that is activated by a surplus imbalance and acts to correct it by stopping the process that brought about the surplus. 10

nephron Anatomical and functional unit of the kidney; kidney tubule. 326

nerve Bundle of long nerve fibers that run to and/or from the central nervous system. 64, 152

nerve deafness Hearing impairment that usually occurs when the cilia on the sensory receptors within the cochlea have worn away. 182

nerve fiber Thin process of a neuron (i.e., axon, dendrite). 142

nerve impulse Change in polarity that flows along the membrane of a nerve fiber. 143

nervous tissue Tissue of the nervous system, consisting significantly of neurons and neuroglia. 64

neuroglia Nonconducting nerve cells that are intimately associated with neurons and function in a supportive capacity. 64, 142

neurolemmocyte Type of neuroglial cell that forms a myelin sheath around axons; also called a Schwann cell. 142

neuromuscular junction Junction between a neuron and a muscle fiber. 118

neuron Nerve cell that characteristically has three parts: dendrite, cell body, and axon. 64, 142

neurotransmitter Chemical made at the ends of axons that is responsible for transmission across a synapse. 145

neutral fat A triglyceride. 26

neutron Electrically neutral particle in an atomic nucleus. 18

neutrophil Phagocytic white blood cell that normally constitutes 60–70% of the white blood cell count. 212

node of Ranvier Gap in the myelin sheath of a nerve fiber. 64

nondisjunction Failure of the chromosomes (or chromatids) to separate during meiosis. 392

noninsulin-dependent diabetes mellitus (NIDDM) Type 2 diabetes mellitus, usually characterized by gradual onset with minimal or no symptoms of metabolic disturbance and no required exogenous insulin to prevent ketonuria and ketoacidosis. 198

norepinephrine Hormone secreted by the adrenal medulla to help initiate the "fight-or-flight" reaction. 145, 193

nose Specialized structure on the face that serves as the sense organ of smell and as part of the respiratory system. 277

nostril One of the external orifices of the nose. 277

nuclear envelope Membrane surrounding the cell nucleus and separating it from the cytoplasm. 39

nuclear pore Opening in the nuclear envelope. 39

nucleic acid Large organic molecule found in the nucleus (DNA and RNA) and in the cytoplasm (RNA). 31

nucleolus Organelle found inside the nucleus and composed largely of RNA for ribosome formation (pl., *nucleoli*). 36

nucleotide Building block of a nucleic acid molecule, consisting of a sugar, a nitrogen-containing base, and a phosphate group. 31

nucleus Large organelle that contains the chromosomes and acts as a cell control center. 36

O

obesity Excess adipose tissue; exceeding desirable weight by more than 20%. 318

occipital condyle One of two processes on the lateral portions of the occipital bone; for articulation with the atlas. 90

occipital lobe Area of the cerebrum responsible for vision, visual images, and other sensory experiences. 149

occluded coronary arteries Blocked blood vessels that serve the needs of the heart. 229

oil Substance, usually of plant origin and liquid at room temperature, formed when a glycerol molecule reacts with three fatty acid molecules. 26

olfactory cell Cell located high in the nasal cavity that bears receptor sites on cilia for various chemicals and whose stimulation results in smell. 167

oocyte Developing female gamete. 343

oogenesis Production of eggs in females by the process of meiosis and maturation. 351

oophorectomy Surgical removal of one or both ovaries. 352

opportunistic infection Disease that arises in the presence of a severely impaired immune system. 265

optic nerve Nerve composed of the ganglion cell fibers that form the innermost layer of the retina. 171

organ Structure consisting of a group of tissues that perform a specialized function; a component of an organ system. 2

organelle Part of a cell that performs a specialized function. 2, 36

organic molecule Carbon-containing molecule. 24

organism Individual living thing. 2

organ of Corti See *spiral organ*. 179

organ system Group of related organs working together. 2

organ transplantation Replacement of a diseased or defective organ with a healthy one. 8

orgasm Physical and emotional climax during sexual intercourse; results in ejaculation in the male. 347

origin End of a muscle that is attached to a relatively immovable part. 124

oropharynx Portion of the pharynx in the posterior part of the mouth. 298

osmosis Movement of water from an area of greater concentration to an area of lesser concentration across the plasma membrane. 43

osmotic pressure The amount of pressure needed to stop osmosis; the potential pressure of a solution caused by nondiffusible solute particles in the solution. 209

ossicles Tiny bones in the middle ear; malleus (hammer), incus (anvil), and stapes (stirrup). 178

ossification Formation of bone. 86, 370

osteoarthritis Disintegration of the cartilage between bones at a synovial joint. 107

osteoblast Bone-forming cell. 86

osteoclast Cell that causes the erosion of bone. 86

osteocyte Mature bone cell. 86

osteoporosis Weakening of bones due to decreased bone mass. 107

osteoprogenitor cells Cells found on or near all of the free surfaces of bone, which undergo division and transform into osteoblasts. 86

otitis media Inflammation of the middle ear. 286

otolith Granule that lies above, and whose movement stimulates, ciliated cells in the utricle and saccule. 181

otosclerosis Overgrowth of bone that causes the stapes to adhere to the oval window, resulting in conductive deafness. 182

ototoxic Damaging to any of the elements of hearing or balance. 182

outer ear Portion of the ear consisting of the pinna and the auditory canal. 178

oval window Membrane-covered opening between the stapes and the inner ear. 178

ovarian cancer Cancer of an ovary. 352

ovariohysterectomy Surgical removal of the ovaries and uterus. 353

ovary Female gonad; the organ that produces eggs, estrogen, and progesterone. 197, 349

ovulation Discharge of a mature egg from the follicle within the ovary. 351

oxygen deficit Amount of oxygen needed to metabolize the lactic acid that accumulates during vigorous exercise. 120

oxyhemoglobin Hemoglobin bound to oxygen in a loose, reversible way. 285

oxytocin Hormone released by the posterior pituitary that causes contraction of uterus and milk letdown. 188

P

pacemaker Small region of neuromuscular tissue that initiates the heartbeat; also called the *SA node*. 230

palatine tonsil Either of two small, almond-shaped masses located on either side of the oropharynx, composed mainly of lymphatic tissue; believed to act as sources of bacteria-killing phagocytes. 298

pancreas Endocrine organ located near the stomach that secretes digestive enzymes into the duodenum and produces hormones, notably insulin. 196, 308

pancreatic amylase Enzyme that digests starch to maltose. 308

pancreatic islets (of Langerhans) Distinctive groups of cells within the pancreas that secrete insulin and glucagon. 196

papillary muscle Muscle that extends inward from the ventricular walls of the heart and to which the chordae tendineae attach. 226

Pap smear Sample of cells removed from the tip of the cervix and then stained and examined microscopically. 352

paranasal sinus One of several air-filled cavities in the maxillary, frontal, sphenoid, and ethmoid bones that is lined with mucous membrane and drains into the nasal cavity. 277

paraplegia Paralysis of the lower body and legs, due to injury to the spinal cord between vertebrae T1 and L2. 147

parasympathetic division Portion of the autonomic nervous system that usually promotes those activities associated with a normal state. 157

parathyroid gland One of four small endocrine glands embedded in the posterior portion of the thyroid gland. 192

parathyroid hormone (PTH) Hormone secreted by the parathyroid glands that raises the blood calcium level primarily by stimulating reabsorption of bone. 192

parental cell Cell that divides so as to form daughter cells. 59

parietal Pertaining to the wall of a cavity. 66

parietal lobe Area of the cerebrum responsible for sensations involving temperature, touch, pressure, pain, and speech. 149

parietal pericardium Outer layer of the two layers of the serous pericardium, lining the fibrous pericardium. 7, 226

parietal peritoneum Lines the abdominal and pelvic walls and the inferior surface of the thoracic diaphragm. 7

parietal pleura Membrane that lines the inner wall of the thoracic cavity. 7

Parkinson disease Progressive deterioration of the central nervous system due to a deficiency in the neurotransmitter dopamine; also called paralysis agitans. 145

parturition Processes that lead to and include the birth of a human and the expulsion of the extraembryonic membranes through the terminal portion of the female reproductive tract. 384

passive immunity Protection against infection acquired by transfer of antibodies to a susceptible individual. 266

patella Bone of the kneecap. 102

pathogen Disease-causing agents, such as bacteria and viruses. 209

pathologist Person trained in knowledge of diseases and their symptoms, allowing for diagnosis of disease. 66

pectoral girdle Portion of the skeleton that provides support and attachment for the upper limbs. 97

pedigree Chart showing the relationships of relatives and which ones have a particular trait. 397

pelvic cavity Hollow place within the ring formed by the sacrum and coxal bones. 7

pelvic girdle Portion of the skeleton to which the lower limbs are attached. 100

pelvic inflammatory disease (PID) Latent infection of gonorrhea or chlamydia in the vasa deferentia or uterine tubes. 363

penis Male excretory and copulatory organ. 347

pentose Five-carbon sugar; deoxyribose is the pentose sugar found in DNA; ribose is a pentose sugar found in RNA. 24

pepsin Protein-digesting enzyme produced by the stomach. 301

peptidase Enzyme that catalyzes the breakdown of polypeptides. 311

peptide bond Bond that joins two amino acids. 28

peptide hormone Type of hormone that is a protein, a peptide, or derived from an amino acid. 201

perforin Protein released by cytotoxic T cells that attaches to an antigen. 263

pericardial fluid Fluid found in small amounts in the potential space between the parietal and visceral laminae of the serous pericardium. 226

pericardium Protective serous membrane that surrounds the heart. 66, 226

periodontitis Inflammation of the periodontal membrane that lines tooth sockets, causing loss of bone and loosening of teeth. 297

periosteum Fibrous connective tissue covering the surface of bone. 84

peripheral Situated away from the center of the body or an organ. 3

peripheral nervous system (PNS) Nerves and ganglia of the nervous system that lie outside the brain and spinal cord. 141

peristalsis Rhythmical contraction that moves the contents along in tubular organs, such as the digestive tract. 299

peritoneum Serous membrane that lines the abdominopelvic cavity and encloses the abdominal viscera. 66

peritonitis Generalized infection of the lining of the abdominal cavity. 7, 304

peritubular capillary network Capillary network that surrounds a nephron and functions in reabsorption during urine formation. 326

pernicious anemia Insufficiency of mature red blood cells, due to poor absorption of vitamin B$_{12}$. 213

Peyer patches Lymphatic organs located in small intestine. 257

phagocytosis Taking in of bacteria and/or debris by engulfing; also called cell eating. 212

phalanges Bones of the fingers and thumb in the hand and of the toes in the foot (sing., *phalanx*). 103

pharyngeal tonsil Diffuse lymphatic tissue and follicles in the roof and posterior wall of the nasopharynx. 298

pharynx Common passageway for both food intake and air movement; the throat. 277, 298

phenotype Physical manifestation of a trait that results from the action of a particular set of genes. 395

phlebitis Inflammation of a vein. 235

phospholipid Lipid that contains two fatty acid molecules and a phosphate group combined with a glycerol molecule. 27

pH scale Measure of the hydrogen ion concentration; any pH below 7 is acidic, and any pH above 7 is basic. 23

physiology Branch of science dealing with the study of body functions. 2

pia mater Innermost meningeal layer that is in direct contact with the brain and spinal cord. 146

pineal gland Small endocrine gland, located in the third ventricle of the brain, that secretes melatonin and is involved in biorhythms. 200

pinna Outer, funnel-like structure of the ear that picks up sound waves. 178

pituitary dwarfism Condition in which a person has normal proportions but small stature; caused by inadequate growth hormone. 190

pituitary gland (hypophysis) Endocrine gland attached to the base of the brain that consists of anterior and posterior lobes. 188

pivot joint End of a bone moving within a ring formed by another bone and connective tissue. 105

placenta Structure formed from the chorion and uterine tissue, through which nutrient and waste exchange occurs for the embryo and later the fetus. 371

placental membrane Semipermeable membrane that separates the fetal from the maternal blood in the placenta. 378

plaque Accumulation of soft masses of fatty material, particularly cholesterol, beneath the inner linings of arteries. 228

plasma Liquid portion of blood. 61, 209

plasma cell Cell derived from a B lymphocyte that is specialized to mass-produce antibodies. 260

plasma membrane Membrane that surrounds the cytoplasm of cells and regulates the passage of molecules into and out of the cell. 36

platelet Cell-like disks formed from fragmentation of megakaryocytes that initiate blood clotting. 214

platelet plug Platelets that stick and cling to each other in order to seal a break in a blood vessel wall. 214

pleura (pl., *pleurae*) Serous membrane that covers the lungs and lines the walls of the chest and the diaphragm. 7, 66, 279

pneumonectomy Surgical removal of all or part of a lung. 288

pneumonia Infection of the lungs that causes alveoli to fill with mucus and pus. 286

PNS See *peripheral nervous system.* 141

polar body Small, nonfunctional cell that is a product of meiosis in the female. 351

polar molecule Combination of atoms in which the electrical charge is not distributed symmetrically. 22

polycythemia Abnormally high number of red blood cells in the blood. 213

polydipsia Chronic, excessive intake of water. 197

polyp Small, abnormal growth on any mucous membrane, such as in the large intestine. 306

polypeptide A compound formed by the union of many amino acid molecules. 28

polyphagia Excessive eating. 197

polyribosome String of ribosomes simultaneously translating regions of the same mRNA strand during protein synthesis. 39

polysaccharide Carbohydrate composed of many bonded glucose units—for example, glycogen. 25

polyuria Excessive output of urine. 197

poly-X female Female who has more than two X chromosomes. 394

pons Portion of the brain stem above the medulla oblongata and below the midbrain; assists the medulla oblongata in regulating the breathing rate. 151

portal triad Grouping of the tributaries of the hepatic artery, vein, and bile duct at the angles of the lobules of the liver. 308

positive feedback Process by which changes cause more changes of a similar type, producing unstable conditions. 11, 188

posterior Toward the back; opposite of *anterior.* 3

posterior pituitary (neurohypophysis) Portion of the pituitary gland connected by a stalk to the hypothalamus. 190

posterior (dorsal)-root ganglion Mass of sensory neuron cell bodies located in the dorsal root of a spinal nerve. 154

postganglionic fiber In the autonomic nervous system, the axon that leaves, rather than goes to, a ganglion. 157

prefrontal area Association area in the frontal lobe that receives information from other association areas and uses it to reason and plan actions. 150

preganglionic fiber In the autonomic nervous system, the axon that goes to, rather than leaves, a ganglion. 157

premature baby Child born before full term and weighing 5 pounds, 8 ounces, or less. 380

presbycusis Loss of hearing that accompanies old age. 181

primary germ layers Three layers (endoderm, mesoderm, and ectoderm) of embryonic cells that develop into specific tissues and organs. 377

primary motor area Area in the frontal lobe where voluntary commands begin; each section controls a part of the body. 149

primary somatosensory area Area posterior to the central sulcus where sensory information arrives from the skin and skeletal muscles. 149

primary spermatocyte Cell dividing into two secondary spermatocytes. 345

prime mover Muscle most directly responsible for a particular movement. 124

PRL See *prolactin*. 188

progesterone Female sex hormone secreted by the ovaries that, along with estrogen, promotes the development and maintenance of the primary and secondary female sex characteristics. 197

prolactin (PRL) Hormone secreted by the anterior pituitary that stimulates milk production in the mammary glands; also known as lactogenic hormone. 188

pronation Rotation of the forearm so that the palm faces backward. 106

prophase Stage of mitosis when chromosomes become visible. 49

proprioceptor Sensory receptor that assists the brain in knowing the position of the limbs. 164

prostaglandins Hormones that have various and powerful effects, often within the cells that produce them. 200

prostate gland Gland in males that is located about the urethra at the base of the bladder; contributes to the seminal fluid. 343

protein Macromolecule composed of amino acids. 28

prothrombin Plasma protein made by the liver that must be present in blood before clotting can occur. 214

prothrombin activator Enzyme that catalyzes the transformation of the precursor prothrombin to the active enzyme thrombin. 214

proton Positively charged particle in an atomic nucleus. 18

proximal Closer to the midline or origin; opposite of *distal*. 3

proximal convoluted tubule Highly coiled region of a nephron near the glomerular capsule. 326

pseudostratified columnar Appearance of layering in some epithelial cells when, actually, each cell touches a baseline and true layers do not exist. 57

psoriasis Common chronic, inherited skin disease in which red patches are covered with scales; occurs most often on the elbows, knees, scalp, and trunk. 74

PTH See *parathyroid hormone*. 192

puberty Stage of development in which the reproductive organs become functional. 342

pubic symphysis Slightly movable cartilaginous joint between the anterior surfaces of the hip bones. 104

pulmonary artery Blood vessel that takes blood away from the heart to the lungs. 242

pulmonary circuit Path of blood through vessels that take O₂-poor blood to and O₂-rich blood away from the lungs. 242

pulmonary edema Excessive fluid in the lungs caused by congestive heart failure. 257

pulmonary embolism Blockage of a pulmonary artery by a blood clot that commonly originates in a vein of the lower legs. 235

pulmonary fibrosis Accumulation of fibrous connective tissue in the lungs; caused by inhaling irritating particles, such as silica, coal dust, or asbestos. 287

pulmonary tuberculosis Tuberculosis of the lungs, caused by the tubercle bacillus. 286

pulmonary vein Blood vessel that takes blood away from the lungs to the heart. 242

pulse Vibration felt in arterial walls due to expansion of the aorta following ventricular contraction. 238

pupil Opening in the center of the iris that controls the amount of light entering the eye. 170

Purkinje fiber Specialized muscle fiber that conducts the cardiac impulse from the AV bundle into the ventricular walls. 230

pus Thick, yellowish fluid composed of dead phagocytes, dead tissue, and bacteria. 259

pyelonephritis Inflammation of the kidney due to bacterial infection. 334

Q

quadriplegia Paralysis of the entire body and all four limbs, due to injury to the spinal cord between vertebrae C4 and T1. 147

R

radioactive isotope Atom whose nucleus undergoes degeneration and in the process gives off radiation. 19

radius Elongated bone located on the thumb side of the lower arm. 99

recessive allele Hereditary factor that expresses itself only when two copies are present in the genotype. 395

recruitment Increase in the number of motor units activated as intensity of stimulation increases. 123

rectum Terminal portion of the intestine. 304

red blood cell See *erythrocyte*. 61, 211

red bone marrow Blood cell-forming tissue located in spaces within certain bones. 84, 225

reduced hemoglobin (HHb) Hemoglobin that is carrying hydrogen ions. 285

referred pain Pain perceived as having come from a site other than that of its actual origin. 165

reflex action Automatic, involuntary response of an organism to a stimulus. 154, 298

renal artery Vessel that originates from the aorta and delivers blood to the kidney. 325

renal cortex Outer, primarily vascular portion of the kidney. 326

renal medulla Inner portion of the kidney, including the renal pyramids. 326

renal pelvis Inner cavity of the kidney formed by the expanded ureter and into which the collecting ducts open. 326

renal vein Vessel that takes blood from the kidney to the inferior vena cava. 325

renin Secretion from the kidney that activates angiotensinogen to angiotensin I. 194, 238, 332

replication Production of an exact copy of a DNA sequence. 47

repolarization Recovery of a neuron's polarity to the resting potential after the neuron ceases transmitting impulses. 143

residual volume Volume of air that remains in the lungs after normal exhalation. 281

respiration Transport and exchange of gases between the atmosphere and the cells via the lungs and blood vessels. 276

respiratory center Group of neurons in the medulla oblongata that regulates respiration. 283

respiratory membrane Alveolar wall plus the capillary wall, across which gas exchange occurs. 280

retina Innermost layer of the eyeball that contains the rod cells and cone cells. 171

retinal A form of vitamin A. 173

rheumatoid arthritis Persistent inflamation of synovial joints, often causing cartilage destruction, bone erosion, and joint deformities. 107, 269

Rh factor Type of antigen on red blood cells. 219

rhodopsin Light-sensitive biochemical in the rod cells of the retina; visual purple. 172

ribonucleic acid (RNA) Nucleic acid that helps DNA in protein synthesis. 31

ribosomal RNA (rRNA) RNA (ribonucleic acid) occurring in ribosomes, structures involved in protein synthesis. 48

ribosome Minute particle, found attached to the endoplasmic reticulum or loose in the cytoplasm, that is the site of protein synthesis. 39

rickets Defective mineralization of the skeleton, usually due to inadequate vitamin D in the body. 20

RNA See *ribonucleic acid*. 31

rod cell Dim-light receptor in the retina of the eye that detects motion but not color. 172

rotation Movement of a bone around its own longitudinal axis. 106

rotational equilibrium Maintenance of balance when the head and body are suddenly moved or rotated. 181

rough ER Endoplasmic reticulum that is studded with ribosomes on the side of the membrane that faces the cytoplasm. See *smooth ER*. 40

round window Membrane-covered opening between the inner ear and the middle ear. 178

rubella An acute, infectious disease affecting the respiratory tract in children and nonimmune young adults; characterized by a slight cold, sore throat, and fever, and the appearance of a fine, pink rash. 382

rugae Deep folds, as in the wall of the stomach. 301

S

saccule Saclike cavity of the inner ear that contains receptors for gravitational equilibrium. 181

sacroiliac joint Connection between the coxal bone and the sacrum. 100

sacrum Bone consisting of five fused vertebrae that form the posterior wall of the pelvic girdle. 95

saddle joint Two bones joined, having convex and concave surfaces that are complementary. 105

sagittal plane Plane or section that divides a structure into right and left portions. 5

sagittal suture Line of junction between the two parietal bones in the cranium. 104

salivary amylase In humans, enzyme in saliva that digests starch to maltose. 296, 311

salivary gland Gland associated with the mouth; secretes saliva. 296

salpingectomy Surgical removal of the uterine tubes. 352

salt Compound produced by a reaction between an acid and a base. 20

SA node See *sinoatrial node.* 230

sarcoma Cancer that arises in striated muscle, cartilage, or bone. 66

sarcomere Structural and functional unit of a myofibril. 116

saturated fatty acid Organic molecule that includes a fatty acid molecule which lacks double bonds between the atoms of its carbon chain. 26

scapula Large bone in the posterior shoulder area (pl., *scapulae*). 97

Schwann cell Cell that surrounds a fiber of a peripheral nerve and forms the neurilemmal sheath and myelin. 64, 139

SCID See *severe combined immunodeficiency disease.* 270

sclera White, fibrous outer layer of the eyeball. 170

scoliosis Abnormal lateral (side-to-side) curvature of the vertebral column. 94

scrotum Pouch of skin that encloses the testes. 7, 343

sebaceous gland Gland of the skin that secretes sebum. 73

sebum Oily secretion of the sebaceous glands. 73

secondary sex characteristic Trait that is sometimes helpful but not absolutely necessary for reproduction and is maintained by the sex hormones in males and females. 348

secondary spermatocyte One of the two cells into which a primary spermatocyte divides, and which in turn gives rise to spermatids. 345

selectively permeable Membrane that allows some molecules through but not others. 43

sella turcica Saddle-shaped area of the sphenoid bone; houses the pituitary gland. 92

semen Sperm-containing secretion of males; seminal fluid plus sperm. 343

semicircular canal Tubular structure within the inner ear with ampullae that contain the receptors responsible for the sense of rotational equilibrium. 178

semilunar valve Valve resembling a half-moon located between the ventricles and their attached vessels. 226

seminal fluid Sperm-containing secretion of males; also called semen. 343

seminal vesicle Convoluted, saclike structure attached to vas deferens near the base of the bladder in males; contributes to seminal fluid. 343

seminiferous tubule Highly coiled duct within the male testes that produces and transports sperm. 344

sensory neuron Neuron that takes the nerve impulse to the central nervous system; also known as an afferent neuron. 142

sensory receptor Sensory structure specialized to receive information from the environment and to generate nerve impulses. 164

serous membrane Membrane that covers internal organs and lines cavities lacking an opening to the outside of the body; also called serosa. 6, 66

serum Light-yellow liquid left after clotting of the blood. 214

severe combined immunodeficiency disease (SCID) Congenital illness in which both antibody- and cell-mediated immunity are lacking or inadequate. 270

sex chromosome Chromosome responsible for the development of characteristics associated with maleness or femaleness; an X or Y chromosome. 390

sex-linked Allele that occurs on the sex chromosomes but may control a trait that has nothing to do with the sex characteristics of an individual. 396

sexually transmitted disease (STD) Illness communicated primarily or exclusively through sexual intercourse. 362

sickle-cell disease Hereditary disease in which red blood cells are narrow and curved so that they are unable to pass through capillaries and are destroyed, causing chronic anemia. 213

sigmoid colon Portion of the large intestine that is S-shaped and extends from the descending colon to the rectum. 304

simple columnar epithelium Covering of the internal and external surfaces of the body; composed of a single layer of tall, prismatic cells. 57

simple cubodial epithelium Covering of the internal and external surfaces of the body; composed of a single layer of cube-shaped cells. 55

simple goiter Condition in which an enlarged thyroid produces low levels of thyroxine. 191

simple squamous epithelium Covering of the internal and external surfaces of the body; composed of a single layer of flattened, platelike cells. 55

sinoatrial (SA) node Small region of neuromuscular tissue that initiates the heartbeat; also called the pacemaker. 230

sinus Cavity; for example, the sinuses in the human skull. 90

sinusitis Inflammation of the mucous membrane lining a paranasal sinus. 286

sister chromatids Two chromatids of a chromosome, held together by a centromere. 47

skeletal muscle Contractile tissue that comprises the muscles attached to the skeleton; also called striated muscle. 62, 114

SLE See *systemic lupus erythematosus.* 269

sliding filament theory Muscles contract when the thin (actin) and thick (myosin) filaments move past each other, shortening the skeletal muscle cells. 116

small intestine Portion of the digestive tract that extends from the lower opening of the stomach to the large intestine. 302

smooth ER Synthesizes the phospholipids that occur in membranes, among other functions, depending on the particular cell. 40

smooth muscle Contractile tissue that comprises the muscles in the walls of internal organs; also called visceral muscle. 63, 114

soft palate Entirely muscular posterior portion of the roof of the mouth. 296

solute Substance dissolved in a solution. 43

somatic system Portion of the peripheral nervous system containing motor neurons that control skeletal muscles. 152

somatotropin See *growth hormone.* 188

spasm Sudden, violent, involuntary contraction of a muscle or a group of muscles. 136

sperm Male gamete having a haploid number of chromosomes and the ability to fertilize an egg, the female gamete. 345

spermatid Intermediate stage in the formation of sperm cells. 345

spermatogenesis Sperm production in males by the process of meiosis and maturation. 345

spermatozoa Developing male gametes. 345

sphincter Muscle that surrounds a tube and closes or opens the tube by contracting and relaxing. 299

spinal cord Portion of the central nervous system extending downward from the brain stem through the vertebral canal. 146

spinal meningitis Inflammation of the meninges of the spinal cord. 6

spinal nerve Nerve that arises from the spinal cord. 152

spindle Apparatus composed of microtubules to which the chromosomes are attached during cell division. 49

spiral organ Structure in the vertebrate inner ear that contains auditory receptors; also called organ of Corti. 179

spleen Large, glandular organ located in the upper left region of the abdomen that stores and purifies blood. 257

spongy bone Bone found at the ends of long bones; consists of bars and plates separated by irregular spaces. 61, 84

sprain Joint injury in which some of the fibers of a supporting ligament are ruptured, but the continuity of the ligament remains intact. 136

squamosal suture Type of suture formed by overlapping of the broad, beveled edges of the participating bones. 104

stapes The last of three ossicles of the ear; serves with the malleus and incus to conduct vibrations from the tympanic membrane to the oval window of the inner ear. 178

starch Polysaccharide that is common in foods of plant origin. 25

stem cell A precursor cell. 210

sternum Breastbone to which the ribs are ventrally attached. 96

steroid Lipid-soluble, biologically active molecules having four interlocking rings; examples are cholesterol, progesterone, and testosterone. 27

steroid hormone Type of hormone that has the same complex of four-carbon rings, but each one has different side chains. 201

stomach Saclike, expandable digestive organ located between the esophagus and the small intestine. 301

strain An overstretching or overexertion of some muscles. 136

stratified Layered, as in stratified epithelium, which contains several layers of cells. 55

stratified squamous epithelium Covering of the internal or external surfaces of the body; composed of layered, flattened, platelike cells. 57

stratum basale Deepest layer of the epidermis where cell division occurs. 70

stratum corneum Uppermost keratinized layer of the epidermis. 71

stroke See *cerebrovascular accident.* 149, 239

sty Inflammation of a sebaceous gland. 168

subclavian Either of two arteries branching off the aortic arch and supplying the arms. 245

subcutaneous injection Introduction of a substance beneath the skin, using a syringe. 71

subcutaneous tissue Tissue beneath the dermis that tends to contain fat cells. 71

subdural hematoma Accumulation of blood between the dura mater and the brain. 146

superficial Near the surface. 3

superior Toward the upper part of a structure or toward the head. 3

superior vena cava Large vein that enters the right atrium from above and carries blood from the head, thorax, and upper limbs to the heart. 242

supination Rotation of the forearm so that the palm faces forward when in the anatomical position. 106

surface tension Force that holds moist membranes together when water molecules attract. 279

surfactant Agent that reduces the surface tension of water; in the lungs, a surfactant prevents the alveoli from collapsing. 279

suture Type of immovable joint articulation found between bones of the skull. 90

sweat gland Skin gland that secretes a fluid substance for evaporative cooling; also called sudoriferous gland. 73

sympathetic division Part of the autonomic nervous system whose effects are generally associated with emergency situations. 157

synapse Region between two nerve cells where the nerve impulse is transmitted from one to the other, usually from axon to dendrite. 145

synaptic cleft Small gap between the synaptic knob on one neuron and the dendrite on another neuron. 145

syndrome A group of symptoms that characterize a disease condition. 195, 390

synergist Muscle that assists the action of the prime mover. 124

synovial fluid Fluid secreted by the synovial membrane. 104

synovial joint Freely movable joint. 104

synovial membrane Membrane that forms the inner lining of a capsule of a freely movable joint. 66, 104

synthesis reaction To build up, as in the combining of two small molecules to form a larger molecule. 29

syphilis Sexually transmitted disease caused by the bacterium *Treponema pallidum* characterized by a painless chancre on the penis or cervix; if untreated, can lead to cardiac and central nervous system disorders. 364

systemic circuit Part of the cardiovascular system that serves body parts other than the gas-exchanging surfaces in the lungs. 242

systemic disease Illness that involves the entire body or several body systems. 12

systemic lupus erythematosus (SLE) Syndrome involving the connective tissues and various organs, including kidney failure. 269

systole Contraction of the heart chambers, particularly the left ventricle. 232

systolic pressure Arterial blood pressure during the systolic phase of the cardiac cycle. 239

T

tachycardia Abnormally rapid heartbeat. 231

talus Ankle bone. 103

tarsal bones Bones of the ankle in humans. 103

taste bud Organ containing the receptors associated with the sense of taste. 166

Tay-Sachs Lethal genetic disease in which the newborn has a faulty lysosomal digestive enzyme. 40

tectorial membrane Membrane in the spiral organ (organ of Corti) that lies above and makes contact with the receptor cells for hearing. 179

telophase Stage in mitosis when newly formed cells separate. 50

template Pattern or guide used to make copies; parental strand of DNA serves as a guide for the production of daughter DNA strands, and DNA also serves as a guide for the production of messenger RNA. 47

temporal lobe Area of the cerebrum responsible for hearing and smelling and for the interpretation of sensory experience and memory. 149

tendinitis Inflammation of muscle tendons and their attachments. 136

tendon Tissue that connects muscle to bone. 59, 115

teratogen Any substance that produces abnormalities during human development. 382

testis Male gonad; the organ that produces sperm and testosterone (pl., *testes*). 197, 343

testosterone The most potent of the androgens, the male sex hormones. 197, 345

tetanic contraction Sustained muscle contraction without relaxation. 122

tetanus Acute infection caused by the toxin of the tetanus bacterium; results in a rigidly locked jaw. 136

tetany Severe twitching caused by involuntary contraction of the skeletal muscles due to a lack of calcium. 192

thalamus Mass of gray matter located at the base of the cerebrum in the wall of the third ventricle; receives sensory information and selectively passes it to the cerebrum. 151

thoracic cavity Hollow place within the chest. 6

thrombin Enzyme derived from prothrombin that converts fibrinogen to fibrin threads during blood clotting. 214

thrombocyte A blood platelet. 214

thrombocytopenia Insufficient number of platelets in the blood. 214

thromboembolism Obstruction of a blood vessel by a thrombus that has dislodged from the site of its formation. 214, 228

thrombus Blood clot that remains in the blood vessel where it formed. 214

thymosins Hormones secreted by the thymus. 200

thymus gland Lobular gland that lies in the neck and chest area and is necessary for the development of immunity. 200, 256

thyroid gland Endocrine gland, located just below the larynx and in front of the trachea, that secretes thyroid hormones. 191

thyroid-stimulating hormone (TSH) Hormone that causes the thyroid to produce thyroxine. 188

thyroxine (T_4) Hormone produced by the thyroid that speeds the metabolic rate. 191

tibia Shinbone found in the lower leg. 102

tidal volume Amount of air that enters the lungs during a normal, quiet inspiration. 281

tight junction Junction between cells when adjacent plasma membrane proteins join to form an impermeable barrier. 65

tissue Group of similar cells that performs a specialized function. 2, 55

tissue fluid Fluid found around tissue cells that contains molecules that enter from or exit to the capillaries. 216

tissue thromboplastin Clotting factor, released or derived from tissues, that interacts with platelets, calcium ions, and other clotting factors. 215

T lymphocyte One of two types of lymphocytes: a killer T cell that interacts directly with antigen-bearing cells and is responsible for cell-mediated immunity, or a helper T cell that stimulates other immune cells. 212, 260

tone Continuous, partial contraction of muscle. 123

tonicity Osmolarity of a solution compared to that of a cell. If the solution is isotonic to the cell, there is no net movement of water; if the solution is hypotonic, the cell gains water; and if the solution is hypertonic, the cell loses water. 43

tonsil Partly encapsulated lymph nodule located in the pharynx. 257, 286

tonsillectomy Surgical removal of the tonsils. 286

tonsillitis Inflammation of the tonsils. 286

trabeculae Branching bony plate that separates irregular spaces within spongy bone. 61

tracer Substance having an attached radioactive isotope that allows a researcher to track its whereabouts in a biological system. 19

trachea Windpipe; serves as a passageway for air. 278

tracheostomy Creation of an artificial airway by incision of the trachea and insertion of a tube. 278

tract Bundle of neurons forming a transmission pathway through the brain and spinal cord. 146

transcription Manufacturing RNA from DNA. 48

transfer RNA (tRNA) Molecule of RNA (ribonucleic acid) that carries an amino acid to a ribosome engaged in the process of protein synthesis. 48

translation Assembly of an amino acid chain according to the sequence of base triplets in a molecule of mRNA. 48

transverse colon Portion of the large intestine that travels transversely as it extends from the ascending colon to the descending colon. 304

transverse plane Plane or section that divides a structure horizontally to give a cross section. 5

tricuspid valve Atrioventricular valve between the right atrium and the right ventricle. 226

triglyceride Lipid composed of three fatty acids combined with a glyercol molecule. 26

triplet code Three-nucleotide base unit coding for a particular amino acid during protein synthesis. 48

trisomy State of having an extra chromosome—three instead of the normal two. 392

trophoblast Outer cells of a blastocyst that help form the placenta and other extra-embryonic membranes. 373

trypsin Protein-digesting enzyme produced by the pancreas. 308

TSH See *thyroid-stimulating hormone.* 188

T (transverse) tubule Membranous channel that extends inward from a muscle fiber membrane and passes through the fiber. 116

tubal ligation Method for preventing pregnancy in which the uterine tubes are cut and sealed. 359

tubular reabsorption Process that transports substances out of the renal tubule into the interstitial fluid from which the substances diffuse into peritubular capillaries. 329

tubular secretion Process of substances moving out of the peritubular capillaries into the renal tubule. 329

tumor Abnormal growth of tissue that serves no useful purpose. 80

Turner syndrome Condition caused by the inheritance of a single X chromosome. 393

tympanic membrane Membrane located between the external and middle ear; the eardrum. 178

U

ulcer Open sore in the lining of the stomach; frequently caused by bacterial infection. 301

ulna Elongated bone within the lower arm. 99

umbilical Pertaining to the umbilicus. 6

umbilical cord Cord through which blood vessels that connect the fetus to the placenta pass. 377

unsaturated fatty acid Organic compound that includes a fatty acid molecule having one or more double bonds between the atoms of its carbon chain. 26

urea Primary nitrogenous waste of mammals. 324

uremia High level of urea nitrogen in the blood. 334

ureters Tubes that take urine from the kidneys to the bladder. 325

urethra Tube that takes urine from the bladder to the outside of the body. 325, 343

urethritis Inflammation of the urethra. 334

uric acid Product of nucleic acid metabolism in the body. 324

urinalysis Examination of a urine sample to determine its chemical, physical, and microscopic aspects. 334

urinary bladder Organ where urine is stored before being discharged by way of the urethra. 325

urticaria Skin eruption characterized by the development of welts as a result of capillary dilation. 74

uterine tube Tube that extends from the uterus on each side toward an ovary and transports sex cells; also called fallopian tube or oviduct. 352

uterus Female organ in which the fetus develops. 349

utricle Saclike cavity of the inner ear that contains receptors for static equilibrium. 181

uvula A fleshy portion of the soft palate that hangs down above the root of the tongue. 296

V

vaccine Treated antigens that can promote active immunity when administered. 266

vagina Female copulatory organ and birth canal. 349

valve Structure that opens and closes, ensuring one-way flow; common to vessels, such as systemic veins, lymphatic veins, and veins to the heart. 235

varicose vein Irregular dilation of a superficial vein, seen particularly in the lower legs, due to weakened valves within the veins. 235

vascularization Process in which a tumor becomes supplied with blood vessels. 80

vas deferens Tube connecting the epididymis to the urethra; sperm duct (pl., *vasa deferentia*). 343

vasectomy Method for preventing pregnancy in which the vasa deferentia are cut and sealed. 359

vasomotor center Neurons in the brain stem that control the diameter of the arteries. 237

vein Blood vessel that takes blood to the heart. 235

venous duct See *ductus venosus*. 246

ventilation Breathing; the process of moving air into and out of the lungs. 282

ventral Toward the front or belly surface; the opposite of *dorsal*. 6

ventricle Cavity in an organ, such as the ventricles of the brain or the ventricles of the heart. 146, 226

venule Type of blood vessel that takes blood from capillaries to veins. 235

vermiform appendix Small, tubular appendage that extends outward from the cecum of the large intestine. 304

vernix caseosa Cheeselike substance covering the skin of the fetus. 379

vertebra Bone of the vertebral column. 94

vertebral canal Hollow place within the vertebrae containing the spinal cord. 6

vertebral column Backbone of vertebrates, composed of individual bones called vertebrae. 94

vertigo Dizziness and a sense of rotation. 181

vesicle Small, membranous sac that stores substances within a cell. 40

vesicular (Graafian) follicle Mature follicle within the ovaries that houses a developing egg. 351

vestibule Space or cavity at the entrance of a canal, such as the cavity that lies between the semicircular canals and the cochlea. 178, 296, 353

villi Fingerlike projections that line the small intestine and function in absorption (sing., *villus*). 302

visceral Pertaining to the contents of a body cavity. 66

visceral pericardium The inner layer of the serous pericardium; it is in contact with the heart and the roots of the vessels of the heart. 7, 226

visceral peritoneum Membrane that covers the surfaces of organs within the abdominal cavity. 7

visceral pleura Membrane that covers the surfaces of the lungs. 7

visual accommodation Ability of the eye to focus at different distances by changing the curvature of the lens. 171

visual field Area of vision for each eye. 176

vital capacity Maximum amount of air a person can exhale after taking the deepest breath possible. 281

vitamins Organic molecules (usually coenzymes) that must be in the diet and are necessary in trace amounts for normal metabolic functioning of cells. 315

vitreous humor Substance that occupies the posterior cavity of the eye. 171

vocal cords Folds of tissue within the larynx that produce sounds when they vibrate. 278

vulva External genitalia of the female that lie near the opening of the vagina. 349

W

wart Raised growth on the skin due to a viral infection. 74

white blood cell See *leukocytes*. 61, 212

white matter Myelinated nerve fibers in the central nervous system. 146

X

X chromosome Female sex chromosome that carries genes involved in sex determination; see *Y chromosome*. 390

xenotransplantataion Use of animal organs, instead of human organs, in human transplant patients. 269

X-linked Gene found on the X chromosome that controls traits other than sexual traits. 396

XYY male Male who has an X chromosome and two Y chromosomes in each nucleus. 394

Y

Y chromosome Male sex chromosome that carries genes involved in sex determination; see *X chromosome*. 390

yolk sac Extraembryonic membrane that serves as the first site of red blood cell formation. 371

Z

zygote Cell formed by the union of the sperm and egg; the product of fertilization. 342, 370

Credits

Text

Text Pronunciation Guide: Pronunciation guides for chapter terms are from *Dorland's Illustrated Medical Dictionary,* 27th ed., 1988. Philadelphia, W. B. Saunders Co. Reprinted with permission.

Photographs

Chapter 1

Opener: © Scott Camazine/Photo Researchers, Inc; 1.A: Courtesy of Dr. Anthony Atala/Children's Hospital Boston; 1.B: © Scott Camazine.

Chapter 2

Opener: © Alfred Pasieka/Photo Researchers, Inc.; 2.2b: © Biomed Comm/Custom Medical Stock Photos; 2.3a: © Hank Morgan/Rainbow; 2.3b: © Mazzlota et al/Photo Researchers, Inc.; 2.4b: © Charles M. Falco/Photo Researchers, Inc; 2.9: © Dwight Kuhn; 2.10: © Jeremy Burgess/SPL/Photo Researchers, Inc.; 2.11: © Don Fawcett/Photo Researchers, Inc.; 2.14a,b: © Vol. 176/Corbis.

Chapter 3

Opener: © P. M. Motta/S. Makabe & T. Nagur/SPL/Photo Researchers, Inc.; 3.3: Courtesy Dr. Stephen Wolfe; 3.4: © Barry F. King/BPS; 3.6a: Courtesy of Dr. Keith Porter; 3.7a: © Oliver Meckes/Photo Researchers, Inc.; 3.7b: © Manfred Kage/Peter Arnold, Inc.; 3.15(all): © Michael Abbey/Photo Researchers, Inc.

Chapter 4

Opener: © Cabisco/Visuals Unlimited; 4.1, 4.2: © Ed Reschke; 4.3: © Manfred Kage/Peter Arnold, Inc.; 4.4–4.14: © Ed Reschke.

Chapter 5

Opener: © Ed Reschke/Peter Arnold, Inc.; 5.2: Courtesy of Kent Van De Graaff, photo by James M. Clayton; 5.3b: © CNRI/SPL/Photo Researchers, Inc.; 5.6a: © Ken Greer/Visuals Unlimited; 5.6b: © Dr. P. Marazzi/SPL/Photo Researchers, Inc.; 5.6c: © James Stevenson/SPL/Photo Researchers, Inc.; 5.9: Courtesy Dr. George Bogumill.

Chapter 6

Opener: © NHS/Trust/Tony Stone Images/Getty; 6.Aa: © Royce Blair/Unicorn Stock Photos; 6.Ab: © Michael Klein/Peter Arnold, Inc.; 6.23b: © Lennart Nilsson, "Behold Man," Little Brown and Company, Boston.

Chapter 7

Opener: © Don Fawcett/Photo Researchers, Inc.; 7.1(all): © Ed Reschke; 7.2c: © The McGraw-Hill Companies/Dennis Strete, photographer; 7.3: Courtesy of Hugh E. Huxley; 7.9: © G. W. Willis/Visuals Unlimited.

Chapter 8

Opener: © BioPhoto Assoc./Photo Researchers, Inc.; 8.5: Courtesy Dr. E. R. Lewis, University of California, Berkeley; 8.7C: © Manfred Kage/Peter Arnold, Inc.; 8.8b: © Colin Chumbley/Science Source/Photo Researchers, Inc.

Chapter 9

Opener: © Wellcome Dept. of Cognitive Neurology/SPL/Photo Researchers, Inc.; 9.3b: © Omikron/SPL/Photo Researchers, Inc.; 9.9: © Lennart Nilsson, from "The Incredible Machine"; 9.10b: © The McGraw-Hill Companies/Dennis Strete, photographer; 9.13: © P. Motta/SPL/Photo Researchers, Inc.

Chapter 10

Opener: © Ed Reschke; 10.3a: © Bob Daemmrich/Stock Boston; 10.3b: © Ewing Galloway, Inc.; 10 4: From Clinical Pathological Progression of Acromegaly Conference, "Acromegaly, Diabetes, Hypermetabolism, Proteinura and Heart Failure," American Journal of Medicine 20 (1956) 133, with permission from Excerpta Medica; 10.5: © Biophoto Assoc./SPL/Photo Researchers, Inc.; 10.6: © John Paul Kay/Peter Arnold, Inc.; 10.10a,b: © Custom Medical Stock Photos; 10. 11a,b: "Atlas of Pediatric Physical Diagnosis," Second Edition by Zitelli & Davis, 1992. Mosby-Wolfe Europe Limited, London, UK; 10.A: Courtesy of Robert P. Lanza; 10.13: © James Darell/Stone/Getty.

Chapter 11

Opener: © National Cancer Institute/SPL/Photo Researchers, Inc.; 11.B: © Bill Longcore/Photo Researchers, Inc.; 11.5: © Manfred Kage/Peter Arnold, Inc.

Chapter 12

Opener: © Ed Reschke; 12.B: © Biophoto Associates/Photo Researchers, Inc.

Chapter 13

Opener: © Volker Steger/Peter Arnold, Inc.; 13.2(top left): © Ed Reschke/Peter Arnold, Inc.; 13.2(top right): © Fred E. Hossler/Visuals Unlimited; 13.2(bottom left): R. Valentine/Visuals Unlimited; 13.2(bottom right): © Ed Reschke/Peter Arnold, Inc.; 13.3a–e: © Ed Reschke/Peter Arnold, Inc.; 3.6b: Courtesy of Dr. Arthur J. Olson, The Scripps Research Institute; 13.8b: © Boehringer Ingelheim International, photo by Lennart Nilsson; 13.10: Estate of Ed Lettau/Peter Arnold, Inc.; 13.B: © Michael Newman/Photo Edit; 13.C: © K. G. Murti/Visuals Unlimited.

Chapter 14

Opener: © Manfred Kage/Peter Arnold, Inc.; 14.6: © SIU/Visuals Unlimited; 14.11a,b: © Martin Rotker/Martin Rotker Photography.

Chapter 15

Opener: © Omikron/Photo Researchers, Inc.; 15.3b: © Biophoto Associates/Photo Researchers, Inc.; 15.4b: © Ed Reschke/Peter Arnold, Inc.; 15.7c: Photo by Susumu Ito, from Charles Flickinger, "Medical Cellular Biology," W. B. Saunders, 1979; 15.7d: © Manfred Kage/Peter Arnold, Inc.; 15..9c: © Ed Reschke; 15.13: © Donna Day/Stone/Getty Images; 15.14: © Tony Freeman/PhotoEdit.

Chapter 16

Opener: © SPL/Photo Researchers, Inc.; 16.4(top left): © R. G. Kessel and R. H. Kardon, *Tissues and Organs: A Text Atlas of Scanning Electron Microscopy,* 1979; 16.4(top right & bottom): © 1966 Academic Press, from A. B. Maunsbach, J. Ultrastruct. Res. 15:242–282; 16.10: © SIU/Peter Arnold, Inc.

Chapter 17

Opener: © Secchi-Lecaque/CNRI/SPL/Photo Researchers, Inc.; 17.3b: © Biophoto Associates/Photo Researchers, Inc.; 17.9: © Ed Reschke/Peter Arnold, Inc.; 17.15a: © The McGraw-Hill Companies, Inc./Bob Coyle, photographer; 17.15b: © The McGraw-Hill Companies, Inc. Vincent Ho, photographer; 17.15c,d: © The McGraw-Hill Companies, Inc./Bob Coyle, photographer; 17.15e: © Hank Morgan/Photo Researchers, Inc.; 17.15f: © The McGraw-Hill Companies, Inc./Bob Coyle, photographer; 17.D(fish): © Norbert Wu; 17.D(woman): © Steven Peters/Stone/Getty; 17.D(alligator): © J. Brian Alker/Getty; 17.D(birds): © Alan Barnes/Getty; 17.E(left): © Vol. 161/Corbis; 17.E(right): © Vol. 178/Corbis; 17.F: © Argus Fotoarchiv/Peter Arnold, Inc.

Chapter 18

Opener: © Dr. Yorgos Nikas/SPL/Photo Researchers, Inc.; 18.1a: © David M. Phillips/Visuals Unlimited; 18.6a: Lennart Nilsson, "A Child is Born," Dell Publishing Company; 18.8: © James Stevenson/SPL/Photo Researchers, Inc.; 18.B: Streissguth, A. P., Landesman-Dwyer, S., Martin J. C., and Smith D. W. (1980). Teratogenic Effects of Alcohol in Humans and Laboratory Animals. *Science:* 209 (18): 353–361.

Chapter 19

Opener: © Meckes/Ottawa/Photo Researchers, Inc.; 19.1c–e: © CNRI/SPL/Photo Researchers, Inc.; 19.3: © Jill Cannefax/Coyote Crossing, Inc.; 19.4a,b: Photograph by Earl Plunkett. Courtesy of G. H. Valentine; p. 400: © Ron Chapple/Taxi/Getty Images.

Index

Thalamus, 148, 151
Thalidomide, 383
Therapeutic cloning, 374
Thermoreceptors, 164
Thermostat, 10
Thiamin, 316
Thick filament, 116
Thin filament, 116, 119
Third ventricle, 148
Thoracic aorta, 242, 243
Thoracic cavity, 6, 7, 409
Thoracic nerves, 154
Thoracic spine, 94
Thoracic wall muscles, 128
Thrombin, 215
Thrombocytopenia, 215
Thromboembolism, 215, 219, 228
Thrombus, 215
Thymosin, 187, 200, 256
Thymus, 186, 187, 200, 255, 256
Thyroid cartilage, 405, 406
Thyroid gland, 186, 187, 191–92,
    404, 405, 406
    radioactive iodine examination
        of, 198
Thyroid-stimulating hormone, 187,
    188, 189
Thyroxine, 187, 191
Tibia, 89, 102–3
Tibial artery, 243
Tibialis anterior, 125, 132, 134
Tibial vein, 244
Tidal volume, 281
Tight junction, 65
Tissue
    adipose, 58, 59, 70, 200
    connective, 58–61, 114–15
    epithelial, 55–57
    muscular, 62–63
    nervous, 64
Tissue fluid, 12, 216
Tissue thromboplastin, 215
Tone, muscle, 123
Tongue, 166, 277, 296
Tonicity, of solution, 43
Tonsillectomy, 286, 298
Tonsillitis, 286, 298
Tonsils, 257, 277, 298
Tooth (teeth), 297
Touch, 164–65
Trabeculae, 61, 84
Tracer, 198
Trachea, 276, 277, 278, 405, 407, 408
Tracheostomy, 278
Transcription, 48
Transfusion reaction, 212
Transitional epithelium, 55, 57
Translation, 48
Transplantation, 9
    bone marrow, 256
    kidney, 335
    liver, 310
    tissue rejection in, 269
Transport, 44
    active, 44
    carbon dioxide, 216–17, 284–85
    carrier, 44
    facilitated, 44
    oxygen, 216–17, 284–85
    pump, 44
Transverse colon, 296, 304, 305,
    406, 407
Transverse plane, definition of, 5
Transverse section, definition of, 5

Transversus abdominis, 128, 129,
    404, 405, 409
Trapezium, 100
Trapezius, 125, 127, 128, 129,
    131, 403
Trapezoid, 100
Treponema pallidum infection, 364
Triceps brachii, 125, 130, 131
Tricuspid valve, 226, 227
Trigeminal nerve, 152, 153
Triglyceride, 26
Trigone, 325
Triiodothyronine, 187, 191
Triple bonds, 21
Triplet code, 48
Trochanter
    of bone, 87
    of femur, 102
Trochlea, 98
Trochlear nerve, 152, 153, 169
Trochlear notch, 99
Trophoblast, 373, 375
Tropomyosin, 119
Troponin, 119
Trunk, muscles of, 128–29
Trypsin, 308, 311
T (transverse) tubule, 116, 117
Tubal ligation, 359
Tubercles, 87, 98
Tuberculosis, 286–87
Tuberosity, 87, 99, 103
Tubular reabsorption, in urine
    formation, 328, 329
Tubular secretion, in urine
    formation, 328, 329
Tumor, 80. See also Cancer
Tumor angiogenesis factor, 200
Tunica externa, 234
Tunica interna, 234
Tunica media, 234
Turner syndrome, 390, 393
T wave, 231
Tympanic membrane, 178, 180

U

Ulcers
    decubitus, 71
    genital, 363
Ulna, 89, 99
Ulnar artery, 243
Ulnar nerve, 153, 154
Ulnar vein, 244
Ultraviolet radiation, skin cancer
    and, 77
Umbilical, definition of, 4
Umbilical arteries, 246, 247
Umbilical cord, 377, 378
Umbilical vein, 246, 247
Umbilicus, 403
Unsaturated fatty acids, 26
Upper limb, 98–100
    muscles of, 129–31
Urea, 208, 324
Uremia, 334, 335
Ureter, 324, 325, 407, 408
Urethra, 324, 325, 343, 345, 346, 409
Urethritis, 334
Uric acid, 208, 324
Urinalysis, 334
Urinary system, 8, 13, 324–33.
        See also specific components
    functions of, 324
    in homeostasis, 336, 337

Urination, 325
    aging-related changes in, 336
Urine
    composition of, 334
    formation of, 328, 329
Urochrome, 336
Urticaria, 74
Uterine tube, 352, 353, 407
Uterus, 342, 349, 352–53, 407, 408
    contractions of, 384–85
    in menstrual cycle, 354–55
    during pregnancy, 385
Utricle, 181
Uvula, 277, 296

V

Vaccines, 266, 267
    contraceptive, 359
    in elderly individuals, 270
Vacuole, 36
Vagina, 342, 349, 352, 353, 409
Vagus nerve, 152, 153
Valves
    cardiac, 226–27
    venous, 235
Varicose veins, 235, 248
Vas deferens, 343, 344, 345, 346, 406
Vasectomy, 359
Vasomotor center, 237
Vastus intermedius, 133, 408
Vastus lateralis, 125, 133, 406, 407,
    408
Vastus medialis, 125, 133, 406, 407
Veins, 244, 245
    anatomy of, 235
    cardiac, 228
Vena cava
    inferior, 242, 244, 245, 408, 409
    superior, 242, 244, 245, 407, 408
Venous return, 237, 248, 249
Ventilation, 282–83
Ventricles
    cardiac, 407
        left, 227, 228
        right, 226, 227, 228
    cerebral, 148
Ventricular diastole, 232
Ventricular systole, 232
Venules, 235, 276
Vermiform appendix, 296, 304,
    406, 407
Vernix caseosa, 379
Vertebra prominens, 94
Vertebrae, 95, 409
Vertebral, definition of, 4
Vertebral artery, 243, 246
Vertebral canal, 7
Vertebral cavity, 6
Vertebral column, 89, 94–95
Vertigo, 181
Vesicles, 36, 37, 40
Vestibule, 178, 180, 353
Vestibulocochlear nerve, 152, 153
Villi
    chorionic, 377, 378, 390, 391
    intestinal, 303
Viral infection
    emerging, 268
    herpes, 363
    HIV, 264–65
    human papillomavirus, 363
Visceral membrane, 6, 66
Visceral pericardium, 7, 226

Visceral peritoneum, 7
Visceral pleura, 7
Vision, 168–77. See also Eye(s)
    aging of, 181
Visual association are, 150
Visual field, 175
Visual pathway, 175
Vital capacity, 281
Vitamin(s), 315, 316
    in birth defect prevention, 382
    nutrition label for, 30
Vitamin A, 316
Vitamin B_6, 316
Vitamin B_{12}, 316
Vitamin C, 316
Vitamin D, 316
    in calcium metabolism, 88, 192
    skin production of, 78
Vitamin E, 316
Vitamin K, 316
Vitreous humor, 170, 171
Vocal cords, 278
Vomer bone, 90, 91, 92, 93
Vulva, 349

W

Warts, genital, 363
Water, 21, 22–23
    body, skin effect on, 78
    properties of, 22
    reabsorption of, 330–31
    surface tension of, 279
Water intoxication, 45
Water-salt balance, 324
Weight
    gain of, 240, 318
    during pregnancy, 385
Wernicke's area, 149
White blood cells, 61, 208, 213,
    255, 256
    count of, 213, 214
    formation of, 210
    production of, 108
    in wound healing, 75
White matter, 150
Willis, circle of, 246
Wound healing, 74, 75
Wrist, 100

X

X chromosome, 390, 393–94, 396
Xiphoid process, 96
X rays, during pregnancy, 382

Y

Yawning, 284
Y chromosomes, 390, 393–94
Yolk sac, 371, 375

Z

Zinc, dietary, 317
Z line, 117
Zygomatic arch, 92, 93
Zygomatic bone, 91, 92, 93
Zygomaticus, 125, 126, 127
Zygote, 342
    cleavage of, 371, 373
    formation of, 370